# Teacher's Edition

**Discover Health**

**AGS**®

American Guidance Service, Inc.
Circle Pines, Minnesota 55014-1796
800-328-2560

*Consultants:*

**Dr. Malcolm Goldsmith**
Professor
Southern Illinois University
Edwardsville, IL

**Dr. Ruth Rich**
Director, Drug-Free Schools
   Program
Los Angeles Unified School
   District
Los Angeles, CA

**Therese Telepak**
Safe and Drug Free Schools
   Coordinator
Diocese of Greensburg
Greensburg, PA

**Dr. Robert Wandberg**
Health Teacher
John F. Kennedy High School
Bloomington, MN

*The publisher wishes to thank the following educators for their helpful comments during the review
process for* Discover Health. *Their assistance has been invaluable.*

**Martha Bakerjian**
Resource Specialist Teacher
Lewis School
Lower Lake, CA

**Linda Colom**
Special Education Facilitator
Guinn Middle School
Las Vegas, NV

**Alisa E. Debnam**
Healthful Living Supervisor
Cumberland County Schools
Fayetteville, NC

**Kate Engler**
Grade 8 Health Teacher
Orchard Park Middle School
Orchard Park, NY

**Rochelle D. Farinella**
Facilitator of Safety
   and Security
Parkway School District
Chesterfield, MO

**Edith Fulmore**
Staff Associate
Baltimore City Schools
Baltimore, MD

**Helen Geurkink**
Health Coordinator
Parkway School District
Chesterfield, MO

**Karen Hershberger**
Health Teacher
St. Louis Park Junior
   High School
St. Louis Park, MN

**Deborah Horn**
High School Special
   Education Teacher
Wayne City High School
Wayne City, IL

**Mary Kaufman**
Coordinator, DARE Program
Tobacco Use and Prevention
   Education
Los Angeles Unified School
   District
Los Angeles, CA

**Wendy Lewandowski**
Grade 8 Health Teacher
Orchard Park Middle School
Orchard Park, NY

**April Lewis**
Health Facilitator
Baltimore Public Schools
Baltimore, MD

**Connie Mericle**
Special Education Facilitator
Thurman White
   Middle School
Henderson, NV

**Barbara Nunes**
Health Teacher
Twain Mesa Alternative
   Education
San Diego, CA

**Sherri Reynolds**
Supervisor, Health Services
Sarasota County School Board
Sarasota, FL

**Alice C. Richardson**
Special Education Teacher
Central High School
Detroit, MI

**Ina Sickels**
Health Teacher
St. Louis Park Senior
   High School
St. Louis Park, MN

**Jean Young**
Teacher, Independent Study
Simi Valley Unified
Simi Valley, CA

**Paula Young**
Learning Resource Specialist
Orange County Public Schools
Orlando, FL

ISBN 0-7854-1844-X
Product Number 91052
A 0 9 8 7 6 5 4 3 2 1

# Table of Contents

**Lesson Plans**

**Appendices**

## Answer Keys

# Discover Health

**Discover Healthy Sexual Development**

**Discover Life Skills Handbook**

**Student Workbook**

**Teacher's Edition**

**Student Text**

**Teacher's Resource Library**

**Audiocassettes**

A skill-based wellness approach that addresses today's major health issues for middle/junior high school students

Teach your students the basics of a healthy lifestyle with this new curruculum written to meet national and state health guidelines. *Discover Health* provides comprehensive health education for your students reading below grade level. In clear, easy-to-read text, the colorful hardcover book covers health topics important to today's teenagers.

## Student Text Contents
Unit 1  *Personal Health and Family Life*
    The Body Systems
    Hygiene and Fitness
    The Family
Unit 2  *Mental and Emotional Health*
    Emotions
    Maintaining Mental Health
    Relationships

Unit 3  *Nutrition*
    Diet and Health
    Making Healthy Food Choices
Unit 4  *Use and Misuse of Substances*
    Medicines and Drugs
    Drug Dependence—Problems and Solutions
Unit 5  *Preventing and Controlling Diseases and Disorders*
    Disease—Causes and Prevention
    Preventing AIDS and Sexually
       Transmitted Diseases
    Common Diseases
Unit 6  *Injury Prevention and Safety Promotion*
    Preventing Injuries
    First Aid for Injuries
    Preventing Violence
Unit 7  *Health and Society*
    Consumer Health
    Public Health
    Environmental Health

Life Skills
Healthy
Sexual
Development

Life Skills
Handbook

Student
Workbook

Student Text

Teacher's
Resource
Library

Audiocassettes

**Teacher's Edition (also available for *Life Skills Handbook* and *Healthy Sexual Development*)**

## Student Text
Comprehensive health program for high school students reading below grade level. This colorful text addresses the issues and decisions encountered by teenagers.

## Student Workbook
Consumable workbook that contains activities that reinforce and extend lessons in the text. Also available on TRL. (64 pages) Answer Key is also available.

## Life Skills Handbook
This softcover worktext teaches ten essential life skills through real-life vignettes. Students are taught how to handle conflicts, set goals, and overcome obstacles. (36 pages)

## Life Skills Healthy Sexual Development Text
This softcover worktext presents human sexuality with a positive approach, emphasizing abstinence and responsible decision-making skills. (144 pages)

## Teacher's Wraparound Edition
This full-color teacher's edition includes the complete student text. Teaching strategies are presented at point of use.

## Teacher's Resource Library (TRL) CD-ROM
This CD-ROM contains over 300 reproducibles to help teachers tailor instruction to their class. Includes answers to all activities.

## Audiocassette
The entire text is available on cassette for your students who need added reinforcement.

## Human Body Transparencies
This set of 16 full-color transparencies showing the major body systems and organs adds to classroom presentations.

## The Great Health Review Game
This interactive CD-ROM reviews the objectives from the text in highly motivating game format.

# Student Text Highlights

Many special features in the student text enhance learning by making the content relevant to students.

- A special section at the beginning of the text helps students become more independent learners.

- Study skills taught in this section can be applied to all school subjects.

- Features of the text are introduced to help students become familiar with the book.

## Before Beginning Each Chapter

### The Body Systems

**Chapter 1**

The human body is amazing. It is made up of many systems. These systems work together to keep you healthy. One of the most important ways that the body's systems keep you healthy is by maintaining balance. For example, the systems work together to keep your body from getting too cold or too hot. They keep your temperature balanced. They also work together to make sure that all parts of your body get the right amount of food and oxygen.

In this chapter, you will learn about your body's systems and its basic building blocks. You will also learn how the different parts of the body work together.

**Goals for Learning**
- To describe the structure of cells, tissues, organs, and body systems
- To describe the structure and function of the skin
- To explain how the skeletal and muscular systems work together
- To explain digestive and excretory systems
- To explain the respiratory and circulatory systems
- To describe the parts of the nervous system
- To describe the purpose of the endocrine glands
- To describe the reproductive system

- Read the chapter title.

- Study the goals for learning. The chapter review and tests will ask questions related to these goals.

## Before Beginning Each Lesson

Read the lesson title and restate it in the form of a question. For example:

### Lesson 1    A Healthy Diet

Write: *What is a healthy diet?*

Look over the entire lesson, noting . . .

- pictures
- tables
- charts
- figures
- bold words

- text organization
- questions in the margins
- lesson review

Also note these features . . .

**Healthy Subjects**
*Science*

- **Action for Health**—An action you can take
- **Careers**—A health career and its requirements
- **Healthy Subjects**—A subject such as math or literature related to the chapter topic
- **Technology**—A technology advance related to the chapter topic
- **Then and Now**—An explanation of how health was approached in earlier years compared with today
- **Tips**—A short, easy-to-use tip on health, fitness, safety, or nutrition
- **Writing About Health**—Write about how a topic applies to your health and life

**Action for Health**

### As You Read the Lesson

- Read the major headings. Each subhead is a question.
- Read the paragraphs that follow to answer the question.
- Before moving on to the next heading, see if you can answer the question. If you cannot, reread the section to look for the answers. If you are still unsure, ask for help.
- Answering the questions in the lesson will help you determine if you know the lesson's key ideas.

### Using the Bold Words

Knowing the meaning of all the boxed words in the left column will help you understand what you read.

**Bold type**
*Words seen for the first time will appear in bold type*

These words appear in **bold type** the first time they appear in the text and are defined in the paragraph.

**Glossary**
*Words listed in this column are also found in the glossary*

Proteins are made up of smaller units called **amino acids.**

All of the words in the left column are also defined in the **glossary.**

**Amino acids**—The smaller units of protein (p. 144)

---

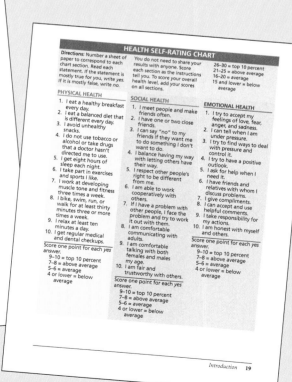

## Introduction

**G**ood health is basic to everything in life. Without health, people have difficulty doing the things they want to do. But health is more than being without illness. Health is a state of being healthy. There are three parts of good health.

- *Physical health* is the body's ability to meet the demands of daily living. It allows a person to do things without getting tired and run-down. For example, it allows you to attend school, to study, and to participate in after-school activities.

- *Social health* is the ability to get along with other people. It is the ability to make friends and to be a friend. Social health is the ability to work with others and to perform effectively as part of a group. It involves contributing to the good of the family and helping out in the community.

### HEALTH SELF-RATING CHART

**Directions:** Number a sheet of paper to correspond to each chart section. Read each statement. If the statement is mostly true for you, write *yes.* If it is mostly false, write *no.*

You do not need to share your results with anyone. Score each section as the instructions tell you. To score your overall health level, add your scores on all sections.

26–30 = top 10 percent
21–25 = above average
16–20 = average
15 and lower = below average

**PHYSICAL HEALTH**
1. I eat a healthy breakfast every day.
2. I eat a balanced diet that is different every day.
3. I avoid unhealthy snacks.
4. I do not use tobacco or alcohol or take drugs that a doctor hasn't directed me to use.
5. I get eight hours of sleep each night.
6. I take part in exercises and sports I like.
7. I work at developing muscle tone and fitness three times a week.
8. I bike, swim, run, or walk for at least thirty minutes three or more times a week.
9. I relax at least ten minutes a day.
10. I get regular medical and dental checkups.

*Score one point for each yes answer.*
9–10 = top 10 percent
7–8 = above average
5–6 = average
4 or lower = below average

**SOCIAL HEALTH**
1. I meet people and make friends often.
2. I have one or two close friends.
3. I can say "no" to my friends if they want me to do something I don't want to do.
4. I balance having my way with letting others have their way.
5. I respect other people's right to be different from me.
6. I am able to work cooperatively with others.
7. If I have a problem with other people, I face the problem and try to work it out with them.
8. I am comfortable communicating with adults.
9. I am comfortable talking with both females and males my age.
10. I am fair and trustworthy with others.

*Score one point for each yes answer.*
9–10 = top 10 percent
7–8 = above average
5–6 = average
4 or lower = below average

**EMOTIONAL HEALTH**
1. I try to accept my feelings of love, fear, anger, and sadness.
2. I can tell when I am under pressure.
3. I try to find ways to deal with pressure and control it.
4. I try to have a positive outlook.
5. I ask for help when I need it.
6. I have friends and relatives with whom I discuss problems.
7. I give compliments.
8. I can accept and use helpful comments.
9. I take responsibility for my actions.
10. I am honest with myself and others.

*Score one point for each yes answer.*
9–10 = top 10 percent
7–8 = above average
5–6 = average
4 or lower = below average

- An introductory section provides students with background information to help them better understand health education.

- Students learn that health has three components: physical, social, and emotional.

- Activities encourage students to evaluate their own health practices.

"Health is a state of complete physical, mental, and social well-being, and not merely the absence of disease . . ."
—World Health Organization Constitution

## Unit 1

# Personal Health and Family Life

List the different things you do in one day. Your list might have walking, reading, laughing, and playing sports on it. Whatever you do, think, or feel—it all happens because your body and all its parts work together. Your body works all the time. It works even when you are asleep.

Good health doesn't just happen. In this unit, you will see what kinds of things you can do to keep yourself healthy. You will learn about the different parts of your body and how they work together. You will learn what you can do to keep your body and its parts working well. You will also learn that your family is important to your health.

▶ Chapter 1  The Body Systems

▶ Chapter 2  Hygiene and Fitness

▶ Chapter 3  The Family

■ Each unit opens with a colorful photo illustrating a related health concept.

■ An opening quote helps students see the relevance of the unit and stimulates discussion about the topic.

■ Introductory paragraphs provide background information to set the stage for learning.

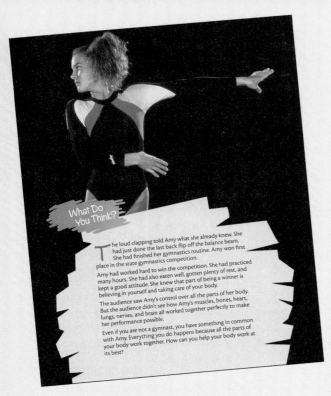

### What Do You Think?

The loud clapping told Amy what she already knew. She had just done the last back flip off the balance beam. She had finished her gymnastics routine. Amy won first place in the state gymnastics competition.

Amy had worked hard to win the competition. She had practiced many hours. She had also eaten well, gotten plenty of rest, and kept a good attitude. She knew that part of being a winner is believing in yourself and taking care of your body.

The audience saw Amy's control over all the parts of her body. But the audience didn't see how Amy's muscles, bones, heart, lungs, nerves, and brain all worked together perfectly to make her performance possible.

Even if you are not a gymnast, you have something in common with Amy. Everything you do happens because all the parts of your body work together. How can you help your body work at its best?

■ Deciding for Yourself activities encourage critical thinking.

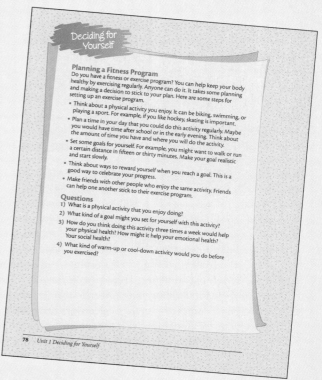

### Deciding for Yourself

**Planning a Fitness Program**
Do you have a fitness or exercise program? You can help keep your body healthy by exercising regularly. Anyone can do it. It takes some planning and making a decision to stick to your plan. Here are some steps for setting up an exercise program.

* Think about a physical activity you enjoy. It can be biking, swimming, or playing a sport. For example, if you like hockey, skating is important.
* Plan a time in your day that you could do this activity regularly. Maybe you would have time after school or in the early evening. Think about the amount of time you have and where you will do the activity.
* Set some goals for yourself. For example, you might want to walk or run a certain distance in fifteen or thirty minutes. Make your goal realistic and start slowly.
* Think about ways to reward yourself when you reach a goal. This is a good way to celebrate your progress.
* Make friends with other people who enjoy the same activity. Friends can help one another stick to their exercise program.

**Questions**
1) What is a physical activity that you enjoy doing?
2) What kind of a goal might you set for yourself with this activity?
3) How do you think doing this activity three times a week would help your physical health? How might it help your emotional health? Your social health?
4) What kind of warm-up or cool-down activity would you do before you exercised?

78  Unit 1 Deciding for Yourself

■ Short vignettes about teenagers highlight the areas of health studied in the unit.

■ Students are encouraged to apply the information to themselves.

Additional features in the chapters and lessons increase student comprehension of the text.

■ Each chapter begins with an introduction to set the stage for learning.

■ Goals for learning help students identify major concepts in the chapter.

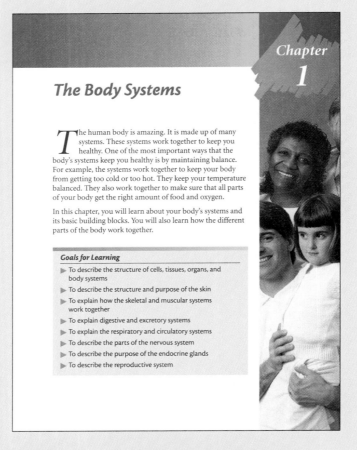

Chapter 1

## The Body Systems

The human body is amazing. It is made up of many systems. These systems work together to keep you healthy. One of the most important ways that the body's systems keep you healthy is by maintaining balance. For example, the systems work together to keep your body from getting too cold or too hot. They keep your temperature balanced. They also work together to make sure that all parts of your body get the right amount of food and oxygen.

In this chapter, you will learn about your body's systems and its basic building blocks. You will also learn how the different parts of the body work together.

### Goals for Learning

▶ To describe the structure of cells, tissues, organs, and body systems
▶ To describe the structure and purpose of the skin
▶ To explain how the skeletal and muscular systems work together
▶ To explain digestive and excretory systems
▶ To explain the respiratory and circulatory systems
▶ To describe the parts of the nervous system
▶ To describe the purpose of the endocrine glands
▶ To describe the reproductive system

Extension features include health and nutrition tips, technology, careers, and cross-curricular topics.

### Healthy Subjects
### Consumer Science

**RUNNING SHOES**

Many people choose running as a way to keep fit. Choosing the right shoes is important for healthy feet. For most runners, "stability shoes" offer good cushioning, center support, and durability. However, "motion-control shoes" are better for people who tend to roll their feet inward as they step. These shoes are heavier but provide much-needed support for runners. Other runners' feet may be less flexible in the center. These people need cushioned shoes without much middle support. Off-road runners should wear "trail shoes." The soles of trail shoes give extra traction. They also include toe "bumpers," durable tops, and stronger stitching. The next time you buy shoes, consider how to keep your feet happy.

### Nutrition Tip

Eat plenty of fruits and vegetables. They can provide vitamins and minerals your skin needs to stay healthy.

- Short, carefully written lessons help students focus on the concepts presented.

- Vocabulary is defined at point of use

- Reader's response notes in the side column help students think more deeply about what they are reading.

- Writing About Health offers students the opportunity to write about various aspects of health-related topics. These can be used for informal assessments.

- Lesson Review questions provide an opportunity for discussion and a way to check understanding.

## Lesson 1

### Cells, Tissues, and Organs

**Cell**
The basic unit that makes up your body

**Cell membrane**
The outer wall of a cell

**Cytoplasm**
The jelly-like material inside the cell membrane

**Microscope**
A tool used to see cells

**Nucleus**
The control center of the cell

Look at your skin. What do you see? You may see lines on the skin or flakes of skin. What you cannot see just by looking at your skin are the tiny **cells** that make up your skin. In fact, tiny living units, called cells, make up each part of your body.

#### What Are Cells?

Cells are the basic units that make up all living things. Your body is made up of trillions of cells. Cells are too small to see without a tool called a **microscope**. A microscope can make a cell look bigger than it really is, so you can see what it looks like. If you were to look at a cell using a microscope, it might look like the cell shown in Figure 1.1.

Your body is made up of many different kinds of cells. Each kind of cell has its own job. For example, skin cells help keep germs out of your body. White blood cells fight the germs that do enter your body. Nerve cells send messages among the different parts of your body and your brain. Each kind of cell carries out a different job.

#### What Are the Main Parts of a Cell?

Look again at the picture of the cell in Figure 1.1. Most cells have three basic parts: a **cell membrane**, the **cytoplasm**, and a **nucleus**.

The cell membrane is the outer wall of the cell. It is like a thin skin around the cell. Food and oxygen can pass into the cell and wastes can pass out of the cell through the cell membrane. The cytoplasm is a jelly-like liquid inside the cell membrane. The cytoplasm often has other cell parts floating in it. Most of the cell's life activities take place in the cytoplasm. The nucleus is sometimes called the control center of the cell. It has all the information that the cell needs to carry out its job and to make new cells like itself.

cytoplasm

cell membrane

nucleus

**Figure 1.1.** A typical cell

24 *Chapter 1 The Body Systems*

**Body system**
A group of organs that work together to carry out a certain job

**Mitosis**
The dividing process that makes new cells

**Organ**
A group of tissues that work together

**Tissue**
A group of cells that do the same job

The nucleus makes new cells by splitting into two, making one cell two cells. When the two cells split, they become four cells, which split to make eight. This dividing is called **mitosis**. Mitosis allows your body to make new cells to grow or to replace dead cells.

#### What Is a Body System?

Cells that do the same job combine to form a **tissue**. Muscles and bones are examples of tissues. Different types of tissues working together form an **organ**, such as the stomach or the kidneys. A group of organs working together to carry out a certain job is called a **body system**. The digestive system is an example of a body system. Each system carries out its own job and works with other systems to keep the body healthy.

**LESSON 1 REVIEW** Write the answers to these questions on a separate sheet of paper. Use complete sentences.

Why are cells called "building blocks of life"?

1) Name three different kinds of cells and what they do.
2) Why is a microscope needed to look at cells?
3) How does mitosis help you grow?
4) How is tissue formed?
5) What are the three main parts of a cell, and what does each one do?

### Writing About Health

All of the systems in your body work together efficiently. Write about how the body must be well organized and balanced for this to happen.

*The Body Systems Chapter 1* **25**

---

### Writing About Health

All of the systems in your body work together efficiently. Write about how the body must be well organized and balanced for this to happen.

---

Then and Now

### GINGER ISN'T JUST FOR COOKING

Many old herbal treatments are now considered useless or even harmful. However, some herbal treatments are now considered useful. For example, about 2,500 years ago, the Chinese used ginger to treat upset stomach, coughing, vomiting, and other ailments. Ginger was used by other groups, too. Nigerians have used it to treat yellow fever and malaria. In Russia, ginger has been used to treat toothaches.

Scientists have found that a chemical in ginger makes it a useful treatment for nausea, vomiting, migraines, and rheumatoid arthritis. Many pregnancy manuals and doctors who care for pregnant women advise taking ginger teas or ginger ale to help with morning sickness. Ginger is also a common treatment for motion sickness.

■ Planning guide saves valuable preparation time by organizing all materials for the unit.

■ Contains a complete listing of all lessons so you can preview the chapters quickly.

■ Assessment options are highlighted for easy reference.  These include:

✓ Writing About Health

✓ Self-Assessments

✓ Chapter Mastery Tests, forms A and B

✓ Unit Mastery Tests

✓ Midterm Mastery Test

✓ Final Mastery Test

■ Additional AGS materials are listed for your convenience. Materials include:

✓ Healthy Sexual Development

✓ Life Skills Handbook

## Unit 1 — Planning Guide

### Personal Health and Family Life

| | Student Pages | Vocabulary | Lesson Review | Writing About Health |
|---|---|---|---|---|
| **Chapter 1  The Body Systems** | 23–53 | | | |
| Lesson 1  Cells, Tissues, and Organs | 24–25 | • | • | • |
| Lesson 2  The Body's Protective Covering | 26–27 | • | • | |
| Lesson 3  Skeletal and Muscular Systems | 28–31 | • | • | |
| Lesson 4  The Digestive and Excretory Systems | 32–35 | • | • | |
| Lesson 5  The Respiratory and Circulatory Systems | 36–39 | • | • | |
| Lesson 6  The Nervous System | 40–43 | • | • | |
| Lesson 7  The Endocrine System | 44–46 | • | • | |
| Lesson 8  The Reproductive System | 47–50 | • | • | |
| **Chapter 2  Hygiene and Fitness** | 54–65 | | | |
| Lesson 1  Hygiene | 55–58 | • | • | |
| Lesson 2  Fitness | 59–62 | • | • | • |
| **Chapter 3  The Family** | 66–77 | | | |
| Lesson 1  The Family Life Cycle | 67–70 | • | • | |
| Lesson 2  Dealing With Family Problems | 71–74 | • | • | • |

*Header: Student Lesson*

### Unit Activities

**Home Connection**
**What Do You Think?**
**Deciding for Yourself**

### AGS-Related Resources

**Discover Life Skills Handbook**
**Discover Healthy Sexual Development**

### Assessment Options

**Student Text**
   **Lesson Reviews**
   **Chapter Reviews**
   **Unit Review**
**Teacher's Resource Library**
   **Chapter Mastery Tests**
   **Unit Mastery Test**

| Student Text Features | | | | | | Teaching Strategies | | | | | | | Learning Styles | | | | | Teacher's Resource Library | | | |
|---|---|---|---|---|---|---|---|---|---|---|---|---|---|---|---|---|---|---|---|---|---|
| Action for Health | Careers | Health, Fitness, and Nutrition Tips | Healthy Subjects | Then and Now | Technology | Background Information | Career Application | Community Application | Environment Application | Global Connection | Home Application | Multicultural Connection | Auditory | Group Learning | LEP/ESL | Tactile/Kinesthetic | Visual | Activities | Mastery Tests | Student Study Guide | Workbook Activities |
| | | | | | | | | | | | | | | | | | | | • | • | |
| | | | | | | | | | | | | | | 25 | | | | 1 | | | 1 |
| | | | | | | | 27 | | | | | | | | | | | 2 | | | 2 |
| | | 28 | 31 | | | 30 | | | | 29 | | | 29 | | 30 | | | 3 | | | 3 |
| | | 34 | | 35 | | 33, 34 | | | | | | | | | | | 34, 35 | 4 | | | 4 |
| | | | | | | 37 | | | | 39 | | | 39 | | | 37 | | 5 | | | 5 |
| | 43 | | | | | 42, 43 | | 42 | | | | | | | | | 41 | 6 | | | 6 |
| | | | | 45 | | 45, 46 | | | | | | | | | | | 45 | 7 | | | 7 |
| 50 | | | | | | | | 50 | 49 | | | | | | | | 48 | 8 | | | 8 |
| | | | | | | | | | | | | | | | | | | | • | • | |
| 57 | | 55 | 58 | | 56 | 57 | | 56 | | 56 | | | | 58 | | | | 9 | | | 9 |
| | 61 | 60 | | 62 | | | | 60 | | 60 | 61 | 62 | | 61 | | | | 10 | | | 10 |
| | | | | | | | | | | | | | | | | | | | • | • | |
| 70 | | 69 | | 69 | | 69 | 70 | | 70 | 68 | 68 | | | | | | | 11 | | | 11 |
| | 73 | 72 | | | | 74 | | | | | | 73 | | | 72 | 72 | 74 | 12 | | | 12 |

Learning style instructions are referenced for quick retrieval. Ideas are provided for tactile/kinesthetic, visual, auditory, group learning, and ESL/LEP.

Teaching strategies are highlighted to help you tailor instruction.

Student text features are listed for easy reference.

Activities from the Teacher's Resource Library CD-ROM are all listed. These include:

✓ Lesson Activities
✓ Mastery Tests
✓ Student Study Guides
✓ Workbook Activities

Learning activities specifically geared toward a block schedule accompany each unit.

## Block Scheduling

Here is a suggested teaching activity if you have extended instructional time, such as a block schedule.

**Sport Watch** *To observe the level of fitness required to participate in various professional sports.*

Select four different athletic sports. Watch an entire game of each sport in person, on video, or on TV, keeping a record of the body systems and degree of fitness needed to perform the sport well. For example, the body systems and level of fitness needed for boxing and billiards are very different.

For each sport, compare the necessary muscular and cardiovascular endurance, muscular strength, flexibility, length of time, intensity of effort, and frequency of effort.

Finally, select an individual athlete from one of the sports. Research and write a brief summary of the person's family history. Is athletic "heredity" evident with this person? Why or why not?

20B

# Teacher's Edition Highlights

- Quick overviews of the units, chapters, and lessons save planning time.

- Lesson objectives are listed for easy reference.

- Page references are provided for convenience.

- All materials needed for the lesson are listed.

- Audiocassettes, which offer added reinforcement for student learning, are referenced with lessons.

- Transparencies are referenced with appropriate lessons.

- An introductory discussion or activity opens each lesson by activating prior knowledge and setting the stage for learning.

- Answers are provided for all questions.

---

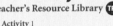

## Lesson at a Glance

### Chapter 1 Lesson 1

**Overview** This lesson describes the parts of a cell and the organization of the body's cells into tissues, organs, and systems.

### Objectives
- To name different kinds of cells in the body.
- To describe parts of a cell and explain what each part does.
- To understand the organization of the body into cells, tissues, organs, and systems.

**Student Pages** 24–25
**Audiocassette** 🎧
**Teacher's Resource Library** (TRL)

Activity 1
Workbook Activity 1

## Teaching Suggestions

### ■ Vocabulary
*cell, cell membrane, cytoplasm, microscope, nucleus, body system, mitosis, organ, tissue*

Point out the vocabulary word *cell* where it appears in both the text and the vocabulary box in the margin. Model how to pronounce difficult words by breaking them into syllables. Read each word and its definition aloud to students, having them locate the word in the text.

### ■ Teaching the Lesson
Use the organization of the textbook to introduce the organization of the human body. Point out that the basic units of the textbook are organized into sections, for example, the section with the heading "What Are Cells?" The sections make up lessons. The lessons make up chapters. The chapters make up units. Have students read the introductory paragraph and the first section on page 24.

### Ask:
- What is a cell? (the basic units that make up all living things)
- Why can't you see cells? (They are too small.)

**24** Chapter 1 The Body Systems

---

### Lesson 1
## Cells, Tissues, and Organs

**Cell**
*The basic unit that makes up your body*

**Cell membrane**
*The outer wall of a cell*

**Cytoplasm**
*The jelly-like material inside the cell membrane*

**Microscope**
*A tool used to see cells*

**Nucleus**
*The control center of the cell*

Look at your skin. What do you see? You may see lines on the skin or flakes of skin. What you cannot see just by looking at your skin are the tiny **cells** that make up your skin. In fact, tiny living units, called cells, make up each part of your body.

### What Are Cells?
Cells are the basic units that make up all living things. Your body is made up of trillions of cells. Cells are too small to see without a tool called a **microscope**. A microscope can make a cell look bigger than it really is, so you can see what it looks like. If you were to look at a cell using a microscope, it might look like the cell shown in Figure 1.1.

Your body is made up of many different kinds of cells. Each kind of cell has its own job. For example, skin cells help keep germs out of your body. White blood cells fight the germs that do enter your body. Nerve cells send messages among the different parts of your body and your brain. Each kind of cell carries out a different job.

### What Are the Main Parts of a Cell?

cytoplasm

cell membrane

nucleus

**Figure 1.1.** A typical cell

Look again at the picture of the cell in Figure 1.1. Most cells have three basic parts: a **cell membrane**, the **cytoplasm**, and a **nucleus**.

The cell membrane is the outer wall of the cell. It is like a thin skin around the cell. Food and oxygen can pass into the cell and wastes can pass out of the cell through the cell membrane. The cytoplasm is a jelly-like liquid inside the cell membrane. The cytoplasm often has other cell parts floating in it. Most of the cell's life activities take place in the cytoplasm. The nucleus is sometimes called the control center of the cell. It has all the information that the cell needs to carry out its job and to make new cells like itself.

**24** Chapter 1 The Body Systems

---

- What is shown in the picture on page 24? (The picture shows the parts of a typical cell. Point out the caption and the labels that convey this fact.)

- How will the picture help you during the lesson? (Point out the words *Parts of a Cell* in the section heading. The picture will help students understand what they read in this section.)

---

The nucleus makes new cells by splitting into two, making one cell two cells. When the two cells split, they become four cells, which split to make eight. This dividing is called **mitosis**. Mitosis allows your body to make new cells to grow or to replace dead cells.

### What Is a Body System?

Cells that do the same job combine to form a **tissue**. Muscles and bones are examples of tissues. Different types of tissues working together form an **organ**, such as the stomach or the kidneys. A group of organs working together to carry out a certain job is called a **body system**. The digestive system is an example of a body system. Each system carries out its own job and works with other systems to keep the body healthy.

**LESSON 1 REVIEW** Write the answers to these questions on a separate sheet of paper. Use complete sentences.

1) Name three different kinds of cells and what they do.
2) Why is a microscope needed to look at cells?
3) How does mitosis help you grow?
4) How is tissue formed?
5) What are the three main parts of a cell, and what does each one do?

**Body system**
*A group of organs that work together to carry out a certain job*

**Mitosis**
*The dividing process that makes new cells*

**Organ**
*A group of tissues that work together*

**Tissue**
*A group of cells that do the same job*

Why are cells called "building blocks of life"?

Writing About Health

All of the systems in your body work together efficiently. Write about how the body must be well organized and balanced for this to happen.

*The Body Systems*   Chapter 1   **25**

---

Have students read about the parts of a cell on pages 24 and 25.

Ask:

- What are the three parts of a cell? Where do you learn this? (cell membrane, cytoplasm, nucleus; in both the picture and the text)

- How are new cells made? What vocabulary word describes this process? (The nucleus of a cell splits into two parts. This dividing process is mitosis. Point out where *mitosis* appears in both the text and the vocabulary box in the margin.)

Have students read about a body system on page 25.

**Lesson 1 Review Answers**
1) Skin cells help keep germs out of the body. White blood cells fight the germs that enter the body. Nerve cells send messages among the different parts of the body and the brain.
2) A microscope is needed because cells are too small to see otherwise.
3) Mitosis allows your body to make new cells.
4) Cells that do the same job combine to form a tissue.
5) Cells are made up of a membrane, the cytoplasm, and a nucleus. The cell membrane is the outer wall of the cell through which food and wastes pass. Most of the cell's life activities take place in the cytoplasm. The nucleus acts as the control center of the cell.

### LEARNING STYLES

**LEP/ESL** Observe as students read the sections of this first lesson to identify those who need help reading the textbook. Partner these students with proficient readers so they can work in teams. The students in a team can read a paragraph or small section silently. Then they can discuss the main idea, supporting details, information in illustrations, and difficult vocabulary words.

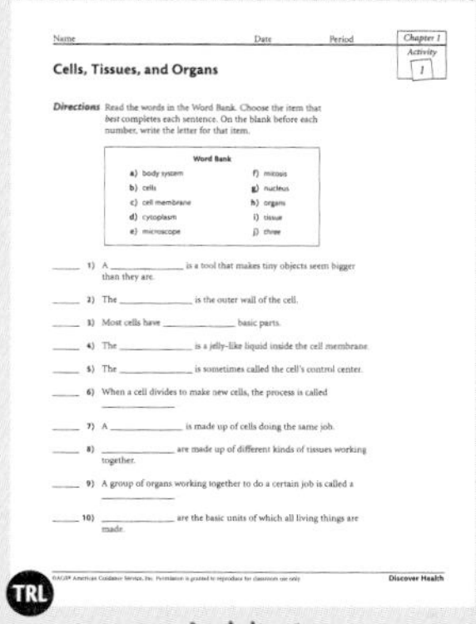

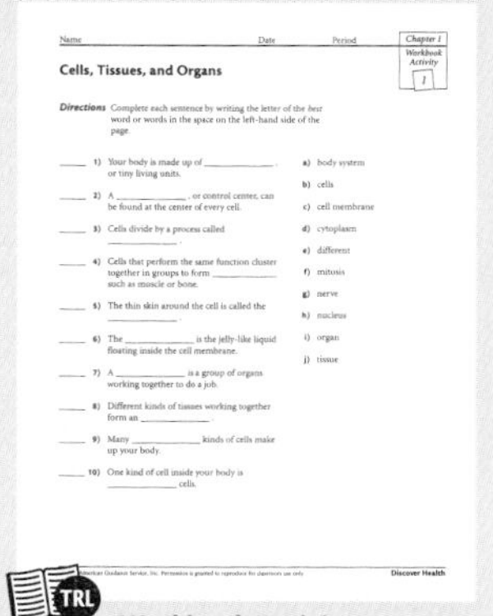

*The Body Systems*   Chapter 1   **25**

---

**Activity 1**

**Workbook Activity 1**

---

Right column teacher notes:

■ **Background Information** provides teachers with additional information to help students understand the lesson.

■ **At Home Applications** offer suggestions for students to apply and practice at home.

■ **Career Connections** provide information on careers in health fields to help students think about future work options.

■ Students are encouraged to relate lessons to the outside world with **Community Applications**.

■ **Learning Styles:** Teaching strategies are provided to help teachers meet the needs of students with diverse learning styles. Modalities included are visual, tactile/kinesthetic, auditory, and group learning. Additional teaching activities are provided for LEP/ESL students.

---

■ Activity, Workbook Activity, Unit Activity, Study Guide, and Mastery Test pages are shown at point of use.

## Discover Health

### Teacher's Resource Library

**AGS®**

© 2000
American Guidance Service, Inc.
Circle Pines, MN 55014-1796
1-800-328-2560

Permission is granted to print and reproduce
the contents of this disk for classroom use only.

### SELECT AN ITEM

- AGS Web Site
- Activities by Component
- Activities by Unit, Chapter, Lesson
- Answer Key
- Activities by National Health Standards
- Instructions

**TRL** All of the activities you'll need to reinforce and extend the text are conveniently located on the AGS Teacher's Resource Library (TRL) CD-ROM. The reproducible activities featured in the Teacher's Edition are ready to view, select, and print. Additionally, you can preview other materials by directly linking to the AGS web site.

### Activities
Lesson activities are available to reinforce vocabulary in each lesson. Activities include fill in the blank, matching, and true/false.

### Workbook Activities
Workbook activities may be reproduced as added reinforcement and practice for lessons. These activities are also available in workbook format.

### Unit Activities
Three unit-level activities include:
**Deciding for Yourself**—activities to encourage students to think more deeply about health issues

**What Do You Think?**—assessments and activities for students to assess their knowledge, set unit learning goals, and describe new learning
**Home Connections**—activities regarding unit content for students and families to share

### Student Study Guides
An outline for each chapter helps students focus on and review main ideas. They provide flexibility for individualized instruction or independent study.

### Mastery Tests
Unit, midterm, and final mastery tests are conveniently referenced as assessment options.

### Answer Key
All answers to reproducible activities are included in the TRL and the Teacher's Edition.

### National Health Education Standards
To focus your instruction on a particular health education standard, you may select from a group of activities that have been organized by standard. This reference will save planning time.

# The Human Body Transparencies

To enhance and clarify instruction of the human body, colorful overheads are available. These 16 overheads reinforce some lessons in the student text.

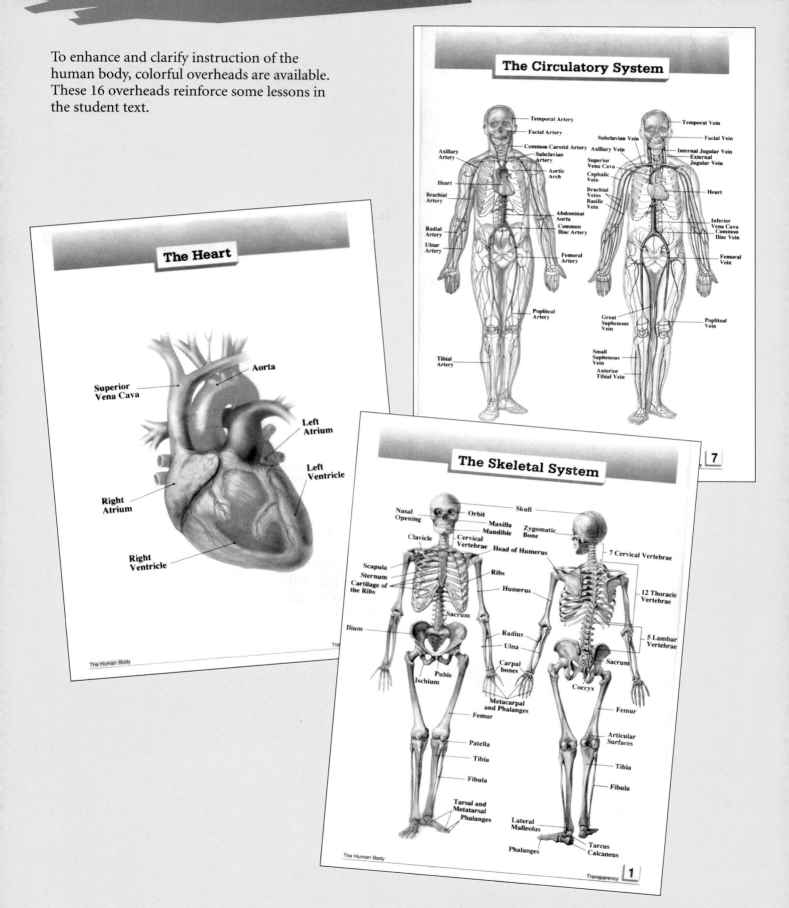

**The Circulatory System**

Temporal Artery
Facial Artery
Common Carotid Artery
Subclavian Artery
Axillary Artery
Aortic Arch
Heart
Brachial Artery
Abdominat Aorta
Common Iliac Artery
Radial Artery
Ulnar Artery
Femoral Artery
Popliteal Artery
Tibial Artery

Temporal Vein
Subclavian Vein
Axillary Vein
Facial Vein
Internal Jugular Vein
External Jugular Vein
Superior Vena Cava
Cephalic Vein
Brachial Veins
Basilic Vein
Heart
Inferior Vena Cava
Common Iliac Vein
Femoral Vein
Great Saphenous Vein
Popliteal Vein
Small Saphenous Vein
Anterior Tibial Vein

7

**The Heart**

Aorta
Superior Vena Cava
Left Atrium
Left Ventricle
Right Atrium
Right Ventricle

The Human Body

**The Skeletal System**

Nasal Opening
Orbit
Skull
Maxilla
Mandible
Zygomatic Bone
Clavicle
Cervical Vertebrae
Head of Humerus
7 Cervical Vertebrae
Scapula
Sternum
Cartilage of the Ribs
Ribs
Humerus
12 Thoracic Vertebrae
Sacrum
Ilium
Radius
Ulna
5 Lumbar Vertebrae
Carpal bones
Sacrum
Pubis
Ischium
Coccyx
Metacarpal and Phalanges
Femur
Femur
Patella
Articular Surfaces
Tibia
Tibia
Fibula
Fibula
Tarsal and Metatarsal Phalanges
Lateral Malleolus
Phalanges
Tarcus
Calcaneus

The Human Body

Transparency 1

# National Health Education Standards

| HEALTH EDUCATION STANDARD 1: Students will comprehend concepts related to health promotion and disease prevention. | Correlation/ Discover Health |
|---|---|
| As a result of health instruction in Grades 5-8, students will: | |
| 1. explain the relationship between positive health behaviors and the prevention of injury, illness, disease, and premature death. | Introduction; Chapter 11: Lesson 2; Chapter 12: Lessons 1, 2; Chapter 14: Lessons 1, 3; Chapter 16: Lesson 3 |
| 2. describe the interrelationship of mental, emotional, social, and physical health during adolescence. | Introduction; Chapter 1: Lesson 1; Chapter 2: Lesson 2; Chapter 4: Lessons 1-3 |
| 3. explain how health is influenced by the interaction of the body systems. | Chapter 1: Lessons 1-8; Chapter 9: Lessons 1-2; Chapter 10: Lesson 1 |
| 4. describe how family and peers influence the health of adolescents. | Chapter 3: Lesson 2; Chapter 4: Lesson 2; Chapter 5: Lesson 3; Chapter 6: Lesson 3 |
| 5. analyze how the environment and personal health are interrelated. | Chapter 8: Lesson 2; Chapter 19: Lessons 1-3 |
| 6. describe ways to reduce risks related to adolescent health problems. | Throughout: Examples; Chapter 2: Lesson 2; Chapter 3: Lesson 2; Chapter 5: Lessons 1, 2, 4; Chapter 6: Lesson 3; Chapter 8: Lessons 1, 4 |
| 7. explain how appropriate health care can prevent premature death and disability. | Throughout: Examples; Chapter 2: Lesson 2; Chapter 3: Lesson 2; Chapter 5: Lesson 4; Chapter 8: Lesson 1; Chapter 9: Lesson 2; Chapter 10: Lesson 1; Chapter 12: Lessons 1, 2 |
| 8. describe how lifestyle, pathogens, family history, and other risk factors are related to the cause or prevention of disease and other health problems. | Chapter 2: Lessons 1, 2; Unit 5: Deciding for Yourself; Chapter 9: Lesson 2; Chapter 10: Lessons 1, 2; Chapter 11: Lesson 1 |

| HEALTH EDUCATION STANDARD 2: Students will demonstrate the ability to access valid health information and health-promoting products and services. | Correlation/ Discover Health |
|---|---|
| As a result of health instruction in Grades 5-8, students will: | |
| 1. analyze the validity of health information, products, and services. | Chapter 7: Lesson 5; Chapter 8: Lessons 1-4; Chapter 17: Lessons 1-6 |
| 2. demonstrate the ability to utilize resources from home, school, and community that provide valid health information. | Chapter 7: Lesson 5; Chapter 8: Lessons 1-4; Chapter 17: Lessons 2, 4, 6 |
| 3. analyze how media influence the selection of health information and products. | Chapter 8: Lesson 2; Unit 3: Deciding for Yourself; Chapter 17: Lessons 4, 5 |
| 4. demonstrate the ability to locate health products and services. | Chapter 3: Lesson 2; Chapter 4: Lesson 2; Chapter 5: Lesson 3; Chapter 6: Lesson 3 |
| 5. compare the costs and validity of products. | Chapter 8: Lesson 3; Chapter 17: Lessons 2-5 |
| 6. describe situations requiring professional health services. | Chapter 5: Lesson 4; Chapter 10: Lesson 2; Chapter 12: Lessons 1, 2; Chapter 18: Lesson 2 |

| HEALTH EDUCATION STANDARD 3: Students will demonstrate the ability to practice health-enhancing behaviors and reduce health risks. | Correlation/ Discover Health |
|---|---|
| As a result of health instruction in Grades 5-8, students will: | |
| 1. explain the importance of assuming responsibility for personal health behaviors. | Introduction; Chapter 2: Lessons 1-2; Chapter 8: Lesson 1; Chapter 10: Lesson 2; Chapter 12: Lessons 1, 2; Chapter 16: Lesson 3; Throughout: Action for Health Features |
| 2. analyze a personal health assessment to determine health strengths and risks. | Introduction; Unit 1: Deciding for Yourself |
| 3. distinguish between safe and risky or harmful behaviors in relationships. | Chapter 4: Lessons 2, 3; Chapter 6: Lessons 2, 3 |
| 4. demonstrate strategies to improve or maintain personal and family health. | Chapter 1: Action for Health; Chapter 2: Lessons 1, 2; Chapter 3: Lessons 1, 2; Chapter 4: Lessons 1, 2, Action for Health |
| 5. develop injury prevention and management strategies for personal and family health. | Chapter 14: Lessons 1-3, 5; Chapter 15: Lesson 2 |
| 6. demonstrate ways to avoid and reduce threatening situations. | Chapter 16: Lesson 3 |
| 7. demonstrate strategies to manage stress. | Chapter 2: Lesson 2; Chapter 3: Lesson 2, Writing About Health; Chapter 4: Lessons 1, 3, Fitness Tip |

| HEALTH EDUCATION STANDARD 4: Students will analyze the influence of culture, media, technology, and other factors on health. | Correlation/ Discover Health |
|---|---|
| As a result of health instruction in Grades 5-8, students will: | |
| 1. describe the influences of cultural beliefs on health behaviors and the use of health services. | Chapter 8: Lesson 2 |
| 2. analyze how messages from media and other sources influence health behavior. | Chapter 8: Lesson 2; Chapter 17: Lessons 4, 5 |
| 3. analyze the influence of technology on personal and family health. | Technology Features Throughout. Examples- Chapter 7: Lesson 5; Chapter 9: Lesson 4; Chapter 17: Lesson 5 |
| 4. analyze how information from peers influences health. | Chapter 5: Lesson 3; Chapter 6: Lesson 3 |

# National Health Standards

| HEALTH EDUCATION STANDARD 5: Students will demonstrate the ability to use interpersonal communication skills to enhance health. | Correlation/ Discover Health |
|---|---|
| As a result of health instruction in Grades 5-8, students will: | |
| 1. demonstrate effective verbal and non-verbal communication skills to enhance health. | Chapter 5: Lessons 1-3; Throughout: Deciding for Yourself, Writing About Health, and Action for Health Features |
| 2. describe how the behavior of family and peers affects interpersonal communication. | Chapter 3: Lesson 2; Chapter 5: Lesson 3 |
| 3. demonstrate healthy ways to express needs, wants, and feelings. | Chapter 4: Lesson 3; Chapter 5: Lessons 1-4; Chapter 6: Lessons 1-3 |
| 4. demonstrate ways to communicate care, consideration, and respect of self and others. | Chapter 4: Lesson 3; Chapter 6: Lessons 1-3 |
| 5. demonstrate communication skills to build and maintain healthy relationships. | Chapter 5: Lesson 3; Chapter 6: Lessons 2, 3; Unit 2: Deciding for Yourself |
| 6. demonstrate refusal and negotiation skills to enhance health. | Chapter 5: Lessons 1-3; Chapter 6: Lesson 3; Chapter 9: Lesson 6, Health Tip; Chapter 10: Lesson 2 |
| 7. analyze the possible causes of conflict among youth in schools and communities. | Chapter 4: Lessons 2, 3 |
| 8. demonstrate strategies to manage conflict in healthy ways. | Chapter 4: Lesson 3; Chapter 5: Lesson 3 |

| HEALTH EDUCATION STANDARD 6: Students will demonstrate the ability to use goal-setting and decision-making skills to enhance health. | Correlation/ Discover Health |
|---|---|
| As a result of health instruction in Grades 5-8, students will: | |
| 1. demonstrate the ability to apply a decision-making process to health issues individually and collaboratively. | Chapter 10: Lesson 2; Chapter 14: Lesson 1; Chapter 16: Lesson 3; Throughout: Action for Health, Deciding for Yourself Features |
| 2. analyze how health-related decisions are influenced by individuals, family, and community values. | Chapter 5: Lesson 3; Chapter 8: Lesson 2; Throughout: Writing About Health, Deciding for Yourself Features |
| 3. predict how decisions regarding health behaviors have consequences for self and others. | Throughout: Examples-Chapter 2: Lesson 2; Chapter 3: Lesson 2; Chapter 6: Lesson 3; Chapter 8: Lesson 1; Chapter 10: Lesson 1 |
| 4. apply strategies and skills needed to attain personal health goals. | Throughout: Writing About Health, Action for Health, Deciding for Yourself Features |
| 5. describe how personal health goals are influenced by changing information, abilities, priorities, and responsibilities. | Chapter 3: Lesson 1; Chapter 6: Lesson 1; Chapter 14: Lesson 1; Chapter 17: Lesson 4 |
| 6. develop a plan that addresses personal strengths, needs, and health risks. | Introduction; Unit 1: Deciding for Yourself; Throughout: Action for Health Features |

| HEALTH EDUCATION STANDARD 7: Students will demonstrate the ability to advocate for personal, family, and community health. | Correlation/ Discover Health |
|---|---|
| As a result of health instruction in Grades 5-8, students will: | |
| 1. analyze various communication methods to accurately express health information and ideas. | Chapter 7: Lesson 4; Chapter 19: Lesson 4; Throughout: Writing for Health, Action for Health Features |
| 2. express information and opinions about health issues. | Throughout: Writing About Health, Action for Health, Deciding for Yourself Features |
| 3. identify barriers to effective communication of information, ideas, feelings, and opinions about health issues. | Chapter 4: Lesson 3; Chapter 5: Lesson 3; Throughout: Writing About Health Features |
| 4. demonstrate the ability to influence and support others in making positive health choices. | Chapter 14: Lessons 3, 5; Chapter 15: Lessons 3, 4; Chapter 16: Lesson 3; Chapter 19: Lesson 4 |
| 5. demonstrate the ability to work cooperatively when advocating for healthy individuals, families, and schools. | Chapter 18: Lesson 3; Throughout: Action for Health Features |

# Block Scheduling

**If you have extended instructional time, such as a block schedule, here are some suggestions:**

■ *Have a short-term and long-term instructional plan.* Focus on what students need to know and what they must be able to do to achieve learner outcomes and standards.

■ *Strive for variety in student assessment strategies.* Allow students to use many different ways to demonstrate that they know or can do something. Some students express their wisdom and achievements by writing, speaking, drawing, or acting or through music, comics, humor, video, or dance. Expand student options for learning—and ways each student can demonstrate that learning.

■ *Strive for student relevance.* Be prepared for the question, "Why do we have to learn this?" Students should be able to answer these questions with each major topic or issue from *Discover Health*:

- Where am I?
- Where is a healthy (or healthier) place to be?
- How do I get there? (What do I need to know and be able to do?)
- How do I stay there? (What do I need to know and be able to do?)
- How can I help others improve?

■ *Expand your classroom.* Extended periods often allow for field trips and alternative learning environments. Take students to nearby libraries, businesses, public and private agencies, and schools. Students can do independent research in the community.

■ *Increase your role as a coach and facilitator.* Be an academic coach. Provide experiences, guidance, and support that increases students' confidence, knowledge, and skills.

**Focus and Warm-Up** 5-15%

**Direct Teaching** 15-25%

**Student Performance** 35-45%

**Review** 15-25%

**Closure** 5-15%

## Focus and Warm-Up
- ✔ review previous learning
- ✔ set stage for next lesson

## Direct Teaching
- ✔ demonstrations
- ✔ lectures
- ✔ multimedia
- ✔ guest speakers

## Student Performance
- ✔ individual/team work
- ✔ computer/technology applications
- ✔ student presentations
- ✔ creations, videos, posters, advocacy strategies
- ✔ inventions, discovery
- ✔ inquiry, analysis, assessments, evaluations

## Review
- ✔ learning journals
- ✔ writing about health
- ✔ active questioning
- ✔ sharing
- ✔ reviewing notes and materials
- ✔ summarizing

## Closure
- ✔ collecting assignments
- ✔ homework
- ✔ reminders

The publisher wishes to thank Dr. Robert Wandberg, John F. Kennedy High School, Bloomington, Minnesota, for these suggestions.

**AGS**

Discover
Health

**AGS**

American Guidance Service, Inc.
Circle Pines, Minnesota 55014-1796
800-328-2560

**Photos:**

pp. 4, 90—Don Smetzer/Tony Stone Images; pp. 6, 186-87, 196, 199, 206—Michael Crousek; p. 10 —Drew Tempe; pp. 16, 126—Lori Adamski Peek/Tony Stone Images; pp. 20-21, 106—Laura Dwight/ Laura Dwight Photography; p. 22—Bill Bachmann/PhotoEdit; pp. 23, 54, 66—Jim Cummins/ Tony Stone Images; p. 24—Bo Veisland, MI&I/Science Photo Library/Photo Researchers, Inc.; pp. 58, 164, 345, 368, 376, 384— Mary Kate Denny/PhotoEdit; pp. 60, 72, 120, 123, 136-37, 215, 265, 328—David Young-Wolff/ PhotoEdit; pp. 68, 82-83— SuperStock International; p. 84—Mark Richards/PhotoEdit; pp. 85, 100, 118—Skjold Photography; pp. 86, 140, 333— David Kelly Crow/PhotoEdit; p. 93—D. MacDonald/ PhotoEdit; pp. 96, 113, 160 bottom, 201, 218, 282, 289, 305, 312, 388—Tony Freeman/ PhotoEdit; pp. 102, 262—Zigy Kaluzny/Tony Stone Images;

p. 109—Penny Tweedie/Tony Stone Images; p. 138—Spencer Grant/PhotoEdit; pp. 139, 158, 173, 185, 212, 264, 296, 307, 347, 359, 378—Michael Newman/ PhotoEdit; pp. 142, 147, 149— Felicia Martinez/PhotoEdit; pp. 143, 184, 280-81—Richard Hutchings/PhotoEdit; p. 145— Steven Needham/Envision; p. 150—Shaun Egan/TSI; p. 151— U.S. Dept. of Agriculture; p. 160 top—Chris Everard/Tony Stone Images; p. 182-83—David Hanover/Tony Stone Images; p. 192—Courtesy of Pathways Magazine and Toronto Public Health; pp. 228-29—Hubbard/ Gamma Liaison International; p. 230—Robin L. Sachs/PhotoEdit; pp. 231, 242, 254—I. Burgum/ P. Boorman/Tony Stone Images; p. 237—Robert Brenner/ PhotoEdit; p. 246—AP/Wide World Photos; pp. 249, 255— Myrleen Ferguson/PhotoEdit; p. 256—John Bavosi/Science Photo Library/Photo Researchers, Inc.; p. 268—Hans-Ulrich

Osterwalder/Science Photo Library/Photo Researchers, Inc.; p. 271—James Shaffer/PhotoEdit; pp. 283, 304, 322—Gary Holscher/ Tony Stone Images; p. 285— Donald Johnston/Tony Stone Images; p. 297—David Weintraub/ Photo Researchers, Inc.; p. 298— A. Ramey/PhotoEdit; p. 310— Courtesy of the American Red Cross. All Rights Reserved in all Countries, American Red Cross; p. 324—Jonathan Nourak/ PhotoEdit; p. 342-43—David Joel/Tony Stone Images; p. 344— Robert E. Daemmrich/Tony Stone Images; p. 352—Chuck Keeler/ Tony Stone Images; p. 355— Bruce Ayres/Tony Stone Images; p. 370—Jeff Greenberg/Unicorn Stock Photos; p. 387—Anne Heller; p. 390—Nello Giambi/ Tony Stone Images; p. 394—David Woodfall/Tony Stone Images; p. 396—David Young-Wolff/Tony Stone Images; p. 398—Robert Cameron/Tony Stone Images; p. 409—1998 PhotoDisc; p. 413— Custom Medical Stock

Printed in the United States of America

ISBN 0-7854-1843-1

Product Number 91050

A 0 9 8 7 6 5 4 3 2 1

# Contents

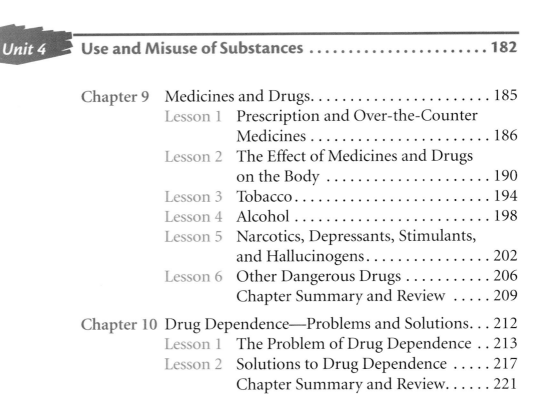

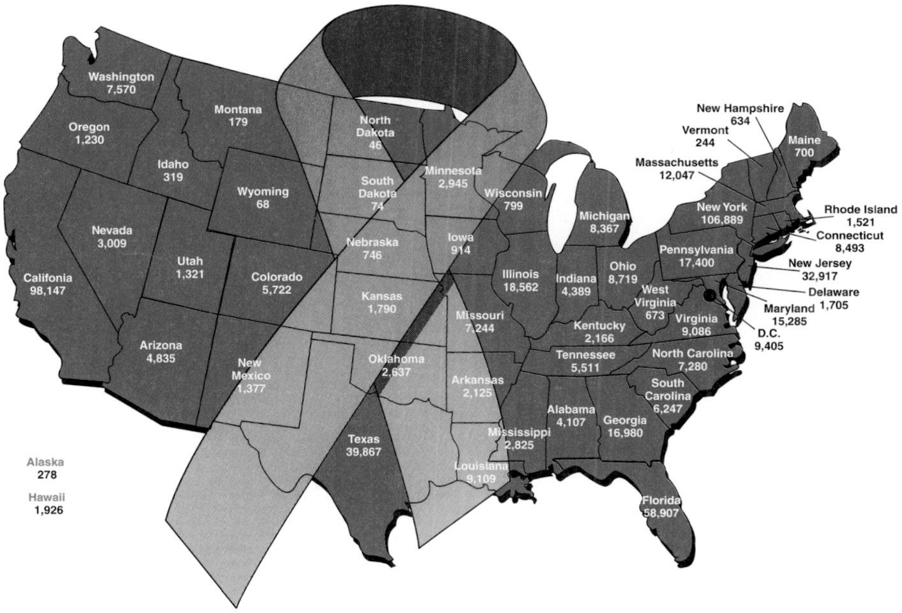

Washington 7,570
Oregon 1,230
Idaho 319
Montana 179
North Dakota 46
Minnesota 2,945
Wisconsin 799
Michigan 8,367
New Hampshire 634
Vermont 244
Maine 700
Massachusetts 12,047
New York 106,889
Rhode Island 1,521
Connecticut 8,493
New Jersey 32,917
Delaware 1,705
Maryland 15,285
D.C. 9,405
Pennsylvania 17,400
Ohio 8,719
West Virginia 673
Virginia 9,086
Indiana 4,389
Illinois 18,562
Iowa 914
South Dakota 74
Wyoming 68
Nebraska 746
Nevada 3,009
Utah 1,321
Colorado 5,722
California 98,147
Kansas 1,790
Missouri 7,244
Kentucky 2,166
Tennessee 5,511
North Carolina 7,280
South Carolina 6,247
Arizona 4,835
New Mexico 1,377
Oklahoma 2,637
Arkansas 2,125
Alabama 4,107
Georgia 16,980
Mississippi 2,825
Texas 39,867
Louisiana 9,109
Florida 58,907
Alaska 278
Hawaii 1,926




*Discover Health Contents* **7**

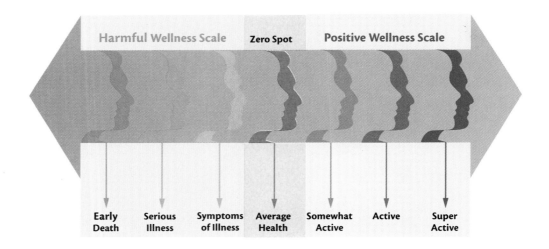

| Harmful Wellness Scale | | | Zero Spot | Positive Wellness Scale | | |
|---|---|---|---|---|---|---|
| Early Death | Serious Illness | Symptoms of Illness | Average Health | Somewhat Active | Active | Super Active |

**How to Use This Book:**
**A Study Guide**

**Overview** This section may be used to introduce the study of health, to preview the book's features, and to review effective study skills.

**Objectives**

- To introduce the study of health.
- To preview the student textbook.
- To review study skills.

**Student Pages** 10–15

**Teacher's Resource Library** **TRL**

**Student Study Guides** 1–6

## Introduction to the Book

Have volunteers read aloud the first two paragraphs of the introduction. Discuss with students why studying health is important and what kinds of things people can learn from studying health.

### ■ How to Study

Read aloud each bulleted suggestion, pausing to discuss with students why the suggestion is a part of good study habits. Distribute copies of Student Study Guide 1, "Study Habits Survey." Read the directions together and then have students complete the survey. After they have scored their surveys, ask students to make a list of the study habits they plan to work on improving. After three or four weeks, have students complete the survey again to see if they have improved their study habits. Suggest that they keep the survey and review it every month or so to see whether they are maintaining and improving their study habits.

# How to Use This Book: A Study Guide

Welcome to the study of health. Everyone wants to have good health and wellness. Studying health helps you to learn ways to promote wellness. It helps you identify causes of health problems and ways to prevent them.

As you read the units, chapters, and lessons of this book, you will learn about promoting emotional, physical, and social health.

## How to Study

- Plan a regular time to study.
- Choose a quiet desk or table where you will not be distracted. Find a spot that has good lighting.
- Gather all the books, pencils, and paper you need to complete your assignments.
- Decide on a goal. For example: "I will finish reading and taking notes on Chapter 1, Lesson 1, by 8:00."
- Take a five- to ten-minute break every hour to keep alert.
- If you start to feel sleepy, take a short break and get some fresh air.

**10** *How to Use This Book: A Study Guide*

---

Name _____ Date _____ Period _____

*Student Study Guide*

*1*

*page 1*

**Study Habits Survey**

*Directions* Here are 25 statements about studying. If a statement describes what you really do—not what you think you should do—mark a *T* for True on the blank. If the statement is not how you study, mark an *F* for False on the blank.

**Study Habits**

_____ 1) I have a regular study time.

_____ 2) I listen to the radio or watch TV as I study.

_____ 3) As I study, I try to express in my own words what the book is saying.

_____ 4) My study time is often interrupted by phone calls or talking to people.

_____ 5) I set goals for how much reading I will complete by a certain time.

_____ 6) I usually sit in an easy chair or lie down to study.

_____ 7) Before reading about a topic, I look over the material to see what it is about.

_____ 8) If I start to feel sleepy, I take a nap.

_____ 9) I try to figure out how what I am studying will be useful to me later.

**Taking Notes**

_____ 10) I try to get the teacher's exact words down when I take notes.

_____ 11) I put my notes in outline form as soon after taking them as possible.

_____ 12) I rewrite all of my notes.

_____ 13) When I rewrite my notes, I put them in outline form and fill in important details.

_____ 14) I seldom take notes on my reading assignments.

_____ 15) As I listen to teachers, I think about what they are saying.

_____ 16) I write down everything the teacher says.

_____ 17) During lectures, I look at the teacher when I am not taking notes.

**TRL** ©AGS® American Guidance Service, Inc. Permission is granted to reproduce for classroom use only. **Discover Health**

**Student Study Guide 1, page 1**

Name _____ Date _____ Period _____

*Student Study Guide*

*1*

*page 2*

**Study Habits Survey,** *continued*

**Taking Tests**

_____ 18) If I have trouble with a question, I don't move on until I can answer it.

_____ 19) I think through the test questions before I begin to answer them.

_____ 20) I only review by rereading or scanning the material on which I am to be tested.

_____ 21) On essay tests, I outline my answers before beginning to write them.

_____ 22) I think many test questions are tricky and are meant to fool me.

_____ 23) I review my notes before a test and think about what questions will be asked.

_____ 24) I stay up late the night before a test to study.

_____ 25) I look over the entire test before I start answering questions.

The odd-numbered questions on this survey reflect good study habits. Give yourself a point for every odd-numbered question you answered with a True. Then give yourself a point for every even-numbered question you answered with a False. Decide on which study habits you would like to improve. Take the survey again after you have worked on improving your study skills. Compare your score on the odd-numbered items to see if you are making progress.

**TRL** ©AGS® American Guidance Service, Inc. Permission is granted to reproduce for classroom use only. **Discover Health**

**Student Study Guide 1, page 2**

## Before Beginning Each Unit

- Read the title and the opening paragraph.

- Study the photograph. What does the photo say to you about health?

- What does the quotation say to you?

- Read the titles of the chapters in the unit.

- Read "What Do You Think?" and consider what you would do in that situation.

- Look at the headings of the lessons and paragraphs to help you locate main ideas.

- Read the chapter and unit summaries to help you identify key issues.

- Read the Deciding for Yourself page at the end of each unit.

Each unit covers a different health topic.

## ■ Before Beginning Each Unit

When students begin their study of Unit 1, you may wish to have them read aloud and follow each of the bulleted suggestions on page 11. Actually trying the suggestions will help them understand what they are supposed to do and recognize how useful the suggestions are when students preview a unit. At the beginning of subsequent units, refer students to page 11 and encourage them to follow the suggestions. You may wish to continue to do this as a class each time or allow students to work independently.

In addition to the suggestions on page 11, the text in the Teacher's Edition that accompanies each Unit Opener offers teaching suggestions and questions for the unit introduction, illustrations, and quotation. The text also includes a list of the chapters and Teacher's Resource Library (TRL) materials in the unit as well as a list of outside resource materials for teachers and students, including books, videos, and software.

A Unit Opener organizes information in an easy-to-read form. To help students organize their time and work in an easy-to-follow form, have them fill out Student Study Guide 2, "Weekly Schedule." Encourage them to keep the schedule in a notebook or folder where they can refer to it easily. Suggest that they review the schedule periodically and update it as necessary.

**TRL**

**Student Study Guide 2**

## ■ Before Beginning Each Chapter

When students begin their study of Chapter 1, have them turn to page 23 in their textbooks. Read aloud the first bulleted statement at the top of page 12. Have a volunteer find and read aloud the Chapter 1 title. Read aloud the second bulleted statement and have volunteers take turns reading aloud the Goals for Learning for Chapter 1. Discuss with students why knowing these goals can help them when they are studying the chapter. Ask students to look at the long narrow photograph on the page. Ask students how it might relate to body systems.

## ■ Before Beginning Each Lesson

Read through the information on page 12 with students. Then assign each of the eight lessons in Chapter 1 to a small group of students. Have them make a list of the features in their lesson and be prepared to report to the class on their findings. Encourage them to speculate on the content of the features based on the features' titles.

Now that students are familiar with the unit, chapter, and lesson structure and features of the textbook, help them become familiar with other features and parts of the book. Distribute copies of Student Study Guide 3, "Finding Information." Point out that there are many possible answers for most of the features in the list, but for several features, there is only one correct answer. You may wish to remind students of a book feature that is particularly useful for completing this activity—the Table of Contents. When students have finished filling in the master, ask volunteers to read some of their answers and have the other students check to see that the page numbers and titles are correct.

## *Before Beginning Each Chapter*

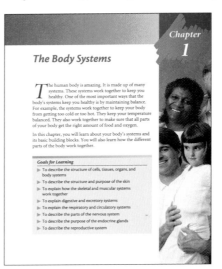

- ■ Read the chapter title.

- ■ Study the goals for learning. The chapter review and tests will ask questions related to these goals.

## *Before Beginning Each Lesson*

Read the lesson title and restate it in the form of a question. For example:

### Lesson 1
*A Healthy Diet*

Write: *What is a healthy diet?*

Look over the entire lesson, noting . . .

- • pictures
- • tables
- • charts
- • figures
- • bold words
- • text organization
- • questions in the margins
- • lesson review

**Student Study Guide 3**

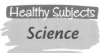
Healthy Subjects
Science

Action for Health

Also note these features . . .

- Action for Health—An action you can take
- Careers—A health career and its requirements
- Healthy Subjects—A subject such as math or literature related to the chapter topic
- Technology—A technology advance related to the chapter topic
- Then and Now—An explanation of how health was approached in earlier years compared with today
- Tips—A short, easy-to-use tip on health, fitness, safety, or nutrition
- Writing About Health—Write about how a topic applies to your health and life

### As You Read the Lesson

- Read the major headings. Each subhead is a question.
- Read the paragraphs that follow to answer the question.
- Before moving on to the next heading, see if you can answer the question. If you cannot, reread the section to look for the answers. If you are still unsure, ask for help.
- Answering the questions in the lesson will help you determine if you know the lesson's key ideas.

### Using the Bold Words

Knowing the meaning of all the boxed words in the left column will help you understand what you read.

These words appear in **bold type** the first time they appear in the text and are defined in the paragraph.

> Proteins are made up of smaller units called **amino acids.**

All of the words in the left column are also defined in the **glossary**.

> **Amino acids**—The smaller units of protein (p. 144)

**Bold type**
*Words seen for the first time will appear in bold type*

**Glossary**
*Words listed in this column are also found in the glossary*

### ■ As You Read the Lesson

Have students turn to page 24 in their textbooks. Read aloud the first bulleted statement on page 13 of this Introduction and have a volunteer read aloud the first subhead in Lesson 1 of Chapter 1—What Are Cells? Then read the second bulleted statement and have volunteers read the two paragraphs under the subhead. After reading the last two bulleted statements, ask students to answer the question in the subhead in their own words, either orally or on paper. You may wish to repeat this procedure using the other two subhead questions in Lesson 1 of Chapter 1.

### ■ Using the Bold Words

Read aloud the information on Using the Bold Words on page 13 of this Introduction. Make sure students understand what the terms *bold type* and *glossary* mean. Then ask students to look at the boxed words on page 24. Have a volunteer read the first boxed word (cell) and then find and read the sentence in the text in which that word appears in bold type. Have another volunteer read the definition of the word in the box and then find and read the definition given in the text. Have a third volunteer find and read the definition of the word in the glossary at the back of the textbook.

Point out that boxed words may appear on other pages in a lesson besides the first page. Have students look at the boxed words on page 25. Explain that these words appear in a box here because they are used in the text on this page. Have volunteers find and read the sentences in the text in which the vocabulary words are used.

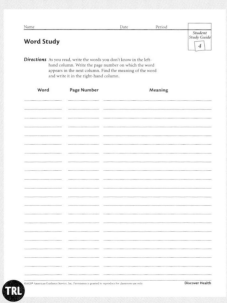

| Name | Date | Period | Student Study Guide 4 |

**Word Study**

*Directions* As you read, write the words you don't know in the left-hand column. Write the page number on which the word appears in the next column. Find the meaning of the word and write it in the right-hand column.

| Word | Page Number | Meaning |
| --- | --- | --- |

Discover Health

TRL

**Student Study Guide 4**

## ■ Taking Notes in Class

Before reading the information in this section on page 14, ask students why note taking is an important study skill. Encourage them to tell what method they use to take notes during class discussions or when reading. Ask them to explain why they use the method they do. Then have volunteers read the information on page 14. Suggest that students who do not have a method for taking notes try one of the methods mentioned and see how it works for them.

## ■ Using an Outline

If students are unfamiliar with outlines, discuss the format of an outline. Using the example shown on page 14, point out the title, the main headings (the ones with Roman numerals), and the sub-headings (the ones with capital letters). Explain that if a subheading has details listed under it, they would be numbered 1, 2, and so on. Then ask students to copy the partial outline onto a sheet of paper and complete the outline using information from Chapter 7. Students may want to include more than two subheadings or add details under the subheadings.

Explain that an outline is only one kind of graphic organizer, or way of organizing information visually to make it easier to understand and remember. Distribute copies of Student Study Guide 5, "Organizing Information," to students. Ask a volunteer to read the directions. Then have students fill in the graphic organizer using the information they wrote earlier on the outline. Discuss with students what they did or did not like about using each method. This Student Study Guide can be used with any lesson or chapter to have students organize the information in the lesson or chapter.

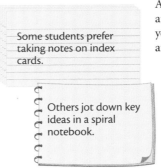

Some students prefer taking notes on index cards.

Others jot down key ideas in a spiral notebook.

As you read, you will be learning many new facts and ideas. Your notes will be useful and will help you remember when preparing for class discussions and studying for tests.

- Always write the main ideas and supporting details.
- Use an outline format to help save time.
- Keep your notes brief. You may want to set up some abbreviations to speed up your note-taking. For example: *with = w/  and = +  dollars = $*
- Use the same method all the time. Then when you study for a test, you will know where to find the information you need to review.

Here are some tips for taking notes during class discussion:

- Use your own words.
- Do not try to write everything the teacher says.
- Write down important information only.
- Don't be concerned about writing in complete sentences. Use phrases.
- Be brief.
- Rewrite your notes to fill in possible gaps as soon as you can after class.

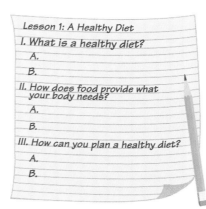

Lesson 1: A Healthy Diet
I. What is a healthy diet?
   A.
   B.
II. How does food provide what your body needs?
   A.
   B.
III. How can you plan a healthy diet?
   A.
   B.

### Using an Outline

You may want to outline the section using the subheads as your main points. An outline will help you remember the major points of the section. An example of an outline is shown at left. Your teacher may have you use the Student Study Guide for this book.

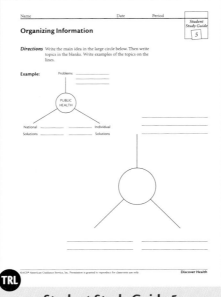

Name _____ Date _____ Period _____

Student Study Guide 5

**Organizing Information**

*Directions* Write the main idea in the large circle below. Then write topics in the blanks. Write examples of the topics on the lines.

**Example:**

Problems

PUBLIC HEALTH

National Solutions            Individual Solutions

**Student Study Guide 5**

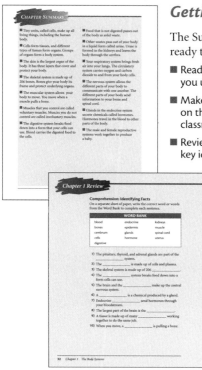

## Getting Ready to Take a Test

The Summaries and Reviews can help you get ready to take tests.

- Read the summaries from your text to make sure you understand the chapter's main ideas.

- Make up a sample test of items you think may be on the test. You may want to do this with a classmate and share your questions.

- Review your notes and test yourself on words and key ideas.

  - Practice writing about some of the main ideas from the chapter.

  - Answer the questions under Identifying Facts.

  - Answer the questions under Understanding the Main Ideas.

  - Write what you think about the questions under Write Your Opinion.

## Use the Test Taking Tip

- Read the Test Taking Tip with each Chapter Review of the text.

**Test Taking Tip**  If you know you will have to define certain terms on a test, write the term on one side of a card. Write its definition on the other side. Use the cards to test yourself, or work with a partner.

**Student Study Guide 6**

## Getting Ready to Take a Test

Begin a general discussion of tests and test taking. Encourage students to offer their opinions about tests and their ideas on test-taking strategies. What do they do to study for a test? List their comments on the board. Then read the first sentence and set of bulleted statements on page 15. Add these suggestions to the list on the board if they are not already there.

## Use the Test Taking Tip

Have students turn to the Chapter Review at the end of any chapter in the textbook and find the Test Taking Tip. You might have several volunteers read aloud the tips they find in the Chapter Reviews.

## Writing Activities

Explain to students that they will be doing writing activities at certain points in the chapters. To show students an example, have them turn to page 25 and look at the Writing About Health feature. Note that this feature asks students to list ways to reach a goal that they have not yet reached. Then distribute copies of Student Study Guide 6 and ask students to write their goal and ways to meet it. This Study Guide can be given to students to use with the Writing About Health features or any other suggested writing activity.

## Introduction

**Overview** This section emphasizes the importance of health and wellness and the connection of physical, social, and emotional health to overall well-being.

## Objectives

- To introduce and describe health and wellness.

- To describe actions that improve the quality of life.

**Student Pages** 16–19

## Teaching Suggestions

Ask students to describe how they react when something upsets them. Prompt them to describe how they feel physically, how their moods change, and how their reactions affect their relationship to the people around them.

Have students read pages 16 and 17 to find out about physical, social, and emotional well-being. Challenge students to think about their own health and well-being as they read and study the introduction.

### Ask:

- What are the three parts of good health? (physical health, social health, emotional health)

- How are physical, social, and emotional health related to each other? (Physical illnesses affect how we feel about ourselves and how we relate to others; emotional illness can contribute to physical illness.)

## Introduction

Good health is basic to everything in life. Without health, people have difficulty doing the things they want to do. But health is more than being without illness. Health is a state of being healthy. There are three parts of good health.

- *Physical health* is the body's ability to meet the demands of daily living. It allows a person to do things without getting tired and run-down. For example, it allows you to attend school, to study, and to participate in after-school activities.

- *Social health* is the ability to get along with other people. It is the ability to make friends and to be a friend. Social health is the ability to work with others and to perform effectively as part of a group. It involves contributing to the good of the family and helping out in the community.

**16** *Introduction*

It involves trust, honesty, respect, responsibility, fairness, and good citizenship.

- *Emotional health* is the ability to handle the problems and pressures of daily living. It also involves feeling good about oneself. It involves controlling and managing anger without turning to violence.

The physical, social, and emotional parts of health are all connected. If people are physically ill, it affects how they feel about themselves. Physical illness affects the ability to relate well with other people. In a similar way, emotional problems can contribute to physical illnesses such as heart disease. For example, you may feel extra tired when you have pressures at home or at school. You may notice you are more likely to have accidents or to get upset when you are worried about something.

### How Is Good Health Achieved?

Good health is something that everyone must achieve for himself or herself. We all should work toward promoting good physical, social, and emotional health and preventing illness. Like playing a musical instrument well, good health requires practicing certain basic rules for keeping healthy. For example, everyone needs to practice developing good friendships. We all need to practice handling our feelings appropriately. Good health requires that we use good judgment and self-control to provide the body with the food, exercise, rest, and care it needs.

- **Exercise regularly.**
- **Eat three balanced, healthy meals daily, including breakfast.**
- **Choose to eat only healthy snacks.**
- **Maintain a normal weight for your height and age.**
- **Sleep eight hours each night.**
- **Do not smoke, drink alcohol, or use drugs that a doctor hasn't directed you to take.**
- **Get reliable medical and dental care and advice.**

Achieving and maintaining good health is largely within our control. By practicing the healthy behaviors listed in the box, we can help increase the quality and length of our life.

All of these behaviors are a way of preventing health problems and achieving wellness.

*Introduction* **17**

Discuss the seven behaviors described on page 17, asking students to suggest how each behavior helps to prevent illness or promote good social or emotional health.

### Ask:

- Why do you think it's important to exercise on a regular schedule? (Exercising once in a while is not as helpful to our bodies as regular exercise. Regular exercise maintains muscle strength and the heart system at a healthier level.)

- What are some healthy snacks? (fruit, vegetables, milk)

- What are some unhealthy snacks? (foods high in fat and sugar, such as candy, french fries, soft drinks)

Invite students to chart their health behaviors for a week. Suggest that they list six behaviors down the side of a sheet of paper and then make seven columns across. At the end of each day, they should put a check after each behavior they have done. At the end of the week, students will be able to review their habits. Point out that students may be surprised to find out what they are doing well and what they can improve.

Have students read page 18 to find out more about wellness. Ask students to look at the Wellness Scale on page 18. On the Harmful Wellness side of the scale, ask students to name some serious illnesses they know about and some of the symptoms associated with those illnesses. On the Positive Wellness side of the scale, encourage students to describe how much time they think somewhat active, active, or super active people spend exercising each day. Point out that guidelines for maintaining a healthy heart suggest vigorous exercise for at least twenty minutes three times a week.

## Ask:

- What is wellness? (a state of health in which a person's physical, social, and emotional health are in balance)

- If a person had average health and didn't do any physical activity, do you think the person would stay healthy for his or her entire life? (It would depend on the person's family health history, whether the person's job involved physical movement, and the person's diet. Most experts agree that regular physical activity promotes better health.)

## The Wellness Scale

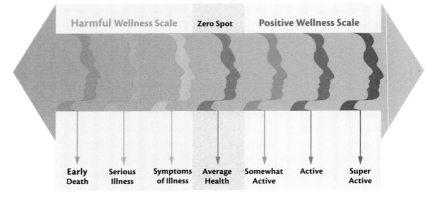

| Harmful Wellness Scale | | | Zero Spot | Positive Wellness Scale | | |

Early Death | Serious Illness | Symptoms of Illness | Average Health | Somewhat Active | Active | Super Active

### What Is Wellness?

Wellness is an active state of health in which an individual moves toward balancing physical, social, and emotional health. The Wellness Scale shows how to chart a person's level of wellness. At one end of the scale is a high state of physical, social, and emotional health. People in the middle of the scale have average health. At the other end of the scale is serious illness and early death.

As you read this textbook, you will learn more about what is involved in achieving good health and wellness. But before you begin, think about your present health and its three parts. Think about where you are on the Wellness Scale. To help you rate your health and wellness, use the Health Self-Rating Chart to rate some behaviors and choices that may affect your health. The chart may help you find areas of your health that you would like to improve.

## HEALTH SELF-RATING CHART

**Directions:** Number a sheet of paper to correspond to each chart section. Read each statement. If the statement is mostly true for you, write *yes*. If it is mostly false, write *no*.

You do not need to share your results with anyone. Score each section as the instructions tell you. To score your overall health level, add your scores on all sections.

26–30 = top 10 percent
21–25 = above average
16–20 = average
15 and lower = below average

### PHYSICAL HEALTH

1. I eat a healthy breakfast every day.
2. I eat a balanced diet that is different every day.
3. I avoid unhealthy snacks.
4. I do not use tobacco or alcohol or take drugs that a doctor hasn't directed me to use.
5. I get eight hours of sleep each night.
6. I take part in exercises and sports I like.
7. I work at developing muscle tone and fitness three times a week.
8. I bike, swim, run, or walk for at least thirty minutes three or more times a week.
9. I relax at least ten minutes a day.
10. I get regular medical and dental checkups.

Score one point for each *yes* answer.
9–10 = top 10 percent
7–8 = above average
5–6 = average
4 or lower = below average

### SOCIAL HEALTH

1. I meet people and make friends often.
2. I have one or two close friends.
3. I can say "no" to my friends if they want me to do something I don't want to do.
4. I balance having my way with letting others have their way.
5. I respect other people's right to be different from me.
6. I am able to work cooperatively with others.
7. If I have a problem with other people, I face the problem and try to work it out with them.
8. I am comfortable communicating with adults.
9. I am comfortable talking with both females and males my age.
10. I am fair and trustworthy with others.

Score one point for each *yes* answer.
9–10 = top 10 percent
7–8 = above average
5–6 = average
4 or lower = below average

### EMOTIONAL HEALTH

1. I try to accept my feelings of love, fear, anger, and sadness.
2. I can tell when I am under pressure.
3. I try to find ways to deal with pressure and control it.
4. I try to have a positive outlook.
5. I ask for help when I need it.
6. I have friends and relatives with whom I discuss problems.
7. I give compliments.
8. I can accept and use helpful comments.
9. I take responsibility for my actions.
10. I am honest with myself and others.

Score one point for each *yes* answer.
9–10 = top 10 percent
7–8 = above average
5–6 = average
4 or lower = below average

Encourage students to complete the Health Self-Rating Chart and score themselves. Point out that this is a tool that each student can use to evaluate his or her own health. Emphasize that it is not a test in which students are competing with one another. Encourage students to be honest with themselves and to focus on identifying their strengths and weaknesses. Suggest that they review the chart on their own to check their progress during the course.

Ask students to tell what behaviors they think are most important to physical, social, and emotional health.

Invite students to start keeping a wellness journal. Point out that they can use the journal to keep daily or weekly records of the actions they take to reduce the risks of disease and to increase their overall physical, social, and emotional well-being. Suggest that students write letters to themselves, expressing their feelings and ideas, as part of their journal. Suggest students use Student Study Guide 6, shown on page 15, as a format for their journal.

# Unit 1 Planning Guide

## Personal Health and Family Life

| | Student Lesson | | | |
|---|---|---|---|---|
| | Student Pages | Vocabulary | Lesson Review | Writing About Health |
| ***Chapter 1 The Body Systems*** | 23–53 | | | |
| Lesson 1 Cells, Tissues, and Organs | 24–25 | • | • | • |
| Lesson 2 The Body's Protective Covering | 26–27 | • | • | |
| Lesson 3 Skeletal and Muscular Systems | 28–31 | • | • | |
| Lesson 4 The Digestive and Excretory Systems | 32–35 | • | • | |
| Lesson 5 The Respiratory and Circulatory Systems | 36–39 | • | • | |
| Lesson 6 The Nervous System | 40–43 | • | • | |
| Lesson 7 The Endocrine System | 44–46 | • | • | |
| Lesson 8 The Reproductive System | 47–50 | • | • | |
| ***Chapter 2 Hygiene and Fitness*** | 54–65 | | | |
| Lesson 1 Hygiene | 55–58 | • | • | |
| Lesson 2 Fitness | 59–62 | • | • | • |
| ***Chapter 3 The Family*** | 66–77 | | | |
| Lesson 1 The Family Life Cycle | 67–70 | • | • | |
| Lesson 2 Dealing With Family Problems | 71–74 | • | • | • |

### Unit Activities

**Home Connection**
**What Do You Think?**
**Deciding for Yourself**

### AGS-Related Resources

**Discover Life Skills Handbook**
**Discover Healthy Sexual Development**

### Assessment Options

**Student Text**
- **Lesson Reviews**
- **Chapter Reviews**
- **Unit Review**

**Teacher's Resource Library**
- **Chapter Mastery Tests**
- **Unit Mastery Test**

| Student Text Features | | | | | | Teaching Strategies | | | | | | | Learning Styles | | | | | Teacher's Resource Library | | | |
|---|---|---|---|---|---|---|---|---|---|---|---|---|---|---|---|---|---|---|---|---|---|
| Action for Health | Careers | Health, Fitness, and Nutrition Tips | Healthy Subjects | Then and Now | Technology | Background Information | Career Application | Community Application | Environment Application | Global Connection | Home Application | Multicultural Connection | Auditory | Group Learning | LEP/ESL | Tactile/Kinesthetic | Visual | Activities | Mastery Tests | Student Study Guide | Workbook Activities |
| | | | | | | | | | | | | | | | | | | | • | • | |
| | | | | | | | | | | | | | | 25 | | | | 1 | | | 1 |
| | | | | | | 27 | | | | | | | | | | | | 2 | | | 2 |
| | | 28 | 31 | | | 30 | | | | | | 29 | | 29 | | 30 | | 3 | | | 3 |
| | | 34 | | 35 | | 33, 34 | | | | | | | | | | | 34, 35 | 4 | | | 4 |
| | | | | | | 37 | | | | 39 | | | | 39 | | 37 | | 5 | | | 5 |
| | 43 | | | | | 42, 43 | | | 42 | | | | | | 41 | | | 6 | | | 6 |
| | | | | 45 | | 45, 46 | | | | | | | | | 45 | | | 7 | | | 7 |
| 50 | | | | | | | 50 | 49 | | | | | | | | | 48 | 8 | | | 8 |
| | | | | | | | | | | | | | | | | | | | • | • | |
| 57 | | 55 | 58 | | 56 | 57 | | 56 | | 56 | | | | 58 | | | | 9 | | | 9 |
| | 61 | 60 | | 62 | | | | 60 | 60 | | 61 | 62 | | | 61 | | | 10 | | | 10 |
| | | | | | | | | | | | | | | | | | | | • | • | |
| 70 | | 69 | | 69 | | 69 | 70 | | 70 | 68 | 68 | | | | | | | 11 | | | 11 |
| | 73 | 72 | | | | | | 74 | | | | 73 | | | 72 | 72 | 74 | 12 | | | 12 |

## Block Scheduling

Here is a suggested teaching activity if you have extended instructional time, such as a block schedule.

**Sport Watch** *To observe the level of fitness required to participate in various professional sports.*

Select four different athletic sports. Watch an entire game of each sport in person, on video, or on TV, keeping a record of the body systems and degree of fitness needed to perform the sport well. For example, the body systems and level of fitness needed for boxing and billiards are very different.

For each sport, compare the necessary muscular and cardiovascular endurance, muscular strength, flexibility, length of time, intensity of effort, and frequency of effort.

Finally, select an individual athlete from one of the sports. Research and write a brief summary of the person's family history. Is athletic "heredity" evident with this person? Why or why not?

## Unit 1:
**Personal Health and Family Life**
pages 20–81

### Chapters

**1) The Body Systems** pages 23–53

**2) Hygiene and Fitness**
pages 54–65

**3) The Family** pages 66–77

**Unit 1 Deciding for Yourself**
page 78

**Unit 1 Summary** page 79

**Unit 1 Review** pages 80–81

**Audiocassette**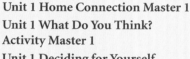

**Teacher's Resource Library** TRL

Unit 1 Home Connection Master 1

Unit 1 What Do You Think?
Activity Master 1

Unit 1 Deciding for Yourself
Activity Master 1

Unit 1 Mastery Test

(Answer Keys for the Teacher's
Resource Library begin on page 433
of this Teacher's Edition.)

## Other Resources
### Books for Teachers
Andes, Karen (Contributor). *The Complete
Book of Fitness: Mind, Body, Spirit.*
Michigan: Three Rivers Press, 1999.

Nuland, Sherwin B. *Incredible Voyage:
Exploring the Human Body.* National
Geographic, 1998.

Schlosberg, Suzanne, and Liz Neporent
(Contributor). *Fitness for Dummies.*
IDG Books Worldwide, 1996.

### Books for Students
Moss, Miriam. *Be Positive (Staying
Healthy).* Crestwood House, 1993.
(Discusses the role of good mental health
in being healthy, covering such aspects
as anxiety, stress management, and the
healing powers of the mind.)

"*Health is a state of complete
physical, mental, and social
well-being, and not merely the
absence of disease . . .*"
—World Health Organization
Constitution

Nottridge, Rhoda. *Care for Your Body!
(Staying Healthy).* Crestwood House,
1993. (A guide to help teens understand
and care for their changing body.)

### Videos
*The Miracle of Life* (60 minutes) NOVA,
1986. (This Emmy Award-winning video
from the PBS NOVA series explores fetal
development from conception to birth.)

*The Job of Your Life: The Reality of Teen
Parenthood* (15 minutes) Human
Relations Media, 1997. (A teen dreams
of becoming a parent and then wakes up
to the responsibility she's not ready to
handle.)

**Home Connection Master 1**

# Unit 1

# Personal Health and Family Life

*L*ist the different things you do in one day. Your list might have walking, reading, laughing, and playing sports on it. Whatever you do, think, or feel—it all happens because your body and all its parts work together. Your body works all the time. It works even when you are asleep.

Good health doesn't just happen. In this unit, you will see what kinds of things you can do to keep yourself healthy. You will learn about the different parts of your body and how they work together. You will learn what you can do to keep your body and its parts working well. You will also learn that your family is important to your health.

## Introducing the Unit

Read aloud the quotation from the World Health Organization Constitution on page 20. Have volunteers read the introductory material on page 21 and examine the picture. Then ask another volunteer to read the quote again. Have several students give their interpretations of the quote.

## Ask:

- **What does the picture show?** (Encourage students to both describe the picture and relate it to what they think they will learn in the unit.)

- **Why will it help you to know about the systems of your body?** (Students may say the following: To understand how the body works; to develop good health habits; to know what to do when something is wrong.)

- **What is fitness?** (keeping the body healthy)

- **What are some things people do to stay fit?** (exercise; eat nutritious food)

- **Hygiene means habits to keep a person healthy and prevent disease. What do you think you will learn in Chapter 2 about hygiene?** (ways to care for physical and mental health; ways to prevent illness)

- **How does what happens in a family relate to good health?** (Students may say the following: The family probably eats many of the same foods. If the foods are nutritious, the family members will stay in good health. Also, family members can encourage one another to exercise.)

- **In what ways do you think families today are made up differently from families in the past?** (Students may realize that single-parent families are much more common today than in the past.)

## What Do You Think?

Have students read the story that introduces some of the key ideas in this unit.

### Ask:

- What is Amy doing in the story? (participating in a gymnastic competition)

- How do you think Amy felt before the competition? After the competition? (Before the competition, Amy was probably excited and nervous; afterwards she might have been relieved, happy, or tired.)

- How did Amy prepare for the competition? (by practicing, eating properly, getting enough rest, and having a positive attitude)

- How do the systems of the body help Amy compete? (by working together so that she can do her best)

- What does everyone have in common with a successful athlete like Amy? (a body that is made of systems working together; needs for rest, proper food, exercise, and good mental attitudes)

- What are some good effects of competitive sports? (a healthy body; keeping weight at a proper level; good self-esteem)

- What can be some bad effects of competitive sports? (too much stress; injuries; temptation to take drugs to do better; stress on other family members)

- Is it necessary to participate in competitive sports to stay fit and healthy? (No; there are many types of exercise that are not competitive.)

Have students complete the Unit 1 What Do You Think? Activity Sheet.

## What Do You Think?

The loud clapping told Amy what she already knew. She had just done the last back flip off the balance beam. She had finished her gymnastics routine. Amy won first place in the state gymnastics competition.

Amy had worked hard to win the competition. She had practiced many hours. She had also eaten well, gotten plenty of rest, and kept a good attitude. She knew that part of being a winner is believing in yourself and taking care of your body.

The audience saw Amy's control over all the parts of her body. But the audience didn't see how Amy's muscles, bones, heart, lungs, nerves, and brain all worked together perfectly to make her performance possible.

Even if you are not a gymnast, you have something in common with Amy. Everything you do happens because all the parts of your body work together. How can you help your body work at its best?

**What Do You Think? Master 1**

# The Body Systems

The human body is amazing. It is made up of many systems. These systems work together to keep you healthy. One of the most important ways that the body's systems keep you healthy is by maintaining balance. For example, the systems work together to keep your body from getting too cold or too hot. They keep your temperature balanced. They also work together to make sure that all parts of your body get the right amount of food and oxygen.

In this chapter, you will learn about your body's systems and its basic building blocks. You will also learn how the different parts of the body work together.

## Goals for Learning

▶ To describe the structure of cells, tissues, organs, and body systems

▶ To describe the structure and purpose of the skin

▶ To explain how the skeletal and muscular systems work together

▶ To explain digestive and excretory systems

▶ To explain the respiratory and circulatory systems

▶ To describe the parts of the nervous system

▶ To describe the purpose of the endocrine glands

▶ To describe the reproductive system

## Introducing the Chapter

Have two volunteers read the introductory information and the Goals for Learning. Discuss what students already know about the systems of the human body. Write these words on the board: *bone, muscle, joint, heart, lungs, stomach, brain, hormone.* Have students match each word with one of the systems described in the Goals for Learning.

---

Name                Date          Period

**Chapter 1 The Body Systems**

*Chapter 1 Student Study Guide 7 page 1*

**Directions** Fill in the outline below. Filling in the blanks will help you as you read and study The Body Systems.

I. **Lesson 1 Cells, Tissues, and Organs (pp. 24–25)**
A. _____ are the basic units that make up all living things.
B. The cell membrane, the _____, and the _____ are the three basic parts of a cell.
C. Different types of _____ work together to form an organ.

II. **Lesson 2 The Body's Protective Covering (pp. 26–27)**
A. Your skin keeps the temperature of your _____ steady.
B. _____, the second layer of skin, is made of living cells.

III. **Lesson 3 Skeletal and Muscular Systems (pp. 28–31)**
A. Your skeletal system provides a _____ for the rest of your body.
B. Muscles move _____ when muscles contract.
C. You control the movements that are caused by _____ muscles.

IV. **Lesson 4 The Digestive and Excretory Systems (pp. 32–35)**
A. The digestive system breaks down _____.
B. Solid waste is stored in the _____.
C. _____ leaves the body through the urethra.

V. **Lesson 5 The Respiratory and Circulatory Systems (pp. 36–39)**
A. The respiratory system brings in _____ and takes out carbon dioxide.
B. The circulatory system pumps _____ through your entire body.
C. Arteries carry blood away from your _____.

TRL  ©AGS® American Guidance Service, Inc. Permission is granted to reproduce for classroom use only.   Discover Health

**Student Study Guide 7, page 1**

---

Name                Date          Period

*Chapter 1 Student Study Guide 7 page 2*

VI. **Lesson 6 The Nervous System (pp. 40–43)**
A. Nerves in the _____ _____ carry messages to and from the brain.
B. The three main parts of the brain are the cerebrum, the _____, and the medulla.

VII. **Lesson 7 The Endocrine System (pp. 44–46)**
A. The endocrine system is made of _____.
B. _____ control reproduction, growth, and emotions.

VIII. **Lesson 8 The Reproductive System (pp. 47–50)**
A. Females store eggs in _____.
B. Males make _____ in testes.
C. For a new life to begin, a female _____ and a male sperm must join.

TRL  ©AGS® American Guidance Service, Inc. Permission is granted to reproduce for classroom use only.   Discover Health

**Student Study Guide 7, page 2**

## Lesson at a Glance

### Chapter 1 Lesson 1

**Overview** This lesson describes the parts of a cell and the organization of the body's cells into tissues, organs, and systems.

### Objectives

■ To name different kinds of cells in the body.

■ To describe parts of a cell and explain what each part does.

■ To understand the organization of the body into cells, tissues, organs, and systems.

**Student Pages** 24–25

**Audiocassette**

**Teacher's Resource Library** **TRL**

Activity 1

Workbook Activity 1

## Teaching Suggestions

### ■ Vocabulary

*cell, cell membrane, cytoplasm, microscope, nucleus, body system, mitosis, organ, tissue*

Point out the vocabulary word *cell* where it appears in both the text and the vocabulary box in the margin. Model how to pronounce difficult words by breaking them into syllables. Read each word and its definition aloud to students, having them locate the word in the text.

### ■ Teaching the Lesson

Use the organization of the textbook to introduce the organization of the human body. Point out that the basic units of the textbook are organized into sections, for example, the section with the heading "What Are Cells?" The sections make up lessons. The lessons make up chapters. The chapters make up units. Have students read the introductory paragraph and the first section on page 24.

Ask:

• What is a cell? (the basic units that make up all living things)

• Why can't you see cells? (They are too small.)

---

## Cells, Tissues, and Organs

**Cell**
*The basic unit that makes up your body*

**Cell membrane**
*The outer wall of a cell*

**Cytoplasm**
*The jelly-like material inside the cell membrane*

**Microscope**
*A tool used to see cells*

**Nucleus**
*The control center of the cell*

Look at your skin. What do you see? You may see lines on the skin or flakes of skin. What you cannot see just by looking at your skin are the tiny **cells** that make up your skin. In fact, tiny living units, called cells, make up each part of your body.

### What Are Cells?

Cells are the basic units that make up all living things. Your body is made up of trillions of cells. Cells are too small to see without a tool called a **microscope**. A microscope can make a cell look bigger than it really is, so you can see what it looks like. If you were to look at a cell using a microscope, it might look like the cell shown in Figure 1.1.

Your body is made up of many different kinds of cells. Each kind of cell has its own job. For example, skin cells help keep germs out of your body. White blood cells fight the germs that do enter your body. Nerve cells send messages among the different parts of your body and your brain. Each kind of cell carries out a different job.

**Figure 1.1.** A typical cell

### What Are the Main Parts of a Cell?

Look again at the picture of the cell in Figure 1.1. Most cells have three basic parts: a **cell membrane**, the **cytoplasm**, and a **nucleus**.

The cell membrane is the outer wall of the cell. It is like a thin skin around the cell. Food and oxygen can pass into the cell and wastes can pass out of the cell through the cell membrane. The cytoplasm is a jelly-like liquid inside the cell membrane. The cytoplasm often has other cell parts floating in it. Most of the cell's life activities take place in the cytoplasm. The nucleus is sometimes called the control center of the cell. It has all the information that the cell needs to carry out its job and to make new cells like itself.

---

• What is shown in the picture on page 24? (The picture shows the parts of a typical cell. Point out the caption and the labels that convey this fact.)

• How will the picture help you during the lesson? (Point out the words *Parts of a Cell* in the section heading. The picture will help students understand what they read in this section.)

## Vocabulary (margin box)

**Body system**
*A group of organs that work together to carry out a certain job*

**Mitosis**
*The dividing process that makes new cells*

**Organ**
*A group of tissues that work together*

**Tissue**
*A group of cells that do the same job*

---

The nucleus makes new cells by splitting into two, making one cell two cells. When the two cells split, they become four cells, which split to make eight. This dividing is called **mitosis**. Mitosis allows your body to make new cells to grow or to replace dead cells.

## What Is a Body System?

Cells that do the same job combine to form a **tissue**. Muscles and bones are examples of tissues. Different types of tissues working together form an **organ**, such as the stomach or the kidneys. A group of organs working together to carry out a certain job is called a **body system**. The digestive system is an example of a body system. Each system carries out its own job and works with other systems to keep the body healthy.

**LESSON 1 REVIEW** Write the answers to these questions on a separate sheet of paper. Use complete sentences.

1) Name three different kinds of cells and what they do.

2) Why is a microscope needed to look at cells?

3) How does mitosis help you grow?

4) How is tissue formed?

5) What are the three main parts of a cell, and what does each one do?

**Why are cells called "building blocks of life"?**

Writing About Health

All of the systems in your body work together efficiently. Write about how the body must be well organized and balanced for this to happen.

---

Have students read about the parts of a cell on pages 24 and 25.

Ask:

- What are the three parts of a cell? Where do you learn this? (cell membrane, cytoplasm, nucleus; in both the picture and the text)

- How are new cells made? What vocabulary word describes this process? (The nucleus of a cell splits into two parts. This dividing process is mitosis. Point out where *mitosis* appears in both the text and the vocabulary box in the margin.)

Have students read about a body system on page 25.

### Lesson 1 Review Answers

1) Skin cells help keep germs out of the body. White blood cells fight the germs that enter the body. Nerve cells send messages among the different parts of the body and the brain.

2) A microscope is needed because cells are too small to see otherwise.

3) Mitosis allows your body to make new cells.

4) Cells that do the same job combine to form a tissue.

5) Cells are made up of a membrane, the cytoplasm, and a nucleus. The cell membrane is the outer wall of the cell through which food and wastes pass. Most of the cell's life activities take place in the cytoplasm. The nucleus acts as the control center of the cell.

### LEARNING STYLES

**LEP/ESL** Observe as students read the sections of this first lesson to identify those who need help reading the textbook. Partner these students with proficient readers so they can work in teams. The students in a team can read a paragraph or small section silently. Then they can discuss the main idea, supporting details, information in illustrations, and difficult vocabulary words.

---

### Activity 1 worksheet

Name ___ Date ___ Period ___  Chapter 1 Activity 1

**Cells, Tissues, and Organs**

*Directions* Read the words in the Word Bank. Choose the item that *best* completes each sentence. On the blank before each number, write the letter for that item.

| Word Bank | |
|---|---|
| a) body system | f) mitosis |
| b) cells | g) nucleus |
| c) cell membrane | h) organs |
| d) cytoplasm | i) tissue |
| e) microscope | j) three |

___ 1) A ___ is a tool that makes tiny objects seem bigger than they are.

___ 2) The ___ is the outer wall of the cell.

___ 3) Most cells have ___ basic parts.

___ 4) The ___ is a jelly-like liquid inside the cell membrane.

___ 5) The ___ is sometimes called the cell's control center.

___ 6) When a cell divides to make new cells, the process is called ___.

___ 7) A ___ is made up of cells doing the same job.

___ 8) ___ are made up of different kinds of tissues working together.

___ 9) A group of organs working together to do a certain job is called a ___.

___ 10) ___ are the basic units of which all living things are made.

©AGS American Guidance Service, Inc. Permission is granted to reproduce for classroom use only.     Discover Health

 **TRL**

**Activity 1**

---

### Workbook Activity 1 worksheet

Name ___ Date ___ Period ___  Chapter 1 Workbook Activity 1

**Cells, Tissues, and Organs**

*Directions* Complete each sentence by writing the letter of the *best* word or words in the space on the left-hand side of the page.

___ 1) Your body is made up of ___, or tiny living units.

___ 2) A ___, or control center, can be found at the center of every cell.

___ 3) Cells divide by a process called ___.

___ 4) Cells that perform the same function cluster together in groups to form ___ such as muscle or bone.

___ 5) The thin skin around the cell is called the ___.

___ 6) The ___ is the jelly-like liquid floating inside the cell membrane.

___ 7) A ___ is a group of organs working together to do a job.

___ 8) Different kinds of tissues working together form an ___.

___ 9) Many ___ kinds of cells make up your body.

___ 10) One kind of cell inside your body is ___ cells.

a) body system
b) cells
c) cell membrane
d) cytoplasm
e) different
f) mitosis
g) nerve
h) nucleus
i) organ
j) tissue

©AGS American Guidance Service, Inc. Permission is granted to reproduce for classroom use only.     Discover Health

**TRL**

**Workbook Activity 1**

# Lesson at a Glance

## Chapter 1 Lesson 2

**Overview** This lesson explains the structure and function of the skin.

### Objectives

- To explain the function of the skin.

- To describe the three layers of the skin.

**Student Pages** 26–27

**Audiocassette**

**Human Body Transparency** 9

**Teacher's Resource Library**

Activity 2

Workbook Activity 2

## Teaching Suggestions

### ■ Vocabulary

*dermis, epidermis, gland, keratin, melanin, perspiration, subcutaneous layer*

Write the vocabulary words on the board. Help students pronounce any difficult words, showing them how to break words into syllables. Then have students read the definitions in the vocabulary boxes.

### ■ Teaching the Lesson

Have students use magnifying glasses to look at the skin on their hands. Help them to identify the epidermis and the pore of the sweat glands. Then have students read the first section of the lesson on page 26.

### Ask:

- What are the tiny holes in your skin called? (pores)

- What do the pores in your skin do? (help cool your body)

- What causes perspiration? (Sweat glands in the skin produce moisture that comes through the pores to the surface.)

---

## Lesson 2

### The Body's Protective Covering

**Dermis**
*The middle layer of the skin*

**Epidermis**
*The outer layer of skin that you can see*

**Gland**
*A group of cells that produces a special substance to help the body work*

**Keratin**
*A protein that makes nails hard*

**Melanin**
*A chemical that gives skin and hair its color*

**Perspiration**
*Sweat*

Your skin is the largest organ of your body. It covers and protects your body.

#### What Does Your Skin Do?

The skin protects your body by preventing germs and other harmful elements from getting inside. Your skin also keeps your body temperature steady. Your skin has more than four million pores, or tiny holes, which help cool your body. A **gland** is a group of cells that produces a special substance to help the body work. For example, if you get too hot, sweat glands in your skin give off moisture called sweat, or **perspiration**. Perspiration comes to the surface of your body through the pores in the skin. As perspiration evaporates from the surface of your skin, your body cools.

Your skin also helps your body adjust to changes around it. Skin detects pressure, pain, heat, and cold. This information is then sent to your brain. The brain interprets the messages and tells different parts of your body how to react.

#### What Is the Structure of the Skin?

Your skin has three main layers. You can see these layers in Figure 1.2. The outer layer, called the **epidermis**, is the part of the skin that you see. It is made up of a thin layer of dead skin cells. Your body is always making new skin cells. It takes about twenty-eight days for new skin cells to form and move to the outer layer of your skin. As the cells travel to the outer layer of skin, they harden and die. When they get to the outside of your body, the dead cells rub off, leaving behind the younger cells. The color of your skin and hair comes from a substance in the epidermis called **melanin**.

Some of the cells in the epidermis develop large amounts of a protein called **keratin**. Keratin hardens into nails, which protect the ends of your fingers and toes.

The second layer of skin is the **dermis**. It is made of living cells. The dermis has blood vessels, nerves, and glands. New

**Why do you think animals have so many different kinds of skin?**

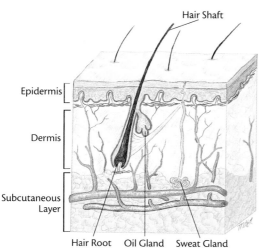

Hair Shaft

Epidermis

Dermis

Subcutaneous
Layer

Hair Root    Oil Gland    Sweat Gland

**Figure 1.2.**
Cross section of the skin

---

**Subcutaneous layer**
*The deepest layer of
the skin*

skin cells are also made in the dermis. Oil glands in the dermis help keep your skin smooth and able to stretch. Sweat glands secrete perspiration. Your hair grows from hair follicles in the dermis.

The **subcutaneous layer** of the skin is closest to your bones. It connects your skin to your muscles. This layer is made of fatty tissue. The fat helps protect your body from very hot or very cold temperatures. It also protects your body when you bump into things.

**LESSON 2 REVIEW** Write the answers to these questions on a separate sheet of paper. Use complete sentences.

1) What are two ways the skin protects your body?

2) What are the three main layers of the skin?

3) What are the similarities and differences between the epidermis and the dermis?

4) What are two types of glands in the skin? What do they do?

5) How does skin respond to changes, such as pain or heat?

*The Body Systems    Chapter 1    27*

---

Have students read the second section of the lesson on pages 26 and 27. Ask them to refer to Figure 1.2 as they read about the layers of the skin.

Ask:

· Use Figure 1.2 to name the three layers of the skin. (epidermis, dermis, subcutaneous layer)

· Where are the oil glands in your skin? (in the dermis)

**Lesson 2 Review Answers**

1) Accept any two of the following: The skin keeps germs out of the body, helps maintain a steady body temperature, and helps the body adjust to changes around it.

2) The three main layers of the skin are the epidermis, the dermis, and the subcutaneous layer.

3) Both are made of skin cells and are part of the outer layer of the skin. The epidermis is made of dead skin cells. The dermis is made of living cells.

4) Oil glands and sweat glands; oil glands secrete oil, which helps keep the skin smooth; sweat glands secrete sweat, which helps regulate body temperature.

5) Skin detects pain or heat and sends messages to the brain. The brain then tells the body how to react.

**GLOBAL CONNECTION**

Discuss the wide range of skin color that exists within the human race. Skin color ranges from pale pink to blue-black with numerous shades of brown in between. Tell students that two other pigments contribute to skin color: hemoglobin gives pale skin a pinkish color; carotene gives skin a yellow-orange cast.

---

Name _____ Date _____ Period _____    Chapter 1 / Activity 2

**The Body's Protective Covering**

*Directions* Read the words in the Word Bank. Choose the item that best completes each sentence. On the blank before each number, write the letter for that item.

Word Bank

a) keratin          f) epidermis
b) follicles        g) pores
c) oil glands       h) skin
d) dermis           i) melanin
e) sweat glands     j) subcutaneous layer

_____ 1) The _____ is the second layer of skin in which nerves and blood vessels are found.

_____ 2) Your body gets rid of perspiration through _____.

_____ 3) Nails contain a protein called _____, which makes them hard.

_____ 4) The skin gets its color from a substance called _____.

_____ 5) Your hair grows from _____ in the dermis.

_____ 6) The _____ is the outer layer of skin.

_____ 7) The _____, the deepest layer of the skin, is fatty tissue that protects the body from heat and cold.

_____ 8) _____ in the dermis help keep your skin smooth.

_____ 9) The _____ is the largest organ in the body.

_____ 10) The _____ are tiny openings in the skin.

©AGS® American Guidance Service, Inc. Permission is granted to reproduce for classroom use only.    **Discover Health**

**Activity 2**

---

Name _____ Date _____ Period _____    Chapter 1 / Workbook Activity 2

**The Body's Protective Covering**

*Directions* Write *T* if the statement is true or *F* if it is false.

_____ 1) Your skin is made up of five layers.

_____ 2) Oil glands in the dermis help keep your skin smooth and stretchable.

_____ 3) Your skin is the second largest organ in the body.

_____ 4) Pores are tiny holes in your skin.

_____ 5) Oil in your skin helps keep your body cool.

_____ 6) The bottom layer of the skin is the subcutaneous layer.

_____ 7) The color of your skin and hair comes from keratin.

_____ 8) Melanin is a protein that hardens into nails.

_____ 9) The outer layer of your skin is called the dermis.

_____ 10) The dermis has blood vessels, nerves, and glands.

©AGS® American Guidance Service, Inc. Permission is granted to reproduce for classroom use only.    **Discover Health**

**Workbook Activity 2**

## Chapter 1 Lesson 3

**Overview** This lesson describes the functions of the skeletal and muscular systems and how these systems work together.

### Objectives

- To explain the functions of the bones and muscles.

- To explain how the skeletal and muscular systems work together.

- To distinguish between voluntary and involuntary muscles.

**Student Pages** 28–31

**Audiocassette**

**Human Body Transparencies** 1–2

**Teacher's Resource Library** **TRL**

    Activity 3

    Workbook Activity 3

## Teaching Suggestions

### ■ Vocabulary

*contract, joint, muscular system, skeletal system, involuntary muscle, voluntary muscle*

Write each vocabulary word on the board. Then read each definition randomly and have students choose the matching word. Provide the correct response if necessary. Have students copy the words on a sheet of paper. As they read the lesson, have them use each word in an original sentence.

### ■ Teaching the Lesson

Read the lesson title and explain that this lesson will be about the bones and muscles in students' bodies. Ask volunteers to name some bones and muscles. Students may know the ribs, backbone, biceps, and hamstrings.

Ask:

- What are joints? (places where two bones connect)

---

## The Skeletal and Muscular Systems

**Contract**
*Shorten*

**Joint**
*A place where two bones come together*

**Muscular system**
*The body system made up of your muscles*

**Skeletal system**
*The body system made up of your bones and joints*

*Fitness Tip*

Instead of watching TV, do something physical—walk, bike, swim, or run.

Two body systems that give your body its shape and help it to move are the **skeletal system** and the **muscular system**. These two systems work together and with other systems to keep you healthy.

### What Is the Skeletal System?

Figure 1.3 shows the skeletal system. It is made up of 206 bones. The places where each bone connects to another bone are called **joints**. Tough bands of tissue hold joints together.

Your skeletal system provides the frame for the rest of your body. Your bones are hard. This hardness provides the frame for your body. Most of the other parts of your body are soft.

Your skeletal system also protects other parts of your body. For example, your ribs form a cage around your heart and lungs. This cage protects your heart and lungs from being crushed when you catch a football or hug someone. The bones of your head protect your brain when you bump your head.

Your skeletal system also allows your body to stand up and to walk and move around. But, in order to move, your skeletal system must work closely with your muscular system.

### What Is the Muscular System?

Bones cannot move by themselves. They are moved by the muscles that make up your muscular system. Muscles move bones by becoming shorter, or **contracting**. When a muscle that is attached to a bone contracts, it pulls the bone. Muscles move bones in only one direction. This is why muscles work in pairs. For example, one set of muscles works to raise your arm up while another set is used to lower it.

---

- What are the functions of bones? (Bones provide a frame for the body and protect the softer parts of the body. Bones also store important minerals and produce certain blood cells.)

- How do bones move? (Muscles are attached to the bones. A muscle contracts and moves a bone.)

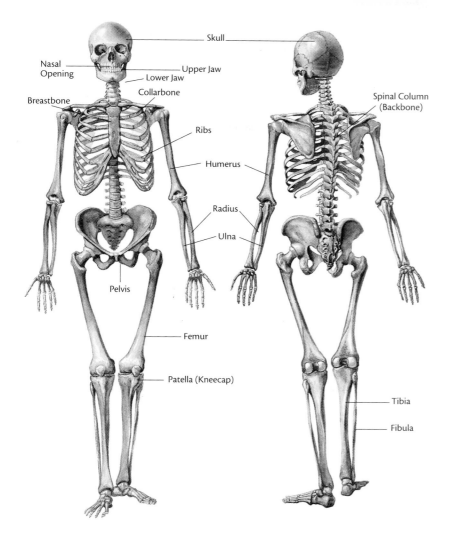

**Figure 1.3.** The skeletal system (front and back views)

Explain that Figure 1.3 shows some bones in the human body. Explain that all the bones make up the skeletal system. Point out the difference between the words *skeleton* and *skeletal*, explaining that one is a noun and one an adjective.

## Ask:

- Which bones are familiar to you? Point to where these bones are on your body. (Answers will vary.)

- Which bones of your skeleton can you feel? Why can't you feel some of your bones? (They are covered with muscles.)

### MULTICULTURAL CONNECTION

Any type of physical activity requires the coordination of bone and muscle movement. A popular form of physical activity is dance. Have students learn about the dances of various cultures, such as the Irish jig, the Spanish flamenco, the Hopi rain dance, the Yoruba apala dance, or the Japanese bugaku. As students investigate the dances, they might learn a few basic steps and demonstrate these for the class.

### LEARNING STYLES

**Group Learning** Have students work in small groups to create collages of the human body. They can gather pictures from magazines, newspapers, and other sources to include in their collages. Explain that the pictures should show positive things about the human body. Students might show people doing exercises or eating healthy food. Provide a bulletin board for groups to display their finished collages.

Explain that Figure 1.4 shows some of the muscles in the human body. Explain that all the muscles make up the muscular system.

Ask:

- Which muscles are familiar to you? Point to where these muscles are on your body. (Answers will vary.)

- Do muscles push or pull your bones? (Muscles pull your bones.)

- Why is it important that muscles and bones be connected? (to allow bones to move)

- Why do muscles work in pairs? (Muscles move bones in only one direction. One muscle might raise your arm; a different muscle would lower it.)

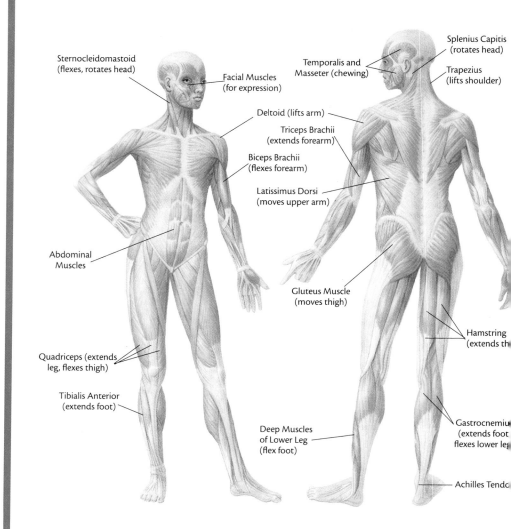

Sternocleidomastoid (flexes, rotates head)

Facial Muscles (for expression)

Splenius Capitis (rotates head)

Temporalis and Masseter (chewing)

Trapezius (lifts shoulder)

Deltoid (lifts arm)

Triceps Brachii (extends forearm)

Biceps Brachii (flexes forearm)

Latissimus Dorsi (moves upper arm)

Abdominal Muscles

Gluteus Muscle (moves thigh)

Hamstring (extends th

Quadriceps (extends leg, flexes thigh)

Tibialis Anterior (extends foot)

Deep Muscles of Lower Leg (flex foot)

Gastrocnemiu (extends foot flexes lower leg

Achilles Tendo

**Figure 1.4.** The muscular system (female front view and male back view)

## RUNNING SHOES

Many people choose running as a way to keep fit. Choosing the right shoes is important for healthy feet. For most runners, "stability shoes" offer good cushioning, center support, and durability. However, "motion-control shoes" are better for people who tend to roll their feet inward as they step. These shoes are heavier but provide much-needed support for runners. Other runners' feet may be less flexible in the center. These people need cushioned shoes without much middle support. Off-road runners should wear "trail shoes." The soles of trail shoes give extra traction. They also include toe "bumpers," durable tops, and stronger stitching. The next time you buy shoes, consider how to keep your feet happy.

---

**Involuntary muscle**
*A muscle that moves whether you think about it or not*

**Voluntary muscle**
*A muscle that moves when you think about it*

## What Kinds of Muscles Are There?

Your body has two basic kinds of muscles. They are called **voluntary muscles** and **involuntary muscles**. When you want to take a walk, your voluntary muscles cause you to walk. You control the movements that are caused by voluntary muscles.

Involuntary muscles cause movements whether you think about them or not. For example, your heart muscle is an involuntary muscle. It pumps blood all the time without you thinking about it. Voluntary muscles move your skeletal and muscular system. For example, voluntary muscles move your arms or legs as you walk and talk.

**Why do you think it hurts to move after a muscle has been injured?**

**LESSON 3 REVIEW** Write the answers to these questions on a separate sheet of paper. Use complete sentences.

1) How many bones make up the skeletal system?
2) How do the skeletal and muscular systems work together?
3) What is the purpose of the skeletal system?
4) Give an example of an involuntary and a voluntary muscle.
5) Explain how the muscle pairs in your arm allow you to lift a glass of milk from a table.

*The Body Systems* Chapter 1 **31**

---

## Healthy Subjects

Discuss the importance of purchasing the right shoes for running, especially to avoid injury. Find out if any of your students enjoy running and discuss factors to consider when choosing a pair of running shoes. Also ask students how they decide when it is time to replace their running shoes.

Have students read about different kinds of muscles on page 31.

Ask:

- What is the difference between voluntary and involuntary muscles? (You can control voluntary muscles. You cannot control involuntary muscles)

- What are some actions you do with voluntary muscles? (walking, reaching, turning the head)

- What are some things involuntary muscles do? (pump blood through the body, help you breathe, help you digest food)

- Why aren't all muscles voluntary? (It would be impossible for a person to think about and direct all the body functions that require muscle action.)

## Lesson 3 Review Answers

1) There are 206 bones in the skeletal system.
2) The muscles move the bones, allowing the body to move.
3) The purpose of the skeletal system is to provide the frame for the body and protect other parts of your body.
4) The muscles in the legs that help you walk are voluntary muscles. Your heart muscle is an involuntary muscle.
5) A set of muscles works together to raise your arm. One muscle contracts and the other expands.

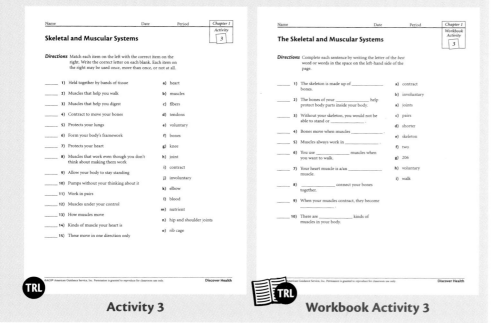

**Activity 3**      **Workbook Activity 3**

## Lesson at a Glance

### Chapter 1 Lesson 4

**Overview** This lesson describes the functions of the digestive and excretory systems.

### Objectives

■ To describe the process of digesting food in the body.

■ To explain how the body removes solid and liquid wastes.

**Student Pages** 32–35

**Audiocassette**

**Human Body Transparencies** 12–13, 16

**Teacher's Resource Library**

Activity 4

Workbook Activity 4

## Teaching Suggestions

### ■ Vocabulary

*digestive system, esophagus, excretory system, saliva, small intestine, anus, large intestine, rectum, ureter, urethra, urine*

Write the vocabulary words on the board. Help students pronounce the difficult words, demonstrating how to break the words into syllables. Then read the definition of each word and have volunteers identify the defined word. As each word is identified, erase it from the board and continue.

### ■ Teaching the Lesson

Give each student an unsalted cracker. Have students chew the crackers for much longer than they usually would before swallowing.

Ask:

• What did you notice about how the cracker tastes as you continue to chew it? (It begins to taste sweeter.)

• Why do you think the cracker begins to taste sweeter? (Accept all answers. Tell students that saliva in the mouth contains enzymes that begin to change the starch in the cracker to sugar.)

---

## Lesson 4 · The Digestive and Excretory Systems

**Digestive system**
*The body system that breaks food down*

**Esophagus**
*The tube that connects the throat and the stomach*

**Excretory system**
*The body system that rids the body of waste and extra water*

**Saliva**
*The liquid in the mouth that begins digestion*

**Small intestine**
*Where most of digestion takes place*

Your body needs food to live and grow. It also has to rid itself of wastes. The **digestive system** works to break food down into a form that your cells can use. The **excretory system** rids your body of its wastes.

### What Does the Digestive System Do?

All the cells in your body use the food you eat to live, grow, and heal. First, the food must be broken down into a form that your cells can use. Breaking food down into a usable form is the job of your digestive system.

Look at the picture of your digestive system in Figure 1.5. Notice that your digestive system is made up of many organs that work together to break down food.

### What Is the Path of Food Through the Body?

As you read, trace the path of food through the picture in Figure 1.5. Food enters your body through your mouth. In your mouth, teeth begin breaking the food down by chewing. **Saliva**, the liquid in your mouth, wets food and makes it easier to swallow. Chemicals in your saliva also begin breaking down the food. Your tongue pushes food to the back of your mouth. Then muscles force the food down your throat and through a tube, called the **esophagus**, into your stomach. Your stomach mixes the food with its own chemicals. Like the chemicals in your saliva, these chemicals also change the food into a form that your cells can use.

From the stomach, the food moves to the **small intestine**. In the small intestine, your blood takes in the digested parts of the food. The blood carries the food parts to every cell in your body.

**Anus**
*The opening through which solid wastes leave the body*

**Large Intestine**
*The tube that connects the small intestine and the rectum*

**Rectum**
*The organ that stores solid waste before it leaves the body*

## How Does the Body Rid Itself of Solid Wastes?

The parts of the food that cells cannot use are wastes. These wastes pass to the **large intestine**. The large intestine is a tube-like organ connected to the small intestine. In the large intestine, most of the water that is mixed with the undigested food returns to the blood. The remaining waste is solid. Solid waste is stored in the **rectum**. Then it passes out of the body through the **anus**.

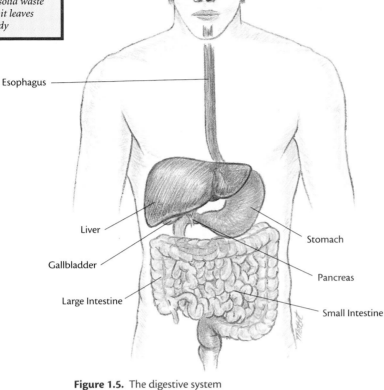

**Figure 1.5.** The digestive system

- Esophagus
- Liver
- Gallbladder
- Large Intestine
- Stomach
- Pancreas
- Small Intestine

Have students read page 33 to find how the body removes solid waste.

Ask:

- Do cells use all parts of the food you eat? (No, the parts of the food that cells cannot use are wastes.)

- What happens to the food your body cannot use? (It passes to the large intestine, water is removed, it is stored in the rectum, and then passes out of the body.)

- Which system removes solid wastes from the body? (digestive system)

Have students study the diagram in Figure 1.5, helping them read the labels. Point out the root word *digest* in *digestive*. Have students trace the path of food through the body as you read aloud the text on page 33.

Ask:

- Which organ looks like a long, thin tube? (esophagus)

- Which organ is between the liver and the intestines? (stomach)

- What happens in the small intestine? (The digested parts of food are taken into the blood.)

- Which organ stores solid waste before it leaves the body? (rectum)

## BACKGROUND INFORMATION

The liver and gallbladder are also digestive organs. The liver produces bile to help digest fats. The gallbladder is a small pouch attached to the liver that stores bile. When bile is needed for digestion, it is pushed into the small intestine. Sometimes bile becomes crystallized in the gallbladder and forms rocklike particles called gallstones. The pancreas produces insulin, which helps cells use sugar. It also gives off enzymes that break down certain foods.

Have students study the diagram in Figure 1.6, helping them read the labels. Point out the root word *excrete* in *excretory*. Then have students read page 34 to find out how the body removes liquid waste.

Ask:

- Which system removes liquid wastes from the body? (excretory system)

- The bladder can stretch to hold urine until it passes out of the body. Which organs carry liquid waste to the bladder? (ureters)

- Which organ carries the urine from the bladder out of the body? (urethra)

**Ureter**
*The tube that carries urine from the kidney to the bladder*

**Urethra**
*The tube through which urine passes out of the body*

**Urine**
*The liquid waste formed in the kidneys*

## How Does the Body Rid Itself of Liquid Wastes?

The excretory system also rids the body of waste products along with extra water. The wastes that leave the body through the excretory system are in the form of **urine**.

The excretory system is made up of two kidneys, two **ureters**, the bladder, and the **urethra**. These organs are shown in Figure 1.6.

*Nutrition Tip*

Drinking at least six to eight 8-ounce glasses of water daily will help the kidneys function properly.

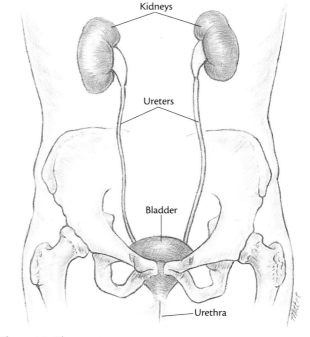

**Figure 1.6.** The excretory system

## GINGER ISN'T JUST FOR COOKING

Many old herbal treatments are now considered useless or even harmful. However, some herbal treatments are now considered useful. For example, about 2,500 years ago, the Chinese used ginger to treat upset stomach, coughing, vomiting, and other ailments. Ginger was used by other groups, too. Nigerians have used it to treat yellow fever and malaria. In Russia, ginger has been used to treat toothaches.

Scientists have found that a chemical in ginger makes it a useful treatment for nausea, vomiting, migraines, and rheumatoid arthritis. Many pregnancy manuals and doctors who care for pregnant women advise taking ginger teas or ginger ale to help with morning sickness. Ginger is also a common treatment for motion sickness.

**What conclusions can you make about what you eat and how it affects your digestive system?**

At the same time that your blood provides food to your cells, it also picks up wastes from your cells. These wastes are processed in your kidneys. Your kidneys are on either side of your backbone. As blood flows through the kidneys, wastes from the blood are absorbed. Water and substances that your body can use are returned to your blood. Inside the kidneys, the wastes become urine. The urine moves from each kidney through one of the ureters to your bladder. Finally, urine leaves the body through the urethra, which leads outside the body.

**LESSON 4 REVIEW** Write the answers to these questions on a separate sheet of paper. Use complete sentences.

1) Where is food first broken down in the body?

2) What part of digestion takes place in the small intestine?

3) What happens to the parts of food that are not used by cells?

4) What waste product is produced by the excretory system?

5) Why is it important to have your kidneys work properly?

*The Body Systems* Chapter 1 **35**

## Then and Now

After students read about the benefits of ginger, discuss any other home remedies students might know to fight flu, colds, or other illnesses. They may have read about these remedies or heard about them through family members, on TV, or in books or magazines. If students are interested in natural remedies, have them research the topic using reference materials or by asking questions at health food stores.

Ask:

- What happens in the kidneys? (Wastes from the blood are absorbed; urine is created.)

- What organ might be hurt if you were hit in the lower back? (one of the kidneys)

- Think of a city. To what processes in a city can you compare the body's ability to get rid of wastes? (garbage collection; sewer systems)

## Lesson 4 Review Answers

1) Food is first broken down in the mouth.
2) Your blood takes in the digested parts of food.
3) The parts of food that are not used by cells are excreted by the body.
4) The wastes that leave the body through the excretory system are in the form of urine.
5) The kidneys clean the blood. If the kidneys did not work properly, the entire body could be contaminated with wastes.

## LEARNING STYLES

**Visual** Have students create a flowchart tracing the path of liquid waste through the body. They should include the following terms in order: kidneys, ureters, bladder, urethra.

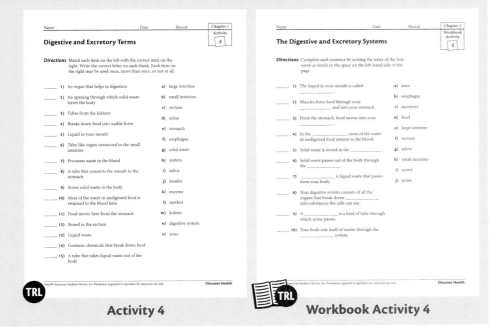

**Activity 4**

**Workbook Activity 4**

## Lesson at a Glance

### Chapter 1  Lesson 5

**Overview**  This lesson explains functions of the respiratory and circulatory systems.

### Objectives

- To explain how the body takes in oxygen.
- To describe the parts of the respiratory system.
- To explain how blood flows through the body.
- To describe the parts of the circulatory system.

**Student Pages** 36–38

**Audiocassette**

**Human Body Transparencies** 6–8

**Teacher's Resource Library**

Activity 5

Workbook Activity 5

## Teaching Suggestions

### ■ Vocabulary

*capillary, circulatory system, respiratory system, trachea, aorta, arteries, plasma, vein*

List the vocabulary words on the board. Help students pronounce the words, breaking them into syllables. As students read the lesson, check off each vocabulary word as it is discussed. After the lesson is finished, have students give definitions of the words. They can then check their definitions against those in the text.

### ■ Teaching the Lesson

Discuss the meaning of heart rate. Show students how to find their pulse and have them count their heartbeats for ten seconds. Then have them multiply by 6 to find their heart rate per minute.

---

**Capillary**
*A tiny blood vessel*

**Circulatory system**
*The body system that pumps blood through the body*

**Respiratory system**
*The body system responsible for breathing*

**Trachea**
*The tube that connects the throat to the lungs*

---

# The Respiratory and Circulatory Systems

When you breathe, you take in oxygen and give off carbon dioxide. Your cells need oxygen to live. They also need a way to rid themselves of their carbon dioxide waste. The **circulatory system** and the **respiratory system** do this job together. They bring oxygen to your cells and take carbon dioxide away from your cells.

### What Does the Respiratory System Do?

Your respiratory system brings fresh air that is rich in oxygen into your body. It also takes air filled with carbon dioxide out of your body.

Look at the picture of the respiratory system in Figure 1.7. When you breathe in air, it passes through your nose or your mouth into your body. The air you breathe in is cleaned and warmed as it passes through your nose.

From your nose or mouth, the air flows into your throat and down the windpipe, or **trachea**. Near your lungs, the trachea splits into two tubes. One tube leads to your left lung. The other tube leads to your right lung. These tubes bring the air to your lungs. Like a tree trunk, each tube divides into many branches that are smaller and smaller. The smallest branches lead into clusters of tiny air sacs.

### How Does Oxygen Get to the Rest of the Body?

The air sacs lie next to tiny blood vessels, called **capillaries**. Both air sacs and capillaries have very thin walls. Oxygen moves through the thin walls of the air sacs into the capillaries.

Blood in the capillaries carries the oxygen from your lungs to all the cells in your body. At the same time, the blood picks up carbon dioxide from the cells. The carbon dioxide passes through the walls of the capillaries and into the air sacs. When you breathe out, your body gets rid of the carbon dioxide waste.

---

**36**    *Chapter 1    The Body Systems*

---

Ask:

- What do you think would happen to your heart rate if you ran for ten seconds? (Accept all answers. Have students run in place for ten seconds and take their heart rates again. Explain that the heart must work harder during exercise.)

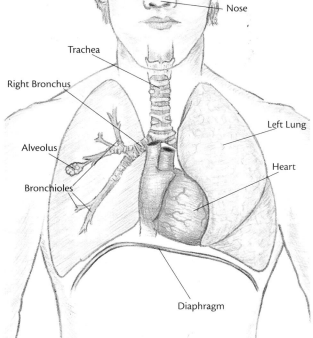

Nose

Trachea

Right Bronchus

Left Lung

Alveolus

Heart

Bronchioles

Diaphragm

**Why do you think your breathing increases when you exercise?**

**Figure 1.7.** The respiratory system

### What Is the Circulatory System?

The main job of the circulatory system is to pump blood through your entire body. The heart and blood vessels are the main organs that carry out this job.

### What Does the Blood Do?

Blood does many jobs in the body. It brings food and oxygen to all parts of the body. It picks up wastes from all parts of the body. Blood also has cells that fight germs in the body. These cells help prevent illnesses.

*The Body Systems    Chapter 1*    **37**

Have students study the picture in Figure 1.7, helping them read the labels. Point out the similarities between the words *respiratory* and *respirator*, explaining that a respirator is a machine to help someone breathe.

Have students trace the path of air on the picture as you read aloud the text on page 37.

Ask:

- Through which organ does air pass after it leaves your nose or mouth? (the trachea)

- Why does the body take in greater amounts of air for a while after exercising? (The body needs more oxygen because of the exercise.)

**BACKGROUND INFORMATION**

The diaphragm is a band of muscle tissue that lies beneath the respiratory organs. When a person inhales, the rib muscles and diaphragm contract to enlarge the chest and allow air to rush in. When a person exhales, the rib muscles and diaphragm expand to force the air out.

**LEARNING STYLES**

**Tactile/Kinesthetic** To demonstrate the function of the lungs, place a balloon inside a plastic detergent bottle as a volunteer squeezes it. Extend the open end of the balloon over the rim of the bottle, screw the cap in place, and leave the cap valve open while the volunteer is still squeezing the bottle. The model functions in much the same way as the chest cavity and lungs of the human body do during breathing. The chest cavity increases when it is filled with air and decreases when the air is exhaled.

Have students read about the circulatory system on pages 37 and 38.

Ask:

- What is the difference between an artery and a vein? (Arteries carry blood away from the heart. Veins carry the blood back to the heart.)

- When you cut your finger, what type of blood vessels are most likely damaged? (capillaries)

- How could damaged lungs affect a person's heart? (Increased amounts of carbon dioxide would eventually damage the heart as it works harder to clear blood of this waste and supply oxygen to tissues.)

**Aorta**
*The largest artery in the body*

**Artery**
*A blood vessel that carries blood away from the heart*

**Plasma**
*The liquid part of blood*

**Vein**
*A blood vessel that carries blood back to the heart*

Your blood is made of cells and a liquid, called **plasma**. Blood cells include white blood cells and red blood cells. White blood cells fight germs. Red blood cells carry oxygen from your lungs to the cells in your body. The red blood cells exchange the oxygen for carbon dioxide. Then they carry the carbon dioxide back to the lungs.

### What Are the Parts of the Circulatory System?

Figure 1.8 shows the parts of the circulatory system. Your heart is not much bigger than your fist. However, it is a strong muscle that pumps blood to every part of your body. Your heart works nonstop, day and night, for your entire life.

Notice that the circulatory system is made up of many blood vessels. Blood vessels that carry blood away from your heart are called **arteries**. Blood vessels that carry blood back to your heart are called **veins**. Capillaries are the tiniest blood vessels. They connect arteries and veins.

The biggest artery is the **aorta**. Blood leaves the heart through the aorta. Other arteries branch from the aorta to reach all parts of the body. Then blood flows into tiny veins, which lead to larger veins and back to the heart.

The right side of the heart pumps blood into the lungs. There the blood gets rid of carbon dioxide and picks up oxygen. The oxygen-rich blood flows into the left side of the heart, through the aorta, and to the rest of the body.

**LESSON 5 REVIEW** Write the answers to these questions on a separate sheet of paper. Use complete sentences.

1) Describe the path of air from your nose to the air sacs in your lungs.

2) What happens in the air sacs?

3) List two purposes of blood.

4) What is blood made of?

5) How do the respiratory system and the circulatory system work together?

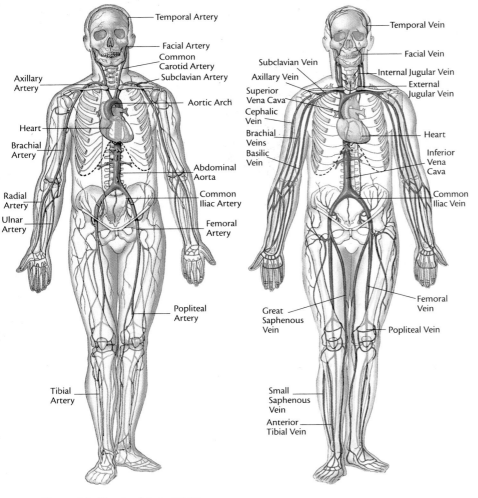

**Temporal Artery**
**Facial Artery**
**Common Carotid Artery**
**Subclavian Artery**
**Axillary Artery**
**Aortic Arch**
**Heart**
**Brachial Artery**
**Abdominal Aorta**
**Radial Artery**
**Common Iliac Artery**
**Ulnar Artery**
**Femoral Artery**
**Popliteal Artery**
**Tibial Artery**

**Temporal Vein**
**Facial Vein**
**Subclavian Vein**
**Axillary Vein**
**Internal Jugular Vein**
**Superior Vena Cava**
**External Jugular Vein**
**Cephalic Vein**
**Brachial Veins**
**Heart**
**Basilic Vein**
**Inferior Vena Cava**
**Common Iliac Vein**
**Great Saphenous Vein**
**Femoral Vein**
**Popliteal Vein**
**Small Saphenous Vein**
**Anterior Tibial Vein**

**Figure 1.8.** The circulatory system

Have students look at Figure 1.8 and locate the heart in each diagram. Point out the root word *circulate* in *circulatory*. Explain that the circulatory system circulates, or moves, blood through the body.

Ask:

- How can the circulatory system be compared to a highway system or a system of roads in a city? (The circulatory system provides for movement of blood necessary for good health. Roads provide for movement of goods and services necessary for a healthy economy.)

## Lesson 5 Review Answers

1) Air flows from your nose or mouth into your throat and down the windpipe, or trachea. Near your lungs, the trachea splits into two tubes. These tubes bring the air to your lungs.
2) Oxygen moves through the thin walls of the air sacs into the capillaries.
3) Blood brings food and oxygen to all parts of the body. Blood picks up wastes from all parts of the body.
4) Blood is made of cells and plasma.
5) The respiratory system and the circulatory system bring oxygen to the body cells and take carbon dioxide away from the cells.

## LEARNING STYLES

**Group Learning** Have students work in groups of four. Ask two students to trace the path of a molecule of oxygen as it travels from the air outside the body to a cell in the foot. Have the other two students trace the path of a molecule of carbon dioxide from the foot to the outside air. Students should name the organs their molecule passes through on its route. When students are finished, choose volunteers to write their routes on the board.

---

# Lesson at a Glance

## Chapter 1 Lesson 6

**Overview** This lesson explains the functions of the nervous system. It also describes the differences between the central and peripheral nervous systems.

## Objectives

■ To describe the parts of the nervous system.

■ To compare the functions of the central and the peripheral nervous systems.

**Student Pages** 40–43

**Audiocassette**

**Human Body Transparencies** 3–5

**Teacher's Resource Library** (TRL)

Activity 6
Workbook Activity 6

# Teaching Suggestions

## ■ Vocabulary

*cerebellum, cerebrum, medulla, nervous system, spinal cord, central nervous system, peripheral nervous system*

Have volunteers read the vocabulary words and their definitions. Then ask students to find as many of the words as they can in the labels on figures 1.9 and 1.10. Tell students that these words describe structures that send messages from the brain to other parts of the body.

## ■ Teaching the Lesson

Ask students to describe what they would see if they looked behind a computer or a stereo system. Students should mention many wires. Ask them what the wires do. (carry electricity from one place to another) Then explain to students that the nerves in their bodies work like the wires—they carry messages from one part of the body to another.

Have students read the first section of the lesson on page 40. Have them study Figure 1.9 on page 41 before they read the second section.

---

## Lesson 6 The Nervous System

**Cerebellum**
*The lower part of the brain, which controls balance and coordination*

**Cerebrum**
*The top part of the brain, which controls thinking*

**Medulla**
*The part of the brain that connects to the spinal cord*

**Nervous system**
*The body system that sends and receives messages throughout the body*

**Spinal cord**
*The cable of nerve cells within the bones of the spine*

Your **nervous system** allows the parts of your body to communicate with one another. It sends and receives messages throughout your body.

### How Does the Nervous System Work?

Your skin, eyes, ears, nose, tongue, and other body parts pick up information about what is happening around and inside your body. This information is sent to your brain through nerve cells. Usually, your brain will receive a message and send a message back, telling that body part what to do. All of this happens very quickly, often without you even knowing about it. Messages to and from the brain are passed from one nerve cell to another at a speed faster than 100 miles an hour!

Your body has billions of nerve cells that reach all parts of your body. These nerve cells form a thick cable called the **spinal cord**. The spinal cord runs through your spinal column to your brain. The nerves in the spinal cord carry messages to and from the brain.

### How Does the Brain Control Your Body?

Your brain runs your body. It determines what you think, do, and feel. Your brain has three main parts: the **cerebrum**, the **cerebellum**, and the **medulla**. Figure 1.9 shows these main parts of your brain.

The top part of your brain is the cerebrum. Find the cerebrum in Figure 1.9. The cerebrum has two halves, called hemispheres. Notice that the figure shows only the left hemisphere. The left hemisphere controls the ability to reason, use language, and do math. The right hemisphere controls your artistic ability and your imagination. However, each person's brain is slightly different. Everything you learn, think, and feel is controlled by your cerebrum. Your cerebrum stores your memories. You also use it when you make decisions or link past experiences to new situations. These are only some of the activities of your cerebrum.

---

Ask:

• What is the function of the spinal cord?
(to send messages to and from the brain)

• What does each half of the brain do?
(The right side controls artistic ability and the imagination. The left side controls the ability to reason, use language, and do math.)

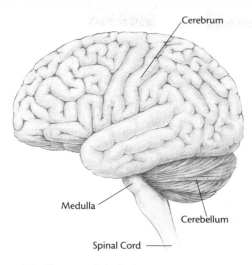

Cerebrum

Medulla

Cerebellum

Spinal Cord

**Figure 1.9.** The parts of the brain

Below your cerebrum is your cerebellum. The cerebellum coordinates voluntary muscles so that they move smoothly. This part of the brain works closely with the cerebrum. The cerebrum, for example, may decide that you need to lift a box off the floor. It sends a message to the muscles to do the work. The cerebellum also sends messages to the muscles so that all the muscles needed for the job work together smoothly.

The third main part of the brain is the medulla. You can see the medulla on the stem-like part of the brain that connects to the spinal cord. The medulla is in charge of your involuntary muscles—those that work without your having to think about them. The medulla works day and night to keep your heart beating, your lungs breathing, and your digestive system breaking down food. It also controls swallowing, coughing, and sneezing.

*The Body Systems    Chapter 1*    **41**

Have volunteers pronounce the words used as labels in Figure 1.9 on page 41.

Ask:
- Which of these labels does not show one of the three parts of the brain? (spinal cord)
- Which part of the brain is the largest? (the cerebrum)

Have students read about the cerebellum and the medulla on page 41.

Ask:
- Which part of the brain coordinates voluntary muscles? (the cerebellum)
- Which part of the brain is in charge of involuntary muscles? (the medulla)
- Suppose a person's spinal cord was damaged in an accident. How could that affect the person? (The ability for messages to go to and from the brain might be damaged or destroyed. Then, the person would not be able to move some parts of the body. The person might be partly or completely paralyzed.)

**LEARNING STYLES**

**LEP/ESL** Show students a globe and explain that this solid figure is called a sphere. Point out the equator, showing that it divides the sphere in half. Each half is called a hemisphere, or one-half of a sphere. Have students find the word *hemisphere* on page 40 where it is used to describe half of the brain.

Have students read about the parts of the nervous system on pages 42 and 43. Then direct their attention to Figure 1.10.

Ask:

- How are messages sent from nerves in the feet to the brain? (along peripheral nerves to the spinal cord and then to the brain)

- What are the two parts of the nervous system? (the central nervous system and the peripheral nervous system)

- What are the parts of the central nervous system? (brain and spinal cord)

- What are the parts of the peripheral nervous system? (all the nerves that are not in the central nervous system)

## BACKGROUND INFORMATION

An EEG (electroencephalogram) is a recording of electrical activity in the brain. The activity results in different kinds of waves, depending on whether a person is awake or asleep, relaxed or excited.

## APPLICATION

**Environment**
Household chemicals, such as soap, bleach, ammonia, affect the nervous system. Depending on the chemical and the amount digested, effects can include dizziness, shortness of breath, nausea, and vomiting. Encourage students to choose three household chemicals. Have students call their local poison center to learn more about the effects of the chemical they have chosen. Invite students to share their information with the class.

**Central nervous system**
*The brain and the spinal cord*

**Peripheral nervous system**
*All the nerves in the body outside the brain and the spinal cord*

## What Are the Parts of the Nervous System?

Your nervous system is really made of two systems. The brain and spinal cord make up the **central nervous system**. The **peripheral nervous system** includes all the nerves outside the central nervous system. Figure 1.10 shows both of these systems.

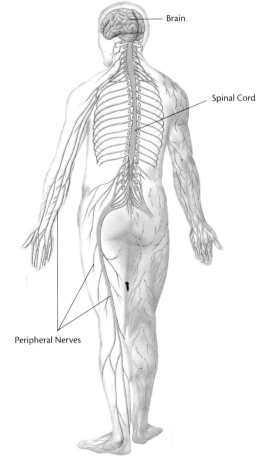

**Figure 1.10.** The nervous system

**ORDERLY**

Health care professionals rely on orderlies. Orderlies assist doctors and nurses in caring for people in hospitals, nursing homes, and clinics. They take care of people's emotional and physical needs. Orderlies check people's health, help keep them clean, and socialize with them. Being an orderly is a good way to try the health care field. Job prospects are excellent. A nursing home association says there is a continued demand for entry-level positions. Some health care facilities offer on-the-job training or pay for classes. Many orderlies like the health field so well, they go back to college or universities to become nurses, therapists, or counselors.

**Why would it be more critical to injure the central nervous system rather than the peripheral nervous system?**

The main job of the peripheral nervous system is to communicate all the information of the body to the central nervous system. Nerves branch from the spine. These nerves are part of the peripheral nervous system. Other nerves go to all parts of the body, including the arms, the legs, and the organs. All of these nerves are also part of the peripheral nervous system. They send and receive messages to the brain.

**LESSON 6 REVIEW** Write the answers to these questions on a separate sheet of paper. Use complete sentences.

1) How does the nervous system send and receive messages throughout the body?

2) What are the main parts of the brain?

3) What are the jobs of the cerebrum and the cerebellum? Compare and contrast the jobs.

4) What are the two systems of the nervous system?

5) What is the main job of the peripheral nervous system?

**Careers**
Have a volunteer read to the class about orderlies. Ask students if any of them would be interested in becoming an orderly. What are some things they might like about the job? What are some things they might not like about it? Encourage students to share information about people they know who work in the health field.

**Lesson 6 Review Answers**

1) Messages are passed throughout the body by nerve cells.

2) The main parts of the brain are the cerebrum, the cerebellum, and the medulla.

3) The cerebrum controls learning, thinking, and memory. The cerebrum may also decide when you need to lift a box off the floor. The cerebellum coordinates voluntary muscles so that they move smoothly. The cerebellum works closely with the cerebrum. The cerebellum also sends messages to muscles so that all the muscles can work together.

4) The two systems of the nervous system are the central nervous system and the peripheral nervous system.

5) The main job of the peripheral nervous system is to communicate all the information about the body to the central nervous system.

 **BACKGROUND INFORMATION**

One part of the peripheral nervous system controls the reflexes. Reflexes are automatic responses to something such as heat or pain. A person has no control over reflexes and cannot stop reflex actions from happening.

To demonstrate reflexes to students, have a volunteer stand in front of the class. Hold a book, ball, or other object and make a movement as if to throw it to the student. Do not actually throw the object. Ask the class to describe what happens.

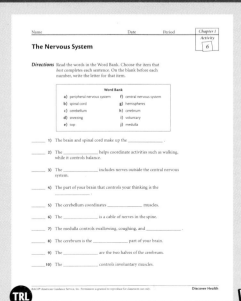

**Activity 6**

**Workbook Activity 6**

# Lesson at a Glance

## Chapter 1 Lesson 7

**Overview** This lesson describes the structure and function of the endocrine system.

### Objectives

■ To explain the functions of the endocrine system.

■ To describe how glands and hormones affect the body.

**Student Pages** 44–46

**Audiocassette**

**Human Body Transparency** 14

**Teacher's Resource Library** **TRL**

Activity 7

Workbook Activity 7

## Teaching Suggestions

### ■ Vocabulary

*endocrine system, hormone, secrete, adrenal gland, adrenaline, pituitary gland, thyroid gland*

Write each vocabulary word on the board. Pronounce each one for students, marking the syllables to help students learn the word. Have students make a list of the words. As they read the lesson, have students write a short definition of each term in their own words.

### ■ Teaching the Lesson

Have students imagine or remember riding a roller coaster or other exciting amusement park ride. Ask volunteers to describe their mental and physical reactions during the ride. Then explain that the endocrine system is the part of the body that responds when a person is excited or afraid.

Direct students' attention to Figure 1.11. Help students pronounce the terms in the labels. Students may already know that the ovaries and testicles are also part of the reproductive system.

---

## The Endocrine System

| Endocrine system |
| --- |
| The body system that uses chemicals to send and receive messages |

*L*ike the nervous system, the **endocrine system** controls many activities of your body. It directs activities such as reproduction, growth, and emotions.

### How Does the Endocrine System Work?

The endocrine system is made of glands. You can see these glands in Figure 1.11.

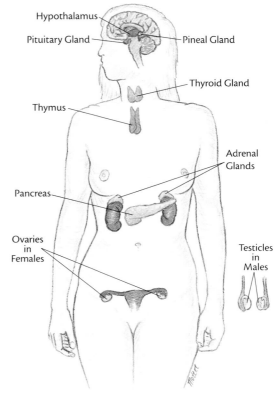

**Figure 1.11.** The endocrine system

---

Ask:

• **What does the endocrine system do?**
(directs activities such as reproduction, growth, and emotions)

• **Where are the adrenal glands located?**
(The adrenal glands are located above the pancreas, on top of the kidneys. Explain that these glands produce a chemical when a person is afraid.)

• **Which organ in the picture is also part of the digestive system?** (the pancreas; refer students to Figure 1.5 on page 33 to confirm this.)

**Hormone**
*A chemical messenger produced by a gland*

**Secrete**
*Form and give off*

Endocrine glands form and give off, or **secrete**, chemicals called **hormones**. Hormones control activities within the body. They control reproduction, growth, and your emotions.

The hormones are sent directly into the blood. When a hormone is secreted into the blood, it travels to another part of the body. For example, a hormone secreted by a gland near your brain may travel to your reproductive organs. These hormones cause development of your reproductive organs during the teenage years.

**Why are hormones secreted only during certain times or during specific phases of life?**

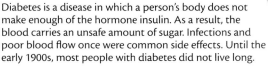

### DIABETES

Diabetes is a disease in which a person's body does not make enough of the hormone insulin. As a result, the blood carries an unsafe amount of sugar. Infections and poor blood flow once were common side effects. Until the early 1900s, most people with diabetes did not live long.

In 1921, Canadian doctor Frederick Banting began to research diabetes. The following year, he perfected an insulin injection for diabetes patients. Since then, millions of people with diabetes have been able to live longer by taking insulin or a pill to stimulate the pancreas to produce insulin. Today, researchers are working on a way to save a person's blood from their umbilical cord at birth to use to grow cells to help stimulate the pancreas or replace diseased tissue. Perhaps in the future, insulin injections will not be needed.

*The Body Systems   Chapter 1*   **45**

## Then and Now

Explain that the symptoms of diabetes include thirst, hunger, and loss of weight. Some people who have diabetes do not need to take insulin. The symptoms of the disease can be controlled by diet. All people with this disease must carefully watch what, when, and how much they eat.

Have students read about how the endocrine system works on pages 44 and 45.

Ask:

- What are hormones and what do they do? (chemicals that control activities in the body)

- What activities in the body do the hormones control? (reproduction, growth, and emotions)

 **BACKGROUND INFORMATION**

Two hormones secreted by the pancreas are insulin and glucagon. The hormones have opposite effects—insulin reduces the level of sugar in the bloodstream; glucagon increases it. Insulin helps the body cells absorb sugar and use it for energy. When the pancreas does not produce enough insulin, the blood sugar level can rise too high.

## LEARNING STYLES

**LEP/ESL** Students whose second language is English may have particular difficulty pronouncing the vocabulary words in this lesson. Partner these students with proficient readers. Have them create their own phonetic spellings to help in pronouncing the words.

Have students read about three of the glands in the endocrine system on page 46.

## Ask:

- Where is the pituitary gland? (at the base of the brain)

- What is the difference between the adrenal gland and adrenaline? (The adrenal gland is an organ. Adrenaline is a hormone produced by the adrenal gland.)

- Which gland helps the body deal with stress? (adrenal gland)

- Which gland releases hormones that cause sex organs to mature? (pituitary gland)

- What does the thyroid gland do? (helps the body change food into energy)

## Lesson 7 Review Answers

1) Endocrine glands form and secrete hormones into the blood.
2) Hormones are chemicals that control activities within the body.
3) The pituitary gland secretes hormones that tell the reproductive organs to begin developing.
4) The pituitary gland secretes many different hormones that control many different activities throughout the body.
5) Adrenaline causes the heart to beat faster.

## BACKGROUND INFORMATION

The word hormone is derived from a Greek word meaning "arouse to activity" or "excite." The term was first used by British physiologist E. H. Starling in 1905 to describe substances secreted by the stomach in the digestive process.

---

**Adrenal gland**
*The endocrine gland that releases several hormones*

**Adrenaline**
*The hormone that increases certain body functions*

**Pituitary gland**
*The endocrine gland attached to the base of the brain*

**Thyroid gland**
*The endocrine gland that affects a person's energy*

## What Do the Pituitary, Thyroid, and Adrenal Glands Do?

The **pituitary gland** has a very important role in the body. It secretes many different kinds of hormones and is sometimes called the body's master gland.

The pituitary gland is a pea-sized gland attached to the base of the brain. It releases hormones that help a child develop into a young adult. These hormones cause the sex organs to mature. The pituitary gland also produces growth hormones that affect a person's size.

The **thyroid gland** is a large endocrine gland. It produces hormones that help the body change food into energy. Too much of these hormones can cause a person to feel overly energetic. Too little of it causes a person to feel tired. The pituitary gland secretes a hormone that causes the thyroid to act.

An **adrenal gland** is on the top of each kidney. These glands secrete hormones that help the body maintain the proper water balance and cope with stress. They also secret a hormone called **adrenaline**. Adrenaline causes your heart to beat faster in an emergency.

**LESSON 7 REVIEW** Write the answers to these questions on a separate sheet of paper. Use complete sentences.

1) What are endocrine glands?
2) What are hormones?
3) How does the endocrine system control development of your reproductive organs?
4) Why is the pituitary gland sometimes called the master gland?
5) How does adrenaline affect the body in an emergency?

---

Name _____ Date _____ Period _____ | Chapter 1 Activity 7

### The Endocrine System

**Directions** Read the words in the Word Bank. Choose the item that *best completes each sentence. On the blank before each number, write the letter for that item.*

**Word Bank**
a) adrenal          f) large
b) adrenaline       g) pea-sized
c) body             h) pituitary
d) endocrine system i) secrete
e) hormones         j) thyroid

1) The _____ controls body activities such as reproduction and growth.
2) Endocrine glands form and _____ hormones.
3) _____ are chemicals that control activities in your body.
4) The _____ gland secretes many kinds of hormones.
5) The _____ gland produces chemicals that change food into energy.
6) The _____ glands secrete hormones that help the body cope with stress.
7) A chemical that causes the heart to beat faster in an emergency is _____.
8) The pituitary gland is a _____ gland.
9) The thyroid gland is a _____ gland.
10) Hormones that are secreted travel to other parts of the _____.

TRL

Activity 7

---

Name _____ Date _____ Period _____ | Chapter 1 Workbook Activity 7

### The Endocrine System

**Directions** Write *T* if the statement is true or *F* if it is false.

____ 1) The endocrine system controls many skin cells.
____ 2) Glands secrete chemicals.
____ 3) Hormones are the same as body organs.
____ 4) The pituitary gland is sometimes called the body's missing gland.
____ 5) The thyroid gland is a large gland.
____ 6) The adrenal glands secrete a chemical called adrenaline.
____ 7) The pituitary gland is the largest gland in the body.
____ 8) Hormones never enter the blood.
____ 9) The endocrine system directs your body's growth.
____ 10) The pituitary gland releases the hormones that cause the development of your reproductive system.

TRL

Workbook Activity 7

## The Reproductive System

**Ovary**
*The female organ that stores eggs*

**Ovulation**
*The monthly process of releasing an egg*

**Puberty**
*The period when children develop into adults and reach sexual maturity*

**Reproductive system**
*The body system responsible for making a baby*

Reproduction is the process through which a male and a female produce a child. The ability to reproduce is one of the most amazing features of the human body. It is carried out by the **reproductive system**. It is the only body system that differs between males and females.

### What Are the Parts of the Female Reproductive System?

The female reproductive system is shown in Figure 1.12. Females are born with more than a million eggs. The eggs are stored in the **ovaries**. The eggs begin to mature when the pituitary gland releases hormones that act on the ovaries. The mature eggs are then released in a monthly process known as **ovulation**. This happens during **puberty**. Puberty is the time when children begin adult development and reach sexual maturity.

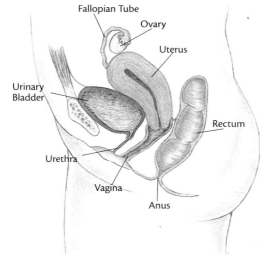

**Figure 1.12.** The female reproductive system

*The Body Systems    Chapter 1*    **47**

- How often does the female reproductive system release eggs? (monthly)

- What is puberty? (the time when a child reaches sexual maturity)

- Why can't very young children have babies? (They have not yet reached sexual maturity.)

## Lesson at a Glance

### Chapter 1  Lesson 8

**Overview** This lesson describes the male and female reproductive systems.

### Objectives

- To describe the male and female reproductive systems.

- To explain how reproduction occurs.

**Student Pages** 47–50

**Audiocassette**

**Human Body Transparency** 15

**Teacher's Resource Library**  **TRL**

Activity 8
Workbook Activity 8

## Teaching Suggestions

### ■ Vocabulary

*ovary, ovulation, puberty, reproductive system, menstruation, sperm, testis, uterus, vagina, penis, sexual intercourse*

Have volunteers copy the vocabulary words on the board. Ask students to find as many of the words as they can in figures 1.12 and 1.13. Then read the definitions in random order and have volunteers choose the correct word for each definition.

### ■ Teaching the Lesson

Stress the physiological aspects of the reproductive systems rather than the sexual aspects. Explain that it is valuable for students to learn the scientific terms for these body organs and functions. Knowing the language can help a person better explain problems or symptoms to a medical professional.

Have students read about the female reproductive system on page 47.

Ask:

- What does the word *reproduce* mean? (make a copy, or duplicate) How are the words *reproduce* and *reproductive* related? (*Reproductive* is the adjective form of the verb *reproduce*.)

Have students read about what happens when an egg is released, how a baby is born, and parts of the male reproductive system on page 48. Encourage students to refer to figures 1.12 and 1.13 as they read.

## Ask:

- In which organ does a baby develop? (the uterus)

- What is menstruation? (the monthly passing of an egg and other tissue from the female body)

- What is the difference between the uterus and the vagina? (The uterus is the organ in which a baby develops; the vagina is the tube leading from the uterus to the outside of the female body.)

- Why is the temperature in the testes lower than the rest of the male body? (so that sperm can survive)

### LEARNING STYLES

**Visual** Prepare very simple diagrams of the male and female reproductive systems. Make copies to distribute to the class. Have students copy labels from figures 1.12 and 1.13 on their diagrams. When students are finished, have them use their diagrams to show where eggs are produced and babies are born, and to trace the path of sperm as it travels through the male reproductive system.

**Menstruation**
*The monthly flow of an egg and extra tissue from the uterus*

**Sperm**
*The male sex cells*

**Testis**
*The male organ that makes sperm*

**Uterus**
*The female organ that holds a growing baby*

**Vagina**
*The birth canal through which a baby is born*

## What Happens When an Egg Is Released?

Once released, an egg moves through a tube to the **uterus**. On its way to the uterus, the egg may be joined by a **sperm**, or male sex cell. If the egg is joined by a sperm, it attaches itself to the wall of the uterus.

The uterus will become larger to make room for the egg and sperm. The egg and sperm will make new cells. The uterus will also provide blood, food, and oxygen to the developing baby.

If the egg is not joined by a sperm, it leaves the body. This monthly passing of an egg and other tissue is called **menstruation**. Menstruation is the blood flow that takes place each month in a woman's body.

## How Is a Baby Born?

A baby will grow in the uterus until it is time for it to be born. Then the uterus opening will expand to allow the baby to move out of the uterus.

The **vagina** is the birth canal. This tube leads from the uterus to the outer sexual organs. It is the path the baby takes when it is born.

## What Are the Parts of the Male Reproductive System?

In males, the sex cells are called sperm. Sperm are made in the male sex organs called **testes**. The testes begin making sperm when the pituitary gland sends hormones to act on the testes during puberty. Figure 1.13 shows the male reproductive system.

The testes are in a sac outside the body. The temperature of the sac is about five degrees lower than the temperature of the rest of the body. Sperm do not live long at the body's normal temperature.

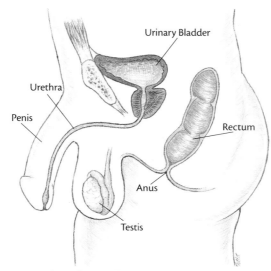

**Figure 1.13.** The male reproductive system

Urinary Bladder

Urethra

Penis

Rectum

Anus

Testis

---

**Penis**
*The male organ used to deliver sperm and to urinate*

**Sexual intercourse**
*Inserting the penis into the vagina*

---

**What reasons might explain why a sperm and an egg are sometimes unable to join?**

### How Are Sperm Released?

The sperm are stored in coiled tubes on the side of the testis. Mature sperm flow into the urethra. The urethra leads to the outside of the body through the penis. Both sperm and urine exit the body through the urethra, but not at the same time.

### How Does New Life Begin?

Once both a male and female reach puberty, it is possible for them to reproduce a new life. **Sexual intercourse** is nature's way of joining a male sperm and a female egg to form a new life.

During intercourse, sperm pass through tubes to the **penis**. The penis is the male reproductive organ. It has many small blood vessels. These vessels fill with blood, making the penis firm. The sperm travel through the penis to enter the female body through the vagina. During intercourse, millions of sperm are released into the female. It takes only one sperm cell to join with an egg. If this happens, the growth of a new baby begins.

*The Body Systems Chapter 1* **49**

---

Have volunteers read the labels in Figure 1.13.

**Ask:**

- Look at Figure 1.13. Which organ produces sperm? (testis)

- Look at the picture on page 49. Which organs are also part of the digestive system? (rectum, anus) Which are part of the excretory system? (urinary bladder)

Have students read the last two sections of the lesson on page 49.

**Ask:**

- Why do you think millions of sperm are released? (to increase the chances that one of them will join with the egg to produce a new life)

- How does the penis get firm during sexual intercourse? (Small blood vessels in the penis fill with blood.)

- Where do the sperm travel after they enter the female body? (through the vagina and into the uterus)

---

**APPLICATION**

 **In the Community**
The testes produce the male hormone testosterone. Anabolic steroids, derived from this hormone, are sometimes used by athletes to increase body mass and strength. However, the use of steroids can have serious and dangerous side effects. Many sports organizations now discourage or prohibit the use of steroids. Have students check with local sports groups and health clubs to find out what information is available about using steroids.

---

## Action for Health

Self-exams are the first step in preventive health care. Brochures on self-exams can be obtained from a local public health office or offices of gynecologists and urologists. Encourage students to share this information with family members. These self-exams should be done at least monthly to ensure early detection and treatment.

## Lesson 8 Review Answers

1) Females are born with all the eggs they will ever have. Sperm are made in the testes and are produced throughout a male's lifetime starting at puberty.
2) Ovulation is the monthly release of an egg. Menstruation is the monthly passing of an unfertilized egg and other tissue.
3) Once released, an egg travels through a tube to the uterus. If the egg is joined by a sperm, it plants itself in the wall of the uterus. If it is not fertilized, it will pass out of the body through the vagina.
4) The sperm are stored in coiled tubes. Then the sperm flow into the urethra. The urethra leads to the outside of the body through the penis.
5) The male reproductive system produces and deposits sperm into the female reproductive system. The female reproductive system stores and releases eggs. When a sperm joins with an egg, the female reproductive system nurtures the growing baby.

### APPLICATION

**Career Connection**
Doctors and nurses specially trained in obstetrics care for a woman's medical needs before and during the birth of her baby. However, a woman can enlist the help of a labor coach called a doula while in labor. Most doulas take certification classes in labor and delivery, and then teach classes to expectant parents on what to do during labor and how to care for a newborn. Have interested students research this career and report back to the class.

## Action for Health

### SELF-EXAM FOR EARLY SIGNS OF CANCER

Learn to examine yourself for changes that may be early warning signs of cancer.

**For Females: Self-Exam of the Breasts**
Females should do a self-examination after each menstrual period. The three ways to examine breasts are before a mirror, in the shower, or lying down.

Stand before a mirror and look at your breasts for any unusual depressions or lumps. Look for unusual changes.

In the shower or lying down, use the left hand to examine the right breast and the right hand to examine the left breast. Use your first three fingers. Examine each breast in a circle around the nipple until you cover the entire breast. Also, check the nipple and the area between the armpit and the breast.

**For Males: Self-Exam of the Testes**
Cancer of the testes is one of the most common cancers in males between the ages of 20 and 35. Most testicular cancers are first discovered during self-examination. Examine the testicles once a month after bathing. Gently roll each testicle between the thumb and fingers, noting any abnormal lumps.

**LESSON 8 REVIEW** Write the answers to these questions on a separate sheet of paper. Use complete sentences.

1) Compare how eggs are produced with the way sperm are produced.
2) What is the difference between ovulation and menstruation?
3) Describe the path of an egg through the female reproductive system.
4) Describe the path of sperm out of the male's body.
5) How do the male and female reproductive systems work together to reproduce?

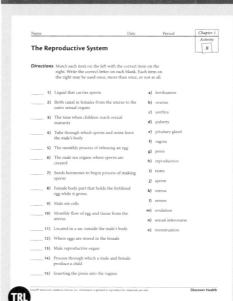

**Activity 8**

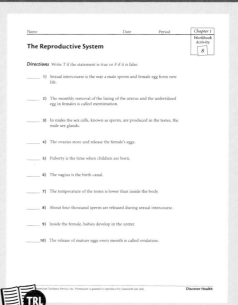

**Workbook Activity 8**

■ Tiny units, called cells, make up all living things, including the human body.

■ Cells form tissues, and different types of tissues form organs. Groups of organs form a body system.

■ The skin is the largest organ of the body. It has three layers that cover and protect your body.

■ The skeletal system is made up of 206 bones. Bones give your body its frame and protect underlying organs.

■ The muscular system allows your body to move. You move when a muscle pulls a bone.

■ Muscles that you control are called voluntary muscles. Muscles you do not control are called involuntary muscles.

■ The digestive system breaks food down into a form that your cells can use. Blood carries the digested food to the cells.

■ Food that is not digested passes out of the body as solid waste.

■ Other wastes pass out of your body in a liquid form called urine. Urine is formed in the kidneys and leaves the body through the urethra.

■ Your respiratory system brings fresh air into your lungs. The circulatory system carries oxygen and carbon dioxide to and from your body cells.

■ The nervous system allows the different parts of your body to communicate with one another. The different parts of your body send information to your brain and spinal cord.

■ Glands in the endocrine system secrete chemicals called hormones. Hormones travel in the blood to other parts of the body.

■ The male and female reproductive systems work together to produce a baby.

## ■ Using the Chapter Summary

To further reinforce the facts and concepts presented in the chapter, read and discuss with students the questions that follow.

### Ask:

- How are tissues related to organs? (Organs are made up of different kinds of tissues.)

- What are the three layers of the skin? (epidermis, dermis, subcutaneous layer)

- What do bones do? (give your body its frame and protect underlying organs)

- Describe the difference between voluntary and involuntary muscles. (Voluntary muscles can be controlled; involuntary muscles cannot be controlled.)

- What are capillaries and veins? (Capillaries are blood vessels that carry blood away from the heart. Veins carry the blood back to the heart.)

- How do the circulatory and respiratory systems work together? (The respiratory system provides oxygen for the blood that is transported through the body by the circulatory system.)

- What is the difference in the functions of the right and left sides of the brain? (The left side controls the ability to reason, use language, and do math. The right side controls artistic ability and the imagination.)

- What does the endocrine system do? (secretes hormones to control activities in the body)

- How does reproduction occur? (Sperm from the male testes joins with an egg in the uterus of the female to create a new life.)

# Chapter 1 Review

The Teacher's Resource Library includes two parallel forms of the Chapter 1 Mastery Test. The difficulty level of the two forms is equivalent. You may wish to use one form as a pretest and the other form as a posttest.

## Review Answers

### Comprehension: Identifying Facts

1) endocrine  2) blood  3) bones
4) digestive  5) spinal cord  6) hormone
7) glands  8) cerebrum  9) cells
10) muscle

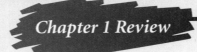

## Comprehension: Identifying Facts

On a separate sheet of paper, write the correct word or words from the Word Bank to complete each sentence.

| WORD BANK | | |
|---|---|---|
| blood | endocrine | kidneys |
| bones | epidermis | muscle |
| cerebrum | glands | spinal cord |
| cells | hormone | uterus |
| digestive | | |

1) The pituitary, thyroid, and adrenal glands are part of the _____ system.

2) The _____ is made up of cells and plasma.

3) The skeletal system is made up of 206 _____.

4) The _____ system breaks food down into a form cells can use.

5) The brain and the _____ make up the central nervous system.

6) A _____ is a chemical produced by a gland.

7) Endocrine _____ send hormones through your bloodstream.

8) The largest part of the brain is the _____.

9) A tissue is made up of many _____ working together to do the same job.

10) When you move, a _____ is pulling a bone.

---

**11)** The three layers of the skin are the _____, the dermis, and the subcutaneous layer.

**12)** Urine is formed by the _____.

**13)** After a sperm joins an egg, the egg attaches itself to the wall of the _____.

## Comprehension: Understanding Main Ideas

Write the answers to these questions on a separate sheet of paper. Use complete sentences.

**14)** How does your skin protect your body?

**15)** How do the respiratory and circulatory systems work together to bring oxygen to your cells?

**16)** What are three purposes of your blood?

**17)** How is the endocrine system different from the nervous system?

**18)** How do the muscular and skeletal systems work together so that you can move?

## Critical Thinking: Write Your Opinion

**19)** Which body system do you think is more important than the others? Explain your answer.

**20)** Many doctors specialize in treating one specific body system. Suppose you were a doctor. Which body system would you specialize in? Why?

**Test Taking Tip** Sometimes it is easier to learn vocabulary words if you break them into their word parts.

---

11) epidermis  12) kidneys  13) uterus

## Comprehension: Understanding Main Ideas

**14)** The skin prevents germs from entering the body. It keeps the body's temperature steady. It also helps the body adjust to changes around it.

**15)** The respiratory system and the circulatory system bring oxygen to the body cells and take carbon dioxide away from the cells.

**16)** Blood brings food and oxygen to all parts of the body. Blood picks up wastes from all parts of the body. Blood also has cells that fight germs.

**17)** The endocrine system communicates with other parts of the body through hormones that are secreted in the blood. The nervous system communicates by sending messages through nerve cells.

**18)** The muscles move bones, allowing the body to move in different ways.

## Critical Thinking: Write Your Opinion

**19)** Answers will vary. Students should back up their opinion with information about the body system they choose.

**20)** Answers will vary. Students should back up their opinion with information about the body system they choose.

---

**Chapter 1 Mastery Test B**

| Name | Date | Period | Chapter 1 Mastery Test B page 1 |

**Chapter 1 Mastery Test B**

**Directions** Circle the response that *best* completes each sentence.

1) The nervous system _____
   a) carries oxygen and carbon dioxide to and from your body cells.
   b) allows the different parts of your body to communicate with one another.
   c) allows your body to move.
   d) works to produce a baby.

2) The _____ are part of the endocrine system.
   a) vagina, uterus, and ovaries
   b) saliva, esophagus, and small intestine
   c) nose, trachea, and lungs
   d) pituitary, thyroid, and adrenal glands

3) The three layers of skin that cover and protect your body are the _____
   a) pituitary, thyroid, and adrenal.
   b) cerebrum, cerebellum, and medulla.
   c) epidermis, dermis, and subcutaneous.
   d) arteries, veins, and aorta.

4) Groups of organs form _____
   a) hormones.
   b) muscles.
   c) bones.
   d) body systems.

5) The main parts of the circulatory system are the _____ and blood vessels.
   a) heart
   b) spinal cord
   c) pituitary gland
   d) ovaries

6) Cells are _____
   a) the largest organ of the body.
   b) tiny units that make up your body.
   c) the frame for your body.
   d) waste that is removed from the body.

7) The _____ breaks food down into a form that your cells can use.
   a) central nervous system
   b) endocrine system
   c) reproductive system
   d) digestive system

**TRL**    ©AGS® American Guidance Service, Inc. Permission is granted to reproduce for classroom use only.    **Discover Health**

| Name | Date | Period | Chapter 1 Mastery Test B page 2 |

**Chapter 1 Mastery Test B, continued**

8) The central nervous system is made up of the _____ and the spinal cord.
   a) heart
   b) lungs
   c) brain
   d) kidneys

9) Your skeletal system _____
   a) protects parts of your body.
   b) is made up of your muscles.
   c) breaks down food.
   d) pumps blood through the body.

10) If the egg is joined by a _____, it attaches to the wall of the uterus.
   a) sperm
   b) testes
   c) cell
   d) gland

11) _____ is formed by the kidneys.
   a) blood
   b) urine
   c) sperm
   d) medulla

12) A hormone is a chemical produced by a _____
   a) gland.
   b) muscle.
   c) large intestine.
   d) dermis.

13) The respiratory system brings to your body fresh _____ that is rich in oxygen.
   a) blood
   b) hormones
   c) air
   d) cells

14) Muscles that move when you think about it are _____
   a) joints.
   b) voluntary.
   c) trachea.
   d) contractual.

15) The _____ system is the only body system that differs between males and females.
   a) circulatory
   b) reproductive
   c) digestive
   d) endocrine

**TRL**    ©AGS® American Guidance Service, Inc. Permission is granted to reproduce for classroom use only.    **Discover Health**

**Chapter 1 Mastery Test B**

(Answer Keys for the Teacher's
Resource Library begin on page 433
of this Teacher's Edition.)

## Introducing the Chapter

Have students stand. Conduct some simple
exercises with them such as running in
place, jumping jacks if there is room, or
stretching and bending exercises.

Have a volunteer read the introductory
information. Discuss the material with
students, as well as the Goals for Learning.

### Ask:

- What physical activities do you enjoy?
  (Lead students to understand that physical
  activity includes more than sports.)

- Do you feel that you get enough physical
  exercise? (If students say no, ask them if
  they would like to get more and what
  prevents them from doing so.)

- Why is exercise important? (Lead students
  to relate exercise to good health.)

# Chapter 2

# Hygiene and Fitness

*T*aking care of yourself can be one of the most
important things you do for yourself. Caring for your
skin, hair, nails, teeth, eyes, and ears can help keep
you healthy. Exercising and getting enough rest also are
important for your health. Taking care of yourself can help
you look and feel better. When you feel good about yourself,
other people usually feel good about you, too.

In this chapter, you will learn about ways to take care of
yourself. You will learn how keeping clean and taking care of
your body are important. You will also learn how exercise and
rest can help you. Finally, you will learn how taking care of
yourself can help your physical, social, and emotional health.

### Goals for Learning

▶ To explain the purpose of basic hygiene

▶ To describe ways to protect skin, hair, nails, teeth, eyes,
and ears

▶ To define cardiovascular fitness and explain its importance

▶ To identify the benefits of regular exercise and the parts of
an exercise program

▶ To explain why the body needs rest and sleep

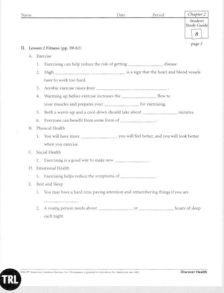

**Student Study Guide 8, page 1**       **Student Study Guide 8, page 2**

**Acne**
*Clogged skin pores
that causes pimples
or blackheads*

Practicing good hygiene is important for your health. Hygiene refers to things that you do to promote your health. Caring for your skin, hair, nails, teeth, eyes, and ears is a part of hygiene.

### How Can You Take Care of Your Skin?

Your skin covers and protects your body. Keeping your skin clean is part of good skin care. Washing with soap and water is the best way to keep your skin clean. This can help remove dirt and germs from the outside of your skin.

**What are some reasons why one person might need to bathe more often than another person?**

Washing with soap and water also helps reduce body odor. Perspiration has no odor. Odor results when perspiration contacts germs on your skin. How often you bathe depends on how active you are and what skin type you have. People who are very active or who have oily skin need to bathe more often.

Strong winds, cold, and sun dry the skin's outer layer. Covering your face and hands in cold or windy weather helps protect your skin. Too much sun can cause sunburn, wrinkled skin, and skin cancer. Wearing sunscreen helps protect your skin. Sunscreens are rated by a sun protection factor (SPF). An SPF of 15 or higher gives the best protection.

*Nutrition Tip*

**Eat plenty of fruits and vegetables. They can provide vitamins and minerals your skin needs to stay healthy.**

### Skin Problems

A common skin problem for teenagers is **acne**. Acne is clogged skin pores, or openings in the skin. Teenagers have a normal increase in hormones. Hormones cause oil glands to produce more oil. If the oil plugs your pores, you may get blackheads or pimples. A blackhead is an oil plug that gets dark when air contacts it. A pimple forms when the skin around the blackhead becomes red and filled with pus. Here are some things you can do to help control acne.

- Wash right after exercise to clean away sweat and germs that can clog pores. Use a clean washcloth every day.

- Shampoo your hair often to limit acne on your forehead, neck, and shoulders.

*Hygiene and Fitness   Chapter 2*   **55**

---

## Lesson at a Glance

## Chapter 2  Lesson 1

**Overview** This lesson explains the purpose of basic hygiene and what students can do to protect their skin, hair, nails, teeth, sight, and hearing.

### Objectives

- To describe how to protect the skin, hair, nails, and teeth.

- To describe how to protect sight and hearing.

**Student Pages** 55–58
**Audiocassette**
**Teacher's Resource Library**

  Activity 9
  Workbook Activity 9

## Teaching Suggestions

### ■ Vocabulary

*acne, caries, dermatologist, plaque, decibel, ophthalmologist, optometrist, orthodontist*

Have students copy each vocabulary word on an index card. As they study the lesson, tell students to write the definition of the words on the back of the card. Have them also use the word in two different sentences.

### ■ Teaching the Lesson

Read the lesson title and the first paragraph to students. Ask them to define *hygiene*. (a group of practices or habits to prevent disease and to maintain good health)

Have students read about how to take care of their skin on pages 55 and 56.

---

Ask:

- What is the best way to keep your skin clean? (wash with soap and water)

- How does body odor form? (when perspiration comes in contact with germs on the skin)

- What damaging effects can too much sun have? (sunburn, wrinkled skin, skin cancer)

- Will the information you have learned about skin care cause you to change any of your habits or actions? (Students might decide to limit time in the sun or to use a sunscreen.)

- What is a skin doctor called? (dermatologist)

Have students read about caring for their hair, nails, and teeth on page 56.

Ask:

- How do you help your hair when you brush it? (Brushing distributes oils and makes hair shiny.)

- How can you take care of your nails? (scrubbing, cutting, and filing them)

- Do you floss every day? (Most people do not. Stress that this is an important way students can protect their teeth.)

- Does your toothpaste contain fluoride? (Encourage students to read the label on the toothpaste tube when they get home. You might bring a tube of toothpaste to class and show students how to read the information on the label.)

## GLOBAL CONNECTION

 Point out to students that skin cancer is now one of the most common forms of cancer worldwide. It is especially prevalent among light-skinned people living in California, Australia, and Africa. Repeated exposure to the sun over a long period of time can contribute to skin cancer. Skin cancer can be cured if it is diagnosed and treated while it is in its early states. Have students investigate the use of sunscreens and sunblocks as protection against sunburn and skin cancer.

## APPLICATION

 **In the Community**
Because fluoride can help prevent tooth decay, many communities across the country have added fluoride to the drinking water. Encourage students to call the water department in their town to ask if there is fluoride in the drinking water.

---

technology

### LASER SURGERY

Science fiction movies show lasers as a weapon used against the enemy. Today lasers are often used for surgery. Laser surgery was first used in the mid-1960s. A laser produces a strong, narrow beam of light. It can be controlled accurately. Lasers can seal blood vessels. They can cut through skin and remove scars and wrinkles. They can change the shape of part of the eye. Some lasers can help nearsighted people see without glasses or contacts. Lasers can help people who snore. Dentists can even use lasers to whiten teeth.

- Eat a well-balanced diet. Get plenty of rest and exercise.
- Do not squeeze or pick pimples and blackheads.

If you have a skin problem, you might visit a **dermatologist**. A dermatologist is a doctor who takes care of skin problems.

**Caries**
*Cavities in the teeth*

**Dermatologist**
*A doctor who takes care of skin*

**Plaque**
*A layer of bacteria on teeth*

### How Can You Care for Your Hair and Nails?
Shampooing your hair often helps keep it clean. Brushing your hair distributes natural oils and makes your hair shiny. Too much heat can damage your hair. If you use a hair dryer or curling iron, use a low heat setting.

Nails protect the ends of your fingers and toes. Scrubbing your nails will get rid of dirt and germs under them. Cutting your nails evenly and filing rough edges will help protect them.

### How Can You Take Care of Your Teeth?
Brushing and flossing your teeth at least once a day can help remove **plaque**. Plaque is a sticky, colorless layer of bacteria that forms on teeth. Plaque causes **caries**, or cavities, in the teeth. Dental caries is a leading cause of tooth loss in children. Plaque also causes gum disease, a leading cause of tooth loss in adults.

**Decibel**
*A unit that measures sound*

**Optometrist**
*A specialist in eye examinations and corrective lenses*

**Orthodontist**
*A dentist who treats crooked or crowded teeth*

Making regular visits to the dentist is important. A dentist can check your teeth for cavities or other dental problems. Visits to the dentist also include a thorough cleaning of the teeth.

Many people have teeth that are crowded or crooked. Teeth that are out of position are harder to clean. This makes tooth decay and gum disease more likely. An **orthodontist** is a dentist who treats crowded or crooked teeth. Treatment can include braces or wires to move the teeth into the proper position.

### How Can You Care for Your Eyes and Sight?

You can help protect your eyes from infection, disease, and injury. Wearing safety glasses, goggles, or a helmet can protect your eyes from damaging light, dirt, or sports injuries. Wearing glasses or contact lenses helps you see better and prevents eyestrain. If you wear contact lenses, it is important to follow instructions for cleaning and wearing them.

Your vision is normal if you see a clear image. If you do not see clearly, an **optometrist** can prescribe glasses or contact lenses. An optometrist is a specialist in eye examinations and corrective lenses. Regular checkups with an optometrist can

 **Action for Health**

### PROTECT YOUR HEARING

The loudness of sound is measured in **decibels** (db). Here are some decibel levels of some common sounds:

| | |
|---|---|
| Normal breathing | 10 db |
| Whisper | 30 db |
| Normal conversation | 60 db |
| Truck traffic | 90 db |
| Rock concert | 120 db |
| Jet engine at takeoff | 140 db |

You can help protect your hearing from harmful noise. Keep the volume low on radios, CD players, and TVs, especially when wearing headphones. Get away from any sound that is too loud. Decibel levels higher than 85 can cause hearing loss. In jobs where noise is greater than 85 db, workers must wear earplugs or earmuffs to protect their hearing.

Have students read about caring for their vision and hearing on pages 57 and 58.

### Ask:

- What are some activities during which you should wear safety glasses to protect your eyes? (using tools, using paint or other chemicals, some types of sports)

- What is the most common reason for hearing loss? (loud noise)

- What is the loudest noise you have ever heard? (Accept all answers.)

- What can you do to protect your hearing and your ears? (avoid loud music, don't put objects in ears, swim in clean water, wear a head guard when playing contact sports)

- Doctors have a saying that you should never clean your ears with anything smaller than your elbow. What do you think that means? (Students may realize it's impossible to get the elbow in the ear. The point is not to put anything in the ear.)

 **BACKGROUND INFORMATION**

"Normal" vision is described as 20/20 vision. People with 20/15 vision have better-than-normal vision. An object that a person with normal vision can see clearly at 15 feet can be seen clearly by someone with 20/15 vision at 20 feet. People with 20/100 vision have poorer-than normal vision. They must move up to 20 feet to see what a person with normal vision sees at 100 feet.

### Technology

Ask students if they know anyone who has had laser surgery. Encourage students to research the various types of laser surgery that have been developed. Discuss what the future possibilities of laser surgery might be, as well as the advantages and disadvantages of this type of surgery.

## Action for Health

Ask students if they enjoy listening to loud music. Stress the importance of avoiding extremely loud music. Encourage students to wear ear plugs if they are in a very noisy place such as at a concert or near a construction site.

Ask each student to describe the loudest sound they can remember hearing. Challenge students to estimate a decimal value for each sound. Encourage students to use resources to check their predictions.

## Lesson 1 Review Answers

1) Accept any two of the following: washing with soap and water; protecting skin from winds, cold, and sun by keeping skin covered in cold or windy weather; wearing sunscreen.
2) You can remove plaque from your teeth by brushing and flossing at least once a day.
3) You can protect your eyes by wearing safety glasses, goggles, or a helmet to protect eyes from damaging light, dirt, or sports injuries.
4) You can protect your ears and hearing by wearing a head guard when playing contact sports, swimming only in clean water, cleaning only the outside of the ears, and staying away from loud noises as much as possible.
5) Answers will vary. Answers may include concerts, constructions sites, airports, or other places where the noise level is high.

## Healthy Subjects

Ask students for ideas about what else could be done to prevent hearing loss from noise pollution. Discuss whether students would be willing to work in a place where it is extremely loud, and if so, under what conditions.

### LEARNING STYLES

**Group Learning** In small groups, have students create a pamphlet including information on basic hygiene. Students can use information from the text as well as other facts they research. Encourage students to include illustrations, charts, and diagrams in their pamphlets.

---

If you wear contacts, be sure to follow instructions for cleaning them.

**Ophthalmologist**
*A doctor who specializes in diseases of the eye*

help correct vision problems and prevent disease. An **ophthalmologist** is a doctor who specializes in eye diseases.

### How Can You Care for Your Hearing?

A common reason for hearing loss is loud noise. Infection, allergy, buildup of wax, and injury can also cause hearing loss. If you have problems with your hearing, see a doctor.

There are things you can do to help protect your ears and your hearing. Wear a head guard when playing contact sports. Be careful to swim only in clean water. Clean only the outside of your ears. Never put a swab or other object into your ear. Stay away from loud noises as much as you can.

**LESSON 1 REVIEW** Write the answers to these questions on a separate sheet of paper. Use complete sentences.

1) What are two ways you can take care of your skin?
2) How can you remove plaque from your teeth?
3) How can you protect your eyes?
4) How can you protect your ears and hearing?
5) What are some noisy places where you think wearing earplugs might be a good idea?

### Healthy Subjects

**Science**

**NOISE POLLUTION**

Noise pollution is a health problem. Loud noise can cause hearing loss. Many industries and companies have worked to reduce loud noise. They use special materials in walls and ceilings to reduce sound levels. They place noisy machines in cases that cut down noise. Airport workers wear earplugs or earmuffs when jets take off. Other people who work in noisy places also wear ear protectors.

---

**Activity 9**

**Workbook Activity 9**

## Fitness

**Aerobic exercise**
*An exercise that raises the heart rate*

**Blood pressure**
*The force of the blood against the walls of the arteries when the heart beats*

**Cardiovascular fitness**
*The condition of the heart, lungs, and blood vessels*

**Heart rate**
*The number of times the heart pumps blood each minute*

**Physical fitness**
*The body's ability to work, exercise, and play without tiring*

**P**hysical fitness is your body's ability to exercise, work, and play without tiring easily. If you are physically fit, you have enough energy to do all the things you want to do. Physical fitness is an important part of your good health. It affects your emotional, social, and physical well-being.

### How Is Exercise Important to Your Health?

**Cardiovascular fitness** is the condition of the heart, lungs, and blood vessels. You can improve your cardiovascular fitness by exercising. Heart disease is the leading cause of death in this country. Heart disease often begins in childhood. Exercising to improve cardiovascular fitness can help reduce the risk of getting heart disease.

Your heart is a muscle. When you exercise, more blood enters the heart. The heart works harder to push more blood into the blood vessels. Then your heart muscle gets stronger.

Your heart pumps blood containing oxygen through your body. Your arteries are blood vessels that carry blood away from the heart to the rest of your body. Your veins carry blood from your body to your heart. Exercising helps blood flow through your body and back to your heart.

How well your heart and blood vessels are moving blood through your body can be measured. Your **heart rate**, or pulse rate, is the number of times your heart pumps blood each minute. **Blood pressure** is the force of blood against the walls of the arteries when the heart beats. High blood pressure is a sign that the heart and blood vessels have to work too hard. High blood pressure can lead to stroke, heart attacks, and kidney failure.

**Aerobic exercises** can help improve cardiovascular fitness. These are exercises that raise your heart rate. When you do aerobic exercises, your body takes in more oxygen. Some kinds of aerobic exercises are walking, running or jogging, biking, swimming, and cross-country skiing.

*Hygiene and Fitness    Chapter 2* **59**

---

## Lesson at a Glance

### Chapter 2  Lesson 2

**Overview** This lesson describes the benefits of exercise, how to exercise properly, and the body's need for sufficient sleep and rest.

### Objectives

- To explain the benefits of exercise.
- To describe ways to exercise safely.
- To explain the benefits of sufficient sleep and rest.

**Student Pages** 59–62

**Audiocassette**

**Teacher's Resource Library**

Activity 10

Workbook Activity 10

## Teaching Suggestions

### ■ Vocabulary

*aerobic exercise, blood pressure, cardiovascular fitness, heart rate, physical fitness*

Have volunteers read the definitions of each vocabulary word. Then have students describe a situation or an activity that is an example of each word.

### ■ Teaching the Lesson

Ask students to share the kinds of exercise they enjoy. Discuss with students the benefits of regular exercise.

Have students read about cardiovascular fitness on page 59.

Ask:

- Why is exercise important for your heart? (Exercise keeps the heart muscle strong so it can pump blood to all parts of the body.)

- What are some kinds of aerobic exercise? (walking, running, jogging, biking, swimming, and cross-country skiing)

Have students read about proper ways to exercise on page 60.

Ask:

- Have you ever seen people doing warm-ups? Where? (Students may have seen professional and high school athletes do stretching or running exercises before a sports event.)

- What could happen if you exercise vigorously without having warmed up? (Students may know that strains and sprains can occur.)

- Besides warming up and cooling down, what other things should you do to exercise safely? (wear proper protective clothing and exercise in a safe place such as bicycling in bike lanes and watching for traffic)

## APPLICATION

### Career Connection

A physical therapist works with people whose physical activity has been curtailed due to accidents, physical handicaps, arthritis, or heart disease. Physical therapists need to be flexible, physically strong, and supportive of their clients. A physical therapist must have at least a Bachelor of Science degree. Many physical therapists pursue a Master's degree in a particular area.

## APPLICATION

### Environment

Discuss with students that many people engage in jogging and aerobics to increase their physical well-being. Exercise causes the rate of breathing to increase. Therefore, any pollutants in the air are taken in more rapidly. Cigarette smoke is one such pollutant. Although most restaurants and other public places have designated smoking areas, some people believe that smoking should also be banned in all public places, including parks and other recreation areas. Ask students what they think about banning smoking in these areas.

*Fitness Tip*

Wear washable clothes when you exercise. Make sure the clothes are comfortable and loose. Clothes made of cotton allow your body to stay cool. Wearing proper shoes for physical activities can help prevent injuries.

## How Can You Exercise Properly?

No matter what kind of exercise you do, your workout should include a warm-up, an exercise period, and a cool-down. Skipping the warm-up and cool-down can be harmful to your body.

Warming up increases the blood flow to your muscles and prepares your body for exercising. Warming up allows your heart rate to increase gradually. A warm-up should take about five minutes. Walking and then stretching is a good way to warm up.

The exercise period should include exercises that make your heart and lungs work hard. It may include exercises such as sit-ups and push-ups to improve muscle strength. You can do stretching and bending exercises as part of the exercise period. These exercises help the body twist and turn easily. They help the body move and change positions smoothly.

Every workout should end with a cool-down. If you stop exercising suddenly, you can become dizzy. To cool down, continue to exercise gently at a slower pace. Do some stretching exercises. The cool-down should take about five minutes.

## Who Benefits From Exercise?

People who have a risk of heart disease can be greatly helped by exercise. In fact, everyone can benefit from some form of exercise. Regular exercise is a healthy habit that can have a positive effect on your physical, social, and emotional health. The top calorie burning exercises to help you be physically fit are found in Appendix A.

Regular exercise can improve your health. Exercise gives you more energy and helps you feel better.

## FITNESS INSTRUCTOR

Do you like to stay fit? If so, you might like to become a fitness instructor. Many companies have health and wellness programs. These programs can help workers develop healthy habits. Fitness instructors work with companies to help plan these programs. They teach workers how exercise helps the body. They help workers make exercise plans. They also show workers the correct way to exercise. Instructors may work with doctors and therapists to help workers with medical problems. You need special certification classes to become a fitness instructor. You need to study about the parts of the body and how they work together.

### Physical Health

Exercise firms and strengthens your muscles and helps your body move more smoothly. It also helps your heart and lungs to work better. When you exercise, you have more energy, you feel better, and you look better

Regular exercise helps you keep in shape at a weight that is right for you. Exercise burns calories. It also helps the body continue to burn calories at a faster rate.

**What might you say to a person who does not exercise because he or she thinks it is boring?**

### Social Health

Exercise is fun. It helps you enjoy your extra time. Exercising is a good way to make new friends. Walking, jogging, skiing, bicycling, swimming, and many other sports are good exercises and good activities to do with friends.

### Emotional Health

Exercise helps reduce the symptoms of stress. It helps you take your mind off your problems. After exercising, you feel refreshed and relaxed.

### Why Are Rest and Sleep Important to Fitness?

When you rest and sleep, your heart rate and breathing slow down. Your blood pressure drops and your muscles relax. Your body uses less energy.

*Hygiene and Fitness   Chapter 2*   **61**

Have students read about the benefits of exercise on pages 60 and 61.

Ask:

- What are some physical benefits of exercise? (firming and strengthening muscles, keeping at the right weight, increasing energy)

- What are some emotional benefits of exercise? (reducing stress, taking your mind off problems, relaxing)

## Careers

Ask students if they think that fitness instructors have an important job and give reasons to support their conclusion. Ask if any students would like to become fitness instructors and discuss the advantages and disadvantages of this type of career. You may want students to research other related careers such as physical therapist, exercise physiologist, or therapeutic recreation specialist.

## APPLICATION

**At Home**
Encourage students to develop with their family or friends a list of activities they can do together to improve heart and lung fitness. Invite students to share their lists with the class for comparison.

## LEARNING STYLES

**LEP/ESL** When discussing the importance that exercise plays in maintaining a healthy body, explain the slang expression "couch potato." Working in cooperative groups, have students write a paragraph describing the habits of a couch potato. Then ask students to design a plan to help the couch potato become a healthier person. Suggest that different groups compare their plans.

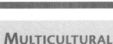

## MULTICULTURAL CONNECTION

Martial arts and yoga are two forms of exercise that are part of the cultures in many Asian countries. Tae kwon do and hapkido are forms of exercise from Korea. Tai chi and kung fu come from China. Yoga came primarily from India. Have students work in groups to research one of these types of exercise.

Have students read about the benefits of sleep on pages 61 and 62.

## Ask:

- What happens when someone does not get enough sleep? (A person becomes tired or cranky. Small problems seem bigger than they are. There is a greater possibility of accidents, injury, or poor performance at school or work.)

- What are some other ways to rest besides sleep? (lying down for a brief time, doing a calming activity such as reading or listening to soft music)

## Lesson 2 Review Answers

1) Heart rate and blood pressure measure how well the heart is moving blood through the body.
2) When you exercise, more blood enters the heart. The heart works harder to push more blood into the blood vessels. Then your heart muscle gets stronger. Exercising also helps blood flow through the body and back to the heart.
3) The three important parts of a workout are a warm-up, an exercise period, and a cool-down.
4) The three parts of overall health that can be improved by exercise are emotional, social, and physical well-being.
5) Lack of sleep might make it difficult to concentrate and to study.

## Then and Now

Conduct a class discussion on the following questions: How do students feel about coed sports teams? Should females be allowed to play football? What are some other sports in which females still do not participate? Are there any sports in which males do not participate? What are students' favorite events in the Olympics? Are the events male- or female-dominated?

### Writing About Health

Think about a physical activity that is fun for you. Write about when you do the activity. Tell why you enjoy it.

When you are tired, you may have a hard time paying attention and remembering things. You may make more mistakes than you usually do. You are more likely to get ill or injure yourself when you are tired. You might find that you are less able to cope with upsetting situations.

Most young people need about eight or nine hours of sleep each night. If you are active, you may need extra rest. Relaxing is a way to rest during the day.

**LESSON 2 REVIEW** Write the answers to these questions on a separate sheet of paper. Use complete sentences.

1) What two things measure how well the heart is moving blood through the body?
2) How does exercise improve your cardiovascular fitness?
3) What are three important parts of a workout?
4) Name three parts of overall health that can be improved by exercise.
5) How might lack of sleep affect how well you study?

### WOMEN IN SPORTS

Around 1900, women in America were not allowed to play most sports. They did play croquet and archery. Women had to wear long dresses with long sleeves when they played. These clothes made it hard for women to play.

Over the years, women started playing volleyball, baseball, and basketball. Today, women play as many sports as men do. They have become champion figure skaters, runners, and tennis players. They have succeeded in gymnastics, water sports, and many other sports.

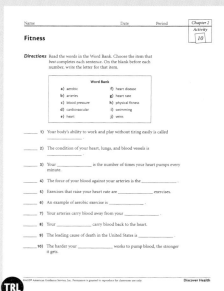

**Activity 10**

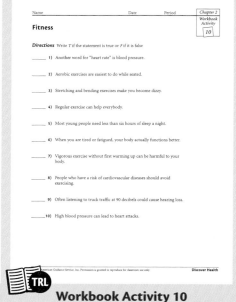

**Workbook Activity 10**

■ Caring for skin, hair, nails, teeth, eyes, and ears is a part of hygiene.

■ One important way to care for the skin is to wash with soap and water.

■ Protecting skin from strong winds, cold, and sun is important.

■ Acne can be controlled by washing often and avoiding squeezing pimples and blackheads.

■ Shampooing hair often helps keep it clean.

■ Keeping nails clean will get rid of dirt and germs under the nails.

■ Brushing and flossing teeth helps remove plaque.

■ People can help protect their eyes and their sight by wearing safety equipment as needed and having regular checkups.

■ People can protect their ears and hearing by wearing head guards for playing sports and avoiding loud noise as much as possible.

■ People can improve cardiovascular fitness by exercising.

■ How well the heart and blood vessels move blood through the body can be measured by heart rate and blood pressure.

■ Aerobic exercises help improve cardiovascular fitness.

■ A good exercise program includes a warm-up, an exercise period, and a cool-down.

■ An exercise period can include exercises to improve muscle strength, exercises to make the body move more smoothly, and stretching exercises.

■ Everyone can benefit from some form of exercise.

■ Exercise has a positive effect on physical, social, and emotional health.

■ A person who is tired may experience difficulty paying attention and other difficulties.

■ Most teenagers need about eight or nine hours of sleep each night.

*Hygiene and Fitness    Chapter 2*    **63**

■ **Using the Chapter Summary**
To further reinforce the facts and concepts presented in the chapter, read and discuss with students the questions that follow.

Ask:

• Why is it important to have good hygiene habits? (to promote good health)

• What two things can you do to protect your eyes? (wear safety equipment when needed and have regular checkups)

• What are some things you can do to protect your ears? (avoid loud noises and music, don't put anything into the ears, swim in clean water, wear head gear for contact sports)

• How can you take care of your skin? (keep the skin clean, wear sunscreen)

• What two things can you do to take care of your teeth? (brush and floss)

• Who should get regular exercise? (Everyone can benefit from regular exercise.)

• Why should you warm up before vigorous exercise? (Warming up increases the flow of blood and warms up muscles to reduce risk of injury.)

• What is aerobic exercise? (any type of exercise that raises the heart rate)

## Chapter 2 Review

The Teacher's Resource Library includes two parallel forms of the Chapter 2 Mastery Test. The difficulty level of the two forms is equivalent. You may wish to use one form as a pretest and the other form as a posttest.

### Review Answers

**Comprehension: Identifying Facts**

1) physical fitness  2) ophthalmologist
3) Crooked teeth  4) heart rate  5) plaque
6) dermatologist  7) Gum disease
8) orthodontist  9) cardiovascular fitness

---

## Comprehension: Identifying Facts

On a separate sheet of paper, write the correct word or words from the Word Bank to complete each sentence.

| WORD BANK | |
| --- | --- |
| acne | gum disease |
| aerobic exercises | heart rate |
| blood pressure | ophthalmologist |
| cardiovascular fitness | optometrist |
| caries | orthodontist |
| crooked teeth | physical fitness |
| dermatologist | plaque |

1) The ability to work, exercise, and play without tiring is called _____.

2) An _____ is a doctor who specializes in diseases of the eye.

3) _____ can be treated with braces or headgear.

4) The number of times the heart pumps blood each minute is called the _____.

5) Brushing and flossing can help remove _____ from the teeth.

6) A doctor who takes care of skin is called a _____.

7) _____ is the leading cause of tooth loss in adults.

8) A dentist who treats crooked or crowded teeth is called an _____.

9) Exercises that improve _____ can help reduce the risk of heart disease.

---

Name _____ Date _____ Period _____ | Chapter 2 Mastery Test A page 1

**Chapter 2 Mastery Test A**

**Directions** Read each sentence. Write *T* if the statement is true or *F* if it is false.

_____ 1) Sunscreen is not important for protecting your skin from the sun.

_____ 2) People can improve cardiovascular fitness by exercising.

_____ 3) A good exercise program includes one long exercise period.

_____ 4) Most teenagers need about five or six hours of sleep each night.

_____ 5) Acne is a common skin problem among teenagers.

_____ 6) Exercise has a negative effect on physical, social, and emotional health.

_____ 7) A decibel is a unit that measures sound.

_____ 8) Brushing and flossing your teeth at least once a day can help remove plaque.

_____ 9) The ability to work, exercise, and play without tiring is called aerobic exercise.

_____ 10) Loud noise, infection, allergy, buildup of wax, and injury are all causes of hearing loss.

_____ 11) Dental caries is the leading cause of tooth loss in adults.

**TRL**  ©AGS® American Guidance Service, Inc. Permission is granted to reproduce for classroom use only.  **Discover Health**

Name _____ Date _____ Period _____ | Chapter 2 Mastery Test A page 2

**Chapter 2 Mastery Test A, continued**

_____ 12) High blood pressure is a sign that the heart and blood vessels have to work too hard.

_____ 13) Not everyone can benefit from some form of exercise.

_____ 14) Caring for skin, hair, nails, teeth, eyes, and ears is part of hygiene.

_____ 15) A doctor who takes care of skin is called a dermatologist.

**TRL**  ©AGS® American Guidance Service, Inc. Permission is granted to reproduce for classroom use only.  **Discover Health**

**Chapter 2 Mastery Test A**

**10)** The leading cause of tooth loss in children is dental
_____.

**11)** High _____ is a sign that the heart and blood vessels have to work too hard.

**12)** An _____ can give eye examinations and prescribe glasses or contact lenses.

**13)** _____ are exercises that raise the heart rate.

**14)** _____ is a common skin problem among teenagers.

## Comprehension: Understanding Main Ideas

Write the answers to these questions on a separate sheet of paper. Use complete sentences.

**15)** Why should a person avoid squeezing pimples or blackheads?

**16)** How can you remove plaque from your teeth?

**17)** How does exercise help your heart?

**18)** What are some kinds of aerobic exercise?

## Critical Thinking: Write Your Opinion

**19)** Why do you think it might be a good idea to do exercises other than those that are part of team sports?

**20)** What advice might you give to a friend who uses headphones to listen to loud music?

**Test Taking Tip**  If you know you will have to define certain terms on a test, write the term on one side of a card. Write its definition on the other side. Use the cards to test yourself or work with a partner to test each other.

**10)** caries  **11)** blood pressure
**12)** optometrist  **13)** Aerobic exercises
**14)** Acne

## Comprehension: Understanding Main Ideas

**15)** A person should avoid squeezing pimples or blackheads because doing so can cause infections or scars.

**16)** Brushing and flossing remove plaque from teeth.

**17)** When you exercise, more blood enters the heart. The heart works harder to push more blood into the blood vessels. Then your heart muscle gets stronger. Exercising also helps blood flow through the body and back to the heart.

**18)** Answers will vary and may include the following aerobic exercises: walking, running, jogging, swimming, biking, cross-country skiing.

## Critical Thinking: Write Your Opinion

**19)** Answers will vary. Students may say that it is a good idea to exercise in order to learn how to become familiar with exercises that can be done throughout life.

**20)** Answers will vary. Students should mention suggesting that the friend lower the volume as well as explaining how loud music can harm one's hearing.

---

Name _____ Date _____ Period _____   *Chapter 2 Mastery Test B page 1*

**Chapter 2 Mastery Test B**

*Directions* Read each sentence. Write *T* if the statement is true or *F* if it is false.

_____ **1)** Dental caries is the leading cause of tooth loss in adults.

_____ **2)** A good exercise program includes one long exercise period.

_____ **3)** A decibel is a unit that measures sound.

_____ **4)** Acne is a common skin problem among teenagers.

_____ **5)** Exercise has a negative effect on physical, social, and emotional health.

_____ **6)** People can improve cardiovascular fitness by exercising.

_____ **7)** Caring for skin, hair, nails, teeth, eyes, and ears is a part of hygiene.

_____ **8)** The ability to work, exercise, and play without tiring is called aerobic exercise.

_____ **9)** Most teenagers need about five or six hours of sleep each night.

_____ **10)** Loud noise, infection, allergy, buildup of wax, and injury are all causes of hearing loss.

_____ **11)** Sunscreen is not important for protecting your skin from the sun.

Name _____ Date _____ Period _____   *Chapter 2 Mastery Test B page 2*

**Chapter 2 Mastery Test B, continued**

_____ **12)** High blood pressure is a sign that the heart and blood vessels have to work too hard.

_____ **13)** A dentist who takes care of skin is called a dermatologist.

_____ **14)** Brushing and flossing your teeth at least once a day can help remove plaque.

_____ **15)** Not everyone can benefit from some form of exercise.

**Chapter 2 Mastery Test B**

## Introducing the Chapter

Ask volunteers to name the members of their family in the following form: father, mother, two sisters, and so on. Some might mention two parents and a sibling. Others might mention one parent and no siblings. Some students might name grandparents as well. List the family members of each student on the board to show that the word *family* can describe different combinations of people.

Have a volunteer read the information on page 66. Discuss the Goals for Learning

### Ask:

• When we talk about a family, are we all referring to the same type of group? (No. When we talk about a family, we are often referring to different types of groups.)

• What do you think all of these types of families have in common? (Accept all reasonable answers. Possible answer include: All families are made up of people who live together and support and take care of one another.)

# The Family

ost people belong to a family and depend on the support they gain from their family. There are many different types of families. However, all families provide similar benefits for their family members. Families help their members act responsibly, both as a group and as individuals.

In this chapter, you will learn about the family life cycle and how new families are formed through marriage. You will learn about parenting and the responsibilities that parents have. You will also learn about different types of families and what makes a family healthy. Finally, you will learn about problems in families and where to get help with the problems.

### Goals for Learning

▶ To explain the place of marriage in the family life cycle

▶ To identify some characteristics of a healthy marriage

▶ To describe parenting and responsibilities parents have

▶ To describe some characteristics of a healthy family

▶ To identify where families can get help for problems

---

Name _____ Date _____ Period _____ | Chapter 3 Student Study Guide 9 page 1

**Chapter 3 The Family**

*Directions* Fill in the outline below. Filling in the blanks will help you as you read and study The Family.

I. **Lesson 1 The Family Life Cycle (pp. 67-70)**
   A. Families
      1. The first stage in the family life cycle is when two people _____ .
      2. The second stage in the family life cycle is when a _____ is born into the family.
   B. Marriages
      1. Characteristics of a healthy marriage include having similar _____ , accepting and supporting each other, and sharing household _____ .
   C. Adolescence
      1. Parents continue to set _____ for their teenagers.
      2. During the third stage in the family life cycle, families can use _____ , patience, and caring skills to address challenges.
   D. Aging
      1. In the fourth stage in the family life cycle, children leave _____ and begin leading their own lives.
      2. Married couples might develop new interests or _____ during the fourth stage.
      3. In the fifth stage in the family life cycle, couples learn to accept growing _____ and disabilities.
      4. Older family members share their _____ , knowledge, and family history.

TRL

Discover Health

**Student Study Guide 9, page 1**

---

Name _____ Date _____ Period _____ | Chapter 3 Student Study Guide 9 page 2

II. **Lesson 2 Dealing With Family Problems (pp. 71-74)**
   A. Stress and Families
      1. _____ events can increase family stress and cause problems.
      2. With the loss or disability of a family member, other family members may feel they have less _____ support.
   B. Separation and Divorce
      1. Children may feel _____ or depressed due to divorce or separation.
   C. Dealing With Problems
      1. When people are not ready to cope with a problem, they are in the _____ stage.
      2. When a family makes successful attempts to adjust with a problem, they've reached the _____ stage.
   D. Violence and Abuse
      1. _____ abuse victims may suffer bruises, broken bones, or even death.
      2. _____ abuse victims are often depressed and scared.
      3. Abuse victims are not _____ for abuse.
   E. Getting Help
      1. Asking for help and working together to solve problems _____ the family.
      2. It is helpful to keep a positive _____ while working on solving family problems.

TRL

Discover Health

**Student Study Guide 9, page 2**

**Commitment**
*Love, dedication; a pledge of trust*

**Extended family**
*A family who includes many people from different generations*

**Family life cycle**
*The changes in a family over time*

*F*amilies change, just as individuals do. The changes in families over time are known as the **family life cycle**. A family life cycle includes events such as marriage and the birth of children.

Each stage in the family life cycle presents the family with new challenges and tasks. Families who meet these challenges lay the foundation for health and strength in the family.

### What Is a Family?

Families come in many forms. Some families are small and some are large. Family members can include many people, such as parents, children, grandparents, aunts, uncles, brothers, and sisters. Families who include many people from different generations are called **extended families**.

A new family is formed when two people marry. This is the first stage in the family life cycle. The newly married couple must adjust to each other and the demands of married life. The couple will form new relationships with each other's extended family and friends. The couple will also share the duties of the family. Every family will solve these challenges in its own way. Discussion and **commitment** are important keys to making the relationship work.

### What Happens When the Family Grows?

Once a married couple has adjusted to the challenges of marriage, many new changes can occur. Children may be added to the family group. Family members and their roles change as the family changes.

When a child is born into the family, the married couple has new responsibilities as parents. This is the second stage in the family life cycle. The parents must meet the needs of the new child while staying healthy themselves.

*The Family    Chapter 3*    **67**

---

## Chapter 3 Lesson 1

**Overview** Students learn about the family life cycle, or the changes in families that happen over time.

■ To explain the place of marriage in the family life cycle.

■ To identify some characteristics of a healthy marriage.

■ To describe parenting and responsibilities parents have.

■ To describe some characteristics of a healthy family.

**Student Pages** 67–70

**Audiocassette**

**Teacher's Resource Library**

Activity 11
Workbook Activity 11

## Teaching Suggestions

### ■ Vocabulary

*commitment, extended family, family life cycle, discipline, adolescent*

Have students read the definitions of the vocabulary words. Then call students to the board in groups of five or six. Challenge each student in the group to write an original sentence using one of the vocabulary words.

### ■ Teaching the Lesson

Do families always stay the same in size and composition? Briefly discuss that question with students. What happens when new family members are born or when family members move away or die? Have students consider how their own families may have changed under such circumstances.

Then have students read about the family life cycle on page 67.

### Ask:

• What is the family life cycle? (The family life cycle is the changes that a family undergoes over time.)

---

• What is an extended family? (An extended family is a family that includes many people from different generations.)

• What is the first stage in the formation of a family? (A new family is formed when two people get married.)

• Commitment is an important part of any relationship. What is commitment? (Commitment involves love, dedication, and trust in a relationship.)

• What is the second stage in the family life cycle? (The second stage in the family life cycle comes when children are born and the couple takes on new responsibilities as parents.)

Talk with students about their concepts of a good marriage. Have them call out characteristics of a good marriage, as you list them on the board.

Then have students read the list explaining characteristics of a healthy marriage on page 68.

Ask:

- Children must be taught discipline as they grow. What is discipline? (Discipline is correct behavior. Explain that discipline involves self-control and being respectful to other people.)

- What are the characteristics of a healthy marriage? (Characteristics of a healthy marriage include: agreeing on money matters, having similar interests, knowing each other well before marriage, accepting and supporting each other, agreeing about having children and about how to discipline children, having common goals, sharing household tasks, having similar family backgrounds and good relationships.)

## APPLICATION

### At Home
Encourage students to ask their parents' or guardians' opinions about what it takes to have a healthy marriage. Parents might discuss what is necessary in a marriage partner and what obstacles are most difficult to overcome. Continue the discussion in class, comparing the opinions with the characteristics described on page 68.

## GLOBAL CONNECTION

Have each student do research to discover what the average family is like in another country. Tell students to find out about the average number of family members, whether extended families are common, and how members of the family relate to one another. Lead a class discussion about how these characteristics compare with those of American families.

---

**Discipline**
*Correct behavior*

One of the challenges of this stage is understanding the new child's needs. Infants need love and attention, as well as food, clothing, and shelter. As the child grows, the parents need to set limits for the child and teach **discipline**. It is also important for parents to sometimes see "through the eyes of a child" and not get angry or impatient at normal mistakes that the child makes.

### What Are Characteristics of Healthy Marriages?
There is no single recipe for a successful marriage, but the following are some things that have been identified as important.

Parents need to teach limits and understand their children's needs.

- Agreeing on money matters
- Having similar interests
- Knowing each other well before marriage
- Accepting and supporting each other
- Agreeing about having children and about how to discipline children
- Having common goals
- Sharing household tasks
- Having similar family backgrounds and good relationships

---

**Then and Now**

## ORPHANAGES AND ADOPTION

Since the 1400s, European orphans were often placed in orphanages. Orphans are children whose parents have died. Orphanages were special buildings where orphans could live. In 1740, the first American orphanage opened in Georgia. As America grew, so did the number of orphanages.

In the 1900s, adoptions of children into families began to replace orphanages. Often, orphans live with a foster family while waiting for adoption. U.S. adoption figures show that the number of adopted children has increased since the 1960s. About 50,000 American children where adopted during the 1990s. In 1997, there were 13,620 adoptions of children from foreign countries.

**Adolescent**
*A child between the ages of 13 and 17*

When children become teenagers, they begin to prepare to live an independent life. This is the third stage in the family life cycle. Parents will continue to set rules for the safety of their **adolescents**. Parents also allow them to become independent and form close relationships outside the family.

This stage of the life cycle is often a time when both adolescents and parents struggle for the right balance between too many and too few rules. Sometimes adolescents want more freedom but are not ready to take the responsibility that goes along with it. Communication, patience, and caring are some skills that families can use while they try to address the challenges of this stage.

*Health Tip*

Talk about and work out problems for healthy relationships.

### How Does Aging Affect the Family?

As family members age, their roles and relationships within the family change. Some may leave and form families of their own. Older family members may die, and the family will adjust and cope with their loss.

When they are old enough, children leave home and begin leading their own lives. This is the fourth stage in the family life cycle. The family returns to being a couple again for the second time. Parents often feel a sense of loss when their

---

**Then and Now**

In some cases, children who are adopted cannot find out the identities of their biological parents. Have a class discussion during which students discuss whether this is the best policy. Have students identify reasons for wanting to know or not wanting to know the identities of biological parents.

Have students read about adolescence and aging on page 69.

### Ask:

- What is the third stage in the family life cycle? (The third stage in the family life cycle is when children become teenagers and begin to prepare for independent lives.)

- What is the fourth stage of the family cycle? (The fourth stage of the family cycle comes when children leave home and begin to lead lives of their own.)

- What negative effects can parents experience when children leave home? (When children leave home, parents often feel a sense of loss and can sometimes feel that they have lost their importance in the family.)

 **BACKGROUND INFORMATION**

Hundreds of years ago, the average American family was much larger than it is today. Most people lived on farms. Having many children was useful because they provided extra hands to get all of the farm work done. Children were also relied on to take care of their parents when the parents grew old. In some countries, this is still the case.

## Action for Health

Ask students if they know a child who goes to a day-care facility or an older adult who uses an elder-care facility. Interview that person about their experiences at the facility. Have students report their findings to the class.

## Lesson 1 Review Answers

1) An extended family is a family that includes many people from different generations.
2) During the second stage of the family cycle, parents must meet the needs of the new child while staying healthy themselves.
3) Answers will vary. Some characteristics of a healthy marriage may include: having common goals, accepting and supporting each other, sharing household tasks, agreeing on money matters, having similar interests.
4) The first stage in the family life cycle begins when two people marry. They share duties of the family. Stage two begins when a child is born into the family and the couple has parental responsibilities. Stage three is when the children become teenagers and begin preparing for living independent lives. The fourth stage is when children leave home and begin their own lives. In the fifth and final stage, a couple must learn to accept growing limitations and disabilities.
5) Older family members contribute to the family by sharing wisdom, knowledge, and family history.

### APPLICATION

**Career Connection**
Invite a day-care provider to talk to your class about working with children. Invite students to ask questions about job responsibilities and qualifications as well as education requirements.

### APPLICATION

**Environment**
Ask students to interview older family members, friends, or neighbors about their environment. Encourage students to write their findings in a report.

---

children leave home. Sometimes they even feel they have lost their importance in the family.

Married couples may change and renew their relationship to each other. They may also develop new interests or hobbies to keep themselves occupied. Eventually, the parents will form new relationships with their children's friends, spouses, and in-laws. Parents may also learn new roles as grandparents.

In the fifth and final stage of the family life cycle, a couple must learn to accept growing limitations and disabilities. Sometimes, couples must adjust to a new home or community. At this stage, a family member may learn to cope with the death of the spouse. Older family members continue to contribute to the family by sharing their wisdom, knowledge, and family history.

**LESSON 1 REVIEW** Write the answers to these questions on a separate sheet of paper. Use complete sentences.

1) What is an extended family?
2) What are some of the challenges in the second stage of the family life cycle?
3) What are some characteristics of a healthy marriage?
4) What are the five stages of the family life cycle? Briefly describe each stage.
5) How do older relatives contribute to a family?

### FINDING CARE FOR FAMILY MEMBERS

Caring for the elderly is an important issue in the United States. The number of elderly people has grown steadily over the years, and will continue to grow as the baby boom generation ages. Most people are familiar with day care programs for children, which provide care and education while parents work. Similar programs are available for older relatives as well. Investigate which facilities are available in your community for both younger and older family members. Compare their similarities and differences. If you were to choose a facility for a child or grandparent, what qualities would you look for?

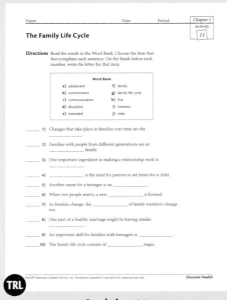

**Activity 11**

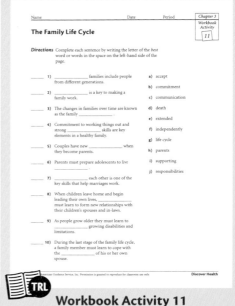

**Workbook Activity 11**

**Depressed**
*Extremely sad*

**Divorce**
*The end of a marriage*

**Separation**
*A period when a married couple stops living together*

When families successfully deal with changes and challenges, they lay the foundation for a healthy family unit. However, some changes, such as divorce, illness, and death, may be too difficult for families to deal with on their own. Troubled families can get help to survive and recover from such problems.

### How Does Stress Affect a Family?

Some of the stresses that families deal with are a normal part of everyday life. Family members work the problems out by changing the way they relate to one another. For example, the birth of a new child or relocation of an older family member may require people to take on new roles and responsibilities.

Unexpected events can increase family stress and cause problems. If a family member loses a job, the family must change to deal with lost income. This may cause a physical and emotional burden for all family members. Tragedy, such as an illness, injury, or the death of a family member, is also a stressful change. The loss or disability of a family member who has a strong, supportive role in the family can be very difficult. Other family members may feel they have less emotional support and no one to turn to.

**What are some special challenges for children in single-parent households?**

### How Do Separation and Divorce Affect a Family?

Sometimes a couple decides that they cannot live together anymore. They may agree to a **separation** so that they can think about how to make their marriage work. If they believe that the marriage is not healthy and that they cannot improve it, they may decide to **divorce**.

Separation and divorce can be difficult for children. They may worry or feel **depressed**. They may feel that they are losing a parent. Children may even believe that they have caused the divorce.

*The Family    Chapter 3    71*

---

### Ask:

- List some sources of stress in a family. (Sources of family stress include the birth of a child; relocation of an older family member; loss of a job; illness, injury, or death of a family member.)

- Why are separation and divorce often difficult for children? (Separation and divorce are often difficult for children because the children may feel they are losing a parent. Some children might even believe that they have caused the divorce.)

---

## Lesson at a Glance

### Chapter 3  Lesson 2

**Overview**  Students learn about the problems families can encounter. Students also learn how families can get help to overcome their problems.

### Objectives

- To identify stresses and problems that can affect families.

- To identify where families can get help for problems.

**Student Pages** 71–74

**Audiocassette**

**Teacher's Resource Library**

Activity 12

Workbook Activity 12

## Teaching Suggestions

### ■ Vocabulary

*separation, depressed, divorce, violent, child abuse, emotional abuse, sexual abuse*

Before beginning the lesson, list the vocabulary words on the board. Have students write definitions of the words based on their current understanding of their meanings. Then have students compare the definitions they have written with the definitions in the text.

### ■ Teaching the Lesson

Explain to students that stress is a state of physical or emotional pressure. People often face stress when demands are put on them, when they feel threatened, or when they are in new and challenging situations. Lead a classroom discussion in which students talk about the situations that they find stressful, and what they do to alleviate stress.

Then have students read about sources of family stress, including separation and divorce of parents, on page 71.

Discuss with students the way they deal with problems. After a brief discussion, have students read about the ways families deal with problems on page 72.

Ask:

- Why do people react to problems with denial? (Denial is a common initial response when people are not ready to cope with a problem.)

- What feelings often follow denial and help overcome it? (Feelings of denial are often followed by feelings of anger, sadness, or loneliness.)

- What stage often follows denial and anger? (The stage of adjustment often follows denial and anger.)

- Some family members may deal with problems in an unhealthy way, by using violence. What is violence? (Violence involves actions or words that hurt others.)

## LEARNING STYLES

**Tactile/Kinesthetic** Have students break into groups to create skits that present a problem, then show how family members deal with it. Encourage students to incorporate some or all of the stages of denial, anger, adjustment, and acceptance that they have just read about. After each skit, allow students to have a class discussion during which they evaluate how the "family" dealt with the problem.

## LEARNING STYLES

**LEP/ESL** Draw the attention of LEP/ESL students to the photograph at the bottom of page 72. Have students write simple sentences stating the positive characteristics of the family that are being displayed in the picture. Characteristics might include helping one another, having fun, and spending time together.

**Violent**
*Doing actions or words that hurt people*

*Fitness Tip*

Go for a walk or a run when you feel unhappy.

## How Do Families Deal With Problems?

People often react to serious problems in several stages: denial, anger, adjustment, and acceptance. *Denial* is a common response when people are not ready to cope with a problem. However, denial does nothing to solve the problem. Feelings of *anger,* sadness, or loneliness often overcome the denial. If high stress levels continue, family members may argue and ignore one another's needs and feelings. The *adjustment* stage happens when the family recognizes the problem and begins working on a solution. Healthy family solutions include setting goals for change and being willing to compromise. *Acceptance* is reached when a family makes successful attempts to adjust. Family members must learn to accept that some events are beyond their control. However, they can work to change those things that can be changed and to move on.

## How Do Violence and Abuse Affect a Family?

Most families find ways to deal with stress and problems. However, problems in some families are so severe that the family becomes unhealthy. Family members no longer support one another and may even become **violent**.

Family members can help each other.

**FAMILY COUNSELOR**

Many families need help solving their problems. Some families today face problems such as alcohol and drug abuse, depression, and violence. Some families may just need help adjusting to normal stresses and changes. Family counselors help families with these problems. Crisis intervention may be necessary if there is substance or physical abuse. Family counselors must be able to understand how all the members of the family feel. They must be able to help the family members form trusting, caring relationships with one another. Requirements vary from on-the-job experience to college level programs in social work or psychology. Never before has the need for family counselors been so great.

---

**Child abuse**
*An action that harms a child*

**Emotional abuse**
*A mistreatment through words, gestures, or lack of affection*

**Sexual abuse**
*Any sexual contact that is forced on a person*

---

Violence may be caused by anger, stress, drugs, or alcohol. Sometimes people learn to be violent because that was how they were raised. **Child abuse** is a form of violence. Victims of physical abuse may suffer bruises, broken bones, or even death. Harsh words, threats, and lack of affection are forms of **emotional abuse**. Victims of emotional abuse are often depressed and scared. They may avoid contact with others. **Sexual abuse** is any sexual contact that is forced on someone.

Every state has laws to protect children from abuse. These laws require people who work with children to notify local authorities if abuse is suspected. Victims may be afraid to report abuse because they feel shame or fear. Sometimes children may feel responsible for the abuse. However, in *no* case are victims responsible for abuse. Telling a trusted adult is very important. It is the first step in getting help. With help, victims of abuse are able to overcome the pain. Without help, victims sometimes become abusers themselves.

*The Family    Chapter 3    **73***

Have students read about violence and its effects on families on page 73.

## Careers

Invite students to write classified ads for the job of a family counselor. Tell them to concentrate on characteristics that they think a good family counselor needs. Have students share their ads with one another in class.

## Ask:

- **What are some of the causes of violence?** (Violence can be caused by anger, stress, or by the use of alcohol and other drugs. People can also turn to violence because they were raised in a violent household.)

- **What is child abuse?** (Child abuse is a form of violence in which an action harms a child.)

- **What is emotional abuse?** (Emotional abuse is mistreatment through words, gestures, or lack of affection.)

- **What is sexual abuse?** (Sexual abuse is any sexual contact that is forced on someone.)

- **What should children do if they are being abused?** (Children who are victims of abuse should tell a trusted adult about the problem.)

- **How do laws protect children from abuse?** (Laws require people who work with children to notify authorities if they suspect that a child is the victim of abuse.)

**MULTICULTURAL CONNECTION**

Direct students to research the way divorce is handled in other countries. Have students share what they learn with the class. Then have the class evaluate whether the handling of divorce is fair and effective.

Have students read about where family members can go for help with problems on page 74.

## Lesson 2 Review Answers

1) Some events that cause stress in families are the birth of a child, relocation of an older family member; loss of job; illness, injury, or death of a family member.

2) Most communities have support groups to help families deal with problems. Caring adults or friends are good sources of support. Professional counselors, social workers, and psychologists can also help the family.

3) The stages for reacting to serious problems are denial, anger, adjustment, and acceptance.

4) A victim of abuse should seek help from a trustworthy adult or friend. The victim should also understand that the abuse is not his or her fault.

5) Families can respond positively to stressful situations by working together to find a way to change and adapt to stresses.

### APPLICATION

**In the Community**
Have students find the names, addresses, and phone numbers of family counselors and family counseling facilities in your community. Then have students work together to compile the information in a flyer that can be handed out to other students who might be interested.

### LEARNING STYLES

**Visual** During one week, ask students to watch for examples of violence and abuse in television shows and movies. Have them take notes on how the violence or abuse occurred and how it was handled. Discuss the examples in class. Were the situations handled constructively? How might students have handled the situations better?

### Writing About Health

You have read about some of the stresses that can cause problems in families. Write about the effects of one kind of stress on a family. Tell how the family might respond to maintain a healthy family.

## Where Can Family Members Go for Help?

Sometimes a family needs help to solve a problem. Admitting that a problem exists and asking for help is the most important step. Denying the problem or failing to address it can cause greater stress later.

Stressful events occur in all families. Asking for help and working together to solve problems strengthens the family. Most communities have support groups to help families deal with serious problems.

Caring adults or friends are good sources of support. Sometimes a parent, sibling, or other relative can help a family through difficult times. In school, some staff members are trained to assist students as they work through problems. When family problems become too difficult to handle, professional counselors, social workers, and psychologists can help the family.

It is helpful to keep a positive attitude while working on solving family problems. Talking with a caring friend or adult or writing feelings down in a diary can help avoid depression. This can give family members more confidence as they concentrate on solving a problem.

**LESSON 2 REVIEW** Write the answers to these questions on a separate sheet of paper. Use complete sentences.

1) What are some events that cause stress in families?

2) Who can offer support to you about your problems or stress?

3) What are the stages for reacting to serious problems?

4) What should a person do if he or she is being abused?

5) How can families respond positively to stressful situations?

**Activity 12**

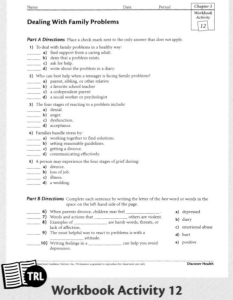

**Workbook Activity 12**

■ A new family life cycle begins with marriage. Each stage in the family life cycle presents the family with new challenges.

■ Parents are responsible for the health, safety, and well-being of their children.

■ Parents need to learn certain skills to help their children grow physically and emotionally. They must set rules and provide discipline.

■ Similar family backgrounds and having common interests and goals contribute to a healthy marriage.

■ The family life cycle is always growing and changing.

■ In the fifth stage of the family life cycle, a family deals with the aging of older family members.

■ Separation, divorce, aging, illness, and death are changes that affect families. To be successful, family members support each other as they adjust to these changes.

■ Normal stresses as well as unexpected events occur in all families. In most cases, family members work to solve these problems together.

■ Families can seek help for serious problems. Caring friends, professional counselors, and trained school staff offer support and help.

■ Family members often go through several stages when they react to problems: denial, anger, adjustment, and acceptance.

■ A family in which violence and abuse occur is unhealthy. Violence and abuse are never acceptable.

## ■ Using the Chapter Summary

To further reinforce the facts and concepts presented in the chapter, read and discuss with students the questions that follow.

Ask:

- **What is the family life cycle?** (The family life cycle consists of the changes in the family over time.)

- **What are the responsibilities of parents?** (The responsibilities of parents include seeing to the health, safety, and well-being of their children.)

- **List some characteristics that contribute to a healthy marriage.** (The characteristics of a healthy marriage include: agreeing on money matters, similar interests, knowing each other well, accepting and supporting each other, agreeing about having children and how to discipline them, having common goals, sharing household tasks, having similar family backgrounds and good relationships.)

- **What is the first stage of the family life cycle?** (The first stage of the family life cycle begins when a couple gets married.)

- **What is the fifth stage of the family life cycle?** (The fifth stage of the family life cycle involves dealing with the aging of family members.)

- **What are some sources of stress for families?** (Sources of stress for families include the birth of a child; relocation of an elderly member; loss of a job; illness, injury or death of a family member.)

- **Where can families turn for help with problems?** (Families can turn to several sources for help including caring friends, professional counselors, other family members, trained school staff, or other professionals such as counselors and psychologists.)

- **What are the stages that families go through when they have to deal with problems?** (When families have to deal with problems, they often go through the stages of denial, anger, adjustment, and acceptance.)

# Chapter 3 Review

The Teacher's Resource Library includes two parallel forms of the Chapter 3 Mastery Test. The difficulty level of the two forms is equivalent. You may wish to use one form as a pretest and the other form as a posttest.

## Review Answers
### Comprehension: Identifying Facts
**1)** family life cycle  **2)** challenges
**3)** responsibilities  **4)** rules
**5)** independence  **6)** cope  **7)** Adoption
**8)** elderly  **9)** roles  **10)** depression

## Comprehension: Identifying Facts

On a separate sheet of paper, write the correct word or words from the Word Bank to complete each sentence.

| WORD BANK | | |
|---|---|---|
| adoption | divorce | roles |
| challenges | elderly | rules |
| cope | family life cycle | sexual abuse |
| counselor | independence | violence |
| depression | responsibilities | |

1) A new _____ begins when two people marry.

2) Each stage in the family life cycle presents the family with _____.

3) A married couple must share family _____.

4) Parents need to set _____ for children to keep them safe.

5) When children grow into adolescents, they begin to prepare for _____.

6) When older family members die, the family must _____ with their loss.

7) _____ has replaced most orphanages.

8) It is important to find ways to care for the _____ as they grow older.

9) When families change to meet challenges, family members may take on new _____.

10) When you experience a loss, you may feel _____, or a feeling of deep sadness.

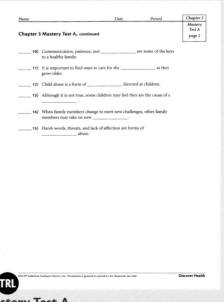

**Chapter 3 Mastery Test A**

**11)** Although it is not true, children sometimes feel they are the cause of a _____.

**12)** A professional _____ can help a family work through difficult problems.

**13)** Child abuse is a form of _____ directed at children.

**14)** Victims of _____ are never responsible for the other person's behavior.

## Comprehension: Understanding Main Ideas

Write the answers to these questions on a separate sheet of paper. Use complete sentences.

**15)** What are some ways families address the challenges of their changing lives?

**16)** Why do people sometimes react by denying a difficult problem?

**17)** Give an example of emotional abuse and describe how it might affect the victim.

**18)** List five characteristics of a healthy marriage.

## Critical Thinking: Write Your Opinion

**19)** How can keeping a positive attitude help you solve a problem?

**20)** What could you do to help a friend who is suffering from abuse?

---

**Test Taking Tip** Before you begin a test, look it over quickly. Try to set aside enough time to complete each section.

---

---

**11)** divorce  **12)** counselor  **13)** violence
**14)** sexual abuse

## Comprehension: Understanding Main Ideas

**15)** Communication, patience, and caring are some ways families can address new challenges.

**16)** Denial allows people to avoid a problem when they feel they are not ready to cope with it.

**17)** Harsh words, threats, and lack of affection are some examples of emotional abuse. The victim may be depressed, scared, or reluctant to come in contact with others.

**18)** Answers will vary. Accept any five of the following: agreeing on money matters, having similar interests, knowing each other well before marriage, accepting and supporting each other, agreeing about having children and about how to discipline children, having common goals, sharing household tasks, having similar family backgrounds and good relationships.

## Critical Thinking: Write Your Opinion

**19)** Keeping a positive attitude can help you avoid becoming depressed and help you concentrate on the problem.

**20)** Convince the friend to tell a trusted adult about the abuse. Help your friend understand that it is not his or her fault and that it is the abuser who is wrong. Accept all reasonable answers.

---

Name _____ Date _____ Period _____   | Chapter 3 / Mastery Test B / page 1 |

**Chapter 3 Mastery Test B**

**Directions** Read the words in the Word Bank. Choose the item that *best* completes each sentence. On the blank before each number, write the letter for that item.

**Word Bank**

a) adjustment     f) elderly          k) independent
b) caring          g) emotional       l) professional counselor
c) depressed       h) extended family  m) responsibilities
d) discipline      i) family life cycle  n) safety
e) divorce         j) goals            o) violence

____ **1)** Families can seek help for serious problems from a _____ .

____ **2)** Having common interests and _____ contribute to a healthy marriage.

____ **3)** When family members change to meet new challenges, other family members may take on new _____ .

____ **4)** Harsh words, threats, and lack of affection are forms of _____ abuse.

____ **5)** When children become teenagers, they begin to prepare to live an _____ life.

____ **6)** As children grow, parents need to set rules and provide _____ .

____ **7)** When you experience a loss, you may feel _____ , or a feeling of deep sadness.

____ **8)** An _____ is one that includes people from different generations.

____ **9)** Family members may go through four stages when they react to problems: denial, anger, _____ , and acceptance.

TRL   ©AGS® American Guidance Service, Inc. Permission is granted to reproduce for classroom use only.   Discover Health

---

Name _____ Date _____ Period _____   | Chapter 3 / Mastery Test B / page 2 |

**Chapter 3 Mastery Test B, continued**

____ **10)** Parents are responsible for the health, _____ , and well-being of their children.

____ **11)** Changes in families over time are known as the _____ .

____ **12)** Communication, patience, and _____ are some of the keys to a healthy family.

____ **13)** It is important to find ways to care for the _____ as they grow older.

____ **14)** Child abuse is a form of _____ directed at children.

____ **15)** Although it is not true, some children may feel they are the cause of a _____ .

TRL   ©AGS® American Guidance Service, Inc. Permission is granted to reproduce for classroom use only.   Discover Health

**Chapter 3 Mastery Test B**

## Deciding for Yourself

Explain that regular exercise can keep the body healthy. Ask students if they already exercise regularly. Then have students read "Planning a Fitness Program" in the Deciding for Yourself lesson on page 78.

### Ask:

- What does it take to have an exercise program? (It takes planning and making a decision to stick to the plan.)

- In what ways can you reward yourself when you reach your goal? (Students may say that they take a day off from their exercise program. Accept any reasonable answers.)

- What is the advantage of making friends with other people who enjoy the same activity? (Friends can help you stick to your exercise program.)

### Deciding for Yourself Answers

1) Students may say biking, swimming, playing tennis, jogging, and so forth.
2) Goals will vary, depending on the activity. Here are some examples:
Biking: 30 minutes or 2 miles
Swimming: 20 laps
Tennis: three times a week
Jogging: 5 miles per week
3) Exercise helps your physical health because you will be able to do things without getting tired. Exercising helps your emotional health because you will feel better about yourself and will be able to handle the problems and pressures of daily living better. Exercising helps your social health because you can make friends and be friends with others.
4) Answers will vary, depending on the chosen exercise. Warm-up activities might include walking or doing stretching exercises. Cool-down activities might include continuing the exercise at a slower pace and/or stretching exercises.

### ■ Deciding for Yourself Activity

Have students complete the Unit 1 Deciding for Yourself Activity.

Deciding for Yourself

### Planning a Fitness Program

Do you have a fitness or exercise program? You can help keep your body healthy by exercising regularly. Anyone can do it. It takes some planning and making a decision to stick to your plan. Here are some steps for setting up an exercise program.

- Think about a physical activity you enjoy. It can be biking, swimming, or playing a sport. For example, if you like hockey, skating is important.
- Plan a time in your day that you could do this activity regularly. Maybe you would have time after school or in the early evening. Think about the amount of time you have and where you will do the activity.
- Set some goals for yourself. For example, you might want to walk or run a certain distance in fifteen or thirty minutes. Make your goal realistic and start slowly.
- Think about ways to reward yourself when you reach a goal. This is a good way to celebrate your progress.
- Make friends with other people who enjoy the same activity. Friends can help one another stick to their exercise program.

### Questions

1) What is a physical activity that you enjoy doing?
2) What kind of a goal might you set for yourself with this activity?
3) How do you think doing this activity three times a week would help your physical health? How might it help your emotional health? Your social health?
4) What kind of warm-up or cool-down activity would you do before you exercised?

Name _____ Date _____ Period _____ | Unit 1 Deciding for Yourself Activity 1

**Making a Fitness Plan**

1) Choose a physical fitness activity that you will do for one week.
Name the activity _____

2) Write down the number of times that you will do the activity during the week. Then write down how long you will do it. Do the activity for 15 minutes, 30 minutes, or one hour. You may want to plan to do this activity with another person.
- What I plan to do _____
- How many times a week _____
- How long _____
- What I did _____

3) Record the number of times you exercise and how long you exercise each time.
- How many times _____
- How long each time _____

4) At the end of the week, compare what you did with your plan.
- What made keeping your plan easy? _____
- What made sticking to the plan difficult? _____
- Did doing the activity with someone else help you keep your goal? Why or why not? _____

TRL ©AGS® American Guidance Service, Inc. Permission is granted to reproduce for classroom use only. Discover Health

**Deciding for Yourself Master 1**

■ Tiny cells make up all living things. Your body is made of trillions of cells.

■ Your body is organized into cells, tissues, and organs. Tissues that work together to do a similar job are called organs. Many organs work together in a body system.

■ Your body systems include the skin, skeletal, muscular, digestive, excretory, respiratory, circulatory, nervous, endocrine, and reproductive systems.

■ Body systems work together to provide your cells with oxygen and nutrients.

■ Caring for your skin, hair, nails, teeth, eyes, and ears is a part of hygiene.

■ Exercise can improve your physical, social, and emotional health.

■ An exercise program should include a warm-up period, an exercise period, and a cool-down period.

■ Most teenagers need eight or nine hours of sleep each night.

■ Each stage in the family life cycle brings new challenges to a family.

■ The family life cycle begins with marriage.

■ The second stage in the family life cycle occurs when a child is born into the family.

■ The third stage in the family life cycle is when children become teenagers and begin to prepare to live on their own.

■ The fourth stage in the family life cycle is when children leave home and begin their own lives.

■ The final stage in the family life cycle is learning to deal with aging.

■ Stress occurs in all families. In healthy families, members learn to work together to solve problems.

■ Family members often feel denial, anger, adjustment, and acceptance as they react to problems.

■ Violence and abuse are never acceptable in a family.

*Unit 1 Summary* **79**

## Using the Unit Summary

To further reinforce the facts and concepts presented in the unit, read and discuss with students the questions that follow.

### Ask:

- Name one function of each of the following body systems: **skin** (protects the body from germs; controls the body's temperature); **skeletal** (provides support for the body; protects internal organs); **muscular** (movement; pumps blood; controls breathing); **digestive** (breaks down food; gets rid of solid waste); **excretory** (gets rid of liquid waste; filters blood); **respiratory** (brings in oxygen; gets rid of carbon dioxide); **circulatory** (transports blood); **nervous** (sends messages); **endocrine** (produces hormones); **reproductive** (produces new life).

- What is the most common reason for hearing loss? (loud noise)

- How can you protect your skin from the weather? (wear sunscreen in the sun, wear a hat, dress warmly in cold weather)

- What is cardiovascular fitness? (the condition of the lungs, heart, and blood vessels)

- Why is it important to warm up before exercising vigorously? (to increase the flow of blood and reduce risk of injury)

- What is the difference between a nuclear family and an extended family? (A nuclear family consists of mother, father, and their children. An extended family includes a nuclear family plus other relatives.)

- Why is stress a normal part of family life? (Changing circumstances can challenge a family; the members can have different needs and desires.)

## Unit 1 Review

The Teacher's Resource Library includes a two-page Unit Mastery Test pictured on this page. Answers are in the Answer Keys beginning on page 433 of this Teacher's Edition.

### Review Answers

**Comprehension: Identifying Facts**

**1)** plasma **2)** endocrine **3)** brain
**4)** bone **5)** skeletal **6)** cells **7)** epidermis
**8)** Acne **9)** hygiene

## Comprehension: Identifying Facts

On a separate sheet of paper, write the correct word or words from the Word Bank to complete each sentence.

| WORD BANK | | |
| --- | --- | --- |
| plasma | extended | safety |
| cardiovascular | cells | acne |
| skeletal | epidermis | endocrine |
| bone | hygiene | abuse |
| physical | brain | |

**1)** Your blood is made of cells and _____.

**2)** Hormones are chemicals released by _____ glands.

**3)** The cerebrum is the largest part of your _____.

**4)** When a muscle pulls a _____, it causes your body to move.

**5)** Your _____ system is made of 206 bones.

**6)** Your digestive system breaks food down into a form your _____ can use.

**7)** The _____ is made of dead skin cells.

**8)** _____ is blocked skin pores.

**9)** Caring for your skin, hair, nails, teeth, eyes, and ears is a part of _____.

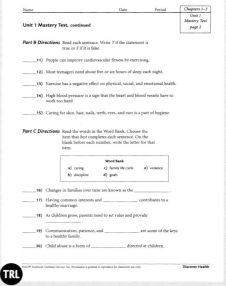

**Unit 1 Mastery Test, page 1**          **Unit 1 Mastery Test, page 2**

10) _____ fitness is the condition of the heart, lungs, and blood vessels.

11) _____ fitness is your body's ability to exercise, work, and play without tiring easily.

12) A family that includes people from different generations is called an _____ family.

13) Every state has laws to protect children from _____.

14) Parents are responsible for the health, _____, and well-being of their children.

## Comprehension: Understanding Main Ideas

Write the answers to these questions on a separate sheet of paper. Use complete sentences.

15) Describe the five stages in the family life cycle.

16) Explain how exercise affects physical, social, and emotional health.

17) What does the word *family* mean?

18) Choose two body systems and explain how they work together to do a job in the body.

## Critical Thinking: Write Your Opinion

19) What are two things you can do to improve your personal hygiene?

20) What role does your family play in your everyday life?

10) Cardiovascular  11) Physical
12) extended  13) abuse  14) safety

## Comprehension: Understanding Main Ideas

15) The family life cycle begins with marriage. The second stage occurs when a child is born into the family. The third stage is when children begin to prepare to live on their own. The fourth stage happens when families adjust to their children leading their own lives. The final stage in the family life cycle is learning to deal with aging and death.

16) Regular exercise keeps your muscles, bones, heart, and lungs working properly. It also keeps your body strong and at a healthy weight. Exercising is a good way to make friends, spend leisure hours, and have a good time. Finally, exercise helps reduce the symptoms of stress.

17) A family is a group of people usually joined by a marriage who support one another and are committed to making the relationships within the family work.

18) Answers will depend on the body systems selected. Students should select two of the following body systems for their discussion: skin, skeletal, muscular, digestive, excretory, respiratory, circulatory, nervous, endocrine, or reproductive.

## Critical Thinking: Write Your Opinion

19) Answers will vary. Students should back up their opinion with information about proper hygiene.

20) Answers will vary. Students should back up their opinion with information about their family and its role in their life.

# Unit 2 Planning Guide

## Mental and Emotional Health

| | Student Lesson | | | |
|---|---|---|---|---|
| | Student Pages | Vocabulary | Lesson Review | Writing About Health |
| ***Chapter 4 Emotions*** | 85–99 | | | |
| Lesson 1 Emotions and Their Causes | 86–89 | • | • | |
| Lesson 2 Social Emotions | 90–92 | • | • | • |
| Lesson 3 Emotions and Behavior | 93–96 | • | • | |
| ***Chapter 5 Maintaining Mental Health*** | 100–117 | | | |
| Lesson 1 Managing Frustration | 101–103 | • | • | |
| Lesson 2 Managing Stress and Anxiety | 104–107 | • | • | • |
| Lesson 3 Responding to Peer Pressure | 108–111 | • | • | |
| Lesson 4 Eating Disorders | 112–114 | • | • | |
| ***Chapter 6 Relations*** | 118–131 | | | |
| Lesson 1 Being a Friend to Yourself | 119–121 | • | • | |
| Lesson 2 Making Friends | 122–124 | • | • | • |
| Lesson 3 Healthy Relationships | 125–128 | • | • | |

### Unit Activities

**Home Connection**
**What Do You Think?**
**Deciding for Yourself**

### AGS-Related Resources

**Discover Life Skills Handbook**
**Discover Healthy Sexual Development**

### Assessment Options

**Student Text**
- **Lesson Reviews**
- **Chapter Reviews**
- **Unit Review**

**Teacher's Resource Library**
- **Chapter Mastery Tests**
- **Unit Mastery Test**

| Student Text Features | | | | | | Teaching Strategies | | | | | | | Learning Styles | | | | | Teacher's Resource Library | | | |
|---|---|---|---|---|---|---|---|---|---|---|---|---|---|---|---|---|---|---|---|---|---|
| Action for Health | Careers | Health, Fitness, and Nutrition Tips | Healthy Subjects | Then and Now | Technology | Background Information | Career Application | Community Application | Environment Application | Global Connection | Home Application | Multicultural Connection | Auditory | Group Learning | LEP/ESL | Tactile/Kinesthetic | Visual | Activities | Mastery Tests | Student Study Guide | Workbook Activities |
|  |  |  |  |  |  |  |  |  |  |  |  |  |  |  |  |  |  |  | • | • |  |
|  |  | 88 | 88 |  |  |  |  |  |  |  | 87 | 88 |  |  |  |  | 89 | 13 |  |  | 13 |
| 91 |  | 92 |  |  |  |  |  | 92 |  |  |  |  | 91 |  |  |  |  | 14 |  |  | 14 |
|  | 95 |  | 94 |  |  | 96 | 95 |  | 94 | 95 |  |  |  |  |  |  | 94 | 15 |  |  | 15 |
|  |  |  |  |  |  |  |  |  |  |  |  |  |  |  |  |  |  |  | • | • |  |
|  |  |  |  |  |  |  |  |  |  |  |  |  |  |  |  |  | 102 | 16 |  |  | 16 |
|  |  | 105 |  |  | 107 | 107 |  |  | 106 |  |  |  |  |  | 106 | 105 |  | 17 |  |  | 17 |
| 111 |  |  |  |  |  |  | 109 |  |  | 114 |  | 110 | 109 | 110 |  |  |  | 18 |  |  | 18 |
|  | 114 | 114 |  | 113 |  |  |  |  |  |  |  |  |  |  |  |  |  | 19 |  |  | 19 |
|  |  |  |  |  |  |  |  |  |  |  |  |  |  |  |  |  |  |  | • | • |  |
| 121 |  | 120 |  |  |  | 120 |  |  | 121 |  |  |  |  |  | 120 | 120 |  | 20 |  |  | 20 |
|  | 124 | 122 |  |  |  |  |  | 124 |  |  |  |  |  |  |  | 123 |  | 21 |  |  | 21 |
|  |  |  |  | 127 |  | 126 | 127 |  | 128 |  | 128 | 126 |  |  | 126 |  |  | 22 |  |  | 22 |

## Block Scheduling

Here is a suggested teaching activity if you have extended instructional time, such as a block schedule.

Bio Me  *To examine and increase your understanding and management of your mental health by creating a Bio Me silhouette.*

Standing between an overhead projector and a large sheet of paper taped to the wall, have another person trace your silhouette on paper. Divide your silhouette into five random but nearly equal sections. Label the sections: Physical Needs, Safety, Important People, Feeling Good About Myself, Goals. For each section, use drawings, photographs, magazine pictures, or other illustrations to represent what is important to you in that area of your life. On the paper outside of your silhouette, write three things:

1. What you think is important to do to stay healthy.
2. How someone you admire handles problems.
3. Things that you enjoy doing with friends or family.

**Other Resources**

**Books for Teachers**

Chester, Eric, ed. *Teen Empower*. Lakewood, CO: ChesPress Publication, 1997.

Cormier, Sid. *Am I Normal? Personal Guide to Understanding Yourself and Others*. New York: Carrol and Graf, 1993.

**Books for Students**

Chester, Eric, ed. *Teen Power*. Lakewood, CO: ChesPress Publication, 1997. (Presents teens with words of wisdom, advice, and encouragement from America's foremost youth speakers.)

McCoy, Kathy, and Charles Wibbelsman. *Life Happens*. New York: Berkeley, 1996. (Offers advice on how to cope with sadness, anger, anxiety, and other feelings related to problems that teens face.)

*A strong positive mental attitude will create more miracles than any wonder drug.*
—Patricia Neal

**Videos**

*C.H.I.L.L.: Straight Talk About Stress* (22 minutes). Waco, TX: Health EDCO (1-800-299-3366), 1994. (Provides teens with ways to handle stress in their lives.)

*Mental Illness* (23 minutes). Princeton, NJ: Films for the Humanities and Sciences (1-800-257-5126), 1990. (Describes common mental illnesses and the progress medical research is making in understanding them.)

*Without Pity: A Film About Abilities* (56 minutes). Princeton, NJ: Films for the Humanities and Sciences (1-800-257-5126), 1996. (Narrated by Christopher Reeve, this award-winning film shows how several disabled individual overcome their physical obstacles with a positive mental attitude.)

**TRL**  **Home Connection Master 2**

# Mental and Emotional Health

For most people, some days are better than others. You can have good days and bad days. Sometimes outside events influence the kind of day you have. But your thoughts, emotions, and beliefs also play a role. Learning how to maintain good mental and emotional health is important. It can help you enjoy the good days more and not be as upset by the bad days.

Your beliefs about yourself affect what you do. They can have a big impact—either positive or negative—on your physical health. These beliefs also influence how you handle relationships with other people. In this unit, you will learn about mental and emotional health. You will also learn ways to create and maintain healthy relationships.

▶ Chapter 4  Emotions

▶ Chapter 5  Maintaining Mental Health

▶ Chapter 6  Relationships

## Introducing the Unit

Have students look at the picture and think about what it shows. While they are doing this, read aloud the quote by Patricia Neal on page 82. Then have volunteers read the introductory material on page 83.

### Ask:

- **What does the picture show?** (Encourage students to both describe the picture and relate it to what they think they will learn in the unit.)

- **The people in the photograph are having a positive group experience. What positive group experience have you had?** (Answers will vary. Examples of positive group experiences: participating in band, orchestra, or theater performances; winning an important football, soccer, basketball, or softball game; raising money for a special cause; and so forth.)

- **What do you think Patricia Neal is saying about mental attitude?** (Students may have different interpretations, but they may suggest a positive attitude can get you through daily life, including pressures, better than any drugs.)

- **Do you think that the people in the picture have good mental and emotional health? Why do you think that?** (Students may say yes for several reasons: the people look happy, they look like they enjoy life, they seem to enjoy doing things together.)

- **How do you think a positive mental attitude can help your mental and emotional health?** (It can help you enjoy the good days more and not be so upset by the bad days.)

## What Do You Think?

Tell students that in this unit they will learn positive ways to handle emotions. Then have students read the story on this page.

Ask:

- While Lucia was getting ready for school, what things went wrong? (Lucia overslept, she didn't have time to eat breakfast, the sweater she wanted to wear had a stain, and she yelled at her brother for getting in the way.)

- What went wrong after Lucia left the house? (It rained and she didn't have an umbrella, she had to stand on the bus, she had an argument with a friend over nothing.)

- What did Lucia discover during math class? (She had left the homework on the kitchen counter.)

- Lucia then finds out that there is a surprise quiz. How does she feel? (frustrated, panicked, embarrassed to be so upset)

- Why was Lucia so upset? (Answers will vary. Students may suggest that Lucia is upset at herself because she realized nothing major had gone wrong and that she got very emotional over small things.)

- What could Lucia have done to not get so upset? (Answers will vary. Students may suggest that Lucia could have organized herself better by doing the following the night before: put the math assignment away, check the sweater for stains, set the alarm so she would not have overslept.)

Have students complete the Unit 2 What Do You Think? Activity Sheet.

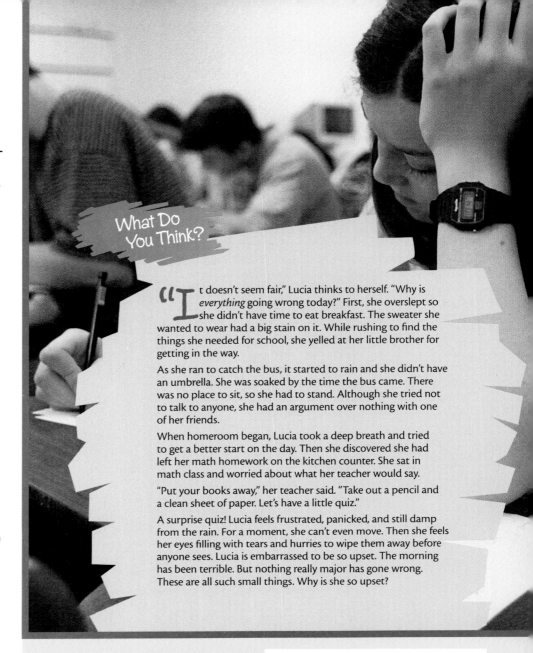

### What Do You Think?

"It doesn't seem fair," Lucia thinks to herself. "Why is *everything* going wrong today?" First, she overslept so she didn't have time to eat breakfast. The sweater she wanted to wear had a big stain on it. While rushing to find the things she needed for school, she yelled at her little brother for getting in the way.

As she ran to catch the bus, it started to rain and she didn't have an umbrella. She was soaked by the time the bus came. There was no place to sit, so she had to stand. Although she tried not to talk to anyone, she had an argument over nothing with one of her friends.

When homeroom began, Lucia took a deep breath and tried to get a better start on the day. Then she discovered she had left her math homework on the kitchen counter. She sat in math class and worried about what her teacher would say.

"Put your books away," her teacher said. "Take out a pencil and a clean sheet of paper. Let's have a little quiz."

A surprise quiz! Lucia feels frustrated, panicked, and still damp from the rain. For a moment, she can't even move. Then she feels her eyes filling with tears and hurries to wipe them away before anyone sees. Lucia is embarrassed to be so upset. The morning has been terrible. But nothing really major has gone wrong. These are all such small things. Why is she so upset?

**What Do You Think? Master 2**

# Emotions

*B*eing healthy involves both the body and the mind. Feeling happy can help your whole body feel well. If you are worried about something, you might not feel as well. Your mind affects the body. The body also affects the mind. For example, if you get enough rest, you are usually able to think clearly. If you are tired, you may not be able to think as clearly.

In this chapter, you will learn about keeping your mind and body healthy by understanding your emotions. You will find out what causes emotions. You also will learn how emotions affect your relationships with others and the way you behave.

## Goals for Learning

▶ To learn what emotions are

▶ To describe some causes of emotions

▶ To explain how emotions affect relationships with others

▶ To explain how emotions are related to the way a person behaves

## Introducing the Chapter

Give students the chance to think of various types of emotions as you write them on the board. Once the list is complete, have students choose an emotion and write a sentence about the last time they felt that emotion. Collect the sentences without student names. Read them aloud in class so the sentences can serve as a springboard for discussion.

Tell students that the chapter they are about to read will discuss emotions, their causes, and how emotions affect people and those around them.

Have volunteers read page 85 aloud, including the Goals for Learning.

## Ask:

• What kinds of emotions have most people written about? (Answers will vary, depending on the emotions students choose.)

• What seems to be the cause of most of these emotions? (Answers will vary, depending on the events that trigger the emotions.)

---

Name _____ Date _____ Period _____

Chapter 4
Student Study Guide
10
page 1

**Chapter 4 Emotions**

*Directions* Fill in the outline below. Filling in the blanks will help you
as you read and study Emotions.

I. Lesson 1 (pp. 86-89)
  A. Emotions and Their Causes
    1. An emotion has a physical side and a _____ side.
    2. A physical change gets your body ready to _____ .
    3. Emotions start with _____ .
    4. The state of physical and emotional pressure is called _____ .
    5. You will feel uncomfortable and _____ when you are afraid.
    6. It is wise to _____ before you act.
    7. When you act in ways that solve problems, you are _____ .
    8. Normal, healthy living usually has some _____ and some
    _____ .

II. Lesson 2 (pp. 90-92)
  A. Social Emotions
    1. Social emotions are emotions that have to do with _____ with others.
    2. Feeling _____ may keep you from having good relationships with others.
    3. If someone does not approve of you, you feel _____ .
    4. When you have a loss, you feel _____ , which is a mixture of painful
    emotions.
    5. Depression is extreme _____ .
    6. _____ action and thinking may help get rid of depressed feelings.

©AGS® American Guidance Service, Inc. Permission is granted to reproduce for classroom use only.    **Discover Health**

---

Name _____ Date _____ Period _____

Chapter 4
Student Study Guide
10
page 2

III. Lesson 3 (pp. 93-96)
  A. Emotions and Behavior
    1. The _____ responses to your thoughts and experiences are your emotions.
    2. When an emotion signals a _____ , you can identify what causes the
    problem, decide on a way to _____ the problem, and carry out your plan.
    3. You might feel upset if something you don't _____ happens.
    4. Behaving in a _____ way will help you feel good about yourself. It may also
    lead to a _____ .
    5. All emotions are _____ .
    6. _____ action can help you deal with your emotions.

©AGS® American Guidance Service, Inc. Permission is granted to reproduce for classroom use only.    **Discover Health**

---

**Student Study Guide 10, page 1**    **Student Study Guide 10, page 2**

## Chapter 4 Lesson 1

**Overview** This lesson discusses what emotions are, what causes them, and how people can adapt to situations that trigger strong emotions.

### Objectives

- To learn what emotions are.
- To describe some causes of emotions.

**Student Pages** 86–89

**Audiocassette**

**Teacher's Resource Library**  TRL

    Activity 13

    Workbook Activity 13

## Teaching Suggestions

### ■ Vocabulary

*emotions, stress, adapt*

Make up sentences using each vocabulary word and write them on the board. Ask volunteers to give a definition of each word based on its context. Write the definitions on the board and have students compare them to the definitions in the textbook.

### ■ Teaching the Lesson

Ask students to brainstorm a list of "needs" and "wants" as you list them on the board. Tell students to think about the difference between the two. After reading and discussing the lesson, ask students how they might change the lists of "needs" and "wants."

Have students start reading about what emotions are and how they manifest themselves physically on page 86.

Ask:

- What are your emotions? (Emotions are your feelings.)

---

| Emotions |
|---|
| *Feelings* |

*E*very person has feelings. Your feelings make you different from every other person. Your feelings affect the way you react to things. Different people may react to the same thing in different ways.

**What Are Emotions?**

Your feelings are called **emotions**. Emotions are our reactions to events and experiences. They let us know when something is right as well as when something is wrong. Learning about your feelings can help you to understand yourself better.

An emotion is made up of two parts. One part is the physical reaction you have to a situation. For example, you might feel angry. Then your face might become flushed, or reddish. Your muscles may feel tight. You might even want to shout or hit something. The second part of an emotion is the mental side. The mental side of an emotion explains why you feel the way you do.

Before you act, think about why you feel the way you do.

**The Physical Side**

Different kinds of physical changes can be part of emotions. For example, when you are excited, your blood may flow more quickly through your body. Then you might feel stronger and have more energy. If you are sad or afraid, the muscles in your legs might feel tight. You might feel like you are ready to run away. You might even cross your arms to protect your body. Physical changes get your body ready to act. Before you act, it is wise to think about why you feel the way you do.

**86**   *Chapter 4   Emotions*

---

- What are the two parts of an emotion? (Emotions have a physical side, which consists of changes that happen to your body. Emotions also have a mental side, which explains why you feel the way you do.)

- List two physical changes that can happen as the result of emotions. (Physical changes can include increased blood flow as the result of excitement and tightening of the muscles as the result of fear.)

### The Mental Side

Understanding why you feel a certain way can help you decide how to act. Suppose you are angry and act before you think about the reasons for your feelings. You might do something you will feel sorry about later. For example, if you say unkind things to a friend you might end your friendship. If you think before you act, you might behave differently.

### What Causes Emotions?

Emotions start with thoughts. When we think about something that happens, we may feel a certain way about that event. Our thinking triggers an emotion. **Stress**, fear, and anger are common emotions.

### Stress

When we feel threatened, we may experience stress. Stress is a state of physical and emotional pressure. Stress can be "good" or "bad." For example, you may be excited about a project and do a good job on it. Then good stress helps you. Usually we hear about bad stress because its effects are harmful. Changing schools or the death of someone you love are examples of bad stress. Bad stress can interfere with healthy living. The emotions of fear and change are linked to bad stress. The following chart lists events that commonly cause stress for teens.

#### Common Stressful Life Events for Teens

| | |
|---|---|
| • Death of a parent | • An outstanding personal achievement |
| • A visible deformity | • Being accepted to college |
| • Parents' divorce or separation | • Being a senior in high school |
| • Being involved with alcohol or other drugs | • A change in acceptance by peers |
| • Death of a brother or sister | • A change in parents' financial status |
| • Beginning to date | |

Have students read about the mental side of emotions and the causes of emotions on page 87.

### Ask:

- Why is it important to think about why you feel a certain way before acting on it? (People should think about how they feel before acting because it might stop them from doing something they will regret.)

- What is stress? (Stress is the way the body reacts to a change or to something that can hurt you.)

- What is bad stress? (Bad stress makes someone fearful and interferes with healthy living.)

- Give two examples of situations that can lead to bad stress. (Bad stress can result from the following: death of a close relative, a visible deformity, parents' divorce or separation, being involved with alcohol and other drugs, nervousness about dating, a decrease in the income of parents.)

- How can stress be good? (Stress can be good if it pushes someone to succeed and do a good job.)

- Give two examples of situations that can lead to good stress. (Good stress can result from the following: an outstanding personal achievement, acceptance at a college, becoming a senior in high school, feeling accepted by peers, an increase in the income of parents.)

### APPLICATION

 **At Home**
Have student talk with family members about situations that they find stressful and how they handle that stress. Invite students to compare notes on what they find in class. Lead a discussion in which students talk about the main sources of stress that they have found and the solutions people have developed for dealing with them.

## Then and Now

Talk with students about what it would have been like to live in a place such as Sparta. What type of society would be formed by people who knew nothing but the most basic skills such as fighting and planting crops? Encourage students to find out more about Sparta, including what life was like for women in this society.

Have students read about fear and anger on page 88.

### Ask:

- How can fear be useful? (Fear can be useful if it helps you protect yourself or avoid a situation in which something is being done that you think is wrong.)

- What are some negative ways that people express anger? (People express anger negatively by screaming and physically hurting others. Accept any other reasonable answers.)

- What are some ways to deal constructively with anger? (People can deal constructively with anger by thinking about why they are angry and talking to someone who can help, expressing why they feel angry in words, and staying calm. Accept any other reasonable answers.)

### MULTICULTURAL CONNECTION

In some cultures, it is acceptable to display emotions openly. In others, emotions are hidden. Have students look for information about how people express emotions in various cultures. Have students prepare reports in which they compare the expression of emotions in different cultures. Encourage students to share their findings with the class.

Then and Now

### ANCIENT IDEAS

Around 400 B.C., the Spartans of ancient Greece believed in physically strong people. Young boys were trained in sports. They were made to exercise so they became strong soldiers. They learned only how to fight and farm. They did not have any other schooling.

At the same time, the Greek people of ancient Athens believed in strong minds and bodies. They wanted their people to learn about history, science, and the arts.

Most cultures have followed the Athenians. They believe that the mind and body work together. Developing both the mind and the body helps a person be healthier.

### Fear

When you are afraid, you feel uncomfortable and nervous. You want to get away from whatever is frightening you. Fear is useful when it helps you protect yourself. For example, you may be playing ball and a teammate shouts, "Watch out!" You may feel fear and duck your head. Sometimes you might feel afraid without knowing why. If someone tries to get you to do something you think is wrong, you might feel afraid. Your fear may help you get away from the situation.

### Anger

Anger might cause you to react too strongly. You might start a fight or an argument. If someone bothers you, you may want to fight back. When you feel anger, you can choose how to behave. You can speak or yell. You can complain to someone who can help. You can hurt someone or step away until you calm down. Before you act, it is a good idea to think about what might happen later. Deciding how to act is not always easy.

*Fitness Tip*

**Getting regular exercise can make it easier to deal with stressful situations.**

The best way to express your anger is to say why you are angry. You could say, "I feel hurt when you tease me." Staying calm is a way to control anger. Self-talk helps, too. For example, it can calm your body to tell yourself, "Stay calm. Relax."

### How Can You Change Your Behavior?

When you feel the emotions of stress, you can **adapt**, or change, the way you behave. Adapting means that you act in ways that solve problems. You adapt to cold weather by wearing warm clothing. You also can adapt to situations that cause stress. If you are worried about a test, you can study. If someone hurts your feelings, you can tell the person how you feel. You can ask the person to apologize. Keep in mind that the person might not agree to apologize. Nevertheless, by trying, you will feel that you have done all you can.

**How can walking away from a fight help you feel better?**

The emotions of relief and joy are a sign that the stressful situation is over. Relief can feel like a wave of good feelings. It ends the fear or anger that stress starts. Joy is a happy feeling. People show joy in different ways. Some people smile shyly. Others laugh out loud.

Feeling good is important for mental health. Normal, healthy living usually has some ups and some downs. Changes in emotions help you keep a healthy balance in life. It is important to recognize what your emotions are trying to tell you.

**LESSON 1 REVIEW** Write the answers to these questions on a separate sheet of paper. Use complete sentences.

1) What are two sides of an emotion?

2) What emotions prepare people to protect themselves?

3) Name one way you can deal with anger in a way that can help solve problems.

4) What emotions can be a sign that a stressful situation is over?

5) What is one way you could adapt your behavior if you are afraid about acting in the school play?

*Emotions* Chapter 4 **89**

Have students read about ways to change behavior on page 89.

Ask:

- How can learning how to adapt help you deal with stressful emotions? (Adapting to stressful emotions means that you change your behavior in a way that helps to solve the problem causing the stress.)

- Why is it important to pay attention to your emotions? (Accept all reasonable answers including the following: Paying attention to your emotions can help you deal with problems that cause them, react more positively in difficult situations, and improve your mental and physical health.)

### Lesson 1 Review Answers

1) The two sides of an emotion are the physical and mental sides.

2) Fear and anger are emotions that prepare people to protect themselves.

3) Answers will vary. One way you can deal with anger is to talk to a parent or teacher about your feelings instead of having a fight or an argument.

4) Relief and joy are emotions that tell you a stressful situation is over.

5) Answers will vary but might include the following behaviors: studying hard to memorize the lines, practicing the lines in front of others, asking a teacher for extra help.

## LEARNING STYLES

**Tactile/Kinesthetic** Have students split into small groups to create skits in which they show people expressing strong emotions in certain situations. The skit should include a mechanism the person uses to deal with negative emotions or adapt to a stressful situation, such as taking a few deep breaths or counting to ten. Have students present their skits in class. Then have other students evaluate the way the situation was handled.

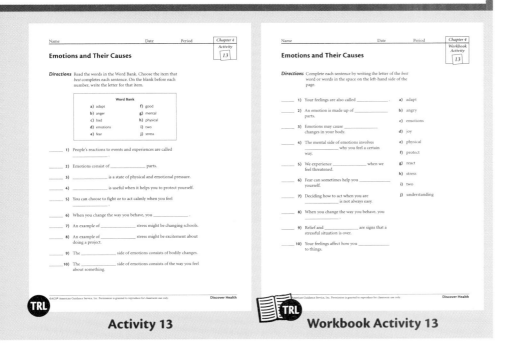

**Activity 13**

**Workbook Activity 13**

## Lesson at a Glance

### Chapter 4 Lesson 2

**Overview** In this lesson, students learn what social emotions are and how to deal with them.

### Objectives

- To explain how emotions affect relationships with others.

**Student Pages** 90–92

**Audiocassette**

**Teacher's Resource Library** **TRL**

Activity 14

Workbook Activity 14

## Teaching Suggestions

### ■ Vocabulary

*social emotions, guilt, shame, grief, depression*

Read the vocabulary words and discuss their meanings with the class. Then have students write sentences, leaving blanks for the missing vocabulary words. Ask students to exchange papers and write in the missing words.

### ■ Teaching the Lesson

Ask students to think about emotions they have shown in their relationships with parents, sisters and brothers, and close friends. These could be good or bad emotions. One example might be a feeling of love toward a friend or competitiveness toward a sibling. Then have students read about social emotions on page 90.

### Ask:

- What are social emotions? (Social emotions are those that have to do with relationships with other people.)

- Explain the social emotion called love. (Love is a positive way to think, feel, or act toward another person such as a parent, sibling, or friend. It involves mutual feelings of sharing and respect.)

- What are some ways to show respect to a family member you love? (Accept all reasonable answers. Possible answers include: telling the person how you feel about them, offering to help the person, doing something for the person that you know they will enjoy.)

- What triggers emotions of guilt? (You feel guilt when you disappoint yourself or others. You also feel guilt when you think you have done something wrong.)

## Lesson 2

### Social Emotions

**Social emotions**
*Emotions that have to do with relationships with others*

**Guilt**
*An emotion felt when a person does something wrong*

**P**eople need other people. Many emotions begin with our relationships with family members, friends, and other people.

#### What Are Social Emotions?

Emotions that have to do with relationships with others are called **social emotions**. The most familiar social emotion is love. Love is a positive way of thinking, feeling, and acting toward another person. People feel different kinds of love. You feel love for parents, brothers, and sisters. You also feel love toward close friends. As you grow older, love can develop for a special person in your life.

Love begins with a baby's need to be near a parent or caregiver. As you grow and meet more people, you choose to have loving feelings toward others. Love involves sharing and respect between people. The person you love feels loving feelings for you, too.

**What are some ways to show respect to a family member you love?**

Love is important for healthy living. Painful social emotions develop when love is lost. You feel the emotion of **guilt** when you disappoint yourself and others. You may feel guilty when you do something you know is wrong. Guilt may not have signs that other people see. Guilty feelings may keep you from having good relationships with others.

You may feel love toward close friends.

**90** *Chapter 4  Emotions*

**Shame**
*An emotion that results from disapproval or rejection*

**Grief**
*A mixture of painful emotions that result from loss*

**Shame** is an emotion you feel if someone does not approve of you. You might feel shame if someone rejects you. Suppose you make a mistake. Suppose you feel that people are making fun of you. You might feel embarrassed and ashamed. Shame sometimes has outward signs. People who are ashamed sometimes blush. When you blush, your face becomes red and warm. If you feel shame, you might perspire. You probably wish to get away from the situation.

Sometimes people lose close relationships. For example, a grandparent dies or a good friend moves away. A person you care about might stop caring for you. You feel **grief**. Grief is a mixture of painful emotions you feel when you have a loss.

Grief is a normal way to react to a loss. A grieving person needs to deal with his or her feelings. It is important to face the loss and talk about the pain it causes.

**Action for Health**

## DEALING WITH LOSS AND DISAPPOINTMENT

How can you learn to deal with grief and disappointment? There are some things you can do to deal with grief in positive ways.

**Accept the loss.** You can keep photographs or objects to remind you of a person you lose. If you are disappointed about something, try writing about your feelings.

**Set a time every day for grieving.** Explain to others that you need some time alone. You may need to cry. Crying expresses sad feelings. It also helps bring relief. When time is up, put your grief away. Remind yourself that you can grieve again the next day.

**Make a plan for living with your loss.** Talking with others may be helpful. Set new goals. A goal might be to exercise every day. Think of new dreams for your life. You might even set a goal for something you want when you are older.

**Reward yourself.** When you reach a goal, be proud of yourself. You might want to tell someone else what you did. As you reach some goals, you can set other goals. Think about all the things you can look forward to in your life.

Have students read about shame, grief, and dealing with loss and disappointment on page 91.

Ask:

- What causes people to feel shame? (People feel shame when someone does not approve of them, rejects them, or when they do something that embarrasses them.)

- What is grief, and what causes it? (Grief is a mixture of painful emotions that result from a loss such as the death of a family member or close friend.)

- Why is it healthy for people to feel grief after a loss? (Grief is a normal way to react to a loss. It is healthy for grieving people to face their grief and talk about how the loss makes them feel.)

## Action for Health

Invite students to write a paragraph about how they have dealt with a loss or disappointment in their lives. The subject can range from the death of a family member to the failure to make a team or get a good grade on a test. Allow students to hand in their paragraphs without their names if they choose. Read some aloud in class and discuss how the person dealt with the loss.

### LEARNING STYLES

**Auditory** Challenge students to find an article in a newspaper or magazine that relates a situation or an action for which students would have felt shame if it had happened to them. Have each student read the article for classmates and explain why he or she would feel shame in this situation. Have other members of the class decide whether they would feel the same way. Discuss any differences in opinion.

Talk about depression with students. Ask what kinds of situations cause them to feel depressed. Also discuss how students can deal with feelings of depression. Then have students read about depression on page 92.

Ask:

- What can cause depression? (Accept all reasonable answers. Depression can be caused by many things, including loss of a person close to you, being rejected by others, or not meeting goals.)

- How can you help someone who is depressed? (You can help a depressed person by allowing him or her to talk to you about the feeling or suggesting that the person go to a professional who can help.)

## Lesson 2 Review Answers

1) Love begins with a baby's need to be near a parent or caregiver.
2) You might feel guilt when you do something you know is wrong. You might also feel shame.
3) If a person feels ashamed, he or she might perspire or blush.
4) Answer will vary and might include the following: a loss due to the death of someone close or a good friend moving away.
5) Answers will vary and might include the following: encourage the person to talk about the pain; encourage the friend to think and act in a positive way; talk with family members, friends, or a mental health professional.

## APPLICATION

### In the Community

Tell students to locate facilities in the community that can offer professional help to people who are dealing with depression. Have students find out how people can get help at these facilities. Encourage students to work together to make up a list of the facilities, including addresses, phone numbers, and hours of operation. Allow students to make the list available to people through the school administration.

---

| Depression |
|---|
| Extreme sadness |

Grief includes **depression**. Depression is extreme sadness. People who feel depressed have low energy. They may feel angry and stay away from others. A grieving person may feel depressed for weeks or months or even longer.

People also feel grief when they have disappointments. For example, you may feel depressed and angry when you do not make a team. Not being chosen for a club can lead to depressed feelings. You may feel depressed when you do not meet one of your goals. If you feel depressed, it is important to tell your feelings to someone who cares about you. If friends feel depressed, it is important to listen to their feelings. Encourage them to express their feelings.

The best "cure" for depressed feelings is positive action and thinking. Sometimes, the depressed person needs the help of a mental health professional, such as a psychologist. Often, family members and friends can help the depressed person get over the pain of losses. Then the person can begin again to be active and to have good relationships.

**LESSON 2 REVIEW** Write the answers to these questions on a separate sheet of paper. Use complete sentences.

1) When does love begin?
2) What emotion might you feel when you do something you know is wrong?
3) What signs might a person show if he or she feels ashamed?
4) What are some things that can cause grief?
5) What might you suggest to a friend who seems depressed?

### Nutrition Tip

Take time to eat healthy meals when you are feeling sad or disappointed about something.

### Writing About Health

Think about a goal you could set that could help you deal with a disappointment. List things you could do to reach your goal.

---

**Activity 14**

**Workbook Activity 14**

## Emotions and Behavior

**Need**
*Something important or necessary to have*

Emotions always lead to some way of behaving or acting. Sometimes controlling your feelings probably seems easy. Other times, you may feel "driven" by your feelings. Then you are more likely to act without thinking carefully. Acting without thinking first can have unpleasant results.

### What Do Emotions Mean?

Emotions are feelings that seem to come from inside you. If you watch a sad movie, you may feel like crying. If you do well on a test, you may feel happy. When you watch a game, you may feel excited. You may feel like jumping up and shouting to cheer your team. Emotions are automatic responses to your thoughts and experiences.

Some emotions are signs of **needs**. You have a need when you are missing something important. If you do not have enough food, you get hungry. You have a need to eat. If you do not feel close to other people, you feel loneliness. You need friendship. When emotions show that you need something, you can do something about the problem. Hungry people think about food and how to get it. They may think of hardly anything else. Lonely people think about being close to others. They may feel sorry for themselves.

When an emotion signals a need, the healthiest response is to think about what you can do. You can do three things:

1. Identify what causes the problem.

2. Decide on a way to solve the problem.

3. Carry out your plan.

When you identify your needs, you can determine how best to meet them. Sometimes all you need to do is ask. If you need help with your homework, simply ask a friend.

You may feel happy and excited after a sporting event.

Emotions *Chapter 4* **93**

---

 **Lesson at a Glance**

## Chapter 4  Lesson 3

**Overview** In this lesson, students learn what emotions mean and how they can trigger certain behaviors.

## Objectives

■ To explain how emotions are related to behavior.

**Student Pages** 93–96

**Audiocassette** 🎧

**Teacher's Resource Library**

Activity 15

Workbook Activity 15

## Teaching Suggestions

### ■ Vocabulary

*need, compromise*

Have students read the definitions of the vocabulary words. Then have students write original sentences using the words. Ask for volunteers to read their sentences to the class.

### ■ Teaching the Lesson

Tell students to recall a time when they acted on a very strong emotion without thinking—possibly out of anger. What were the results of the action? Talk about whether thinking first would have resulted in a more positive result. Then have students read about emotions and behavior on page 93.

Ask:

· Emotions can be signs of needs. What are needs? (Needs are important things that you must have.)

· Give some examples of needs. (Examples of needs are food and companionship. Students might mention other needs such as shelter, clothing, or health care. Accept all reasonable answers.)

· What three steps should you take when an emotion triggers a need? (When an emotion triggers a need, identify what is causing the problem, decide how to solve the problem, and carry out the plan.)

Have students continue to read about needs and emotional action on page 94.

Ask:

- What is the best way to get what you need from others? (It is best to be direct and state what you want, rather than dropping hints that others may not understand.)

- What is the best way to deal with emotions caused by stress? (Accept all reasonable answers. One possible answer is to face the situation that is causing the stress and try to change it.)

## Healthy Subjects

Discuss feelings of envy with students—wanting to have something that someone else has or wanting to be like someone else. Ask students if they have ever felt jealous and what types of things or people have triggered the jealousy. Then discuss the best ways to deal with jealousy. Discuss how accepting yourself as you are is related to good mental health.

### APPLICATION

**Environment**
The conflict between the needs of different groups is common in environmental issues. Challenge students to become familiar with a local, state, or national environmental issue in which the needs of two different groups clash, such as people and animals or farmers and developers. Divide the class into two groups, with each group arguing one side of the issue in a debate.

### LEARNING STYLES

**Visual** Some students with artistic ability might enjoy drawing a cartoon that expresses the clash of needs argued in the above debate, or students might draw a poster that expresses their side of the argument. Display these in class.

Being direct works best. Dropping hints and hoping others will guess what you need usually doesn't work. You may need to work harder to get what you need. If you need high grades to get a job, you may have to study harder.

Emotions can be a sign that you are feeling stress. When something you do not expect happens, you may feel upset. You might want to act but you do not know what to do. If a teacher announces a pop quiz, you may feel angry. You might feel afraid even though you have been studying. Having a surprise test can seem unfair. In such a situation, you may not have many choices. You probably will take the test instead of running from the classroom. Maybe stress will help you work harder and do better on the test.

### Emotional Action

The outcome of an emotional experience depends on what you do. Recognizing how you feel is important. Everyone feels angry or afraid at times. You can control the way you act when you have such feelings. Then you will be better able to deal with problems. Behaving in a reasonable way will help you feel good about yourself.

#### Healthy Subjects
#### Literature

Toni Morrison's novel *The Bluest Eye* tells the stories of two African American girls. The girls come from different families. One girl, Pecola Breedlove, has parents who are angry. Her parents abuse her. Other children laugh at her. She feels ugly for being black. Pecola wishes she were white. She believes that having white skin would make her happy. She even prays for blue eyes. Pecola's sadness just makes her ill. As time passes, her health gets even worse.

The other girl, Claudia McTeer, feels very loved by her family. She likes the way she looks. She accepts herself. She has dreams about her future. Claudia works hard so her dreams may come true someday. Accepting herself helps her stay healthy.

**Careers**

### MENTAL HEALTH ASSISTANT

Do you think of yourself as caring? Would you describe yourself as trustworthy? Then you might want to become a mental health assistant. Mental health assistants work closely with mental health counselors. They help other people solve problems. Counselors help people handle many different kinds of situations. For example, some people have problems with their marriages. Others have trouble getting along with family members or friends. Sometimes people have problems that are related to school or to their jobs. People may need help handling stress. Some people do not think well of themselves. Others may be so depressed that they want to commit suicide. Mental health assistants need to be caring. They need to be able to gain people's trust. Good communication skills are important. Most employers prefer mental health assistants who have had college courses that teach "people skills" or psychology.

**Compromise**
*An agreement in which both sides give in a little*

Suppose that you want to go out with your friends. Your parents are not sure they want you to go. You feel angry at your parents. You are afraid that your friends will think you are a baby if you cannot join them. You can choose how to behave. You can have an angry outburst at your parents. Such behavior might hurt your parents' feelings. It is not likely to bring the results you want. If you think before you act, you might take more positive steps. For example, you could set a time to talk with your parents. You could explain where you want to go. You could tell them who will be with you. If you speak calmly, your parents will be more likely to listen to you. You also could listen to your parents' wishes and concerns. Acting in a reasonable way may lead to a **compromise**. A compromise is an agreement in which both sides give in a little.

## Careers

Tell students to find out more about the training that mental health assistants must have and the types of places where they would work. Suggest that students look into the job opportunities for mental health assistants and what they are likely to earn. If possible, invite a mental health assistant to class to speak to students about this career.

Have students read about compromise on page 95.

### Ask:

- How can compromise help you solve problems? (Accept all reasonable answers, including the following: Compromise can help you solve problems by allowing you to listen to the other side of the issue and coming up with a reasonable response that satisfies you and the other person.)

### APPLICATION

 **Career Connection**
Mediators make a living by bringing groups together and getting them to compromise. Mediators help to settle labor disputes between people such as employee and employer. Have students find out more about what mediators do and what qualities are needed for the job. Direct students to write a report on the subject. Students may want to find information about the role of public figures, such as President Jimmy Carter or General Colin Powell, in settling disputes between countries.

### GLOBAL CONNECTION

 Compromise would often benefit countries that have disagreements and military conflicts. Have each student choose a world conflict—either a verbal or legal disagreement between countries or an actual military conflict—that might have been or might still be worked out by compromise. Have students formulate the compromise, taking both sides of the conflict into account. Students should then make a presentation to the class.

Have students read the last section on dealing with emotions on page 96.

- Expressing your emotions can help you deal with them. What are some ways that you can express your emotions? (Accept all reasonable answers. Answers can include the following: talk with others, write about your feelings, ask others to help you meet your needs or make a decision.)

- What physical activity can help you deal with stress in a positive way? (People can deal with stress in a positive way by patting themselves on the back, jumping in the air, singing, or dancing. Accept any other reasonable answers.)

## Lesson 3 Review Answers

1) Emotions are automatic responses to your thoughts and experiences.
2) Answers will vary. Possible answers include working harder to do well on a test.
3) Thinking before you act can help you act in a reasonable way.
4) Answers will vary. Accept any two of the following: you can compromise, you can act to change a situation that is making you feel afraid or angry, you can express your feelings in a positive way, you can ask others to help you.
5) Answers will vary but should include a situation in which the student and his or her parents, relatives, or friends each give in a little until they reach an agreement.

## BACKGROUND INFORMATION

People who cannot set realistic goals are less likely to feel in control of their emotions and their lives. They might find that they cannot achieve the goals they set or that the decisions they make do not lead to achieving the things they want. Setting and achieving realistic goals is an important part of emotional health and can lead to increased success in school and at work. This success can have a positive effect on personal relationships.

Playing sports, such as basketball, can help you relax.

**What physical action might you choose to do to deal with stress in a positive way?**

Keep in mind that all emotions are normal. Emotions are not "good" or "bad." How you handle an emotion is the important thing to your mental health. First you need to pay attention to the emotions you are feeling. Think about why you feel the way you do. Then you will be ready to act in a positive way. You might be able to change a situation that is causing you to feel afraid or angry. For example, you may be afraid of taking a history test. You can talk to your teacher. He or she can give you some ideas for studying in a better way.

Expressing your emotions can help you deal with them. You can express your emotions in different ways. You can talk with others about your feelings. You can write about your feelings. You can ask other people to help you meet your needs. For example, you can ask parents or teachers to help you make a decision.

Sometimes taking physical action can help you deal with emotions. You might pat yourself on the back. You might jump in the air or sing a song. Doing physical activities, such as running or dancing, can help relax you. Then you can deal with your emotions in a calm way. Sometimes people feel that they cannot handle their emotions themselves. In such cases, talking with a mental health professional is the best thing to do.

**LESSON 3 REVIEW** Write the answers to these questions on a separate sheet of paper. Use complete sentences.

1) What are emotions?
2) What is an example of positive behavior that can come from stress?
3) How can thinking before you act be important?
4) What are two positive ways you can deal with an emotion?
5) What is an example of a situation in which a compromise might be helpful?

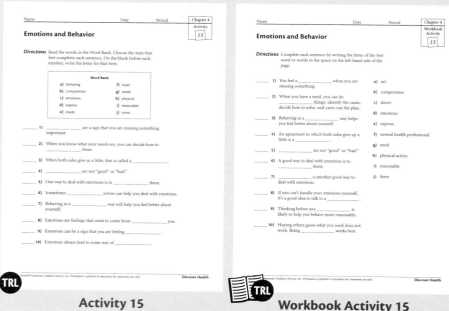

**Activity 15**　　　　**Workbook Activity 15**

■ Emotions are automatic responses to thoughts and experiences.

■ Acting without thinking first can have unpleasant results. Thinking first can help a person act in a reasonable way.

■ Some emotions are signs of needs people have, such as food or friends.

■ When emotions signal a need, a person must decide how to solve the problem.

■ Stress can help a person work harder to solve a problem.

■ Recognizing feelings can help a person control his or her actions.

■ Behaving in a reasonable way helps a person feel good about himself or herself.

■ Angry outbursts are not likely to bring positive results. Acting in a reasonable way may lead to a compromise.

■ How a person handles emotions is important to mental health.

■ Understanding the reasons for emotions can lead to positive behavior.

■ People can often change situations that are causing them to feel angry or afraid.

■ Expressing emotions can help a person deal with them. Talking with a mental health professional is important when people are unable to handle emotions themselves.

■ Physical activity can help a person deal with emotions in a positive way.

*Emotions   Chapter 4*   **97**

## ■ Using the Chapter Summary

To further reinforce the facts and concepts presented in the chapter, read and discuss with students the questions that follow.

### Ask:

• Why is thinking before acting on an emotion important? (Acting without thinking can result in doing something you will regret. Thinking first can lead to more productive and satisfying results.)

• What is stress? (Stress is a way the body reacts to a change or situations that seem threatening or unpleasant.)

• When is it important to know how to adapt? (It is important to adapt when you are in a situation that causes stress or other strong emotions. When you adapt, you can act in a way that solves the problem.)

• How can stress sometimes be good? (Stress can help a person work harder to solve a problem or achieve a goal.)

• What are social emotions? (Social emotions are emotions that have to do with relationships with others.)

• What is the source of feelings of guilt? (Guilt comes from a feeling that you have done something wrong.)

• What is shame? (Shame is an emotion that results from disapproval or rejection.)

• When does a person feel grief? (Grief is a mixture of painful emotions that result when a person feels a loss such as the death of a family member.)

• How should a person deal with grief? (A grieving person should face the loss and talk about the pain it has caused with others.)

• List two ways that people can deal positively with emotions. (Accept all reasonable answers, including the following: express the emotion by talking about the situation, engage in physical activity, talk with a mental health professional.)

## Chapter 4 Review

The Teacher's Resource Library includes two parallel forms of the Chapter 4 Mastery Test. The difficulty level of the two forms is equivalent. You may wish to use one form as a pretest and the other form as a posttest.

### Review Answers

#### Comprehension: Identifying Facts

**1)** Emotions **2)** adapt **3)** guilt
**4)** social emotions **5)** compromise
**6)** depressed **7)** need **8)** Grief **9)** shame
**10)** Stress

## Comprehension: Identifying Facts

On a separate sheet of paper, write the correct word or words from the Word Bank to complete each sentence.

| WORD BANK | |
|---|---|
| adapt | guilt |
| compromise | need |
| depressed | shame |
| emotions | social emotions |
| grief | stress |

**1)** _____ are a person's reactions to events and experiences.

**2)** You can _____ the way you behave to solve problems.

**3)** You may feel the emotion of _____ when you do something you know is wrong.

**4)** Emotions that have to do with relationships with others are called _____.

**5)** A _____ is an agreement in which both sides give in a little.

**6)** A person who feels _____ feels very sad and usually has low energy.

**7)** When emotions show that you have a _____, it is important to do something about the problem.

**8)** _____ is a mixture of painful emotions a person feels because of a loss.

**9)** A person might feel the emotion of _____ if he or she is rejected by someone else.

**10)** _____ is a state of physical and emotional pressure.

Chapter 4 Mastery Test A

## Comprehension: Understanding Main Ideas

Write the answers to these questions on a separate sheet of paper. Use complete sentences.

11) What kinds of physical changes can be part of emotions?

12) Why might some people be frightened of some of their emotions?

13) What are some ways you can choose to behave when you are angry?

14) What are three reasons people behave the way they do?

15) How can the emotion of fear be useful?

16) What are two ways you can express your emotions?

17) What are some ways to deal with feelings of depression?

18) What are some signs of love?

## Critical Thinking: Write Your Opinion

19) Why do you think dealing with stress and other emotions is important to your physical and mental health?

20) What could you do to help a friend who is feeling the emotion of grief?

**Test Taking Tip** When you take a test, be sure to read each question carefully before answering.

*Emotions* Chapter 4 **99**

---

---

Name _____ Date _____ Period _____ | Chapter 4 Mastery Test B page 1

**Chapter 4 Mastery Test B**

*Directions* Read each sentence. Write *T* if the statement is true or *F* if the statement is false.

_____ 1) You can control how you act when you have feelings of fear and anger.

_____ 2) Acting in an unreasonable way may lead to compromise.

_____ 3) A compromise is an agreement in which both sides give in a little.

_____ 4) Emotions are "bad."

_____ 5) Expressing your emotions can help you deal with them.

_____ 6) When you feel the emotions of stress, you should not change the way you behave.

_____ 7) Adapting means that you act in ways that solve problems.

_____ 8) Emotions of relief and joy are a sign that the stressful situation is over.

_____ 9) Feeling good is not too important for mental health.

_____ 10) The most familiar social emotion is guilt.

_____ 11) Sometimes taking physical action can help you deal with emotions.

_____ 12) Running or dancing will add stress to your life.

_____ 13) Depression is extreme happiness.

©AGS® American Guidance Service, Inc. Permission is granted to reproduce for classroom use only. Discover Health

---

Name _____ Date _____ Period _____ | Chapter 4 Mastery Test B page 2

**Chapter 4 Mastery Test B, continued**

_____ 14) Emotions are automatic responses to your thoughts and experiences.

_____ 15) Lonely people think about staying away from people and rarely feel sorry for themselves.

_____ 16) When an emotion signals a need, the healthiest response is to think about how you can fill the need.

_____ 17) An event that may cause stress for teens is a change in acceptance by peers.

_____ 18) Anger never causes a person to react too strongly.

_____ 19) When you are afraid, you feel uncomfortable and nervous.

_____ 20) Love is a positive way of thinking, feeling, and acting toward another person.

_____ 21) If you are ashamed, you may blush or perspire.

_____ 22) A grieving person should not talk about the pain the loss causes.

_____ 23) Different kinds of physical changes can be part of emotions.

_____ 24) Before you act, it is wise to think about why you feel the way you do.

_____ 25) Stress can only be bad.

©AGS® American Guidance Service, Inc. Permission is granted to reproduce for classroom use only. Discover Health

**TRL** **TRL**

**Chapter 4 Mastery Test B**

## Introducing the Chapter

Brainstorm a list of things that describe a
mentally healthy person. Write students'
suggestions and discuss them. Save the
list to compare with students' ideas about
mental health at the end of the chapter.

Have volunteers read page 100 aloud,
including the Goals for Learning.

### Ask:

- What can help your emotional health
  and well being? (getting to know yourself
  and becoming aware of your values and
  beliefs)

- Why might peer pressure be a bad thing?
  (Answers will vary. People may
  influence you to do things you
  know you shouldn't do.)

# Chapter 5

# Maintaining Mental Health

Many things affect your mental health. Getting
to know yourself helps your emotional health.
Becoming aware of your values and beliefs can also
help your well-being. You can do many things to help keep
yourself mentally and emotionally healthy.

In this chapter, you will learn about healthy ways to deal
with frustration and stress. You will find out ways to handle
peer pressure. You also will learn about eating disorders and
how they affect health.

### Goals for Learning

▶ To learn ways to handle frustration

▶ To identify healthy ways to cope with stress

▶ To identify ways to deal with peer pressure

▶ To describe three kinds of eating disorders

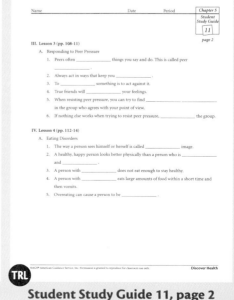

Student Study Guide 11, page 1     Student Study Guide 11, page 2

## Managing Frustration

**Aggression**
*Any act that is meant to harm someone*

**Frustration**
*An unpleasant feeling that happens when goals are blocked*

Everyone has needs. Each person also has goals he or she wants to meet. When you are hungry, you need to eat. When you are lonely, you want to be with people. When you want to do well in school, you study hard.

### How Can You Deal With Frustration?

Sometimes you feel the unpleasant feeling called **frustration**. Frustration happens when you are blocked from meeting your goals. Sometimes someone or something else gets in the way of your goal. For example, Hank wants to take a shower. His brother Ross gets in the shower first. Ross's action makes Hank feel frustrated.

You feel frustrated when something you do gets in the way of your goal. Part of Hank's problem was that he overslept. If he had awakened on time, he could have used the shower first. You frustrate yourself when you do not plan ahead. You frustrate yourself when you make mistakes in meeting your goals. You also feel frustrated when you do not have everything you need to meet a goal.

### Responses That Are Not Helpful

People react to frustration in different ways. Often people react in ways that are harmful. Such responses do not get rid of things that block goals.

**Aggression** is the most common response to frustration. Aggression is any act that is meant to harm someone. For example, Hank's little sister gets in his way. Hank shows aggression when he yells at her. The way Hank acts does not help the problem. Aggressive actions don't solve the problem.

Another reaction to frustration is acting childish. People may whine when they don't get their way. Sometimes people pout or stamp their feet and cry. They may bully other people. Such actions do not help you get what you want.

---

## Chapter 5  Lesson 1

**Overview** This lesson explains how people can cope with problems and describes ways to handle frustration.

### Objectives

- To identify some causes of frustration.
- To explain how some responses to frustration are not helpful.
- To describe some responses to frustration that are helpful.

**Student Pages** 101–103

**Audiocassette**

**Teacher's Resource Library** TRL

   Activity 16
   Workbook Activity 16

## Teaching Suggestions

### ■ Vocabulary

*aggression, frustration, cope, withdraw*

Write definitions for the vocabulary words on the chalkboard. Ask a student to read each definition. Challenge students to describe situations that match the definition. Continue until all the words are reviewed.

### ■ Teaching the Lesson

Ask students how feelings of frustration might affect the way they deal with a situation. (Feelings of frustration might affect their ability to deal with the situation.)

Have students read page 101 about dealing with frustration and responses that are not helpful.

Ask:

- What are some ways that people frustrate themselves? (not planning ahead, making mistakes, not having everything you need to meet a goal)

- Why are aggression and withdrawal not helpful? (They do not get rid of the things that block your goals.)

Have students read page 102 to get an overview of helpful responses to frustration.

Ask:

- How should you respond if you cannot reach one of your goals and it is causing you frustration? (set a new goal that is more reasonable)

- If a problem does not go away, how does coping help? (Coping helps you deal with a problem without feeling stress.)

## LEARNING STYLES

**Visual** Draw a concept map on the chalkboard that illustrates how setting reasonable goals, meeting goals, solving problems, and coping are all branches of positive responses to frustration. The map can be simple like the one shown. Discuss how a failure to do the things in one part of the map might affect the other parts.

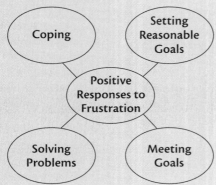

Cope
*Deal with a problem*

Withdraw
*Pull away*

If you feel frustrated a lot, you may **withdraw**, or pull away. People sometimes withdraw if they cannot deal with problems. They may withdraw if they feel frustrated. People who withdraw sometimes give up at the first sign of a problem. They stop trying to deal with the problem. Marty has trouble with math. He has to work harder to learn math than his classmates do. When he is frustrated by learning math, he stops work early. He complains that he'll never figure it out. Sometimes others try to help or explain the math. Marty acts impatient and does not listen. Marty still feels frustrated. Withdrawing does not help a person deal with a problem.

### Responses That Are Helpful

The positive way to respond to frustration is to **cope**. When you cope, you handle the problem. You get rid of whatever is causing your frustration. Coping is not always easy. It does make a positive difference. Coping helps you deal with a problem.

One way to cope with frustration is to take another look at your goal. Think about what is blocking you from meeting the goal. Maybe the goal is too far out of reach. There may be no way to meet it. For example, Bill likes playing softball, but he is not a fast runner. His goal of making the school softball team is blocked. He cannot run fast enough to make the team. Bill sets a new goal. He decides to play softball with friends on weekends. Bill is able to meet his new goal. Making sure your goals are possible is a good idea.

People react to frustration in different ways.

Another way to cope with frustration is to work harder to reach your goals. For example, Maria wants to go to computer camp this summer. Right now, her grades are not high enough to get into the camp. She sets a goal to raise her grades. Maria decides to work harder in school. She talks with her teachers about what to do. She gives up some other activities and spends more time studying. She probably will be able to get better grades. Then she will be able to go to computer camp this summer.

In some cases, there is another way to cope with frustration. You figure out what is blocking you from reaching a goal. Then you can figure out a way to solve that problem. For example, Nina wants to buy a new camera. She has not saved enough money to buy the one she wants. She talks with the owner of the camera store about her problem. Nina and the owner agree that she can trade in her old camera. In this way, Nina will get a lower price on the new camera. Now Nina can afford to buy the camera she wants.

**What reasonable goal can you set for yourself this week?**

In most cases, people need to act in several ways when they feel frustrated. Combining the ideas given above will help you cope with frustration. These ideas work because they solve the problems that are preventing you from reaching your goals.

**LESSON 1 REVIEW** Write the answers to these questions on a separate sheet of paper. Use complete sentences.

1) What causes frustration?

2) How does acting in an aggressive way increase frustration?

3) What are two ways of acting that show aggression?

4) Think about a person who gives up when there is a problem. What word describes the way the person is acting?

5) Suppose you are frustrated because you did not make the school band. What are some things you can do to cope with the frustration you feel?

*Maintaining Mental Health    Chapter 5    103*

---

Have students finish reading about helpful responses on page 103.

**Ask:**

- Suppose you have a goal of making 75 percent of your basketball free throws. If you only make 60 percent of your free throws, how could you respond? (practice hard to reach your goal, ask for advice from someone on how to shoot better free throws, alter your goal to be more realistic)

**Lesson 1 Review Answers**

1) Answers will vary. Some things that may cause frustration include: something getting in the way of a goal, not planning ahead, making mistakes in meeting goals, not having everything you need to meet a goal.

2) Acting in an aggressive way increases frustration because it doesn't solve the problem.

3) Answers will vary and may include whining, pouting, or having temper tantrums.

4) A person who gives up when there is a problem is withdrawing.

5) Answers will vary. Some things you could do to cope with the frustration are to set a different goal and to try harder the next time.

**APPLICATION**

**At Home**
Encourage students to keep a journal at home in which they write realistic personal goals. Suggest they start with one goal and list steps they could take to achieve the goal.

---

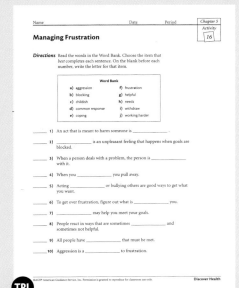

**Activity 16**

**Workbook Activity 16**

# Lesson at a Glance

## Chapter 5 Lesson 2

**Overview** This lesson explains how a person can deal with stress and anxiety.

### Objectives

- To identify causes and signs of stress.

- To explain the things a person can do to manage stress and deal with anxiety.

**Student Pages** 104–107

**Audiocassette**

**Teacher's Resource Library**

Activity 17

Workbook Activity 17

## Teaching Suggestions

### ■ Vocabulary

*hassle, self-esteem, threat, stress response, anxiety*

Write the definitions of the vocabulary words on the chalkboard and ask students to name a word that matches each definition. Prompt students to think about the difference between stress and stress response.

### ■ Teaching the Lesson

Ask students to think about an event in their lives that caused them stress or anxiety. Was the stress good or bad? What might they have learned from this event?

Have students read about the causes of stress on page 104.

### Ask:

- Why might a person feel stress when he or she is put down or criticized? (A person's self-esteem can be threatened by criticism, and the person will feel bad.)

- When can little hassles, like missing the bus or forgetting your book at home, cause stress? (when a number of hassles happen at the same time)

---

**Lesson 2**

## Managing Stress and Anxiety

**Hassle**
*A small, annoying event or problem*

**Self-esteem**
*The way a person feels about himself or herself*

**Threat**
*A situation that puts a person's well-being in danger*

Yyou may recall reading about stress in Chapter 4. Stress is a state of physical and emotional pressure. Some physical activities cause stress. Running to catch the bus or straining to lift a heavy object are stressful. Experiences that take mental effort also cause stress.

### How Can You Learn to Manage Stress?

Stress in itself is not bad. In fact, it helps you do certain things. For example, stress helps you work quickly to finish a paper for school. It gives you energy to run fast to catch the bus. Stress keeps you alert. It helps you take the right action. Too much stress can be harmful to your health.

### Causes of Stress

**Threats** are a common cause of stress. Threats are situations that seem to be dangerous to you. People feel threatened when they cannot meet their basic needs. For example, people are threatened when they do not have enough food. Not having shelter is a threat. People also feel threatened when they do not feel safe. Sometimes stress is caused by threats to **self-esteem**. Self-esteem is how a person feels about himself or herself. Your self-esteem is threatened when someone puts you down or criticizes you.

What is a positive way you have dealt with a hassle?

Other common causes of stress are major life changes. These changes are losses, illness, and injuries. People need to learn new ways of acting when they face major changes. People also need to deal with **hassles**. Hassles are small, annoying events or problems. Think about hassles that make life hard. You might oversleep or miss your bus. You might spill something or drop your books. Someone might get angry at you. One or two hassles are not stressful enough to harm your health. When a number of hassles happen at the same time, they cause stress.

**104** *Chapter 5 Maintaining Mental Health*

---

## Physical Signs of Stress

When you face stress, you may notice changes in your body. For example, suppose your teacher wants to talk with you. You are afraid you may hear bad news. You feel stress. Most of your response may be automatic. Your body's response to stress is called the **stress response**. There are three parts of the stress response. During the first part, your heart beats faster. Your breathing speeds up. You perspire and your muscles get tight. You may blush or cry out. Sometimes people have headaches or stomach pains. They may feel nervous. Some people may not be able to sleep well.

The second part of the stress response takes one of two forms: fight or flight. When something threatens you, you may want to fight to defend yourself. Fighting may be using words to stand up for your beliefs. The other response is flight. When you have this response, you want to flee, or run away. You leave the situation. The fight-or-flight response is natural. It happens without thinking.

Sometimes stressful situations happen over and over. Then the third part of the stress response happens. You feel exhausted, or very tired. You use a lot of energy dealing with stress. Dealing with stress over a long period of time may lead to illness. People may develop health problems such as ulcers or high blood pressure.

*Health Tip*

Taking deep breaths and breathing in and out slowly will help relax you when you feel stress.

### Healthy Subjects
*Geography*

**SEASONAL AFFECTIVE DISORDER**

Scientists have found that Seasonal Affective Disorder (SAD) affects five million Americans. The condition is very stressful. People feel tired and depressed. They may be unable to sleep. They usually feel anxious. Less daylight during winter months causes SAD. Northern parts of the United States have more cases of SAD. Alaska has the greatest number of cases. Florida has the fewest. Less daylight seems to reduce the amount of an important chemical in some people's brains. Treatment with light can increase the amount of the chemical. People sit in front of a light box for thirty minutes a day. When they do, they have fewer signs of SAD.

*Maintaining Mental Health   Chapter 5*   **105**

Have students read about physical signs of stress on page 105.

Ask:

- How does the stress response affect the body? (faster heartbeat and breathing, perspiration, tightening of the muscles, headaches, stomach problems, nervousness, and difficulty sleeping)

- What are two ways people respond to stress? (fight or flight)

## Healthy Subjects

Ask students to think about how they feel on a rainy day. Then ask them how they usually feel on a warm, sunny day. Have a volunteer read the feature. Then ask what kinds of things students can do on cold or rainy days to reduce stress. (go to an indoor gym to play, find enjoyable activities to do at home, read a book)

### LEARNING STYLES

 **Tactile/Kinesthetic** Have students check their pulse, count how many breaths they take in one minute, and feel their forehead for perspiration. Then have them simulate stress by running in place for one minute. Have them check their pulse, breathing, and forehead again. Discuss the changes in what they felt.

Have students read about managing stress and dealing with anxiety on pages 106 and 107.

**Ask:**

- What usually happens to your body after you respond to stress? (Your body calms down.)

- Is anxiety the same as fear? (No, but people who are anxious may feel like they are afraid.)

## LEARNING STYLES

**LEP/ESL** Students whose second language is English can benefit from making a collage or other visual representation of actions that can help to manage stress. Pictures might include scenes of people doing activities that they enjoy, developing talents, completing projects, and enjoying one another's company. Ask students to share and discuss their work with the class.

## APPLICATION

**Environment**
Suggest that students set a goal of helping protect the environment through a program at school or in the community. They might help with or enact a plan to clean up trash, start a recycling program, or plant trees. Lead students to conclude that doing something for the environment can allow them to experience achieving a goal. Working outdoors can also boost their self-esteem and reduce stress.

Anxiety
*An unpleasant feeling like fear but without reasons that are clear*

## Managing Stress

After you first respond to something stressful, your body calms down. Then you can decide what to do. For example, suppose you walk into a dark room and hear a noise. You may jump back. Then you decide to turn on a light to see what is making the noise. You find the noise was nothing to worry about.

Another way to manage stress is to prepare yourself for it. Eating right, exercising, and getting enough sleep help keep your body healthy. You can do things to strengthen your feelings and your thoughts. For example, do something every day that makes you feel good about yourself. You might want to do something you enjoy or finish something you started. Developing your talents is important. Learning how to handle your own problems will help you feel strong. You might ask others to show you how to do things yourself. Don't be afraid to ask others for help when you need it.

Do something you enjoy to reduce stress.

### How Can You Deal With Anxiety?

You have learned about fear, anger, joy, and grief. However, some feelings are hard to describe. You may have mixed emotions about some things. You may not even be sure why you feel good or bad. One unpleasant feeling that is hard to describe is **anxiety**. Anxiety is a feeling something like fear. Yet the reasons for anxiety may not be clear. People who are anxious do not really feel afraid. They feel *like* they are afraid. They often feel nervous or have trouble sitting still. People who are anxious feel uncomfortable. Anxiety is an upsetting feeling.

Anxiety is worse when you don't know exactly what is causing it. Instead of finding the reason for anxiety, you may just try to get rid of it. For example, Keith feels anxious about getting ready for school one morning. He probably feels anxious because he did not study enough for his French test. He doesn't try to find the reason for

## Writing About Health

List three situations that often cause you to feel stress. Next to each item, write about a way to deal with the stress in a positive way.

his anxiety. Instead he tries to get rid of the anxiety by staying home from school. Later when he feels better he must still go to school. He does not understand why he feels anxious. When he gets to school, he still is not ready to take the test.

The best way to deal with anxiety is to find the reason for it. Then you can face the problem and deal with it. When you deal with the problem that is causing anxiety, you will feel relief.

**LESSON 2 REVIEW** Write the answers to these questions on a separate sheet of paper. Use complete sentences.

1) What are some positive effects of stress?

2) What are two common causes of stress?

3) How does the stress response affect your body?

4) What are three signs of anxiety?

5) What are three ways to help you manage stress?

### BIOFEEDBACK

When you hear *biofeedback*, do you think of science fiction? Biofeedback is not science fiction. It is used to help treat illness or anxiety. Technicians place special sensors on a person's head or muscles. Computers measure muscle activity. Changes in muscle activity show on a computer monitor. The monitor shows how much stress a person is feeling. People learn to control pain by using positive thoughts. Biofeedback is used to treat long-term pain. It also is used to treat many other disorders such as headaches, epilepsy, and sleeplessness. Athletes use biofeedback to control anxiety before games. Biofeedback is not always a sure cure. For some people, though, it seems to work.

## Lesson 2 Review Answers

1) Answers will vary and may include: Stress can help you work quickly, give you more energy, keep you alert, and help you take the right action.

2) Answers will vary. Accept any two of the following: threats, major life changes, hassles.

3) The stress response affects your body the following ways: your heart beats faster; breathing speeds up; you perspire; your muscles get tight; you blush; you get headaches or stomach aches; you feel nervous; you may not sleep well.

4) Answers will vary. Accept any three of the following: feeling fearful for a reason that is not clear, uneasiness, nervousness, trouble sitting still, feeling uncomfortable.

5) Answers will vary. Possible activities that can help manage stress may include: making a decision about what to do; preparing for stress by staying healthy; eating right, exercising, getting enough sleep; doing something every day to help you feel good about yourself.

## Technology

Invite students to relax all of their muscles and take slow, deep breaths. After several minutes, ask students if they feel relaxed or stressed. Then have a volunteer read the feature aloud.

### BACKGROUND INFORMATION

Stress can help people get things done. It can motivate a person to finish work. Stress can help an athlete perform difficult tasks. Sometimes stress can help a person achieve extraordinary feats in emergency situations. In the stress response, the brain signals the release of the hormone adrenaline into the bloodstream. Adrenaline can provide the extra strength and speed a person needs for emergency action.

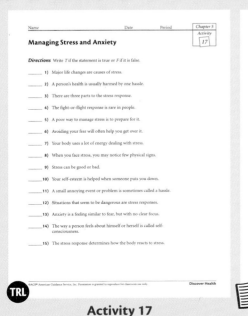

**Activity 17**

**Workbook Activity 17**

## Lesson at a Glance

### Chapter 5 Lesson 3

**Overview** This lesson discusses peer pressure and how to deal with it.

### Objectives

■ To explain how peer pressure works.

■ To identify how to resist negative peer pressure.

**Student Pages** 108–111

**Audiocassette**

**Teacher's Resource Library** TRL

Activity 18

Workbook Activity 18

## Teaching Suggestions

### ■ Vocabulary

*peer, peer pressure, resist*

Have students write clues for the vocabulary words. For example: She is the same age as I am. She is my _____. Allow students to show their clues to classmates who name the word for each clue.

### ■ Teaching the Lesson

Discuss how friends are important for people to feel good about themselves and enjoy life. Then ask if friends always have to agree and do the same things.

Have students read page 108 about how peer pressure works.

### Ask:

· **Who are your peers?** (Your peers are your friends and other people who are close to your age.)

· **How can peer pressure be positive?** (If your friends or other peers challenge you to meet a goal, that can be positive peer pressure.)

---

# Lesson 3

## Responding to Peer Pressure

**Peer**
*A person in the same age group*

**Peer pressure**
*The influence people of the same age have on one another*

When you were younger, you spent most of your time with your family. Your family is still very important to you. As you grow older, your friends are also becoming an important part of your life.

Friends keep you company. They laugh at your jokes. Friends listen to you when you need to talk. They help you do things. Groups of friends give one another a sort of home. The people in the group have a feeling of belonging. Some goals are easier to reach when you are part of a group. Your friends help you do things you could not do alone. For these reasons, you probably belong to some groups. The groups may be teams or clubs. You may have a special group of friends. Your friends and other people who are close to your age are called your **peers**.

### How Does Peer Pressure Work?

Belonging to a group gives you a good feeling. In return for that feeling, others in the group expect something of you. They expect you to pay attention to them. They expect you to support things they do and say. Peers often influence things you say and do. For example, you may wear the same styles of clothing as your peers. You may join the same activities. The influence your peers have on you is called **peer pressure**. Both words and actions are part of peer pressure.

**What is one way you have resisted peer pressure?**

Many times peer pressure is reasonable. It can even be helpful. Your friends and teammates help you meet your goals. They often encourage you to do good things. Lee just moved to a new school. Her new friends make visits to older people at a nursing home. They asked Lee to join them. Lee decided to go with her new friends.

Lee found that she enjoyed talking with older people. The visits made her feel good about herself. Peer pressure helped Lee to do something worthwhile. She did something that went along with her own beliefs. In this case, peer pressure was positive.

**Resist**
*Act against*

Sometimes you may get harmful peer pressure. Then you feel pressure to act in ways that are wrong for you. For example, Lucy planned to study in the library after school. Her friends asked her to go to a movie instead. She was afraid her friends would be angry if she studied. Even though schoolwork was important, she went to the movie. She gave in to the peer pressure by doing something that was against her beliefs.

David had history homework. The night before the homework was due, David's friend Tom called. Tom said that he had not had time to do the homework himself. He asked if he could copy David's answers. David was afraid of losing Tom as a friend. Yet David knew that cheating was wrong. He told Tom that he did not feel right about cheating. He did not let Tom copy the answers to the homework.

Peer pressure can influence a person to do something that is wrong. For example, someone might ask you to speed down a hill on your bike. Someone might dare you to do something that might hurt you. Remember that you need to act in ways that keep you safe. You need to be strong enough to **resist** this kind of peer pressure. When you resist something, you act against it.

People often use peer pressure to get you to go along with the decisions of the group. Groups can be very hard on you if you do not go along. If you do not agree with the others, they may push you out of the group. At such times, you need to stand up for your own beliefs.

Peers can be very hard on you
if you do not go along.

*Maintaining Mental Health    Chapter 5*    **109**

Have students finish reading about how peer pressure works on page 109.

**Ask:**

- When should you resist peer pressure? (when someone is trying to influence you to do something that is wrong or where you could get hurt)

- How should you respond if your peers threaten to push you out of a group because you won't go along with the others? (You should stand up for your beliefs. True friends will not abandon you just because you disagree.)

## LEARNING STYLES

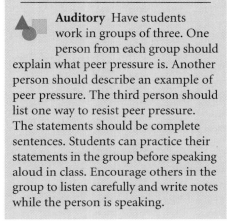

**Auditory** Have students work in groups of three. One person from each group should explain what peer pressure is. Another person should describe an example of peer pressure. The third person should list one way to resist peer pressure. The statements should be complete sentences. Students can practice their statements in the group before speaking aloud in class. Encourage others in the group to listen carefully and write notes while the person is speaking.

## APPLICATION

**Career Connection**
Ask students to write a job description for a school counselor. Their descriptions should include what they think a school counselor does. Prompt students to think about how a school counselor might help students resist harmful peer pressure. (The counselor might start an education program to encourage students to think for themselves and have self-confidence.) Discuss whether students might like to pursue this career.

Have students read about resisting peer pressure on pages 110 and 111.

Ask:

- Why do you not always need to explain your reasons for not wanting to do something? (You have the right to just say "no" or "I don't want to." If a person continues to pressure you, you can just walk away .)

- If you're not sure why your friends are asking you to do something, what should you do? (Ask questions. You have the right to know why people want you to do something.)

## MULTICULTURAL CONNECTION

Ask students to share or think about the experiences of someone who encountered prejudice because of race, nationality, religion, or cultural differences. Discuss whether peer pressure can ever influence people to act or think with prejudice. Ask students to think of some things that they can do to help eliminate prejudice and discrimination. Prompt students to think about whether positive peer pressure can influence a person to abandon a prejudiced attitude. This is a sensitive area, so model sensitivity and suggest that students also show sensitivity.

## LEARNING STYLES

**Group Learning** Have students form small groups. Tell them to prepare a short skit that shows how to use some strategies for resisting unwelcome peer pressure. Each group should have one character who is applying peer pressure and one character who is resisting it. The other characters in the skit can be anywhere in between: applying, resisting, or neutral. Allow groups to present their skits to the class and discuss the strategies.

### How Can You Resist Peer Pressure?

Learning how to deal with peer pressure is an important part of growing up. Choosing whether to go along with others is not always easy. You might be afraid you will lose friends if you do not follow them. You might be afraid that you will no longer be part of a group.

Keep in mind that true friends will respect your feelings. Your ideas will be important to them. They will understand that you need to decide for yourself. True friends will still be friends if you disagree with them.

If people pressure you to do something wrong or dangerous, you *must* resist. You can handle this kind of peer pressure in different ways. Here are some things you can do to resist peer pressure.

- Ask questions. You have the right to know why people want you to go along with them. You may not agree with their reasons. Remember that you have the right to make up your own mind.

- Express your feelings. Starting explanations with "I feel . . ." or "I think . . ." is helpful. Words such as "You just want to get me in trouble" might cause a fight. Instead, talk about your own concerns. You might say "I think I would get into trouble. I'm not going along with you."

- Try to find someone else in the group who agrees with you. It is helpful if at least one other person sees it your way. Try to guess who would be the most understanding. Then ask that person to support you. You may not be able to figure out who would be on your side. You still can give others the idea that you are not alone. You might say "I'm not the only one who thinks this is a bad idea. I might just be the only one who will say so right now."

- You do not always need to explain your reasons. Say "no" or "I don't want to." Speak in a friendly way. Keep your voice calm. Then just walk away. People who are really your friends will not argue with you.

## PRACTICING RESPONSES TO PEER PRESSURE

The best way to respond to peer pressure is to stand up for your rights. At the same time, respect the rights of others to choose differently. It is important for your body language to match your words. That is, you have to look like you believe what you are saying. Act sure of yourself and your decisions. Here are some things you can do when you respond to peer pressure.

• Stand straight and tall. Stand two or three feet away from the other person.

• Look into the other person's eyes. Keep your eyes steady.

• Have a pleasant expression on your face. Your expression can still make it clear that you mean what you say.

• Stay calm. Try not to look nervous. Keep your hands relaxed. Do not slump your shoulders or stuff your hands in your pockets. Try not to show fear.

• Practice your responses by looking in the mirror. If you practice your responses ahead of time, you will handle peer pressure more smoothly.

• If nothing else works, leave the group. You may only need to leave for a short while. Later, people may realize that you were right. Others may decide not to pressure you any more. You may need to leave the group for good. Then remember that you did so for the right reasons. You do not need friends who do not support you. It is better to have friends who think about what is best for you.

**LESSON 3 REVIEW** Write the answers to these questions on a separate sheet of paper. Use complete sentences.

1) What are three ways peers are important to you?

2) What are two examples of positive peer pressure?

3) What are two examples of harmful peer pressure?

4) What are three ways you can resist peer pressure?

5) What can you say to a friend who keeps pressuring you to do something wrong ?

## Action for Health

Challenge students to think about a situation in which they didn't like what their peers were doing. Did they go along with the group anyway or did they say "no" and walk away? Have students take turns reading a paragraph from the feature.

## Lesson 3 Review Answers

1) Answers will vary and may include the following: Peers keep you company; they listen to you and help you do things; they give you a sense of belonging; they help you meet goals.

2) Answers will vary. Accept any two of the following: Positive peer pressure may help you to study, help you meet goals, or encourage you to do good things.

3) Harmful peer pressure discourages you from studying and encourages you to do things that are harmful or dangerous.

4) Answers will vary. Accept any three of the following: ask questions, express your own feelings and concerns, find others to agree with you, say "no," leave the group.

5) Answers will vary. Possible answer: I need to stand by my own values, and I expect my friends to respect my right to do so.

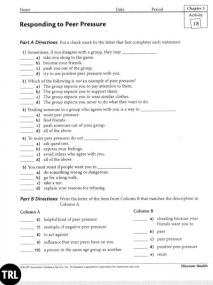

**Activity 18**

**Workbook Activity 18**

## Lesson at a Glance

### Chapter 5 Lesson 4

**Overview** This lesson discusses several eating disorders and their effects on the body.

### Objectives

- To identify eating disorders and their causes.

- To explain how to prevent or treat eating disorders.

**Student Pages** 112–114

**Audiocassette**

**Teacher's Resource Library** TRL

    Activity 19

    Workbook Activity 19

## Teaching Suggestions

### ■ Vocabulary

*anorexia, body image, eating disorder, bulimia*

Read the vocabulary words and discuss their meanings with the class. Ask students to write sentences, leaving blanks for the missing vocabulary words. Then have students exchange papers and write in the missing words.

### ■ Teaching the Lesson

Have students make a list of words that they associate with their own bodies. Tell them that this list is private and they will not share it with anyone else. Ask them if they think their words reflect something they like or don't like about their body image. Ask them to think about why they feel that way.

Have students read about eating disorders on page 112.

### Ask:

- Why might someone develop an eating disorder? (Someone might develop an eating disorder because he or she wants to have a "perfect body.")

- What are some kinds of problems caused by anorexia? (heart problems, emotional problems)

---

**Anorexia**
*An eating disorder in which a person chooses not to eat*

**Body image**
*The way each person sees himself or herself*

**Eating disorder**
*A health problem in which a person loses control over eating patterns*

During the teenage years, people develop their **body image**. Body image is the way each person sees himself or herself. Sometimes people see themselves in a positive way. In many cases, people have a negative body image.

People often get ideas about body image from the media. Most models are thin. Many young people think of a very thin body as a "perfect body." Yet few people really have this body type. When people compare themselves to an image of a "perfect body," they feel bad about themselves.

Teenagers must understand that their own bodies might never be like those of models. People naturally have bodies of many different types. A healthy, happy person looks better than a person who is unhealthy and unhappy.

### What Are Eating Disorders?

Different people have different eating habits. Most people are able to control the way they eat. Some people have serious **eating disorders**. Eating disorders cause people to lose control over their patterns of eating.

### Anorexia

A common eating disorder in the United States is **anorexia**. Anorexia is a serious disorder that happens when a person chooses not to eat. Anorexia results from emotional problems. The disorder affects girls more often than boys. Usually, people who have anorexia think they are too fat. They might begin by dieting. They eat less and less. Soon they feel full after only a few bites of food. They lose too much weight. Often, people with anorexia exercise a lot to lose more weight.

Anorexia can cause heart problems. It can even cause death. People with anorexia need to be treated by a doctor. They may need to spend time in a hospital for treatment. They also need counseling to deal with the emotional causes of the disorder.

**What can you say to a friend who is thin but always complains about being fat?**

Have students read about bulimia on page 113.

**Bulimia**
*An eating disorder in which a person eats large amounts of food and then vomits*

## Bulimia

Another common eating disorder is **bulimia**. A person who has bulimia eats large amounts of food within a short time. Then the person vomits or takes laxatives. In this way, the person gets rid of food before it is digested. Bulimia affects girls more often than boys.

Bulimia causes many health problems. The vomiting causes tooth decay because stomach acids eat away at the teeth. Many people with this disorder keep their normal weight. They might appear to be healthy. Others lose too much weight. People with this disorder do not get enough nutrients to stay healthy. They may develop heart conditions. Bulimia can lead to death. Bulimia is caused by emotional problems. People with this disorder need psychological treatment. They also need medical treatment to deal with their physical health problems.

People with anorexia think they are too fat.

### TREATMENT OF MENTAL ILLNESS

People have always been concerned about mental and emotional disorders. Ancient peoples thought evil spirits caused the problem. Holes were drilled in the person's head to let the spirits escape. Years later, healers performed magic to drive out devils. During the Middle Ages, people with mental illness were often tortured or starved to get rid of demons. At other times, people were locked up in insane asylums. These were buildings used to keep people with mental illness away from others.

Today, mental and emotional disorders are better understood. Counseling and modern medicine can be used to treat these disorders.

**Then and Now**

*Maintaining Mental Health    Chapter 5    **113***

Ask:

• Would a person with bulimia need psychological or medical treatment? (Both. The person needs psychological treatment to deal with the emotional problems that caused bulimia. The person also needs medical treatment to deal with the physical health problems caused by bulimia.)

• What are some health problems caused by bulimia? (tooth decay, malnutrition, heart problems)

## Then and Now

Invite students to discuss why people might have misunderstood and feared mental illness. Have them brainstorm a list of things that can be done to understand mental illness better. (scientific research, better education)

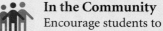

### APPLICATION

**In the Community**
Encourage students to research public and private agencies that offer support to people in your community. Students may want to find out if these agencies can help with treatment for eating disorders or other mental illnesses. Each student should choose one agency and give a report about it to the class. Invite students to use brochures or pamphlets from the agencies as visual aids for their presentations. They should include the name, address, and phone number of the agency in their report. Interested students may want to volunteer at the agency if appropriate.

## Careers

Have a volunteer read the feature. Discuss with students the importance of meeting all the needs of patients in hospitals, nursing homes, and mental health settings. Ask students how a resident assistant helps meet those needs. (Resident assistants help with the everyday needs of patients, such as checking vital signs, bathing them, serving meals, and listening to their needs.)

Have students read the section about overeating on page 114.

## Lesson 4 Review Answers

1) People get ideas about their body image through the media.
2) Anorexia can cause weight loss, heart problems, and even death.
3) People who have bulimia eat large amounts of food within a short period of time and then vomit.
4) Two kinds of treatment that can help eating disorders are medical treatment and psychological treatment.
5) You can develop a good body image by understanding that most people do not have the kind of body presented by the media and understanding the importance of a healthy body.

### GLOBAL CONNECTION

Eating disorders are a growing problem in the United States. The World Health Organization (WHO) focuses on health problems around the globe, including famine and starvation. Have students do research on eating disorders in other countries around the world. Discuss whether or not WHO should address eating disorders as a health problem.

### Careers

### RESIDENT ASSISTANT

Resident assistants work with patients in hospitals, mental health settings, and nursing homes. When patients need help, assistants answer the call. They may check patients' temperatures. They may measure blood pressure, pulse, and breathing rate. Sometimes they bathe patients. Resident assistants help people who must stay in bed or a wheelchair. They serve meals and help some patients eat. Resident assistants listen to patients and help lift their spirits. Sometimes resident assistants are called nurses' aides or nurse assistants. They may get on-the-job training or go through a training program.

### Overeating

For some people, overeating becomes a regular practice. They eat a large amount of food. They eat a lot of snacks. They often eat when they are not hungry. They seem to lose control over the way they eat.

Overeating can cause a person to be overweight. It can also lead to heart disease and many other health problems. People who overeat do not always eat healthy foods. They may not be getting good nutrition.

A person who overeats regularly should see a doctor. A doctor can help the person learn how to eat properly and lose weight. Often overeating is connected to emotional problems. Counseling can help a person deal with the causes of overeating.

**Nutrition Tip**

Eating plenty of fruits and vegetables can help you control your weight in a healthy way.

**LESSON 4 REVIEW** Write the answers to these questions on a separate sheet of paper. Use complete sentences.

1) Where do many people get ideas about their body image?
2) How does anorexia affect health?
3) What pattern of eating is part of bulimia?
4) What two kinds of treatment can help eating disorders?
5) How can you develop a good body image?

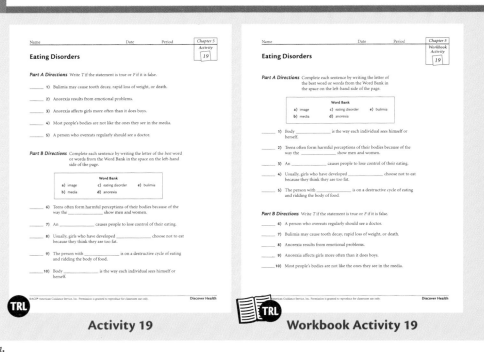

**Activity 19**

**Workbook Activity 19**

■ People become frustrated when they are blocked from achieving a goal.

■ Frustration often causes people to respond with aggression. Aggressive actions do not solve problems.

■ People who don't want to deal with their problems may withdraw.

■ Coping is dealing with a problem. One way to cope with frustration is to set reasonable goals.

■ A person can figure out what is blocking him or her from reaching a goal. Then the person can find ways to solve the problem.

■ Working harder to meet goals can help a person cope with frustration.

■ Stress can be good or bad. It can give you energy to do things. Too much stress can be harmful.

■ Threats, life changes, and hassles cause stress.

■ Physical responses, such as a fast heartbeat, are part of the stress response.

■ Wanting to fight or to flee is the second part of the stress response.

■ Keeping healthy can help a person manage stress.

■ Acting in ways to strengthen thoughts and feelings can help a person manage stress.

■ The best way to deal with anxiety is to find the reason for it and deal with it.

■ Peers often influence the way people act. Peer pressure can be positive or harmful.

■ Asking questions, expressing your feelings, and saying "no" are some ways to resist peer pressure.

■ People who have eating disorders cannot control the way they eat. Anorexia and bulimia are common eating disorders.

■ People with eating disorders need treatment for their physical and emotional health.

■ People who regularly overeat may become overweight and damage their health. Overeating is often connected to emotional health. A doctor can help people learn how to eat healthy foods and lose weight.

## ■ Using the Chapter Summary

To further reinforce the facts and concepts presented in the chapter, read and discuss with students the questions that follow.

### Ask:

• Why doesn't acting childish, stamping your feet, and crying solve problems? (because it does not deal with fixing the problem or removing the things that block your goals)

• How does setting reasonable goals help to reduce frustration? (Being able to achieve a goal creates positive feelings instead of frustration.)

• What could you do if you didn't have enough money to buy something you wanted? (You could work to earn money to buy it.)

• What can happen when stressful situations happen again and again? (A person can become exhausted and prone to illness.)

• Why should you find the reason for a stressful situation? (because knowing the reason can help you deal with the problem)

• Why do people give in to peer pressure? (because they want to be liked and accepted or are afraid of refusing)

• What are some ways to resist peer pressure? (asking questions, expressing your feelings, reasoning with individuals, saying "no," or just leaving)

• Why might people have a poor body image? (They may compare themselves to models or others who look different than they do. People should accept that there are many different body types and they do not need to change theirs.)

• How can eating disorders be treated? (People with eating disorders should get psychological help to deal with emotional problems. They also need medical treatment for the harm the eating disorder has done to their bodies.)

# Chapter 5 Review

The Teacher's Resource Library includes two parallel forms of the Chapter 5 Mastery Test. The difficulty level of the two forms is equivalent. You may wish to use one form as a pretest and the other form as a posttest.

## Review Answers

### Comprehension: Identifying Facts

1) eating disorder  2) Frustration
3) withdraw  4) stress response
5) Self-esteem  6) bulimia  7) Aggression

## Comprehension: Identifying Facts

On a separate sheet of paper, write the correct word or words from the Word Bank to complete each sentence.

| WORD BANK | |
|---|---|
| aggression | peer |
| anorexia | peer pressure |
| anxiety | resist |
| body image | self-esteem |
| bulimia | stress response |
| cope | threat |
| eating disorder | withdraw |
| frustration | |

1) A health problem in which a person loses control over his or her eating is called an _____.

2) _____ is an unpleasant feeling that happens when a person is blocked from meeting goals.

3) Sometimes people pull away, or _____, when they feel frustrated.

4) The _____ is the body's physical signs of stress.

5) _____ is how a person feels about himself or herself.

6) People who eat large amounts of food and then vomit have an eating disorder called _____.

7) _____ is any act that is a common response to frustration.

---

**Chapter 5 Mastery Test A**

Name _____ Date _____ Period _____ | Chapter 5 Mastery Test A page 1

**Chapter 5 Mastery Test A**

**Directions** Circle the letter of the answer that *best* completes each sentence.

1) Frustration happens when you are blocked from meeting your _____
   a) mistakes.
   b) goals.
   c) time.
   d) aggression.

2) The positive way to respond to frustration is to _____
   a) yell.
   b) whine.
   c) withdraw.
   d) cope.

3) A way to cope with frustration is to _____
   a) set reasonable goals.
   b) act aggressively.
   c) withdraw from the situation.
   d) cry.

4) Threats, life changes, and hassles are common causes of _____
   a) goals.
   b) self-esteem.
   c) stress.
   d) coping.

5) Wanting to fight or flee is the second part of the _____
   a) perspiration.
   b) stress response.
   c) anxiety.
   d) self-esteem.

6) Dealing with stress over a long period of time may lead to _____
   a) health problems.
   b) aggression.
   c) coping.
   d) withdrawal.

7) When a person has _____, he or she may feel nervous, afraid, and uncomfortable.
   a) goals
   b) time
   c) aggression
   d) anxiety

Name _____ Date _____ Period _____ | Chapter 5 Mastery Test A page 2

**Chapter 5 Mastery Test A, continued**

8) Your friends and other people close to your age are called your _____
   a) toddlers.
   b) baby boomers.
   c) peers.
   d) groups.

9) Going to a movie when asked by your friends, instead of studying when you should is an example of _____
   a) peer pressure.
   b) resistance.
   c) stress.
   d) anxiety.

10) When peers pressure you to do something wrong or dangerous, you may resist by _____
   a) going along with them.
   b) expressing your feelings.
   c) fighting.
   d) saying "yes."

11) _____ is the way each person sees himself or herself.
   a) Eating disorder
   b) Peer pressure
   c) Anxiety
   d) Body image

12) _____ is a serious eating disorder that happens when a person chooses not to eat.
   a) Body image
   b) Anorexia
   c) Bulimia
   d) Peer pressure

13) People with eating disorders need treatment for their _____ and physical health.
   a) emotional
   b) bulimia
   c) body image
   d) stress

14) An eating disorder in which a person eats large amounts of food and then vomits is called _____
   a) anorexia.
   b) obesity.
   c) bulimia.
   d) self-esteem.

15) The best way to deal with anxiety is _____
   a) to act aggressively.
   b) to find the reason and deal with it.
   c) to break down and cry.
   d) to procrastinate.

**Chapter 5 Mastery Test A**

**8)** _____ is a feeling like fear for which the reasons are not clear.

**9)** _____ is the way a person sees himself or herself.

**10)** A _____ is a person in the same age group.

**11)** When you _____ something, you act against it or withstand it.

**12)** A _____ is a situation that seems dangerous.

**13)** _____ is the influence people of the same age have on one another.

**14)** When you _____ with a problem, you deal with it.

**15)** A person with _____ chooses not to eat.

## Comprehension: Understanding Main Ideas

Write the answers to these questions on a separate sheet of paper. Use complete sentences.

**16)** What physical reactions are part of the stress response?

**17)** What are three harmful responses to frustration?

**18)** What are two ways in which peer pressure can be helpful?

## Critical Thinking: Write Your Opinion

**19)** How can learning to set reasonable goals help you?

**20)** How can resisting peer pressure affect your self-esteem?

**Test Taking Tip**  Sometimes it is easier to learn new vocabulary words if you make them a part of your speaking and writing in other discussions and subject areas.

*Maintaining Mental Health    Chapter 5*    **117**

---

**8)** Anxiety  **9)** Body image  **10)** peer
**11)** resist  **12)** threat  **13)** Peer pressure
**14)** cope  **15)** anorexia

## Comprehension: Understanding Main Ideas

**16)** During the first part of the stress response, your heart beats faster. Your breathing speeds up. You perspire and your muscles get tight. You may blush or cry out. Sometimes people have headaches or stomach pains. They may feel nervous. Some people may not be able to sleep well. The second part of the stress response takes one of two forms: fight or flight. During the third part, you feel exhausted.

**17)** Three harmful responses to frustration are aggression, acting childish, and withdrawing.

**18)** Peer pressure can help you act in positive ways such as studying harder or doing things for others.

## Critical Thinking: Write Your Opinion

**19)** Learning to set reasonable goals can help you avoid situations in which you fail to meet goals and can help you feel better about yourself.

**20)** Resisting peer pressure helps you feel stronger and better about yourself.

---

**Chapter 5 Mastery Test B**

**Chapter 5 Mastery Test B**

*Maintaining Mental Health    Chapter 5*    **117**

## Chapter 6:
### Relationships
pages 118–131

### Lessons

**Audiocassette**

**Teacher's Resource Library**

Activities 20–22

Workbook Activities 20–22

Student Study Guide 12 pages 1–2

Chapter 6 Mastery Tests A and B

(Answer Keys for the Teacher's
Resource Library begin on page 433
of this Teacher's Edition.)

## *Introducing the Chapter*

Have students brainstorm a list of words
they associate with the word *relationship*.
Write students' suggestions and discuss
them. Save the list to compare with
students' ideas about relationships at
the end of the chapter.

Have volunteers read page 118 aloud,
including the Goals for Learning.

### Ask:

- **What do emotionally healthy people have?** (Emotionally healthy people have good relationships with themselves and others.)

- **What can healthy relationships do?** (Healthy relationships can help your outlook on life and have a positive effect on your mental health.)

## Chapter 6

# Relationships

Emotionally healthy people have good relationships
with themselves and others. Getting to know yourself
and thinking about your values can make a difference
in your well-being. Having healthy relationships can help
your outlook on life. It can have a positive effect on your
mental health.

In this chapter, you will learn about being a friend to yourself.
You will find out about things you can do to make friends
with others. You will also learn about relationships and what
makes them healthy.

### Goals for Learning
▶ To learn how to be a good friend to yourself
▶ To explain what you can do to make and keep friends
▶ To describe what makes a relationship healthy

---

Name _____ Date _____ Period _____ | Chapter 6 / Student Study Guide / **12** / *page 1*

**Chapter 6 Relationships**

***Directions*** Fill in the outline below. Filling in the blanks will help you
as you read and study Relationships.

**I. Lesson 1 (pp. 119–21)**
  A. Being a Friend to Yourself
    1. The two things you can do to be a friend to yourself are talking _____ to
        yourself and treating yourself _____.
    2. _____ is what you say to yourself.
    3. Using words such as "_____" and "_____" can lead to harmful
        self-talk.
    4. When you feel proud of what you've done, remember to _____ yourself.
    5. Spending some time _____ with yourself is a way to be good to yourself.

**II. Lesson 2 (pp. 122–24)**
  A. Making Friends
    1. Choosing friends who have traits you _____ is important when considering
        the kind of personality traits you look up to.
    2. Friends usually have things in _____.
    3. You will find lasting friends when you stand up for your own _____.
    4. When you first meet someone, you may make _____ talk as a way to get to
        know that person.
    5. Being a good _____ means paying attention to what the other person is
        saying.
    6. After you've gotten to know someone, you may ask the person to _____
        _____ with you to take the next step in friendship.
    7. A true friend does not _____ a person to act in a certain way.

AGS® American Guidance Service, Inc. Permission is granted to reproduce for classroom use only.      **Discover Health**

**Student Study Guide 12, page 1**

---

Name _____ Date _____ Period _____ | Chapter 6 / Student Study Guide / **12** / *page 2*

**III. Lesson 3 (pp. 125–28)**
  A. Healthy Relationships
    1. It is important to take time _____ in a healthy relationship.
    2. You have a right to say what you _____ to your friend.
    3. You and your friend will give and receive _____ in a healthy relationship.
    4. In a healthy relationship, you will stand up for your _____.
    5. A person who is _____ feels uncomfortable around others.
    6. Asking people questions about _____ shows that you are interested in
        them.
    7. Staying away from _____ shows that you appreciate your friends.
    8. If a friendship ends, the best way to get through it is to be a _____ to
        yourself.

AGS® American Guidance Service, Inc. Permission is granted to reproduce for classroom use only.      **Discover Health**

**Student Study Guide 12, page 2**

## Lesson 1 — Being a Friend to Yourself

**Bond**
*An emotional feeling of closeness*

*T*hink about your friends. You probably are different from one another in many ways. Yet you probably have many things in common. You may be interested in the same things. You may laugh at the same things. You and your friends have a **bond**. A bond is an emotional feeling of closeness.

Your friends help you meet some needs. One of these needs is the need to belong. Friends help you look at things in new ways. They listen to you and give you support. Sometimes they help you decide what do. Friends share your happy feelings and your sad ones. They also allow you to do good for others.

### Why Should You Be Your Own Best Friend?
Before you can be friends with others, you must be a friend to yourself. There are two things you can do to be a friend to yourself. First, you can talk nicely to yourself. Second, you can treat yourself kindly.

### Talking Nicely to Yourself
Think about your self-talk. Your self-talk is what you say to yourself. Are you friendly to yourself? Do you tend to put yourself down?

You might use the words "should," "ought," or "must" too often. You might say "I should be the best student in the class." You may not be able to reach such a goal. Yet you do not need to put yourself down. You can change your self-talk in a positive way. You could say "I study hard in school. I work as hard as I can. I am a good student."

**What are some things you can say to yourself after you do well on a test?**

You might feel you don't do something as well as someone else. Instead, feel proud of what you do. Try not say things such as "I will never be as popular as he is." Instead, you could say "Acting polite and kind to others helps me make friends. My friends and I are important to one another."

---

*Relationships    Chapter 6*    **119**

---

### Lesson at a Glance

#### Chapter 6  Lesson 1
**Overview** This lesson describes how to be a friend to yourself.

**Objective**
- To explain how to be your own best friend.

**Student Pages** 119–121
**Audiocassette**
**Teacher's Resource Library**

Activity 20
Workbook Activity 20

### Teaching Suggestions

■ **Vocabulary**
*bond*

Read the vocabulary word and discuss its meaning with the class. Then ask students to name relationships to which the word would apply.

■ **Teaching the Lesson**
Allow each student to practice improving self-talk by coming up with alternative statements that use positive self-talk. For example, "I should be the best student in the class" can be restated to "I'm doing the best I can in this class."

Have students read about why you should be your own best friend on page 119.

Ask:

- What are two things you can do to be a friend to yourself? (You can talk nicely to yourself and you can treat yourself kindly.)

Have students finish reading about why you should be your own best friend on page 120.

Ask:

- What can you do if you think too much about things you don't like about yourself? (You can think about things you do like about yourself.)

- How can you make your self-talk more helpful? (You can think about the kinds of mistakes you make, catch yourself if your self-talk is a put-down, say something in a positive way instead, or compliment yourself whenever you feel proud of what you do.)

## BACKGROUND INFORMATION

People's emotional health depends on attaining peace with themselves. We can cultivate inner peace by spending time alone.

## LEARNING STYLES

**Tactile/Kinesthetic** Have students cut letters from construction paper and use the letters to create examples of positive self-talk. Invite students to combine their examples by mounting them on poster board. Display the poster in the classroom.

## LEARNING STYLES

**LEP/ESL** Invite students to make a collage or other visual representation of actions that promote good health. Ask students to share and discuss their work with the class.

*Health Tip*

**Take time for yourself. Then you can get to know yourself better. You can think of all the things you like about yourself.**

You might blame yourself for something that is not your fault. Some teenagers say "If I were better, my parents would not be getting a divorce." Instead of putting themselves down, the teenagers could say "I feel sad about my parents' divorce. I know it is not my fault."

You might make a big deal out of something that goes wrong. You might say "I really blew that test. Nothing is going right." You can change your way of thinking. You could say "I did not do well on that test. I can study harder. I can do better on the next test."

You might sometimes think too much about things you don't like about yourself. You might say "I don't know enough about interesting things. I'm boring." Thinking about things you do like about yourself is more useful. You could say "I'd like to learn more about that subject. I'll read about it."

Using words such as "never" and "always" can lead to harmful self-talk. You might say "I'm always messing up." It would be more useful to say "I made a mistake. Making mistakes is okay. I'll try to learn from my mistake."

To make your self-talk helpful, think about the kinds of mistakes you make. Try to catch yourself if your self-talk is a put-down. Then say something in a positive way instead. Remember to compliment yourself whenever you feel proud of what you do.

Remember to compliment yourself when you look or feel good.

## Action for Health

### CREATE YOUR OWN SUPPORT SYSTEM

An important part of mental health is having support. You need to be able to provide support for yourself. You can get ready ahead of time for times when you feel down.

Make a list of things you can do to deal with problems. For example, write down ideas such as "talk it over," or "ask for help." Make sure the names of your close friends and their phone numbers are on your list. Look at your list whenever you have been hurt. Call one of the friends on your list if you need to talk about a problem.

### Doing Nice Things for Yourself

To be good to yourself, you need to spend some time alone with yourself. Ask yourself every day how you are doing. If you feel sad, use self-talk to cheer yourself up. If you feel good, say something nice about yourself. Give yourself a compliment.

Taking care of your health is an important way to be good to yourself. Eating a healthy diet and exercising every day are two things you can do. Practicing good hygiene will help you feel good. Getting enough rest will also help keep you healthy. Remember that you are responsible for meeting your own needs. Taking care of yourself is an important part of having a friendship with yourself.

**LESSON 1 REVIEW** Write the answers to these questions on a separate sheet of paper. Use complete sentences.

1) How do friends help you meet your needs?
2) What are two things you can do to be a friend to yourself?
3) What are three ways you can make your self-talk positive?
4) What are two nice things you can do for yourself?
5) Suppose you and your sister try out for the soccer team. Your sister makes the team. You do not. How can you use positive self-talk to help yourself feel better?

*Relationships    Chapter 6*    **121**

---

## Action for Health

Emphasize that feeling discouraged or sad is normal. Ask volunteers to suggest things people can do to help themselves when they are feeling down. Write students' ideas on the chalkboard. Then read the feature aloud and ask students to complete the activity individually.

Have students read about doing nice things for yourself on page 121.

### Ask:

- What things can you do to take care of your health? (eat a healthy diet, exercise every day, practice good hygiene, get enough rest, meet your own needs)

### Lesson 1 Review Answers

1) Friends help meet the need to belong by doing the following: help you look at things in new ways, listen to you and give you support, share happy and sad feelings, allow you to do good for others.
2) Two things you can do to be a friend to yourself are to talk nicely to yourself and to treat yourself kindly.
3) Accept any three of the following: don't put yourself down; feel proud of what you do; avoid blaming yourself for things that are not your fault; do not make a big deal out of something that goes wrong; think about things you like about yourself; know that making mistakes is okay; compliment yourself.
4) Two nice things you can do for yourself are spending time alone and taking care of your health.
5) Answers will vary and might include not putting yourself down, thinking about the things you do well, and remembering the things you like about yourself.

### GLOBAL CONNECTION

Ask students to research ways in which volunteers of the Red Cross help in other parts of the world. Interested students may want to find out more about the skills required for volunteers of the Red Cross.

---

# Lesson at a Glance

## Chapter 6 Lesson 2

**Overview** This lesson explains the things that are important in friendships and suggests ways to make friends.

### Objectives

■ To explain the importance of values.

■ To describe what you can do to make and keep friends.

**Student Pages** 122–124

**Audiocassette** 🎧

**Teacher's Resource Library** **TRL**

    Activity 21

    Workbook Activity 21

## Teaching Suggestions

### ■ Vocabulary

*small talk*

Ask students if they have heard the vocabulary word. Encourage them to explain what they think the term means. Then read the definition from the textbook. Have students decide if their definition was close to the textbook definition.

### ■ Teaching the Lesson

Invite students to describe their relationship with their best friend in a poem or journal entry. Ask volunteers to share their description with the class.

Have students read about the kinds of friends you need and the importance of values on page 122.

### Ask:

· What are some values you would want in your friends? (Answers will vary and might include not using drugs or cigarettes, being honest, showing kindness to people and animals, and so forth. Accept all reasonable answers.)

---

## Lesson 2

## *Making Friends*

*T*he first step in making friends is to be a good friend to yourself. Your friendship with yourself needs to be strong. Then you will be able to reach out to others. In this lesson, you will learn how to make friends.

### What Kinds of Friends Do You Need?

Think about the kinds of people who make you feel comfortable. Do you like people who are loud or people who are quiet? Do you like being with large groups? Would you rather do things with only one or two people? Feeling relaxed and comfortable with friends is important.

Consider the kind of personality traits you look up to. You might say that a sense of humor is important. Loyalty and trust might be the most important things to you. You will want to choose friends who have traits you respect.

Also think about the part of your life in which you most need friends. Do you want to make more friends at school? Do you want to make more friends in your neighborhood? Maybe you want to make friends who enjoy the same sports you do. Friends usually have things in common. They often like the same things. They often enjoy the same activities.

### Importance of Values

You have thought about the kinds of people you want for friends. You also need to think about your own values. Choosing friends who have the same values as you is important. For example, you know that you want to be drug free. Choosing friends who stay away from drugs would be best for you.

Keep in mind what you believe is right and good. For example, you may feel strongly about treating all people equally. You would not want to join a group that makes fun of others. By standing up for your own values, you will find lasting friends.

#### Fitness Tip

Exercising is a good way to spend time with friends. In this way, you do something together that you enjoy. You also do something that is good for your health.

What are some values that you and your friends have in common?

---

## Forming Friendships

To find friends who like sports, you can go to a local park.

Once you know the kinds of friends you need, you can look for friends. You can let others know you are interested in being friends. Suppose you would like to meet new people in your neighborhood. You especially want to find friends who like sports. You might begin by going to a local park or gym. There you can meet people who also like sports. If you act friendly to people, chances are they'll be friendly to you, too.

**Small talk**
*Talk about things that are interesting but not important*

You may begin by making **small talk** with people. Small talk is talk about things that are interesting but not very important. You might ask for help or give a compliment. You might point out something you noticed. You might ask if you can join in an activity. Remember to be positive. If you practice what to say ahead of time, you will feel calmer. Your pleasant manner will lead people to want to know you better.

You can let the other person know you are interested in him or her. Being a good listener is important. A good listener pays attention to what the other person is saying. Looking at the person is a sign that you are interested. Ask questions from time to time. Let the speaker finish before you talk. You also might lean a little bit toward the person who is speaking. If you smile, the other person will feel comfortable.

### Writing About Health

Think about what you want to find out when you get to know a person. List the things you think are important.

Once you feel relaxed talking with a person, take the next step in friendship. Ask the person to spend time with you. Sharing activities gives you a chance to learn about each other.

Have students read about forming friendships on page 123.

Ask:

- What is small talk? (Small talk is talk about things that are interesting but not very important.)

- How can you let the other person know you are interested in him or her? (be a good listener, look at the person, ask questions from time to time, lean a bit toward the person who is speaking, smile)

### LEARNING STYLES

**Tactile/Kinesthetic** Suggest students work in small groups to role-play approaching new people as potential friends. Students can take turns acting as the person communicating a desire for friendship. Other members of the group can act as people who know each other already. After the activity, discuss as a class how it felt to practice communicating a desire for friendship.

## Careers

Call on a volunteer to read the feature to the class. Then discuss personal qualities and communication skills that would be important for a residential counselor to have.

Have students read page 124 to find out how to treat a friend.

### Ask:

• If you begin a friendship, what can you do to keep that new friend? (You can treat your friend nicely, say things that help your new friend feel good, respect your friend's rights, do not force your ideas on him or her, do not pressure your friend to act a certain way, respect the decisions your friend makes.)

### Lesson 2 Review Answers

1) Accept any three of the following: a kind of person who makes you feel comfortable, personality traits that are important to you, things in common, values that are the same as yours.

2) By standing up for your beliefs, you will find lasting friends.

3) You could join activities for people who have interests similar to yours.

4) Accept any of the following: pays attention to what the other person is saying, looks at the person who is speaking, asks questions from time to time, lets the speaker finish before he or she talks, leans a little bit toward the person who is speaking, smiles.

5) You can be a good friend to another person by thinking about the other person's needs, feelings, and interests; by treating your friend nicely; and by respecting your friend's rights.

### APPLICATION

**In the Community**
Have students research public agencies that offer support to people in your community. Ask each student to choose one agency and give a report about it to the class. Encourage students to use brochures or pamphlets from the agency as visual aids for their presentation.

---

### RESIDENTIAL COUNSELOR

Residential counselors help small groups of people handle their problems. The counselors may live with these groups in halfway houses. Halfway houses help people who are recovering from substance abuse. The counselors may also spend time with people in crisis shelters. People who are abused get help in crisis shelters. Residential counselors give emotional support to people. They help the people learn how to live on their own. Counselors supervise other people who work at the houses or shelters. A residential counselor must have training and be certified. Usually a counselor needs to have two to four years of college.

If you begin a friendship, remember to treat your new friend nicely. You can say things that help your friend feel good. You might thank your friend for coming over. You might say "I had a great time." You might thank your friend for listening. You could say "Thanks for understanding how I feel."

Also respect your friend's rights. Your friend has a right to ideas that are different from yours. You will get along better if you do not force your ideas on others. A true friend does not pressure a person to act in a certain way. If you are a friend, you will respect the decisions the other person makes.

**LESSON 2 REVIEW** Write the answers to these questions on a separate sheet of paper. Use complete sentences.

1) What are three things you need to look for in a friend?

2) How can standing up for your beliefs help you find lasting friends?

3) How can you meet people who have the same interests as you?

4) What are two ways to be a good listener?

5) How can you be a good friend to another person?

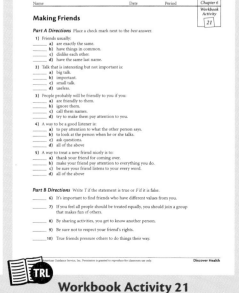

**Activity 21**

**Workbook Activity 21**

## Healthy Relationships

**Relationship**
*A connection between people*

Everyone has a need to belong with people. To meet that need, people have **relationships**. A relationship is a connection to another person. You have relationships with people in your family. You have other relationships, such as those with friends. Having healthy relationships can help keep you happy.

### What Makes a Relationship Healthy?
People in healthy relationships act in certain ways. They accept each other's differences. They also respect each other's values. A person in a healthy relationship thinks about the rights of the other person. The needs of the other person are important.

### Differences Between People
Usually you become friends with people who have something in common with you. You may enjoy doing the same things. Yet, each person has his or her own life.

Perhaps you want to go somewhere alone without inviting your friend. Time alone is important in a healthy relationship. Every person needs time to do things on his or her own. Every person grows and changes as time goes on. Healthy relationships allow people to be themselves.

### Your Rights, Needs, and Values
Your rights, needs, and values are important. A healthy relationship will respect these parts of you. You need to make sure your rights, needs, and values are being respected. Asking yourself the following questions can help you:

#### Your rights
• Can I say what I think to my friend?

• Does my friend like me for who I am instead of wishing I were different?

• Can I make my own decisions without getting pressure from my friend?

---

**Ask:**

• List some ways in which people in a healthy relationship act. (They accept each other's differences, respect each other's values, and think about the rights and needs of the other person.)

## Chapter 6  Lesson 3
**Overview** This lesson describes healthy relationships and how rights, needs, and values contribute to relationships.

### Objectives
■ To explain what makes a relationship healthy.

■ To explain what makes friendship difficult.

■ To explain what to do when a friendship doesn't work.

**Student Pages** 125–128

**Audiocassette**

**Teacher's Resource Library**

Activity 22

Workbook Activity 22

## Teaching Suggestions

### ■ Vocabulary
*relationship, shyness, gossip*

Have students work in small groups to create skits in which each vocabulary word is used. Invite groups to present their skits to the class.

### ■ Teaching the Lesson
Have students name characteristics of a healthy relationship. Write the characteristics in a word web like the one below.

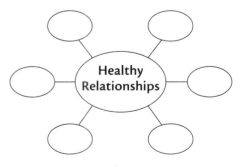

Have students read about what makes a healthy relationship on page 125.

Have students read about needs and values in a relationship on page 126.

## Ask:

- What are some ways to show a friend you appreciate him or her? (Answers will vary. Accept all reasonable answers.)

- What do you think are some ways friends support each other's values and beliefs? (Answers will vary, depending on students' relationships with others. Accept any reasonable response.)

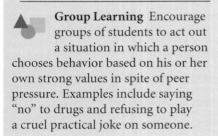

## LEARNING STYLES

**Group Learning** Encourage groups of students to act out a situation in which a person chooses behavior based on his or her own strong values in spite of peer pressure. Examples include saying "no" to drugs and refusing to play a cruel practical joke on someone.

## MULTICULTURAL CONNECTION

Invite students to research the experiences of someone who encountered prejudice because of race, nationality, religion, or cultural differences. Then ask students what they can do to help eliminate prejudice and discrimination. This is a sensitive area, so model sensitivity and suggest to students that they also show sensitivity.

## BACKGROUND INFORMATION

Communication can be nonverbal. For example, sympathy can be communicated by touch. A friendly greeting can be communicated by looking at a person in the eye, smiling, or shaking hands. Facial expressions, body movements, and posture are all forms of body language that communicate feelings to others.

### Your Needs
- Do I feel comfortable with my friend?
- Do I give and receive equally in this friendship?
- Do my friend and I have fun safely?
- Do my friend and I show that we appreciate each other?

### Your Values
- Do my friend and I share many of the same values?
- Do my friend and I respect our own and each other's values?
- Do we each choose to stand up for our values?
- Does my friend support my values and beliefs? Do I support my friend's values and beliefs?

If you can answer "yes" to most of these questions, your friendship is healthy. If you have some "no" answers, you need to think about your friendship. Maybe you can talk with your friend about these questions.

Make friends with people who enjoy the same sports you do.

### CHANGES IN FAMILIES

A Finnish scientist, Alexander Westermarck, suggested that people lived in family groups in prehistoric times. Over the years, family life has changed. For example, years ago, children, parents, grandparents, and other family members usually lived in the same place. In modern times, family members often move far away from one another.

Family members can still remain close. Modern technology has made it easier for people to keep in touch with one another. People talk to each other over the phone. They can keep in touch by using computers. Today family members can remain close even if they live far away from one another.

---

**Shyness**
*Feelings of discomfort around others*

## What Can Make Friendship Difficult?

Sometimes making and keeping friends is not easy. One thing that makes it hard for some people to make friends is **shyness**. People who are shy feel uncomfortable around others. They may feel nervous. They may not try to meet new friends. Other people might think a shy person is stuck-up.

Many people feel shy from time to time. If you feel shy much of the time, you can overcome the shyness. You might work with someone you trust to deal with the shyness. You can practice ways to talk to others.

Remember that most people like to talk about themselves. Asking people questions about themselves shows your interest in them. For example, you might ask someone how long he or she has lived in the area. Asking for other people's ideas makes them feel important. You might ask questions such as "What do you think of the new math teacher?" Giving compliments to others helps them feel good. You might say such things such as "You are a good soccer player. Maybe you could give me some tips." When people answer your questions, they will probably start to feel comfortable around you. Then they might want to get to know you better.

---

## Then and Now

Invite students to discuss ways they keep in touch with relatives (mail, e-mail, telephone call). Challenge students to think of ways people might keep in touch with families in the future.

Have students read about what can make friendship difficult on page 127.

### Ask:

- What makes it hard for some people to make friends? (shyness)

- How do people who are shy feel? (uncomfortable around others, nervous)

- How can a person overcome shyness? (practice ways to talk to others)

### APPLICATION

**Career Connection**
Ask students to write a job description for a school counselor. The description should include what students think a school counselor does. Then ask for volunteers to interview one of the school counselors. Have the volunteers report on the interview to the class. Let students revise their job descriptions based on the new information.

Have students read about gossip and what to do when a relationship doesn't work on page 128.

Ask:

- What are some ways to be your own best friend? (talk honestly with yourself, appreciate yourself, take care of yourself)

## Lesson 3 Review Answers

1) Answers will vary. Accept any of the following: allowing each other to spend time alone and allowing each person to be himself or herself; accepting differences; respecting each other's values, rights, and needs.

2) You have the right to say what you think, the right to be liked for who you are, and the right to make your own decisions.

3) Two things that can make it hard to make and keep friends are shyness and gossip.

4) To get through a painful time when a friendship ends, be a friend to yourself, talk honestly with yourself, appreciate yourself, take care of yourself, and talk to a caring person.

5) If you feel that your friend does not respect your values, talk to your friend about it. Try to work through the problems. If necessary, spend less time in the relationship.

## APPLICATION

### Environment
Challenge students to list environments that might cause gossip to occur. Examples might include work situations, new students at school, new family in the neighborhood, and so forth.

## APPLICATION

### At Home
Invite students to investigate why friendships sometimes fail. Encourage students to find an older friend, family member, or relative who is willing to discuss a failed relationship. Have students share the information with the class.

---

**Gossip**
*The spreading of rumors, usually untrue, about people*

A problem in keeping friends is **gossip**. Gossip is the spreading of rumors or ideas about people. Rumors are not always true. Usually, rumors are about people who are not around to hear what is being said. Gossip can be hurtful. It takes away people's trust. Staying away from gossip shows that you appreciate your friends. Its also shows that you value honesty.

### What Can You Do When a Relationship Doesn't Work?

Sometimes, friendships end. A painful time usually follows. You might feel sad or lonely. You might feel that you failed. The best way to get through this time is to be a friend to yourself. Remember the friendship you have with yourself will last a lifetime. Here are some ways to be your own best friend:

- Talk honestly with yourself. Think about your feelings. Remind yourself that your feelings are normal. Use self-talk to say nice things to yourself.

- Appreciate yourself. Do something you like to do. Give yourself a special treat. Remember to tell yourself what a good person you are.

- Take care of yourself. Eat well, get plenty of rest, and exercise.

You might also want to talk to a caring person about how you feel. Talking to someone is especially important if you are unhappy for several weeks. It also is important if your feelings are very strong. Getting help when you need it is another way of being a good friend to yourself.

**What do you think your friends like about you?**

**LESSON 3 REVIEW** Write the answers to these questions on a separate sheet of paper. Use complete sentences.

1) What is one sign of a healthy relationship?

2) What are two rights you have in a friendship?

3) What are two things that can make it hard to make and keep friends?

4) How can you get through a painful time when a friendship ends?

5) What should you do if you feel that your friend does not respect your values?

---

Name _____ Date _____ Period _____

Chapter 6
Activity
22

**Healthy Relationships**

**Directions** Write *T* if the statement is true or *F* if it is false.

_____ 1) When you are uncomfortable around others, you are shy.

_____ 2) Gossip is positive rumors about someone.

_____ 3) When a relationship ends, be a friend to yourself.

_____ 4) Others might think a shy person is very friendly.

_____ 5) A healthy relationship respects your rights, needs, and values.

_____ 6) Friends need to do everything together.

_____ 7) A good relationship will allow you to be yourself.

_____ 8) Show your interest in others by waiting for them to ask lots of questions about you.

_____ 9) Spreading rumors about a person is a great way to make friends with that person.

_____ 10) A relationship is a connection between people.

©AGS® American Guidance Service, Inc. Permission is granted to reproduce for classroom use only.          Discover Health

**Activity 22**

---

Name _____ Date _____ Period _____

Chapter 6
Workbook
Activity
22

**Healthy Relationships**

**Directions** Write *T* if the statement is true or *F* if it is false.

_____ 1) A relationship is a connection between people.

_____ 2) When you are uncomfortable around others, you are shy.

_____ 3) Gossip is positive rumors about someone.

_____ 4) When a relationship ends, be a friend to yourself.

_____ 5) Others might think a shy person is very friendly.

_____ 6) A healthy relationship respects your rights, needs, and values.

_____ 7) Friends need to do everything together.

_____ 8) A good relationship will allow you to be yourself.

_____ 9) Show your interest in others by waiting for them to ask lots of questions about you.

_____ 10) Spreading rumors about a person is a great way to make friends with that person.

©AGS® American Guidance Service, Inc. Permission is granted to reproduce for classroom use only.          Discover Health

**Workbook Activity 22**

■ Friendship is a special bond between people.

■ Before you can be a friend to others, you need to be a friend to yourself.

■ To be a friend to yourself, you can learn to use positive self-talk. You can also do nice things for yourself every day.

■ Spending time alone with yourself and eating well, exercising, and getting enough rest are important.

■ Before making friends, a person needs to decide what kinds of friends he or she needs.

■ Choosing friends who share your values and have common interests is important.

■ Showing interest in others, asking questions, and listening to others can help a person make friends.

■ Showing friends that you appreciate them and respecting a friend's rights are important.

■ Healthy relationships are important to a person's happiness.

■ In healthy relationships, friends allow each other to be themselves. A friend respects the other person's rights, needs, and values.

■ Friends often can talk about their problems and work them out.

■ Asking people questions about themselves shows your interest in them. It also helps them feel comfortable.

■ Gossip is often hurtful to others. Spreading gossip can damage a friendship.

■ People usually feel sad and lonely when a friendship ends.

■ Remembering to be your own best friend helps you when a friendship ends.

---

## ■ Using the Chapter Summary

To further reinforce the facts and concepts presented in the chapter, read and discuss with students the questions that follow.

### Ask:

- What is friendship? (a special bond between people)

- How can you be a friend to yourself? (You can use positive self-talk and do nice things for yourself.)

- What should you decide before making friends? (Before making friends, decide what kinds of friends you need.)

- What can help a person make friends? (Showing interest in others, asking questions, and listening to others can help a person make friends.)

- What is a healthy relationship? (In a healthy relationship, friends allow each other to be themselves. A friend respects the other person's rights, needs, and values.)

- What can you do to show people you are interested in them? (You can ask questions and smile to make the other person feel comfortable.)

- How do people usually feel when a friendship ends? (sad and lonely)

- When a friendship ends, what is one thing to remember? (to be your own best friend)

## Chapter 6 Review

The Teacher's Resource Library includes two parallel forms of the Chapter 6 Mastery Test. The difficulty level of the two forms is equivalent. You may wish to use one form as a pretest and the other form as a posttest.

### Review Answers

#### Comprehension: Identifying Facts

**1)** small talk  **2)** Gossip  **3)** relationship
**4)** shy  **5)** bond  **6)** self-talk  **7)** values
**8)** Exercising  **9)** needs  **10)** time

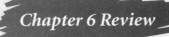
### Comprehension: Identifying Facts

On a separate sheet of paper, write the correct word or words from the Word Bank to complete each sentence.

| WORD BANK | |
|---|---|
| bond | self-talk |
| exercising | shy |
| gossip | small talk |
| needs | time |
| relationship | values |

1) Making _____ is one way to start a conversation with another person.

2) _____ usually happens when a person who is being talked about is not there.

3) Friends who have a healthy _____ respect each other's values.

4) People who are _____ often feel nervous or uncomfortable around others.

5) Friends have a special _____ , or feeling of closeness with each other.

6) Positive _____ helps you be a good friend to yourself.

7) Choosing friends who have the same _____ as you is important.

8) _____ is something healthy you can do for yourself every day.

9) Your values and _____ are important in a friendship.

10) You need to spend _____ with yourself.

---

**Chapter 6 Mastery Test A**

## Comprehension: Understanding Main Ideas

Write the answers to the following questions on a separate sheet of paper. Use complete sentences.

11) What is an example of a way you can change a put-down to positive self-talk?

12) How can spending time alone be a good thing to do for yourself?

13) What kind of personality traits should you look for in a friend?

14) Why is it important to choose friends who have the same values that you have?

15) How should you act if one of your friends makes a mistake?

16) How can you show one of your friends that you appreciate him or her?

17) What might it mean if your friend gets angry when you do things with other people?

18) What should you do if you have very sad feelings that last for several weeks?

## Critical Thinking: Write Your Opinion

19) Why is it difficult for people to accept others who are different? What can you say to a friend who gets angry because your ideas are different?

20) How do you feel when another person does not seem to be listening to you? What could you do to get better at listening to others?

**Test Taking Tip** When studying for a test, use a highlighter to mark things you want to remember. To review your notes, look at the highlighted words.

---

## Comprehension: Understanding Main Ideas

11) Answers will vary. Possible answer: change talk to say things you like about yourself or things you can improve in the future, compliment yourself.

12) Spending time alone can give you a time to ask yourself how you are doing; you can cheer yourself up with self-talk and compliment yourself.

13) The kinds of traits you should look for in a friend should be personality traits you look up to and traits you respect such as loyalty and trust.

14) You should choose friends who have the same values because they will be less likely to pressure you to do things that are harmful; they will be more likely to be lasting friends.

15) Answers will vary and may include to remember that all people make mistakes and to respect the right of others to make mistakes.

16) Answers will vary. Students may suggest the following: tell your friend about your appreciation, thank your friend for listening and for being a friend.

17) If a friend gets angry when you do things with other people, the relationship might not be healthy.

18) If you have sad feelings that last for several weeks, talk with a trusted adult or mental health professional.

## Critical Thinking: Write Your Opinion

19) Answers will vary but may include that other people may feel threatened by those who are different. A person can tell a friend that each person has a right to his or her own ideas.

20) Answers will vary but may include feeling bad if a person does not listen. To get better at listening to others, you could pay attention, look at the person who is talking, ask questions, let the speaker finish, lean toward the person, and smile.

---

### Chapter 6 Mastery Test B

Name _____ Date _____ Period _____

**Chapter 6 Mastery Test B**

*Chapter 6 Mastery Test B page 1*

**Directions** Circle the response that *best* completes each sentence.

1) _____ is important to a person's happiness.
   a) Spending lots of money
   b) Being beautiful
   c) Being a sports star
   d) Having healthy relationships

2) Remembering to be your own _____ helps you when a friendship ends.
   a) best friend
   b) critic
   c) worst enemy
   d) bond

3) Asking people questions about themselves shows your _____ in them.
   a) interest
   b) comfort
   c) respect
   d) relationship

4) People often feel sad and _____ when a friendship ends.
   a) honest
   b) lonely
   c) normal
   d) cheerful

5) Friends help you meet the need to _____.
   a) time.
   b) self-talk.
   c) belong.
   d) have values.

6) To be a friend to yourself you can _____.
   a) talk nicely to yourself.
   b) put yourself down.
   c) never exercise.
   d) blame yourself.

7) Practicing good _____ will help you feel good about yourself.
   a) gossip
   b) hygiene
   c) bonds
   d) needs

---

Name _____ Date _____ Period _____

**Chapter 6 Mastery Test B, continued**

*Chapter 6 Mastery Test B page 2*

8) Spending time alone with yourself, eating well, _____, and getting enough rest are important.
   a) gossiping
   b) talking on the phone
   c) exercising
   d) going to the mall with friends

9) Friends often can talk about their _____ and work them out.
   a) problems
   b) sports
   c) music
   d) television shows

10) You will want to choose friends who have _____ you respect.
   a) common
   b) activities
   c) self-talk
   d) traits

11) Making _____ is one way to start a conversation with another person.
   a) small talk
   b) self-talk
   c) values
   d) a relationship

12) People in healthy relationships accept each other's _____.
   a) differences.
   b) gossip.
   c) mistakes.
   d) subjects.

13) Spreading _____ can damage a friendship.
   a) truth
   b) time
   c) gossip
   d) appreciation

14) Your rights, needs, and _____ should be respected in a relationship.
   a) differences
   b) small talk
   c) bonds
   d) values

15) People who are _____ feel uncomfortable around others.
   a) friends
   b) stuck up
   c) shy
   d) gossips

**Chapter 6 Mastery Test B**

## Deciding for Yourself

Explain that being a good listener is important when making new friends. Ask students if they are good listeners. Then have students read "Being a Good Listener" in the Deciding for Yourself lesson on page 132.

### Ask:

· Why is being a good listener important? (It helps you understand the person who is speaking.)

· What can you do to help yourself hear the message? (Pay attention to body language, facial expression, and tone of voice.)

· After listening to someone, how should you answer? (Take time to think about your answer. When you answer, speak calmly.)

### Deciding for Yourself Answers

1) By watching someone's body language, you can tell whether that person shows interest.

2) Answers will vary. Students may say they feel uncomfortable, frustrated, or upset. Accept all reasonable feelings.

3) Answers will vary. Students may suggest the following: "Please listen to me. This is important to me."

4) Answers will vary. Students may suggest the following: "I don't understand what you said. Please explain it to me." Students might suggest repeating what they think the person said. Accept all reasonable answers.

### ■ Deciding for Yourself Activity

Have students complete the Unit 2 Deciding for Yourself Activity.

---

**Deciding for Yourself**

### Being a Good Listener

Being a good listener is important in relationships with others. When you listen to both the words and feelings in what someone says, it helps you understand the person. For example, your friend might be very upset and say that he or she "hates" someone. By listening carefully and asking questions, you might be able to help your friend calm down.

Good listening begins with body language that shows interest. Looking directly at someone shows your interest. So does your facial expression and posture. Paying attention to body language, facial expression, and tone of voice helps you hear the message.

Sometimes people start thinking about how they will answer a person. When people are thinking about their answer, they do not listen carefully to what is said. After listening to someone, take time to think about your answer. When you answer, speak calmly. Let the person you are talking to know you care about what is happening. It may not be possible for you to solve another person's problem. You might be able to suggest where the person might get some help.

Observe what you do when people are talking with you. Think about whether there are things you want to do to become a better listener.

### Questions

1) How can watching someone's body language help you understand what the person is saying?

2) How do you feel when you are talking to people who cross their arms or frown at you?

3) What can you say to a family member who does not pay attention when you are talking?

4) What can you say to someone when you don't understand what is said?

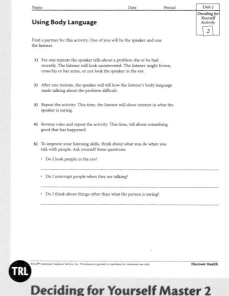

**Deciding for Yourself Master 2**

■ Emotions are automatic responses to thoughts or feelings.

■ Acting without thinking can have bad results. Thinking first helps a person act reasonably.

■ Understanding the reasons for emotions can help a person control actions.

■ Behaving in a reasonable way helps people feel good about themselves.

■ Positive ways to handle emotions include talking about them or doing physical activity.

■ Frustration may occur when someone is blocked from achieving a goal. Frustration can cause anger or aggression.

■ Coping with frustration involves finding what is blocking the goal. Then strategies can be created to get around the block.

■ Stress can be good or bad. It gives you energy to accomplish goals.

■ Too much stress can be harmful. Keeping physically healthy helps a person manage stress.

■ Peer pressure is the influence other people your own age have on you. Peer pressure can be positive or negative. To resist peer pressure, ask questions, express your feelings, or say "no."

■ Anorexia and bulimia are eating disorders caused by emotional problems. People with eating disorders cannot control the way they eat. A person with an eating disorder may need a doctor's care.

■ Before you can be a friend to others, you need to be a friend to yourself.

■ To be a friend to yourself, use positive self-talk, do nice things for yourself, and spend some time alone.

■ Choosing friends who share your values is important.

■ To make friends, show interest in others. Ask questions and listen to what other people say.

*Unit 2 Summary* **133**

■ **Using the Unit Summary**

To further reinforce the facts and concepts presented in the unit, read and discuss with students the questions that follow.

Ask:
_____

- **What are emotions?** (Emotions are automatic responses to thoughts or feelings.)

- **What are two positive ways to handle emotions?** (talking about them or doing physical activity)

- **When may frustration occur?** (Frustration may occur when someone is blocked from achieving a goal.)

- **How do you cope with frustration?** (Coping with frustration involves finding what is blocking the goal. Then strategies can be created to get around the block.)

- **What is peer pressure?** (Peer pressure is the influence other people your own age have on you.) **How can you resist peer pressure?** (Ask questions, express your feelings, or say "no.")

- **What are anorexia and bulimia?** (They are eating disorders caused by emotional problems.)

- **How can you be a friend to yourself?** (Use positive self-talk, do nice things for yourself, and spend some time alone.)

- **How do you make friends?** (Show interest in others, ask questions, and listen to what other people say.)

## Unit 2 Review

The Teacher's Resource Library includes a two-page Unit Mastery Test pictured on this page. Answers are in the Answer Keys beginning on page 433 of this Teacher's Edition.

### Review Answers

#### Comprehension: Identifying Facts

1) grief  2) stress  3) depressed  4) cope
5) blocked  6) self-esteem  7) anxiety
8) peer pressure  9) exercise

### Comprehension: Identifying Facts

On a separate sheet of paper, write the correct word or words from the Word Bank to complete each sentence.

| WORD BANK | | |
| --- | --- | --- |
| anxiety | exercise | self-esteem |
| blocked | grief | self-talk |
| cope | peer pressure | stress |
| depressed | respect | values |

1) The mixture of painful emotions due to loss is called _____.

2) Physical or emotional pressure can cause _____.

3) A person who feels _____ is sad and has low energy.

4) Understanding emotions can help you _____ in a positive way.

5) A frustrated person feels _____ from meeting goals.

6) How a person feels about himself or herself is called _____ .

7) A feeling like fear for which the reasons are not clear is _____ .

8) People your own age can use _____ to influence your decisions and actions.

9) Physical _____ can help you cope with stress and anxiety.

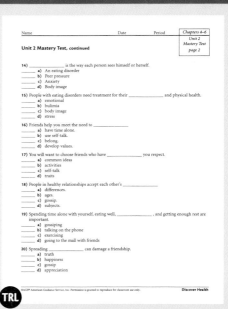

**Unit 2 Mastery Test, page 1**

**Unit 2 Mastery Test, page 2**

10) It is important to choose friends who have the same
_____ .

11) Use positive _____ to be a good friend to
yourself.

12) In a healthy relationship, people _____ each
other's needs and values.

## Comprehension: Understanding Main Ideas

Write the answers to these questions on a separate sheet of
paper. Use complete sentences.

13) Name at least four kinds of emotions.

14) What kinds of physical changes can be part of emotions?

15) How can stress be either positive or negative?

16) What are some ways of coping with stress?

17) What are some positive ways to respond to peer pressure?

18) How can you be a good friend to yourself?

## Critical Thinking: Write Your Opinion

19) Why do some people respond in negative ways to
emotions?

20) Why do some relationships end badly?

10) values  11) self-talk  12) respect

## Comprehension: Understanding Main Ideas

13) Answers will vary. Students may
suggest joy, anger, fear, frustration,
grief, and guilt. Accept all reasonable
answers.

14) Physical changes can include increased
heart rate, tension in muscles, upset
stomach, and perspiration.

15) Positive stress urges a person on to
accomplish goals. Stress is negative
when it is too great or results from
negative experiences.

16) Ways of coping with stress include
positive self-talk, physical exercise,
finding the reasons for the stress, and
talking about the stress to others.

17) Think over the situation and decide
for yourself. Get more information
to help you make a decision. Avoid
situations in which you may be
pressured to make poor decisions.
Say "no" firmly and keep to your
decision.

18) You can be a good friend to yourself
by using positive self-talk, getting
enough exercise and rest, eating
properly, and doing something nice
for yourself every day.

## Critical Thinking: Write Your Opinion

19) Answers will vary. Students may
suggest the following: Some people
have not learned about positive
actions they can take; they may be
tired, hungry, physically sick, or lack
sleep; they may have developed poor
habits in the past; they may need help
from a mental health professional.

20) Answers will vary. Students may
suggest that some relationships end
badly because the people did not
share the same values or they didn't
respect each other's needs and feelings.

# Unit 3 Planning Guide

## Nutrition

| | Student Lesson | | | |
|---|---|---|---|---|
| | Student Pages | Vocabulary | Lesson Review | Writing About Health |
| ***Chapter 7 Diet and Health*** | 139–157 | | | |
| Lesson 1 Food for Energy | 140–141 | • | • | |
| Lesson 2 Carbohydrates and Proteins | 142–44 | • | • | |
| Lesson 3 Fats and Cholesterol | 145–146 | • | • | |
| Lesson 4 Vitamins, Minerals, and Water | 147–150 | • | • | |
| Lesson 5 Dietary Guidelines | 151–154 | • | • | • |
| ***Chapter 8 Making Healthy Food Choices*** | 158–177 | | | |
| Lesson 1 Food Choices and Health | 159–162 | • | • | |
| Lesson 2 Influences on Food Choices | 163–166 | | • | • |
| Lesson 3 Reading Food Labels | 167–170 | • | • | |
| Lesson 4 Making Foods Safe | 171–174 | • | • | |

### Unit Activities

**Home Connection**
**What Do You Think?**
**Deciding for Yourself**

### AGS-Related Resources

**Discover Life Skills Handbook**
**Discover Healthy Sexual Development**

### Assessment Options

**Student Text**
- **Lesson Reviews**
- **Chapter Reviews**
- **Unit Review**

**Teacher's Resource Library**
- **Chapter Mastery Tests**
- **Unit Mastery Test**

| Student Text Features | | | | | | Teaching Strategies | | | | | | | Learning Styles | | | | | Teacher's Resource Library | | | |
|---|---|---|---|---|---|---|---|---|---|---|---|---|---|---|---|---|---|---|---|---|---|
| Action for Health | Careers | Health, Fitness, and Nutrition Tips | Healthy Subjects | Then and Now | Technology | Background Information | Career Application | Community Application | Environment Application | Global Connection | Home Application | Multicultural Connection | Auditory | Group Learning | LEP/ESL | Tactile/Kinesthetic | Visual | Activities | Mastery Tests | Student Study Guide | Workbook Activities |
| | | | | | | | | | | | | | | | | | | | • | • | |
| | 141 | 141 | | | | | | | | 141 | | | | | | | 141 | 23 | | | 23 |
| | | | | | | 143 | | | | 144 | | | | | | | | 24 | | | 24 |
| | | 146 | | | | | | 146 | | | | | | | | | | 25 | | | 25 |
| | | | 149 | | | 149 | | | 150 | | | | | 150 | | | | 26 | | | 26 |
| 152 | | 154 | | | 153 | 153 | | | | | 152 | | | | | | | 27 | | | 27 |
| | | | | | | | | | | | | | | | | | | | • | • | |
| | | 159 | 161 | | | | 162 | | | 162 | 160 | | | 161 | | | | 28 | | | 28 |
| 166 | 163 | 165 | | | | | 166 | | | | | 165 | 164 | | | | | 29 | | | 29 |
| 170 | | | 167 | | | 170 | | | | | | | | 169 | | | 168 | 30 | | | 30 |
| | | | | | | 172 | | 173 | | | | | | | | | | 31 | | | 31 |

## Block Scheduling

Here is a suggested teaching activity if you have extended instructional time, such as a block schedule.

Display  *To examine the eating habits of individuals in your community and to create a display of interesting or important findings.*

Create an observational survey to determine the kinds of food people eat. Go to a grocery store on several different days and, if possible, at several different times to observe and tabulate the information for your survey. The display should contain: (1) the observational survey, (2) the date, time, and length of each observation, (3) the collected data, (4) a concise summary of data, (5) interesting or important findings, and (6) based on the findings, suggestions for people that will assist them in making healthy food selections.

## Unit 3:

### Nutrition
pages 136–181

### Chapters

**Audiocassette**

**Teacher's Resource Library** **TRL**

(Answer Keys for the Teacher's Resource Library begin on page 433 of this Teacher's Edition.)

## Other Resources

### Books for Teachers

Brody, Jane E. *The New York Times Book of Health: How to Feel Fitter, Eat Better, and Live Longer.* New York: Times Books, 1997.

Duyff, Roberta Larson. *The American Dietetic Association's Complete Food and Nutrition Guide.* Minneapolis: Chronimed, 1996.

*The PDF Family Guide to Nutrition and Health.* Montvale, NJ: Medical Economics, 1995.

### Books for Students

Salter, Charles A. *The Vegetarian Teen.* Brookfield, CT: The Millbrook Press, 1991. (Provides guidance for teens and others who wish to cut down on their meat intake while eating a well-balanced diet.)

*"We are indeed much more than we eat, but what we eat can nevertheless help us be much more than what we are."*
—Adele Davis, *Let's Get Well*

### Videos

*Life in the Fast food Lane* (20 minutes). Cambridge Educational Production. Princeton, NJ: Films for the Humanities (1-800-257-5126), 1997. (Offers tips for making healthy fast food choices that will cut down on fat and calories and add fiber and complex carbohydrates to the diet.)

*Nutrition for Living.* (59 minutes). Princeton, NJ: Films for the Humanities (1-800-257-5126), 1998. (Discusses how society shapes our food habits and how to eat well and avoid nutritional problems.)

**Home Connection Master 3**

# Unit 3

# Nutrition

What are your favorite foods? How do you decide what to eat? How does the food you eat affect your health? Eating can be a pleasure. If you know which foods to eat, eating can also keep your body healthy. Eating well means eating more than just the foods you like. It also means choosing foods that meet your body's needs.

Making wise food choices isn't hard. In this unit, you will learn what affects your food choices. You will also learn why it is important to make wise food choices.

▶ Chapter 7  Diet and Health

▶ Chapter 8  Making Healthy Food Choices

## Introducing the Unit

Have volunteers read the introductory material on this page. Then have students look at the picture while you read aloud the quotation by Adele Davis.

### Ask:

- **What is the quotation trying to say?** (Accept all reasonable answers. Help students recognize that Adele Davis is saying people can make better food choices to improve their health.)

- **What is happening in the picture?** (The students are eating healthy food.)

- **Why are they doing this?** (Students may say they are doing this because the students want to improve their health. Other answers may include watching calories, trying to maintain a good weight, or trying to keep a well-balanced diet.)

- **What are your favorite foods?** (Answers will vary, depending on students' preferences.)

- **Do you eat these foods often?** (Answers will vary, depending on students' eating habits.)

- **Do you think the foods you eat often are healthy foods?** (Answers will vary. Some students will think the foods they like are healthy, while others will not.)

- **If you know you are not eating healthy foods, why do you still eat them?** (Answers will vary. Students might say that the foods taste good, or the foods are the only ones available.)

- **How do you think you could make better food choices?** (Answers will vary. Students might say that they should eat more vegetables, or eat fewer sweets or less fat.)

## What Do You Think?

Have volunteers read aloud the story on page 138 to the class.

### Ask:

- Why does Kylie think she won't like the sandwich? (Accept all reasonable answers. Students may suggest that Kylie doesn't eat raw vegetables and whole wheat bread often and doesn't think it will taste food.)

- Would you have had the same reaction as Kylie? (Answers will vary.) Why? (Students should give reasons for their answers.)

- What lesson did Kylie learn? (Accept all reasonable answers. Answers might include: She learned that healthy food can also taste good and not to judge a food before tasting it.)

- What do you think when you hear the word *nutrition*? (Answers will vary. Students might say that they think of vegetables or foods that are healthy.)

- Are you usually willing to try new foods, or do you stick with foods you know? (Answers will vary, depending on students' eating habits.)

- After reading What Do You Think?, would you be more willing to try new, healthy foods? (Answers will vary, depending on the effect the reading has on students' attitudes.)

Have students complete the Unit 3 What Do You Think? Activity sheet.

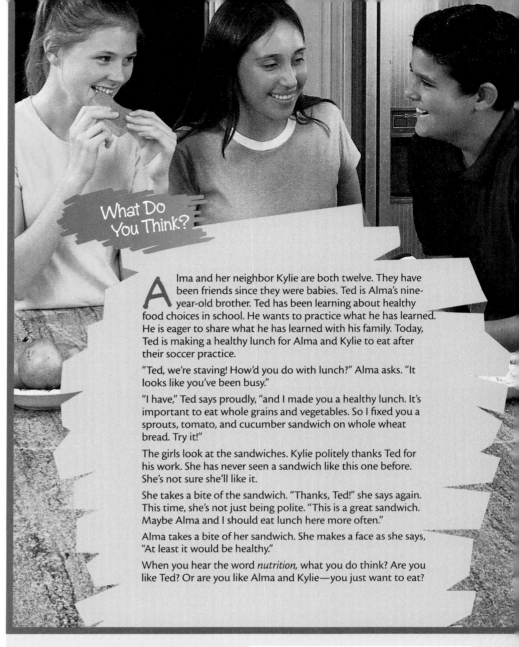

## What Do You Think?

Alma and her neighbor Kylie are both twelve. They have been friends since they were babies. Ted is Alma's nine-year-old brother. Ted has been learning about healthy food choices in school. He wants to practice what he has learned. He is eager to share what he has learned with his family. Today, Ted is making a healthy lunch for Alma and Kylie to eat after their soccer practice.

"Ted, we're staving! How'd you do with lunch?" Alma asks. "It looks like you've been busy."

"I have," Ted says proudly, "and I made you a healthy lunch. It's important to eat whole grains and vegetables. So I fixed you a sprouts, tomato, and cucumber sandwich on whole wheat bread. Try it!"

The girls look at the sandwiches. Kylie politely thanks Ted for his work. She has never seen a sandwich like this one before. She's not sure she'll like it.

She takes a bite of the sandwich. "Thanks, Ted!" she says again. This time, she's not just being polite. "This is a great sandwich. Maybe Alma and I should eat lunch here more often."

Alma takes a bite of her sandwich. She makes a face as she says, "At least it would be healthy."

When you hear the word *nutrition*, what you do think? Are you like Ted? Or are you like Alma and Kylie—you just want to eat?

**What Do You Think? Master 3**

# Chapter 7

## Diet and Health

A s you learned in Chapter 1, food is the body's fuel. Food has the nutrients that all the cells of your body need. However, not all food is equally healthy.

In this chapter, you will learn how food provides energy for the body. You will also learn what kinds of nutrients food can give the body. You will learn which foods contain these different nutrients. Finally, you will learn about dietary guidelines that can help you make healthy choices about the foods you eat.

### Goals for Learning

▶ To describe how the body uses food for energy

▶ To explain that food provides calories and nutrients to the body

▶ To explain the importance of carbohydrates, proteins, fats, vitamins, and minerals in a healthy diet

▶ To identify healthy dietary guidelines

▶ To use the Food Guide Pyramid to judge food choices

### Introducing the Chapter

Make a simple poster with cut-out pictures of the following food items: a cheeseburger, an ice-cream sundae, a soft drink, a bag of potato chips. Show the poster to students, and have a discussion in which you have students evaluate these foods as a meal.

Have volunteers read page 139 aloud, including the Goals for Learning.

#### Ask:

• What kinds of foods do you think would be in a healthy lunch? (Accept all answers as a basis for discussion. Have students give reasons for their answers. Return to the discussion at the end of the chapter to have students evaluate the meal again.)

---

**Student Study Guide 13, page 1**

Name _____ Date _____ Period _____ Chapter 7 / Student Study Guide / 13 / page 1

**Chapter 7 Diet and Health**

*Directions* Fill in the outline below. Filling in the blanks will help you as you read and study Diet and Health.

**I. Lesson 1 (pp. 140-41)**
  A. Food for Energy
   1. _____ are the basic units of food that the body can use.
   2. Nutrients move from the walls of the small intestine into the _____ during absorption.
   3. Nutrients are used for _____ once they are inside cells.
   4. Extra calories are stored in the body as _____ .

**II. Lesson 2 (pp. 142-44)**
  A. Carbohydrates and Proteins
   1. Your body breaks down carbohydrates into a sugar, which your body uses as its main _____ .
   2. The two main kinds of carbohydrates are simple carbohydrates and _____ carbohydrates.
   3. Fiber helps move foods through the _____ system.
   4. About 12 to 15 percent of your diet should come from _____ each day.
   5. A complete protein is a protein with nine _____ acids.

**III. Lesson 3 (pp. 145-46)**
  A. Fats and Cholesterol
   1. The two main kinds of fats are saturated fats and _____ fats.
   2. Cholesterol is found only in foods that come from _____ .
   3. Too much cholesterol makes it hard for your _____ to flow.

©AGS® American Guidance Service, Inc. Permission is granted to reproduce for classroom use only. **Discover Health**

**Student Study Guide 13, page 2**

Name _____ Date _____ Period _____ Chapter 7 / Student Study Guide / 13 / page 2

**IV. Lesson 4 (pp. 147-50)**
  A. Vitamins, Minerals, and Water
   1. Vitamins A, D, E, and K are easily _____ in the body.
   2. Different foods contain different vitamins, so you should eat a wide _____ of foods every day.
   3. Substances that are formed in the _____ are called minerals.
   4. _____ and iron are needed for growth.
   5. The blood pressure of a person who has _____ blood pressure and who gets too much sodium may become worse.
   6. Each day, drink at least _____ glasses of water.

**V. Lesson 5 (pp. 151-54)**
  A. Dietary Guidelines
   1. The Food Guide _____ helps people decide how much and what to eat.
   2. The _____ of a serving depends on how many nutrients and calories the particular food has.
   3. Children and teenagers have different _____ needs.
   4. Boys usually need more calories than girls; girls who are _____ need more iron than boys.

©AGS® American Guidance Service, Inc. Permission is granted to reproduce for classroom use only. **Discover Health**

## Lesson at a Glance

### Chapter 7 Lesson 1

**Overview** This lesson describes the processes that change food into energy the body can use: digestion, absorption, and metabolism.

### Objectives

■ To describe how the body turns food into energy.

■ To explain that food provides calories and nutrients to the body.

**Student Pages** 140–141

**Audiocassette**

**Teacher's Resource Library** **TRL**

    Activity 23

    Workbook Activity 23

## Teaching Suggestions

### ■ Vocabulary

*absorption, digestion, metabolism, nutrient, calorie*

Write the vocabulary words on the chalkboard and ask students which words they have heard. Have them explain what they think the words mean. Then read and review each definition with students.

### ■ Teaching the Lesson

Have students brainstorm reasons that people eat food, besides that it tastes good. Have them concentrate on what they think food does for the body. Then have students read about digestion and absorption on page 140.

### Ask:

• Your body breaks food down into tiny parts that it can use as energy. What are the three steps that turn what you eat into energy? (The three steps in turning food into energy are digestion, absorption, and metabolism.)

• What happens in the body during digestion? (During digestion, food is broken down into basic units that the body can use, called nutrients.)

---

## Lesson 1 *Food for Energy*

**Absorption**
*The moving of nutrients from the digestive system to the circulatory system*

**Digestion**
*The breaking down of food into nutrients*

**Metabolism**
*The process of cells using nutrients for energy and other needs*

**Nutrient**
*The basic unit of food that the body can use*

*T*he food you eat must be broken down into tiny parts. Only then can your body use it as energy. There are three main steps to turning the food you eat into energy. These steps are called **digestion**, **absorption**, and **metabolism**.

### What Happens During Digestion?

During digestion, food is broken down into basic units that your body can use. These basic units of food are called **nutrients**. Digestion begins in your mouth. Chewing and chemicals in your saliva begin to break the food down. Digestion continues in the stomach. Once food is broken down, it moves into the small intestine.

### What Happens During Absorption?

During absorption, nutrients are moved from the walls of the small intestine into the bloodstream. The circulatory system then carries the nutrients to all the cells in your body. If absorption did not occur, your cells would not receive the nutrients they need to live.

You need to eat healthy food so that your body can do all the things you like to do.

---

• **Explain the stages in the process of digestion.** (Digestion begins in the mouth, as chewing cuts up food into smaller pieces, and chemicals in saliva begin to break it down. Digestion continues in the stomach. Once the process of breaking food down is completed, the food moves into the small intestine.)

• **What is absorption?** (Absorption is the process that moves nutrients from the digestive system to the circulatory system so they can be used by the body's cells.)

## FOOD TECHNOLOGIST

Careers

Eating right can be a challenge. Food technologists work for universities, industries that make food or process food, and government agencies that make the guidelines for proper food storage and handling. To do this, a food technologist uses his or her knowledge of chemistry, microbiology, and other sciences to develop new ways to preserve, process, package, and store food. Usually a four-year college degree or higher is needed.

**Calorie**
*The unit used to measure the amount of energy in foods*

### What Happens During Metabolism?

Metabolism occurs inside your cells. During metabolism, nutrients are taken into the cells. Inside the cells, nutrients are changed so the cells can use them for energy and other needs. As nutrients are used, wastes form. The cells remove these wastes.

### What Are Calories?

You have learned that the body uses nutrients for energy. **Calories** measure how much energy different foods give the body. The more calories a food has, the more energy it gives the body. Extra calories are stored in the body as fat. Some foods have calories but few nutrients. Other foods have nutrients but few calories.

*Fitness Tip*

Go for a run or swim to burn off extra calories.

**LESSON 1 REVIEW** Write the answers to these questions on a separate sheet of paper. Use complete sentences.

1) List the three steps of using food for energy.

2) What happens during metabolism?

3) Where do the following steps occur in the body: digestion, absorption, and metabolism?

4) What do calories measure?

5) What might happen if you ate a diet high in calories but low in nutrients? Would this be healthy?

*Diet and Health Chapter 7* **141**

## Careers

Invite the food technologists and registered dietitians who plan meals for your school to speak to the class about what they do. Have them talk about how they plan meals and the nutritional requirements they must follow. Encourage the guests to also include facts, such as how much peanut butter is used in one week or the food that is most popular or least popular with students.

Have students read about metabolism and calories on page 141.

### Lesson 1 Review Answers

1) The three steps of using food for energy are digestion, absorption, and metabolism.

2) During metabolism, nutrients are taken into the cells and are changed in a way that allows the cells to use them for energy and other needs.

3) Digestion occurs in the mouth, stomach, and small intestine. Absorption occurs in the small intestine. Metabolism occurs in body cells.

4) Calories measure the amount of energy in food.

5) If you ate a diet high in calories but low in nutrients, you would not be healthy because of a lack nutrients.

## APPLICATION

**At Home**
Invite students to count calories for one day. Encourage students to compare that number with what a person of their height should take in. Encourage students to discuss what they discover about their daily calorie intake.

## LEARNING STYLES

**Visual** Challenge students to draw a diagram of the human body showing the location of parts of the digestive system mentioned in the text, such as the mouth, stomach, and small intestine. Encourage students to label the diagram with the steps in the digestive process.

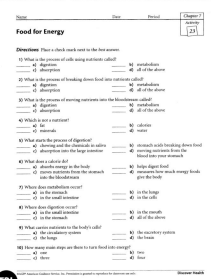

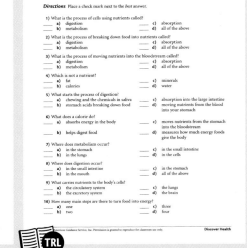

**Activity 23**

**Workbook Activity 23**

## Lesson at a Glance

### Chapter 7 Lesson 2

**Overview** In this lesson, students learn about carbohydrates and proteins.

### Objectives

■ To describe the importance of carbohydrates and proteins in a healthy diet

**Student Pages** 142–144

**Audiocassette**

**Teacher's Resource Library**

   Activity 24

   Workbook Activity 24

## Teaching Suggestions

### ■ Vocabulary

*carbohydrate, protein, fiber, amino acid, complete protein*

For each vocabulary word, have students find two sentences from the text that contain the word. Have students read the sentences, then write an original sentence containing that word.

### ■ Teaching the Lesson

Draw students' attention to the picture on page 142 showing foods rich in carbohydrates, and the picture on page 143 showing foods high in protein. Discuss with students how often they eat such foods. Have students keep their responses in mind as they read the next two pages.

Have students read about carbohydrates on page 142.

Ask:

· Why should you eat foods containing nutrients? (You should eat food containing nutrients because your body cannot make them on its own.)

· One of the essential nutrients your body needs is carbohydrate. What is carbohydrate? (Carbohydrate is a nutrient your body uses to make energy.)

---

## Carbohydrates and Proteins

**Carbohydrate**
*A nutrient needed mostly for energy*

**Protein**
*A nutrient needed for growth and repair of body tissues*

Six nutrients are essential to life, but your body cannot make them on its own. Therefore, the foods you eat must contain these six essential nutrients for your body to be healthy. Two essential nutrients you need are **carbohydrates** and **proteins**.

### What Are Carbohydrates?

Look at the foods in the picture below. Do you ever eat any of these foods? If so, you have been eating carbohydrates. When you eat foods with carbohydrates, your body breaks down the carbohydrates into a sugar. Your body uses this sugar as its main fuel. Extra sugar is stored in your liver for use later. Sometimes it is stored as fat. When you don't eat for a long time, your body can use the stored sugar for fuel. More than half of the foods you eat each day should contain carbohydrates.

### What Kinds of Carbohydrates Are There?

There are two main kinds of carbohydrates: simple carbohydrates and complex carbohydrates. Table sugar, candies, cookies, and cakes all contain simple carbohydrates. These foods are sometimes called "empty calories" because they contain sugars and calories but few other nutrients.

Carbohydrates give the body much of the daily energy it needs.

142    *Chapter 7   Diet and Health*

---

· How does your body process carbohydrates? (Your body breaks carbohydrates down into sugar, which it uses as its main fuel.)

· Name two foods that contain simple carbohydrates. (Foods such as table sugar, candy, cookies, and cake contain simple carbohydrates.)

· Why are foods that contain simple carbohydrate called "empty calories"? (Foods that contain simple carbohydrate are called "empty calories" because they contain sugars and calories but few other nutrients.)

| Food | Total Carbohydrates (in grams) | Simple Carbohydrates (in grams) | Complex Carbohydrates (in grams) |
|---|---|---|---|
| Bread, 1 slice | 13 | 1 | 12 |
| Corn flakes, 1 oz. (low sugar) | 24 | 2 | 22 |
| Pasta or rice, $\frac{1}{2}$ cup, cooked | 20 | 0 | 20 |

**Fiber**
*The parts of food that the body cannot digest*

Complex carbohydrates are found in fruits, vegetables, grains, and many other foods. The foods in the table above are good sources of complex carbohydrates. Complex carbohydrates also have **fiber**. Fiber is not a nutrient, but it is important to your digestion and to your health. Fiber is the part of food that your body cannot digest. It helps move foods through the digestive system. Fiber is found in fruits, vegetables, grains, and beans.

### What Are Proteins?

The picture below shows foods that contain proteins. Proteins are important for building muscles and repairing tissues. Proteins also provide energy.

First, your body uses the calories in proteins to build and repair tissues. Then, it stores the extra calories as body fat. About 12 to 15 percent of your diet should come from proteins each day.

Some protein foods are fish, meat, eggs, milk, poultry, peanuts, seeds, peas, and beans.

Have students continue reading about carbohydrates and proteins on page 143.

Ask:

- What important ingredient is a part of complex carbohydrates? (Complex carbohydrates contain fiber.)

- Why is fiber important? (Fiber is important because it aids digestion by helping foods move through the digestive system.)

- Name two foods that contain complex carbohydrates. (Foods that contain complex carbohydrates include fruits, vegetables, cereal, and pasta.)

- Name two foods that are high in fiber. (Foods that are high in fiber include fruits, vegetables, grains, and beans.)

- Why are proteins important for the body? (Proteins are important because they help build muscles and repair tissues. Proteins also can provide energy.)

- How much of your daily diet should come from protein? (About 12 to 15 percent of your daily diet should come from protein.)

- Name three protein-rich foods. (Protein-rich foods include eggs, fish, meat, milk, poultry, seeds, peas, beans, and nuts.)

### BACKGROUND INFORMATION

Carbohydrates are the chief source of energy for the body. In fact, carbohydrate snacks packed with sugars and starches provide almost instant energy because of the rise in blood sugar level that they cause. But the blood sugar level drops again quickly, causing a craving for more sweets. The main problem with diets very high in refined carbohydrates (such as cookies, candies, and snack foods) is that they crowd out other foods and cause the diet to be low in vitamins, minerals, and fiber.

Have students read about complete proteins on page 144.

Ask:

- Why is it important to eat foods that contain complete proteins? (It is important to eat foods that contain complete proteins because your body cannot make some amino acids, which you must get from food. Foods that are complete proteins contain all of the nine amino acids that your body cannot make.)

- What types of foods contain complete proteins? (Foods from animal sources such as meat, chicken, fish, eggs, milk, and milk products contain complete proteins.)

## Lesson 2 Review Answers

1) Simple carbohydrates are sometimes called "empty calories" because they contain sugars and calories but few other nutrients. Complex carbohydrates (found in fruits, vegetables, and grains) contain both nutrients and fiber.

2) Answers will vary. Accept examples of fruits, vegetables, and grains.

3) Answers will vary. Answers may include meats, poultry, fish, cheese, eggs, milk and milk products, nuts, peas, and beans.

4) A protein that has all nine amino acids the body cannot make is a complete protein. You can get complete proteins by eating foods that contain the nine amino acids, such as meat, chicken, fish, eggs, milk, and milk products.

5) Answers will vary, depending on the foods listed.

**GLOBAL CONNECTION**

How do the diets of people in other countries compare to the typical American diet in terms of nutrients? Have students answer this questions by studying the typical diet of a young person from another country. Have students share their findings in class. Students from other countries might want to report on the differences between the American diet and the diet of their homeland.

---

Amino acid
*The smaller units of protein*

Complete protein
*A protein that has all nine essential amino acids*

## What Is a Complete Protein?

Proteins are made up of smaller units called **amino acids**. There are twenty-two amino acids. They join together to form all the different proteins that we eat. Your body can make some amino acids on its own. However, your body cannot make nine amino acids. You must eat these amino acids for your body to get them. A protein that has all nine of these amino acids is a **complete protein**.

Only foods that come from animal sources have complete proteins. These foods include meat, chicken, fish, eggs, milk, and milk products. Foods that come from only one plant do not have complete proteins. However, you can eat several different foods from plants at the same time to get complete proteins. For example, eating rice with beans gives you complete proteins.

**LESSON 2 REVIEW** Write the answers to these questions on a separate sheet of paper. Use complete sentences.

1) Compare simple carbohydrates with complex carbohydrates.

2) List five foods that are a good source of complex carbohydrates.

3) List five foods that contain proteins.

4) What is a complete protein? How can you get complete proteins?

5) Write down a meal you had today. List the carbohydrates and proteins in that meal.

*Nutrition Tip*

Skipping meals can rob your brain of the sugar it needs. Eating at least three meals a day at regular times can help ensure that your brain has enough sugar.

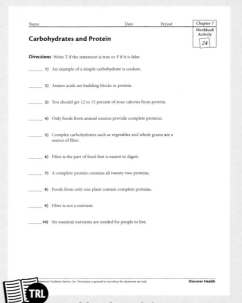

Activity 24

Workbook Activity 24

## Fats and Cholesterol

**Cholesterol**
*A waxy, fatlike substance found in animal products*

**Polyunsaturated fat**
*A fat that is found mostly in plant foods*

**Saturated fat**
*A fat that is found mostly in animal products*

The picture below shows foods that are high in fats. Like carbohydrates, fats also provide energy. Fats are found in all the cells of your body. Fats help the body use vitamins.

### How Much Fat Should You Eat?

You need only small amounts of fats. Too much fat can lead to heart disease and cancer. Too little fat can also be harmful. Less than 30 percent of the calories you eat each day should come from fats. Salad dressings, margarine, dips, and gravies all add extra fat to your foods.

### What Kinds of Fats Are There?

There are two main kinds of fats: **saturated fats** and **polyunsaturated fats**. Saturated fats are found mostly in animal products. They are usually solid at room temperature. Polyunsaturated fats are usually liquid at room temperature. They come mostly from plants.

Fats provide the body with energy but should be eaten sparingly.

### What Is Cholesterol?

**Cholesterol** is a waxy, fatlike substance that is found in every cell of the body. Cholesterol is found in most of the foods that are high is saturated fats. It is found *only* in foods that come from animals.

*Diet and Health    Chapter 7*    **145**

---

- What is the danger of eating too much fat? (Too much fat can lead to heart disease and cancer.)

- What is cholesterol? (Cholesterol is a waxy, fatlike substance found in animal products.)

---

## Lesson at a Glance

### Chapter 7  Lesson 3

**Overview**  This lesson discusses fat and cholesterol in the diet.

### Objectives

- To identify the importance of fats and cholesterol in a healthy diet.

**Student Pages** 145–146
**Audiocassette**
**Teacher's Resource Library**  **TRL**

Activity 25
Workbook Activity 25

## Teaching Suggestions

### ■ Vocabulary

*cholesterol, polyunsaturated fat, saturated fat*

Ask students if they have heard any of the vocabulary words in TV food ads. Discuss how the words were used and what students think they mean. Then read the definition of each word aloud. Have students compare what they thought the words meant based on advertising to what they actually mean.

### ■ Teaching the Lesson

Direct students' attention to the picture at the bottom of page 145. Ask students to identify the high-fat foods in the picture. Write the words on the board. Ask students to name other high-fat foods. Write these on the board as well. Ask students to think about whether they eat large quantities of any of these foods as they read the next lesson.

Then have students begin to read about fats and cholesterol on page 145.

Ask:

- What is the function of fats in the body? (Fats help the body use vitamins. They also give the body energy.)

## Healthy Subjects

Have students do research to find a typical dinner menu for someone in Greenland, Japan, and the United States. Compare the fat and cholesterol content of the three menus. Which foods on the menus from Greenland and Japan make them more heart healthy? Would the students eat the foods on those menus? What could be substituted into the American menu to reduce the amount of fat and cholesterol?

Have students finish reading the information about cholesterol on page 146.

## Lesson 3 Review Answers

1) Fats provide energy and help your body use vitamins. A diet lacking fat might prevent your body from carrying out these functions.

2) Answers will vary. Answers can include butter, oils, salad dressings, gravies, cheese, nuts, and meats.

3) Saturated fats are found mostly in animal products and are usually solid at room temperature. Polyunsaturated fats come mostly from plants and are usually liquid at room temperature.

4) Too much cholesterol can build up in blood vessels, making it hard for blood to flow.

5) Answers will vary and may include the fact that the pasta and vegetables in the sauce would be high in carbohydrates, while oil, butter, meat, and cheese would be high in fat.

## APPLICATION

### In the Community

Invite students to look at the typical meals served in fast-food restaurants in the community. Have students determine whether these meals are high in fat. If so, have students suggest changes in the meals that would make them more healthy and lower in fat. Are these items on the menu? If not, challenge students to write letters to the management of the restaurants to suggest changes. Have students share any replies with the class.

### Healthy Subjects

### Geography

A study was done of 1,800 Greenland natives during a 25-year period. In that time, only three people in the group studied had heart attacks. There have been similar findings in Japan and other Asian countries. This rate seems to be due to the large amount of fish that people in those places eat.

The rate of heart attacks in North America is more than ten times higher than in these other countries. Many Americans eat more meat, which has "bad" cholesterol, which clogs blood vessels. The oils in fish, on the other hand, contain "good" cholesterol, which helps blood flow. Many experts recommend eating fish twice per week.

You have probably heard of cholesterol as something bad. Your body needs some cholesterol to stay healthy. Too much cholesterol, however, can build up in your blood vessels. This makes it hard for your blood to flow. To protect your health, watch the amount of cholesterol and fats you eat each day.

**LESSON 3 REVIEW** Write the answers to these questions on a separate sheet of paper. Use complete sentences.

1) How might eating no fat harm your health?

2) List foods that contain fats.

3) How can you tell a saturated fat from a polyunsaturated fat?

4) How might eating too much cholesterol harm your health?

5) What percent of your daily calories should come from fat?

---

Name _____ Date _____ Period _____ | Chapter 7 Activity 25

**Fats and Cholesterol**

**Directions** Write *T* if the statement is true or *F* if it is false.

_____ 1) Polyunsaturated fats usually come from plants.

_____ 2) Cholesterol comes only from animal foods.

_____ 3) Cholesterol can be good or bad.

_____ 4) Too much fat can lead to heart disease.

_____ 5) Protein is a waxy, fat-like substance found in every cell in the body.

_____ 6) Salad dressings, dips, and gravies are part of a low-fat diet.

_____ 7) More than a third of your daily calories should come from fat.

_____ 8) Cholesterol can build up in your blood vessels.

_____ 9) Your body needs some cholesterol to stay healthy.

_____ 10) There are three main kinds of fats.

**Activity 25**

---

Name _____ Date _____ Period _____ | Chapter 7 Workbook Activity 25

**Fats and Cholesterol**

**Directions** Write *T* if the statement is true or *F* if it is false.

_____ 1) Too much fat can lead to heart disease.

_____ 2) Polyunsaturated fats usually come from plants.

_____ 3) Cholesterol comes only from animal foods.

_____ 4) Cholesterol can be good or bad.

_____ 5) Protein is a waxy, fat-like substance found in every cell in the body.

_____ 6) Salad dressings, dips, and gravies are part of a low-fat diet.

_____ 7) More than a third of your daily calories should come from fat.

_____ 8) There are three main kinds of fats.

_____ 9) Cholesterol can build up in your blood vessels.

_____ 10) Your body needs some cholesterol to stay healthy.

**Workbook Activity 25**

**Mineral**
*A nutrient from the earth that is needed to help the body use energy from other nutrients*

**Vitamin**
*A nutrient needed to help the body use energy from other nutrients*

Not all nutrients give your body energy. Carbohydrates, proteins, and fats do give your body energy. The other three essential nutrients do not provide energy. They are **vitamins**, **minerals**, and water. These nutrients help your body use the energy in food. Compared with carbohydrates, proteins, and fats, your body needs small amounts of vitamins and minerals. Your body needs enough water to replace the amount it loses each day.

**What Are Vitamins?**

The picture below shows foods that are rich in vitamins.

Vitamins A, D, E, and K dissolve in fats. They are easily stored in the body. This means that you can go a day without eating some of these vitamins if you have to. Also, if you take supplements, you could get too much of these vitamins.

Vitamin C and the B vitamins dissolve in water. Because they do, they can be lost by too much washing of foods or soaking them in water. They also do not stay in your body for long. Thus, you need to eat foods with these vitamins every day.

The body needs foods high in vitamins for normal growth.

*Diet and Health* Chapter 7 **147**

---

**Lesson at a Glance**

**Chapter 7 Lesson 4**

**Overview** This lesson discusses vitamins, minerals, and water.

**Objectives**

■ To identify the importance of vitamins, minerals, and water in a healthy diet.

**Student Pages** 147–150

**Audiocassette**

**Teacher's Resource Library**

Activity 26

Workbook Activity 26

## Teaching Suggestions

### ■ Vocabulary

*mineral, vitamin*

Ask students to write the vocabulary words and what they think they mean on a sheet of paper. Then have students list any names of minerals and vitamins that they know. As students read the lesson, have them compare their definitions of the words with those in the textbook.

### ■ Teaching the Lesson

Show students a bottle of multivitamin supplements and a varied group of fruits and vegetables. Tell students that the supplements and the vegetables can provide the same vitamins. Ask students why the foods are a better source of vitamins. Accept all reasonable answers, but tell students that the wide variety of fruits and vegetables have an advantage because they contain other substances the body needs such as fiber.

Then have students read about vitamins on page 147.

Ask:

• How is the function of vitamins, minerals, and water different from the function of carbohydrates, proteins, and fats? (Vitamins, minerals, and water help your body use energy in food. Carbohydrates, proteins, and fats provide the energy.)

---

• Do you need to eat foods with vitamins A, D, E, and K each day? (No.) Why not? (You do not need to eat foods containing these vitamins each day because the body stores them. You can go a day without taking in these vitamins.)

• Do you need to eat foods with vitamins B and C each day? (Yes.) Why? (You need to eat foods containing these vitamins each day because they dissolve in water and don't stay in the body very long.)

Have students read the vitamin chart and the section on minerals on page 148.

## Ask:

- What does vitamin A do for the body? (Vitamin A keeps the skin, hair, and eyes healthy.)

- List some foods that contain vitamin A. (Foods that contain vitamin A include milk, egg yolk, liver, carrots, and spinach.)

- Name three B vitamins. (Three B vitamins are niacin, thiamin, and riboflavin. Inform students that there are other B vitamins.)

- What does vitamin C do for the body? (Vitamin C helps form bones and teeth and helps the body resist infections.)

- List some foods that contain vitamin C. (Foods that contain vitamin C include citrus fruits, tomatoes, and potatoes. Tell students that citrus fruits include oranges, grapefruits, and lemons.)

- What does vitamin D do? (Vitamin D helps form strong bones and teeth.)

- Which foods are good sources of vitamin D? (Vitamin D is in milk and fish oils.)

- What does vitamin E do for the body? (Vitamin E is good for the body's cells.)

- Name some foods that contain vitamin E. (Vegetable oils and margarine contain vitamin E.)

- What is the function of vitamin K? (Vitamin K helps the blood clot.)

- From which foods do we get vitamin K? (Vitamin K comes from green vegetables, soybeans, and bran.)

- What are minerals? (Minerals are substances formed in the earth.)

- Why do you need to eat a wide variety of foods? (Eating a wide variety of foods will allow you to get all of the vitamins and minerals your body needs.)

The chart below shows some of the jobs of different vitamins. It tells you which foods have which vitamins. Because different foods contain different vitamins, you should eat a wide variety of foods every day.

| Vitamin | Job in the body | Foods that have this vitamin |
|---|---|---|
| Vitamin A | Keeps the skin, hair, and eyes healthy | Milk, egg yolk, liver, carrots, spinach |
| B Vitamins | | |
| Niacin | Protects the skin and nerves | Meat, cereal, whole wheat, milk, fish, legumes |
| Thiamin | Protects nervous system, aids digestion | Pork, whole grains, green beans, peanut butter |
| Riboflavin | Protects the body from disease | Milk, eggs, bread, meat (especially liver), green vegetables |
| Vitamin C | Helps form bones and teeth, and resist infections | Citrus fruits, tomatoes, potatoes |
| Vitamin D | Helps form strong bones and teeth | Milk, fish oils |
| Vitamin E | Good for cells | Vegetable oils, margarine |
| Vitamin K | Helps blood clot | Green vegetables, soybeans, bran |

## What Are Minerals?

The picture on the following page shows foods that are high in minerals. Minerals are substances that are formed in the earth. Like vitamins, minerals do not give the body energy. You need to eat a wide variety of foods to get all the vitamins your body needs. You also need to eat many different foods to get all the minerals your body needs.

Foods high in minerals are important for digestion and fluid balance.

## Which Minerals Does the Body Need?

Calcium, iron, and sodium are important minerals. Calcium and iron are needed for growth. Calcium helps bones and teeth form and stay strong. It is found in milk, yogurt, cheese, ice cream, green leafy vegetables, and beans. Girls and boys need about the same amount of calcium. This keeps their skeleton strong and their bones growing properly. Iron is found in meats, beans, and eggs. Red blood cells need iron to carry oxygen to other cells.

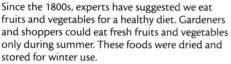

### FOODS IN AND OUT OF SEASON

Since the 1800s, experts have suggested we eat fruits and vegetables for a healthy diet. Gardeners and shoppers could eat fresh fruits and vegetables only during summer. These foods were dried and stored for winter use.

After 1900, canned foods became available. Since 1930, we have been able to buy frozen fruits and vegetables. Because of better transportation, more countries can sell fresh produce. Now we can buy apples from New Zealand, pineapples from Hawaii, and cabbages from China. Even when some fruits and vegetables are out of season in the United States, our stores import and sell them.

*Diet and Health    Chapter 7*    **149**

Have students read about the minerals the body needs on page 149.

### Ask:

- Why is the mineral calcium important for the body? (Calcium helps form strong bones and teeth.)

- Which foods are good sources of calcium? (Foods such as milk, yogurt, cheese, ice cream, green leafy vegetables, and beans are good sources of calcium.)

- Why is iron an important mineral? (Iron is important because red blood cells need iron to carry oxygen to other cells.)

- What foods contain iron? (Meat, beans, and eggs contain iron.)

## Then and Now

Have students visit various supermarkets in your area to find out where the fresh fruits and vegetables come from. Students can find the information by looking on labels on produce or boxes or by asking those selling the produce. Have students compile their information in a large chart for classroom display. Discuss where most produce comes from. Is it local? Does it come from other states or other countries? Have students do research in the library or on the Internet to find out whether there are drawbacks to eating produce from other countries. Discuss the pros and cons of this issue in class.

### BACKGROUND INFORMATION

About seventeen minerals are needed by the body. A very small percentage of the body's weight consists of minerals. Minerals work with vitamins, with some vitamins needed to absorb minerals and some minerals needed to absorb vitamins. For example, the body needs the mineral phosphorus to absorb some B vitamins. Vitamin C increases the body's ability to absorb the mineral iron.

Have students read about sodium and the importance of water on page 150.

## Lesson 4 Review Answers

1) Vitamins and minerals do not provide the body with energy, as carbohydrates do.
2) Answers will vary. See vitamin table on page 148 for possible answers.
3) Answers will vary. Answers include the following: Calcium helps bones and teeth form; iron helps red blood cells carry oxygen; sodium aids nerve cell communication.
4) Water is needed to move nutrients through the blood and maintain the proper body temperature.
5) Eating a wide variety of foods improves the chances that you will get all the vitamins, minerals, and other nutrients the body needs.

### APPLICATION

 **Environment**
Drinking water is important. Have students find out about the water you drink in your community. Where does it come from? Are there any problems with pollution at its source? If so, how does the utility that provides your water treat it to make sure it is safe? How often is the water tested for harmful bacteria and other harmful substances? Have students report to the class on what they find. (If possible, arrange a tour of the facility that supplies water for your community.)

### LEARNING STYLES

**Group Learning** Many foods are mostly water. Encourage each student to research the water content of one food. Provide a chart on a bulletin board or chalkboard that students can fill in with the information they find. The chart should have the following two columns: Food, Percent Water. When all information is listed, have students arrange the foods in order, starting with the food that has the highest water content. Invite students to compare the types of foods that contain the most water with those that contain the least.

Drink at least eight glasses of water daily to replace what the body loses.

Sodium is important for nerve cells to communicate with one another. It is the main ingredient in table salt. It is also used to preserve foods. Sodium is common in packaged foods, for example. It's usually easy to get enough or even too much sodium from a typical American diet. Too much sodium can worsen high blood pressure.

### How Is Water Important?

You body is about 60 percent water by weight. Water is needed to move nutrients through the blood and keep your body the right temperature. You can get the water you need each day by drinking eight glassfuls and from juices and soups.

**LESSON 4 REVIEW** Write the answers to these questions on a separate sheet of paper. Use complete sentences.

1) How are vitamins and minerals different from carbohydrates?
2) List three vitamins and the jobs they do in the body.
3) List three minerals and the jobs they do in the body.
4) How is water important to a healthy diet?
5) Why is it important to eat a wide variety of foods every day?

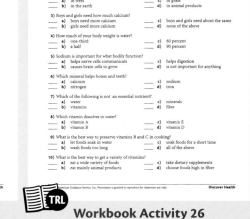

**Activity 26**

**Workbook Activity 26**

**Food Guide Pyramid**
*A chart that can be used to choose a healthy diet*

There are so many things to consider when deciding which foods you should eat. How do you know if you are eating a healthy diet and getting all the nutrients your body needs? One aid is the **Food Guide Pyramid**, shown in Figure 7.1.

### What Is the Food Guide Pyramid?

The U.S. government made the Food Guide Pyramid to help people decide how much and what to eat. Notice that the foods are divided into six groups.

Breads and grains form the base of the pyramid. This shows that more of these foods should be eaten than the other foods. As you move up the pyramid, fewer servings of each kind of food are needed in a healthy diet. Fats and sweets form the top of the pyramid. This group you should avoid or eat only in very small amounts.

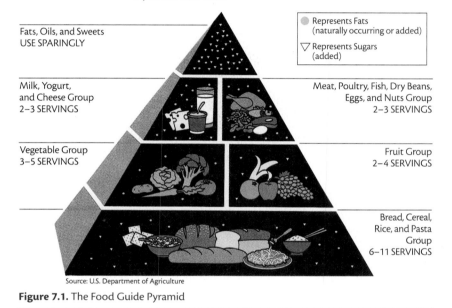

Fats, Oils, and Sweets
USE SPARINGLY

● Represents Fats (naturally occurring or added)
▽ Represents Sugars (added)

Milk, Yogurt, and Cheese Group
2–3 SERVINGS

Meat, Poultry, Fish, Dry Beans, Eggs, and Nuts Group
2–3 SERVINGS

Vegetable Group
3–5 SERVINGS

Fruit Group
2–4 SERVINGS

Bread, Cereal, Rice, and Pasta Group
6–11 SERVINGS

Source: U.S. Department of Agriculture

**Figure 7.1.** The Food Guide Pyramid

---

## Lesson at a Glance

### Chapter 7  Lesson 5

**Overview** In this lesson, students learn to use the Food Guide Pyramid to plan a healthy diet. They also learn about dietary guidelines.

### Objectives

- To identify healthy dietary guidelines.
- To use the Food Guide Pyramid to identify daily food needs.

**Student Pages** 151–154

**Audiocassette**

**Teacher's Resource Library**

   **Activity** 27
   **Workbook Activity** 27

## Teaching Suggestions

### ■ Vocabulary

*Food Guide Pyramid, serving size*

Read the definitions of the vocabulary words to students. Then direct them to write a question that they would like answered about each word. Tell students to look for answers to their questions as they read the lesson. Encourage students to do research about food guidelines in the library or on the Internet.

### ■ Teaching the Lesson

Direct students' attention to the illustration of the Food Guide Pyramid at the bottom of page 151. Have students locate on the pyramid the types of foods they eat most. Tell students to keep this information in mind as they read about dietary guidelines in this lesson so they can evaluate whether they are eating a healthy diet.

Then have students read about the Food Guide Pyramid on page 151.

Ask:

- What is the Food Guide Pyramid? (The Food Guide Pyramid is a chart that shows the amount of various foods needed for a healthy diet.)

- According to the Food Guide Pyramid, which group of foods should people eat the most? (People should eat most foods from the bread, cereal, rice, and pasta group.)

- Which foods should people avoid or eat only in small amounts? (People should avoid or eat only small amounts of foods containing lots of fat, oil, or sugar.)

Have students read about recommended serving sizes and general dietary guidelines on page 152.

Ask:

• What is a serving size? (A serving size is a way to measure the amount of each type of food that should be eaten each day.)

• Why isn't the serving size the same for each type of food? (The serving size depends on the number of nutrients and calories the particular food has.)

• List the five general guidelines for eating a healthy diet. (The five general guidelines for eating a healthy diet are the following: eat a wide variety of foods; balance food with physical activity; eat many grains, fruits, and vegetables each day; choose a diet low in fat, saturated fat, and cholesterol; choose a diet low in sugar.)

## Action for Health

While they are recording their eating patterns, have students also record their drinking habits. Ask students to recall how much water each person should drink each day. (eight glasses) Tell students to keep track of the amount of water they drink each day. Discuss whether it is easy or difficult to drink eight glasses of water each day. Discuss any difference in how consuming this amount of water makes students feel.

### MULTICULTURAL CONNECTION

The U.S. Department of Agriculture has helped to develop the Food Guide Pyramid and the general dietary guidelines. Challenge students to find out whether governments in other countries have developed dietary guidelines that they recommend to their citizens. Have students share what they find in class. How are any other guidelines similar to those supported by the U.S. government? How are they different? What might account for the differences?

---

**Serving size**
*A way to measure the amount of different foods that should be eaten each day*

## What Is a Serving Size?

Note that the Food Guide Pyramid suggests that you eat a certain number of *servings* from each food group each day. **Serving size** for each food group varies. The size of a serving depends on how many nutrients and calories the particular food has. For example, a serving in the fruit group might be a slice of melon, one medium banana, or $\frac{3}{4}$ cup of juice. For meat, which has more calories and fat than fruit, a serving size is 5–7 ounces. Each serving has about the same number of calories and major nutrients for each food.

Also, notice that the Food Guide Pyramid gives a range of servings. The smallest number of servings listed is the minimum amount of that group to be eaten each day. By eating the minimum amount, you'll still get the right amount of nutrients. Below is a list of more general guidelines to help you choose a healthy diet.

### General Dietary Guidelines

• Eat a wide variety of foods.
• Balance the food you eat with physical activity.
• Eat many grains, fruits, and vegetables each day.
• Choose a diet low in fat, saturated fat, and cholesterol.
• Choose a diet low in sugar.

### KEEPING A FOOD RECORD

Use the Food Guide Pyramid to plan a menu for yourself for next week. At the end of each day, check to see how many of the planned foods you actually ate. Monitor your energy level. Think about how you feel as you follow the suggested daily servings for each food group. Do you notice any difference in your ability to keep going without feeling tired or hungry between meals?

## Writing About Health

Think about how your eating pattern compares with the suggestions in the Food Guide Pyramid. Write how you might change your eating pattern to make it more healthy.

### Are Dietary Guidelines Different for Different People?

During different stages of your life, your body will need the same nutrients but in different amounts. Your body will also need different amounts of calories. It depends on your stage of growth or development.

For example, during pregnancy, a woman needs more calories, protein, calcium, iron, and some vitamins than usual. These extra nutrients keep her healthy and make sure the baby will grow properly. In a family with small children and teenagers, each person might have different dietary needs. Each person does not need to eat different foods. Each needs to eat the same foods in different amounts, depending on age, activity level, and gender.

## technology

### COMPUTER PROGRAMS FOR DIET MANAGEMENT

Did you know that computer programs can help people improve their food choices? Some programs use the Food Guide Pyramid to make sure your diet is healthy and well-balanced. Others use an index to show how different foods affect the amount of sugar in your bloodstream. This is especially useful in controlling obesity and diabetes.

Using a computer program, you can make a daily menu. The program may also suggest sports, activities, and exercises to improve your health. Quizzes rate how well you are eating.

Some computer games help make healthy eating habits. As healthy food shoots down junk food, health suggestions seep into your awareness. These computer programs also include a healthy eating guide, body weight logs, body mass index, and a calorie tracking system. Would you like to try one of these computer programs?

Have students read about recommended dietary guidelines for different people on page 153.

### Ask:

- How does age affect the foods that the body needs? (The body needs different amounts of some nutrients and calories at different stages of development. Therefore, people need to eat foods in different amounts depending on factors such as age and gender.)

- How does pregnancy affect the body's nutritional needs? (A pregnant woman needs more calories and an increased amount of foods with protein, calcium, iron and certain vitamins to ensure that the baby will develop properly.)

## Technology

Encourage students to try a computer food planning program if they have access to a computer and the appropriate software. Ask students to evaluate the program in a review. Invite volunteers to share their review with the class.

### APPLICATION

**Career Connection**
Have students research and write a report about the educational requirements and job opportunities for nutritionists. Students should also explain what a nutritionist does and situations in which a person would consult one. Then have students interview a nutritionist about the importance of nutrition in maintaining health and treating illness.

## Healthy Subjects

The Body Mass Index (BMI) factors in the amount of body fat on the body, rather than just weight. After students calculate their BMI, have them compare it to the following chart:

| BMI | Health Risk |
|---|---|
| 20–25 | very low risk |
| 26–30 | low risk |
| 31–35 | moderate risk |
| 36–40 | high risk |
| 40+ | very high risk |

Emphasize that falling into the higher-risk categories doesn't mean a person is ill. It means that a person has an unhealthy amount of body fat and might want to lose weight to decrease the chance of getting some illnesses. This determination should be made by a doctor.

Have students read about the special dietary guidelines that apply to them on page 154.

## Lesson 5 Review Answers

1) The Food Guide Pyramid is an aid to help people decide what and how much to eat.
2) Answers will vary. Answers may include any three of the following: eat a wide variety of foods; balance the food you eat with physical activity; eat many grains, fruits, and vegetables each day; choose foods low in fat, saturated fat, and cholesterol; choose foods low in sugar.
3) Serving size is a way to measure the amount of different foods that should be eaten each day.
4) Answers will vary. Possible answers include: boys typically need more calories; girls usually need more iron.
5) Answers will depend on students' diet.

---

### Healthy Subjects

## Math

Have you ever wondered if your weight is right for your height and build? Find out by figuring out your body mass index. Let's say you weigh 145 pounds and are 6 feet tall.

1. Multiply your weight in pounds by 0.45.
   145 lb. × 0.45 = 65.25

2. Multiply your height in inches by 0.025.
   72 in. × 0.025 = 1.8

3. Multiply this number by itself.
   1.8 × 1.8 = 3.24

4. Divide the answer in step 1 by the answer in step 3.
   (65.25 ÷ 3.24 = 20.1).

Your number should fall between 19 and 25.

### What Special Dietary Guidelines Do You Have?

Because you are growing and changing, you probably need more calories, calcium, and iron than your parents do. Boys are usually larger and have more muscle mass than girls. Boys usually need more calories than girls do. Girls who are menstruating need more iron than boys. That's because girls lose iron each month when menstruating.

**LESSON 5 REVIEW** Write the answers to these questions on a separate sheet of paper. Use complete sentences.

1) What is the Food Guide Pyramid?
2) List three general dietary guidelines.
3) What is serving size?
4) Give one way that dietary guidelines differ for girls and boys.
5) Why might you need more calories, calcium, and iron than your parents?

---

**Name** _____ **Date** _____ **Period** _____  Chapter 7 / Activity / 27

## Dietary Guidelines

**Part A Directions** Place a check mark next to the *best* answer.

1) What is a serving size?
   a) 16 ounces or more
   b) a way to measure how much of a food should be eaten
   c) a measure of the fat in a serving of food
   d) a way to measure the calories in a serving of food

2) Who needs more calories, calcium, and iron?
   a) parents
   b) teenagers
   c) grandparents
   d) active businesspeople

3) Which of these is a general dietary guideline?
   a) Eat a wide variety of foods.
   b) Balance the foods you eat with physical activity.
   c) Eat many grains, fruits, and vegetables every day.
   d) all of the above

4) Different people need different amounts of foods depending on _____
   a) age.
   b) activity level.
   c) gender.
   d) all of the above

5) A chart that can be used to choose a healthy diet is _____
   a) the Food Guide Pyramid.
   b) the Recommended Daily Allowance chart.
   c) the Percent of Daily Diet chart.
   d) the Nutrition Facts label.

**Part B Directions** Write *T* if the statement is true or *F* if it is false.

____ 6) Choosing a diet low in sugar is part of a healthy diet.
____ 7) You should always choose the smaller serving on the Food Guide Pyramid.
____ 8) Breads and grains form the base of the Food Guide Pyramid.
____ 9) The National Food Service (NSF) created the Food Guide Pyramid.
____ 10) Teenage girls need more iron than teenage boys require.

**Activity 27**

---

**Name** _____ **Date** _____ **Period** _____  Chapter 7 / Workbook Activity / 27

## Dietary Guidelines

**Part A Directions** Write *T* if the statement is true or *F* if it is false.

____ 1) Teenage girls need more iron than teenage boys require.
____ 2) Choosing a diet low in sugar is part of a healthy diet.
____ 3) You should always choose the smaller serving on the Food Guide Pyramid.
____ 4) Breads and grains form the base of the Food Guide Pyramid.
____ 5) The National Food Service (NSF) created the Food Guide Pyramid.

**Part B Directions** Place a check mark next to the *best* answer.

6) A chart that can be used to choose a healthy diet is:
   a) the Food Guide Pyramid.
   b) the Recommended Daily Allowance chart.
   c) the Percent of Daily Diet chart.
   d) the Nutrition Facts label.

7) What is a serving size?
   a) 16 ounces or more
   b) a way to measure how much of a food should be eaten
   c) a measure of the fat in a serving of food
   d) a way to measure the calories in a serving of food

8) Who needs more calories, calcium, and iron?
   a) parents
   b) teenagers
   c) grandparents
   d) active businesspeople

9) Which of these is a general dietary guideline?
   a) Eat a wide variety of foods.
   b) Balance the foods you eat with physical activity.
   c) Eat many grains, fruits, and vegetables every day.
   d) all of the above

10) Different people need different amounts of foods depending on:
   a) age.
   b) activity level.
   c) gender.
   d) all of the above

**Workbook Activity 27**

# CHAPTER SUMMARY

■ The body uses three main steps to turn food you eat into energy. These steps are digestion, absorption, and metabolism.

■ Digestion is the process of breaking down food into nutrients that the body can use.

■ Absorption is the process of moving nutrients from the digestive system to the circulatory system. Once in the circulatory system, the nutrients are taken to cells throughout the body.

■ Metabolism is the process by which cells use nutrients for energy and other jobs.

■ Calories are used to measure the amount of energy in food.

■ The body needs six essential nutrients. These are carbohydrates, proteins, fats, vitamins, minerals, and water.

■ Carbohydrates, proteins, and fats give the body energy. Vitamins, minerals, and water do not give the body energy.

■ Fiber is the part of food that the body cannot digest. Although fiber is not a nutrient, it is an important part of a healthy diet.

■ Carbohydrates are found in grains, fruits, and vegetables. Complex carbohydrates give the body energy and fiber.

■ Protein also gives the body energy. Proteins are important for building and repairing tissue. Meat, cheese, eggs, and beans are good sources of protein.

■ A complete protein is one that contains the amino acids that the body cannot make. You can get complete proteins by eating foods from animals or by combining different foods from plants.

■ The body needs fats. Saturated fats are less healthy than polyunsaturated fats. However, too much of any fat can lead to or worsen heart disease.

■ The body also needs cholesterol. Too much cholesterol can build up in the blood vessels and prevent proper blood flow.

■ Vitamins and minerals help the body get and use the energy in other nutrients.

■ The Food Guide Pyramid can help you choose healthy foods in healthy amounts.

## ■ Using the Chapter Summary

To further reinforce the facts and concepts presented in the chapter, read and discuss with students the questions that follow.

### Ask:

- What is digestion? (Digestion is the process that breaks food down into nutrients that the body can use.)

- What is metabolism? (Metabolism is the process by which cells use nutrients for energy and other jobs.)

- What is a calorie? (A calorie is used to measure the amount of energy in food.)

- What are the six essential nutrients needed by the body? (The six essential nutrients are carbohydrates, protein, fats, vitamins, minerals, and water.)

- What is the importance of fiber in the diet? (The body cannot digest fiber, so it helps moves other foods along as it passes through the digestive system.)

- What is a complex carbohydrate, and why is it important? (Complex carbohydrates contain fiber and give the body energy.)

- What is a complete protein, and why is it important? (A complete protein contains all of the amino acids that the body cannot make. It is important because it is the body's only source of these amino acids.)

- What is the danger of eating too much fat? (Too much fat in the diet is unhealthy and can lead to problems such as heart disease and cancer.)

- How does the body use vitamins and minerals? (Vitamins and minerals help the body get and use other nutrients that provide energy.)

- Why is it important to drink enough water each day? (The body needs water to move nutrients through the blood.)

# Chapter 7 Review

The Teacher's Resource Library includes two parallel forms of the Chapter 7 Mastery Test. The difficulty level of the two forms is equivalent. You may wish to use one form as a pretest and the other form as a posttest.

## Review Answers

### Comprehension: Identifying Facts

1) digestion  2) absorption
3) metabolism  4) Calories
5) carbohydrates  6) fiber
7) amino acids  8) saturated

---

## Comprehension: Identifying Facts

On a separate sheet of paper, write the correct word or words from the Word Bank to complete each sentence.

### WORD BANK

| | |
|---|---|
| calories | polyunsaturated |
| digestion | metabolism |
| fiber | cholesterol |
| saturated | vitamins |
| Food Guide Pyramid | water |
| carbohydrates | absorption |
| amino acids | |

1) Food is broken down into nutrients by a process called _____.

2) When nutrients move from the small intestine into the bloodstream, _____ is taking place.

3) The process of _____ takes place inside cells.

4) _____ are used to measure the amount of energy in different foods.

5) Simple _____ are sometimes called "empty calories."

6) The part of food that the body cannot digest is called _____.

7) A complete protein is one that contains all nine of the _____ that the body cannot make on its own.

8) Fats that are usually solid at room temperature are called _____.

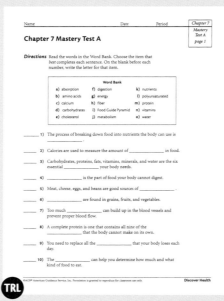

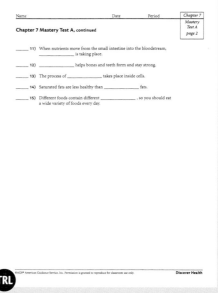

## Chapter 7 Mastery Test A

9) _____ fats come mostly from plants.

10) Too much _____ can clog blood vessels.

11) _____ and minerals do not give the body energy.

12) You need to replace all the _____ that your body loses each day.

13) The _____ can help you determine how much and what kind of foods to eat.

## Comprehension: Understanding Main Ideas

Write the answers to these questions on a separate sheet of paper. Use complete sentences.

14) What is a nutrient?

15) Give an example food for each of the six nutrients.

16) What does the body do with extra calories?

17) Give five dietary guidelines that most people should try to follow.

18) How can eating a wide variety of foods help you get the nutrients your body needs?

## Critical Thinking: Write Your Opinion

19) Do you eat a healthy diet? Explain your answer using the Food Guide Pyramid.

20) Which of your favorite foods are healthy? List the foods and the nutrients they contain.

**Test Taking Tip** Always read test directions more than once. Underline the words that tell you how many examples or items you are to give. Check the directions again after you have finished the test to make sure you have not forgotten anything.

9) Polyunsaturated 10) cholesterol
11) Vitamins 12) water
13) Food Guide Pyramid

## Comprehension: Understanding Main Ideas

14) A nutrient is a basic unit of food that the body can use.

15) Answers will vary. Answers include the following: carbohydrates—bread; proteins—meat; fats—margarine; vitamins—vitamin C in oranges; minerals—sodium in table salt; water.

16) The body stores extra calories as fat.

17) The five dietary guidelines that most people should try to follow are the following: eat a wide variety of foods; balance the food you eat with physical activity; eat many grains, fruits, and vegetables each day; choose a diet low in fat, saturated fat, and cholesterol; choose a diet low in sugar.

18) Different foods contain different nutrients, and no foods contain all the nutrients the body needs; therefore, eating a wide variety of foods can help you get the nutrients you need every day.

## Critical Thinking: Write Your Opinion

19) Answers will vary. Students should back up their opinion with information about what constitutes a healthy diet and their own food choices.

20) Answers will vary. Students should include information about the nutritional values of the foods they choose.

**Chapter 7 Mastery Test B**

## Introducing the Chapter

Ask students to pretend they are sitting
in a restaurant looking at a menu and
are about to choose a meal. What do they
consider when making their choice? Have
students call out their answers as you write
them on the board. Encourage students
to discuss the responses, including how
important nutrition is to them when
making the choice.

Have volunteers read page 158 aloud,
including the Goals for Learning.

### Ask:

• When you make a choice from the
  menu, what is the main thing that you
  consider? (Answers will vary. Student
  answers might include foods that they
  find tasty, foods other people are ordering,
  foods that look good, foods they don't
  eat at home, or foods that are nutritious.)

# Chapter 8

# Making Healthy Food Choices

The eating patterns you begin now will probably stay
with you for the rest of your life. That's why now is
a good time to learn about making wise food choices.

In this chapter, you will learn about healthy eating patterns.
You will learn about the factors, such as advertising, that
affect your food choices. You will also learn how to read a
food label. Finally, you will learn how the government helps
make sure foods are safe.

### Goals for Learning

▶ To recognize healthy eating patterns

▶ To describe what influences your food choices

▶ To read a food label to make a healthy food choice

▶ To describe how the government makes sure our food
   is safe to eat

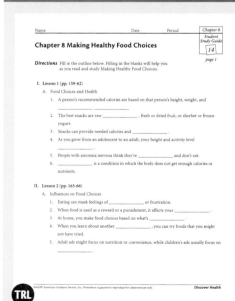

**Student Study Guide 14, page 1**

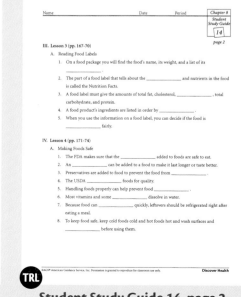

**Student Study Guide 14, page 2**

## Food Choices and Health

Your lifestyle and food choices affect your health. You face important food issues as you grow into a teenager. Some of these are your personal energy needs, snacking, weight changes, and diet-related problems. It's important to learn more about these issues and how they affect you.

### How Much Energy Do You Need Each Day?

Your energy needs will vary during different stages of your life. Until you were one year old, you needed only 650–850 calories each day. Your energy needs increased each year as you grew older. Beginning at about age 11, energy needs begin to differ among boys and girls. Boys usually need more calories than girls starting at this time. Between the ages of 11 and 14, an average boy will need about 2,500 calories. An average girl of the same age will need about 2,200 calories. The number of calories recommended for a person is based on his or her height, weight, and activity level. Around the age of 50, both males and females need fewer calories. Pregnant women and women who are breast-feeding babies need about 500 extra calories each day.

### Why Is Choosing Healthy Snacks Important?

Snacking is an important part of your diet. Your energy needs are high right now. This means that you need to eat more than you did just a few years ago. Snacks can help you get those extra calories and nutrients.

Snacks are also an important part of your lifestyle. You probably had some snacks with your family or friends over the last week. Look at the chart below. Did you choose any of these foods? For healthy snacks, choose these foods over cakes, candies, and high-fat cookies.

| Best Choices | Okay Choices |
| --- | --- |
| raw vegetables | flavored gelatin |
| fresh or dried fruit | fruited yogurt |
| sherbet or frozen yogurt | low-fat crackers or cookies |

*Nutrition Tip*

Nutritious snacks can be part of a healthy diet. Be careful to avoid snacking in place of regular meals. Late night snacking can disturb your sleep and affect your weight.

---

## Lesson at a Glance

### Chapter 8 Lesson 1

**Overview** This lesson explains why making healthy food choices is important. It also discusses how eating disorders affect health.

### Objectives

■ To recognize healthy eating patterns.

**Student Pages** 159–162

**Audiocassette**

**Teacher's Resource Library** TRL

    Activity 28

    Workbook Activity 28

## Teaching Suggestions

### ■ Vocabulary

*bloated, malnutrition, obesity*

Write the vocabulary words on the chalkboard and ask students to think about what they think these words mean. Then ask them to write down the meanings on a sheet of paper. As students read the chapter and learn the definitions of the words, have them revise their definitions if necessary.

### ■ Teaching the Lesson

Have students help you make a concept map that identifies major influences on food choices. Draw a circle on the board and write "Our Food Choices" in the center. Draw several spokes out from the circle. Ask students to brainstorm influences on food choices. Write each answer in a circle at the end of a spoke.

Have students read about energy needs and healthy snacks on page 159.

Ask:

• How do your energy needs change as you grow older? (As you grow older, you need increasing amount of energy until about age 50. Then energy needs decrease.)

• Why is it important to know about your energy needs? (Knowing your energy needs can help you determine how many calories you need to take in each day.)

• Why is snacking an important part of your diet? (Snacks can help you get the extra calories and nutrients you need.)

• Look at the snacks in the chart on the bottom of the page. How are they different from the snacks most people eat? (The snacks contain more fiber and complex carbohydrates and less fat and sugar than most snacks.)

Have students continue to read about snacking and ways to maintain a healthy weight on page 160.

Ask:

- Why is choosing healthy snacks especially important for teens? (Healthy snacks are especially important for teens because about one-third of a teen's diet comes from snacks rather than from meals.)

- How is body weight either gained or lost? (Body weight is either gained or lost depending on how many calories a person takes in through food and how many calories are used by the body.)

- Who should you consult before you go on a diet? (Before starting a diet, consult a doctor or dietitian to find out if you really need to lost weight. )

## APPLICATION

### At Home
Invite students to check their refrigerator and kitchen cabinets for snack foods. Suggest that students discuss with their parents how snack foods could be made more healthy. Also have students bring their lists of snack foods to class. Write some of them on the board. Are there certain types of foods that are found in many homes? Encourage students to talk about how healthy their snacking choices are.

Make good choices when you choose snacks.

A study of teenagers' eating habits was conducted. It found that about one-third of a teen's diet comes from snacks rather than from meals. You can see then why choosing healthy snacks is important. Snacks are an important part of your diet. They also provide needed calories and nutrients.

### How Can You Maintain a Healthy Weight?
Because adolescents grow at different rates, it is hard to give an exact number of calories. Body weight is either gained or lost depending on how many calories are taken in and how many are used by the body. As you grow into a young adult, your height and activity level will change. This will affect the number of calories your body needs and your weight.

Before you go on a diet, have a doctor or dietitian confirm that you need to change your weight. They can also help you make a healthy plan for changing your weight.

**160** *Chapter 8   Making Healthy Food Choices*

**Then and Now**

**RECIPES OLD AND NEW**

Compare the two recipes for plum pudding. One is from 1903. The other is from 1990.

**Plum Pudding (1903)**

3 cups beef fat

3 cups raisins

3 cups water

1 tsp. salt

$\frac{3}{4}$ cup sugar

3 cups flour

4 eggs

3 tsp. spices

**Plum Pudding (1990)**

$1\frac{1}{2}$ cups vegetable oil

6 cups raisins and chopped fruit

4 cups whole wheat bread crumbs

$1\frac{3}{4}$ cups fruit juice

1 cup brown sugar

2 cups whole wheat flour

6 eggs

3 tsp. spices

3 tbsp. lemon rind

The new recipe has less fat and more vitamins from fruit. It also has fiber from whole wheat. Today, many recipes can be made healthier.

## What Are Some Diet-Related Health Problems?

You know that eating too much or too little can affect your weight. It can also be a part of a larger eating disorder. An eating disorder is a pattern of eating that affects your health in a bad way. Eating disorders include anorexia and bulimia.

People who have anorexia choose not to eat because they think they are fat. A person with anorexia may eat little and exercise often until becoming life-threateningly thin.

People with bulimia tend to eat large amounts of food at one time. Then, they either throw up the food or use laxative drugs to rid their body of the food. A person with bulimia may appear to be the correct weight. However, the person can die from the unhealthy pattern of eating and ridding the body of food.

Have students look at the recipes and read about diet-related health problems on page 161.

## Then and Now

Ask students to get a family recipe from a parent or guardian. Challenge students to evaluate their recipes and figure out how they might change them to make the recipes more healthy. Suggest that students print or type up their recipes. Photocopy and bind the recipes in a "Healthy Family Recipes" booklet for each member of the class to take home.

### Ask:

- **What is an eating disorder?** (An eating disorder is a pattern of eating that is harmful to health.)

- **What is anorexia?** (Anorexia is an eating disorder in which a person avoids eating.)

- **What is bulimia?** (Bulimia is a pattern of eating too much food, then purging it from the body, usually by vomiting.)

- **What is obesity?** (Obesity is a condition in which one is more than 20 percent overweight.)

### LEARNING STYLES

**Group Learning** Challenge groups of students to find out more about the eating disorders introduced on this page. Encourage students to report on the causes and symptoms of the disorder, how it can affect health, and how it is treated. If possible, have students identify famous people who have had these disorders and have managed to become healthy again. Ask students to make reports to the class.

Have students continue reading about eating disorders and malnutrition on page 162.

Ask:

- Why is bulimia dangerous to health? (Bulimia is dangerous because the constant eating and artificially forcing the body to rid itself of food damages the body and can even cause death.)

- What is malnutrition? (Malnutrition is a condition in which the body does not get enough food.)

## Lesson 1 Review Answers

1) Weight, growth stage, age, activity level, and gender are factors that affect a person's energy needs.
2) Yes, snacking is part of a healthy diet. Snacking can help a person meet his or her energy and nutritional needs.
3) Answers will vary. Accept answers that include fruits, vegetables, and low-fat yogurt.
4) Anorexia is an eating disorder in which people choose not to eat because they think they are fat. Bulimia is an eating disorder in which people eat large amounts of food and then throw up the food to rid their body of the food.
5) Answers will vary. Answers should include the fact that choosing healthy foods affects a person's weight, overall health, and how they feel.

## GLOBAL CONNECTION

Have students look into the problem of malnutrition in many parts of the world. Challenge students to find out where people are malnourished and what the causes are. Have them also report on what, if anything, is being done to solve the problem.

## APPLICATION

### In the Community
Have students gather information about shelters and food banks in your community that feed the hungry and then report on their findings. Encourage students to volunteer at such a facility.

**162** *Chapter 8 Making Healthy Food Choices*

---

**Bloated**
*Swollen*

**Malnutrition**
*A condition in which the body does not get enough to eat*

**Obesity**
*A condition in which one is more than 20 percent overweight*

**Obesity** results when a person is more than 20 percent above a healthy weight. This condition often is caused by unhealthy eating habits and lack of activity. Obesity stresses the body and its organs. It can also cause related disorders.

Many people in the United States are overweight because they eat too much food. However, there are people around the world who do not have enough food to keep them healthy. Sometimes people even die from lack of enough food.

**Malnutrition** occurs when the body does not get enough calories or nutrients. There are two types of malnutrition. One type of malnutrition is caused by a lack of calories from protein. You may have seen pictures of children with this type of malnutrition. The children have thin legs and arms and huge, **bloated**, or swollen, stomachs. The second type of malnutrition occurs when a person does not get enough calories. This person is starving to death due to lack of food.

**LESSON 1 REVIEW** Write the answers to these questions on a separate sheet of paper. Use complete sentences.

1) What factors affect your energy needs?
2) Is snacking a part of a healthy diet? Explain.
3) Give three examples of healthy snacks.
4) Describe two eating disorders.
5) Explain why choosing healthy foods is important.

**162** *Chapter 8 Making Healthy Food Choices*

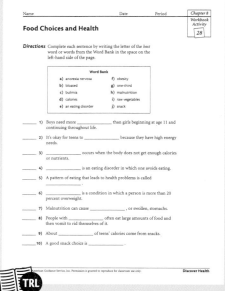

**Activity 28**

**Workbook Activity 28**

## Influences on Food Choices

Many things affect the way you eat. Usually, you probably are not even aware of all the reasons you eat certain foods. As a child, you ate foods that tasted good or that were prepared by people who cared for you. As you grew older, your friends and ads began to influence you.

### How Do Feelings Affect Your Food Choices?

Sometimes you eat foods just because they help you feel good. For example, after a hard day at school, have you ever headed for the refrigerator to find something to eat? Eating is usually a good experience. It can mask feelings of anger or frustration. Sometimes, people eat food to avoid facing their feelings or problems.

Other times, food is used as a reward or a punishment. Have you ever been rewarded with a special meal when you had a good report card? Or have you ever been sent away from the table because you were misbehaving? In both cases, your feelings were probably affected.

**Careers**

### DIETARY AIDE

Hospitals and nursing homes need dietary aides. These workers help prepare food for residents. Many dietary aides work on a tray assembly line. They follow directions about what should go on each person's tray. Then they deliver the trays. After a meal, they pick up the trays and return them to the kitchen. They record the amount of food patients eat. Aides may help sort recyclables and trash, wash dishes, and do other clean-up tasks. Dietary aides are sometimes called food service workers. Dietary aides usually receive on-the-job training.

*Making Healthy Food Choices*    Chapter 8    **163**

---

## Lesson at a Glance

### Chapter 8  Lesson 2

**Overview** In this lesson, students learn how environment, culture, people around us, and advertising influence our food choices.

### Objectives

- To identify what influences food choices.

**Student Pages** 163–166

**Audiocassette**

**Teacher's Resource Library** **TRL**

Activity 29
Workbook Activity 29

## Teaching Suggestions

### ■ Teaching the Lesson

Show students two pictures of the same food, one appetizing and the other less so. Ask students which food they would choose. Remind students that the foods are the same. Ask them why they chose one over the other. Discuss with students the effect that making a food look attractive can have on the choice of a food.

Then have students read about how feelings affect food choice on page 163.

Ask:

- How is eating food sometimes connected with the way people feel? (Accept all reasonable answers. Answers can include: eating to hide anger or frustration, eating to avoid problems, eating as a reward or punishment.)

### Careers

Invite a dietary aide to class to speak to students about his or her job. Have the speaker concentrate on the duties of a typical day. Also have the speaker talk about the training he or she received. Tell students to prepare questions for the speaker before the class visit.

Have students read about how environment affects food choice on page 164.

Ask:

- How does eating at home affect your choice of foods? (When you eat at home, your choices are limited by the foods that are in the house.)

- What limits your food choices at a restaurant? (At a restaurant, you are limited by what is on the menu.)

- What influences your food choices when you eat in the school cafeteria? (When you eat in the school cafeteria, you can only eat what is available. You also may be influenced by the choices of your friends.)

Children choosing what to eat in the school cafeteria.

### How Does Your Environment Affect Your Food Choices?

Your environment also affects your food choices. You may make most of your food choices in your home environment. You make choices based on which foods are available.

**Writing About Health**

Think about the food choices you have made. Compare one influence that resulted in a healthy meal with one that resulted in poor food choices.

A restaurant is another environment that can affect your food choices. The foods you can choose are limited to those on the menu. A restaurant may offer only foods high in fat and calories. Then your healthy food choices will be limited.

You also make food choices at school. You may choose to eat in the school cafeteria or to bring your own lunch. At school, the foods available in the cafeteria line affect you. So do the food choices of your friends and peers.

**164**    *Chapter 8    Making Healthy Food Choices*

### How Do People Affect Your Food Choices?

You might make some food choices for social reasons. For example, you might eat a food you don't like just because your friends eat it. Suppose a friend makes fun of a food you like to eat. Then you might decide not to eat it around that friend. You might decide that you don't really like the food after all.

As a baby, you couldn't make many food choices. Your family gave you foods that they thought were good for you. Your family probably still has a lot of influence on your food choices. Sometimes family members can influence you to eat foods that you don't really want. For example, after seeing your parents eat certain foods over time, you may be influenced to try those foods.

This family influence can be positive because you might try vegetables that you otherwise would not. But it can also be less positive. For example, you might find it hard to say no to sweets and desserts. You might not want to hurt someone's feelings.

### How Does Culture Affect Your Food Choices?

Culture can have a lot of influence on your food choices. Many foods you eat with your family may be recipes passed down from generation to generation. You might also eat traditional foods on holidays that are special to your culture or religion. One benefit of learning about other cultures is that you can try foods that you might not be used to.

### How Does Advertising Affect Your Food Choices?

Food companies spend millions of dollars studying why people buy certain foods. Using this information, they target different groups of people in their ads and food packages. When advertisers target young children, for example, they make their ads using cartoons or toys. These ads usually show how much fun the food is to eat. Adult ads might focus on nutrition or convenience rather than on fun.

*Fitness Tip*

Take a walk after a large meal.

Have students read about how people, culture, and advertising affect food choices on page 165.

Ask:

- How can your friends influence your choice of foods? (You might be influenced to eat a food you might not have tried because a friend eats it or to avoid a food you like because a friend makes fun of it.)

- How does your family affect your food choices? (When you are young, your family chooses your foods for you. You also might be influenced to eat foods you often see your family eat.)

- How does your family's culture affect the foods you choose? (You might eat many foods that are family recipes or holidays dishes that are special to your culture or religion.)

- How does advertising affect your choice of foods? (Advertisers study why people buy certain foods, then produce ads that use the information to make the foods seem appealing.)

 **MULTICULTURAL CONNECTION**

Most families have special dishes that are connected with their cultural or religious background. Invite students to share one of these dishes with the class, either by describing it, drawing it, bringing in a photo of the dish, or bringing a sample in for the class to taste. Have the student list the foods that are in the dish and how they are connected to the geography of the area from which the dish comes. For example, northern European dishes might contain potatoes because they grow plentifully there, while dishes from Hawaii might contain more fish or tropical fruits. Have students evaluate the dish nutritionally as well.

Have students read the Action for Health feature on page 166.

## Action for Health

While students are looking at food and drink ads on TV, have them apply what they have learned about advertising. Have students tape a TV commercial, then play the tape in class while explaining how the advertisers have constructed the ad to make the food seem more appealing. Have the class decide whether or not the ad is effective.

## Lesson 2 Review Answers

1) Any of the following can affect food choices: feelings, environment, culture, people, advertising.

2) Answers will vary, depending on the feelings and food choices.

3) Answers will vary, depending on the food available at your school's cafeteria.

4) Answers will vary, depending on students' cultural and religious backgrounds.

5) Answers will vary, depending on reasons why students make particular choices during a day.

## APPLICATION

**Career Connection**
Have students research product advertising to find out the strategies that advertisers use to sell foods to the public. Direct students to also interview someone in the advertising business on the same subject. Discuss the marketing strategies they discover.

---

### Action for Health

### EXAMINE FOOD ADVERTISING

For a few days, look for food and drink ads on TV and radio, in magazines and newspapers, and on billboards. Then walk through your local grocery store. Find two or three products that you saw ads for. Notice where in the store these items are located.

Then, carefully read the list of ingredients on the packages. The ingredients that are listed first will make up more of the food than the other ingredients. What are the main ingredients in the products? How healthy do you think these products are? Do you think the advertising that you saw presented a fair picture of the product?

A food's package is also made to attract a person's attention. Often the food is put in a large or colorful package. Then, it is easier to spot in the store. Foods are put into large displays in supermarkets to get your attention. Foods that small children like are put on low shelves that they can reach.

**LESSON 2 REVIEW** Write the answers to these questions on a separate sheet of paper. Use complete sentences.

1) List four things that affect your food choices.

2) Describe a time when your feelings affected your food choices.

3) What kinds of food choices are available in your school cafeteria?

4) What is the purpose of a large, colorful food display in a grocery store?

5) Make a list of the reasons you choose certain foods during one day.

**Activity 29**

**Workbook Activity 29**

## Lesson 3

### Reading Food Labels

**Lot number**
*A number that identifies a group of packages*

$A$n important part of healthy eating is being able to read and understand the labels on packages. By reading food labels, you can determine the nutritional value of foods. You can also compare one product with another one, so you can make the healthier choice.

#### What Does the Package Tell You?

In the United States, food sold in packages must have certain information on the label. The package must include what is inside and how it should be stored. The package should give the weight and **lot number** of the food. A lot number is a number that identifies a group of packages. Many packages have a certain date by which the food should be used.

Some things that must be on the package are listed below:

- the name of the product
- the product's weight
- a list of the product's ingredients
- the manufacturer's name and address
- a food label

**Healthy Subjects**

**Math**

In the past, scientists used the calorie to measure energy. However, the popularity and widespread use of the International System of Units changed the unit scientists use to measure energy. The International System of Units is usually abbreviated SI, for *le Système International d'Unités*. It is sometimes referred to as metric units.

The SI unit for measuring energy is the joule. Because scientists still have to use the old research, they sometimes have to convert back and forth from calories to joules. One calorie is 4.184 joules.

*Making Healthy Food Choices  Chapter 8*  **167**

### Healthy Subjects

Have students convert the calories in the foods below to joules:

| Food | Calories | Joules |
|---|---|---|
| pear | 97 | 405,848 |
| cookie | 34 | 142,256 |
| slice cheese | 93 | 389,112 |

Ask students if they see a potential problem in working with joules instead of calories. (Students might suggest that the units are much larger and harder to use in calculations.)

## Lesson at a Glance

### Chapter 8  Lesson 3

**Overview** In this lesson, students learn about the information on food labels.

### Objectives

- To read and understand a food label.

**Student Pages** 167–170
**Audiocassette**
**Teacher's Resource Library** (TRL)

Activity 30
Workbook Activity 30

## Teaching Suggestions

#### ■ Vocabulary
*lot number, Nutrition Facts, Daily Values*

Have students read the definitions of these vocabulary words. Then have students write original sentences using the words. Ask for volunteers to read their sentences to the class.

#### ■ Teaching the Lesson
Ask students to write a short paragraph on what they look for on a food label. Have students take turns reading their paragraphs aloud. Write some of their ideas on the board. Have students compare what they know now about labels with what they learn after reading the lesson.

Have students read about what a package can tell you on page 167.

Ask:

- What is a lot number? (a number that identifies a group of packages)

- Name some things that must be on a food package. (the name of the product, the product's weight, a list of the product's ingredients, the manufacturer's name and address, a food label)

Have students read the material on food labels on page 168.

Ask:

- **What information can you get from a food label?** (A food label contains the following information: number of servings in the package, number of calories per serving, number of calories from fat, amount of nutrients.)

- **What are nutrition facts?** (Nutrition facts is the part of a food label that tells the number of calories and amount of nutrients in food.)

Direct the attention of students to the food label on the page.

- **How many servings are in this can of tuna?** (There are about 2.5 servings in the can.)

- **How many total calories are in the can?** (There are 150 calories in the can.)

- **What vitamins and minerals are in the tuna?** (Sodium, iron, niacin, vitamins B-6 and B-12, and phosphorus are in the tuna.)

## LEARNING STYLES

**Visual** Invite students to imagine that they are packaging a favorite food they prepare. Their task is to create a food label for it. The information will not be exact, but students should include as many parts of the label as they can approximate: ingredients, serving size, calories, vitamins and nutrients in the food. Encourage students to draw their labels on large poster board and present them in class.

## CHUNK LIGHT TUNA IN WATER

| Nutrition Facts | Amount/Serving | %DV* | Amount/Serving | %DV* |
|---|---|---|---|---|
| Serv. Size 2 oz. drained (56g / about ¼ cup) Servings about 2.5 | Total Fat 0.5g | 1% | Total Carb. 0g | 0% |
| | Sat. Fat 0g | 0% | Fiber 0g | 0% |
| Calories 60 Fat Cal. 5 | Cholest. 30mg | 10% | Sugars 0g | |
| | Sodium 250mg | 10% | Protein 13g | 23% |

\* Percent Daily Values (DV) are based on a 2,000 calorie diet.

Vitamin A 0% • Vitamin C 0% • Calcium 0% • Iron 2% • Niacin 20% • Vitamin B-6 8% • Vitamin B-12 20% • Phosphorus 8%

**INGREDIENTS:** LIGHT TUNA, WATER, VEGETABLE BROTH, HYDROLYZED CASEIN, HYDROLYZED SOY PROTEIN, SALT.

**Figure 8.1.** What can you find out by reading this food label?

Nutrition Facts
*The part of a food label that tells about the calories and nutrients in the food*

## What Are Food Labels?

You have probably seen many food labels. Figure 8.1 above shows a food label from a can of tuna. Food labels are one piece of information that must be included on a food's package. The United States government sets guidelines that tell which information must be on a food label.

## What Information Can You Get From a Food Label?

Find the heading **Nutrition Facts** on the food label above. The Nutrition Facts tell the size of one serving. Note that one serving of tuna is 2 oz., or about $\frac{1}{4}$ cup. The label also tells how many servings are in the whole package. If you eat the whole can of tuna, you will get 2.5 servings. Nutrition Facts also list the number of calories per serving and the number of calories from fat. For each serving of the tuna that you eat, you will get sixty calories. Five of these sixty calories will be from fat.

## What Are Daily Values?

Another part of the Nutrition Facts is the percent of the **Daily Value** for each nutrient in the food. These percentages tell you how much of that nutrient is found in the food. These numbers are based on a diet of 2,000 calories per day. Find the Daily Value percentage for sodium on the food label in Figure 8.1. One serving of tuna has 10 percent of the Daily Value for sodium.

Under Daily Values, a food label must give the amounts of total fat, cholesterol, sodium, total carbohydrate, and protein. Amounts are given in either grams (g) or milligrams (mg). You learned in Chapter 7 that these are important nutrients to track in your diet. Thus, you can see how helpful food labels can be in choosing to eat a healthy diet.

## What Other Information Is on the Food Label?

The Nutrition Facts must also show the amount of vitamin A, vitamin C, calcium, and iron in the food. What percentage of these vitamins and minerals are found in tuna? Notice that the label may list other vitamins and minerals. This information is also listed as a percentage of the 2,000 calories daily diet.

The food label must also give all the ingredients that are in the food. Find the list of ingredients on the food label in Figure 8.1. These ingredients are listed in order by weight, from the most to the least. For example, in the can of tuna, light tuna is the first ingredient. This means that the weight of the tuna weighs more than any other ingredient in the can.

Look at the food label for a can of soup. You will probably find that water is the first ingredient. The water in the soup probably weighs more than any other ingredient. The list of ingredients can help you find out whether the food has an ingredient you are allergic to. It's also helpful for people who need to avoid certain ingredients for other health reasons.

Have students read about daily values and other information on food labels on page 169.

Ask:

- What do daily values on a food label tell you? (Daily values are the part of the label that tells the percentage of nutrients in food based on 2,000 calories per day.)

- Why is the daily values part of a label important for people who want to plan a nutritious diet? (The daily values section tells you how much of important nutrients such as cholesterol, fat, sodium, carbohydrate, and protein the food contains.)

- If you see a can of juice with the following list of ingredients, what can you tell about the amount of juice the can contains: water, sugar, corn syrup, grape juice. (The label tell you that the juice is mostly water and sugar and contains little grape juice.)

- How can labels help people who have allergies? (The labels can tell people with allergies if a food contains an ingredient to which they are allergic.)

### LEARNING STYLES

 **Group Learning** Challenge groups of students to research the nutrition descriptions that appear on labels, such as "fat free," "low fat," "light," and "good source of iron." Have them find out what these terms mean and whether there are strict guidelines for them. For example, "fat free" doesn't mean a food has no fat at all. It just means that the amount is small and probably won't affect the body. Allow students to share their findings with the class.

## Action for Health

Have students check grocery store shelves to compare the prices of the brands of food labels they collected. Are they different? If so, is this based on size? Is one package bigger than another? Or does the price seem to be based on something else, such as different types of ingredients, nutrition claims on the label, or the fact that one brand is advertised more than the others? Invite students to discuss their ideas.

## Lesson 3 Review Answers

1) Answers include any three of the following: the name of the product, the product's weight, a list of the product's ingredients, the manufacturer's name and address, the product's Nutrition Facts, information comparing the product's nutrients to Daily Values.

2) Daily Values are based on a 2,000-calorie diet.

3) The order of ingredients on a food label can tell you which ingredients are most prominent in the food.

4) It is important to know the serving size of a food because you then know if you are eating too much or too little of the food.

5) Tuna provides niacin and vitamin B12.

## BACKGROUND INFORMATION

Labels contain dates that are clues to the food's age or freshness. These dates are common on dairy products such as milk and ice cream, on eggs, and on baked foods such as breads and cakes. "Sell by" dates are also called pull dates. This is the last date that the food should be sold by the store. The "best if used by" date indicates that the food should be used by that date for best quality. However, the food might still be good beyond this date.

---

## Action for Health

### COMPARING FOOD LABELS

Collect food labels from several brands of a similar food. For example, you might collect the food labels for five different kinds of chips or cold cereals. Make sure the foods are similar.

Then, carefully read the food labels for each food. First, check the serving sizes. Are they the same? Why might a company alter its suggested serving size? Then compare the Nutrition Facts for each food. What does your comparison show? Is one brand healthier than another? Will this information change your food choices in the future?

### Why Should You Read Food Labels?

All of the information on the food label can be helpful in making healthy food choices. If you are trying to limit a substance in your diet, the label tells you how much is in one serving of the food.

By using the information on the food label, you can tell if the food is priced fairly. You can look at the price and the number of servings and figure out how much each serving costs. Then, compare that amount with other brands to see which product is the best value.

**LESSON 3 REVIEW** Write the answers to these questions on a separate sheet of paper. Use complete sentences.

1) What three pieces of information can you find on a package of food?

2) What are Daily Values based on?

3) What can the order of ingredients on a food label tell you about the food inside?

4) Why is it important to know the serving size of a food?

5) Look at the food label for tuna in Figure 8.1. For which vitamins does tuna provide more than 10 percent Daily Values?

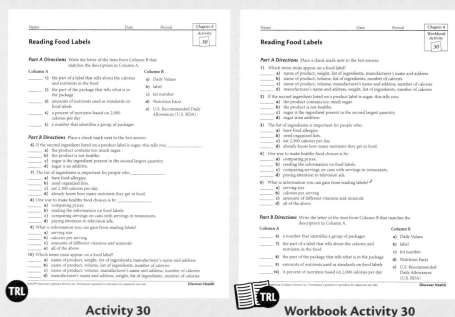

Activity 30            Workbook Activity 30

**Additive**
*A chemical added to food to make it better in some way*

**Enrichment**
*Adding extra nutrients to a food*

**Fortification**
*Adding a nutrient that a food lacks*

**Preservative**
*A chemical added to food to prevent spoiling*

$M$any government agencies monitor the safety of all food sold in the United States. These agencies make rules that help keep foods safe. They can also help if you feel that food safety is at risk in places that sell food. You can take steps in your own home to reduce the risk of illness from foods.

### What Does the FDA Do?

You learned about food labels in Lesson 3. The U.S. Food and Drug Administration (FDA) determines what information to include on food labels. The FDA also determines which foods can be sold and what claims manufacturers can make about the foods they sell. An example of a nutritional claim is "low fat" or "high in fiber." Manufacturers must follow the guidelines set up by the FDA when they make such claims.

If you have read the list of ingredients on many food labels, you know that many chemicals are added to foods. The FDA makes sure that these chemicals are tested and are safe to eat.

### Why Are Chemicals Added to Food?

Chemicals are added to foods for many reasons. For example, **additives** are added to a food to make it better. An additive may be added to a food to make it last longer. Additives also make foods taste better. They improve the texture and appearance of foods, too.

**Preservatives** are added to food to keep germs from growing in them. Preservatives allow food to travel long distances across the United States without spoiling. This allows more people to be fed.

Sometimes vitamins and minerals are added to foods for **enrichment** or **fortification**. Enrichment means nutrients are added to the food because they have been lost during processing. Breads and cereals are often enriched with minerals to make them healthier.

*Making Healthy Food Choices* Chapter 8 **171**

---

- **What are food additives, and why are they used?** (Food additives are chemicals added to foods to improve them in some way. Additives can make foods last longer, taste better, or improve texture or appearance.)

- **What does a preservative do when added to a food?** (Preservatives keep food from spoiling.)

- **What is the enrichment of a food?** (Enrichment is the addition to foods of nutrients that have been lost during processing.)

---

## Teaching Suggestions

### ■ Vocabulary

*additive, enrichment, fortification, preservative, contaminate*

Have students read the definitions of the vocabulary words. Which of the words might be found on a food label? (*additive, enrich* or *enrichment, fortified* or *fortification, preservative*) Which word would probably not be found on a food label? (*contaminate*)

### ■ Teaching the Lesson

Ask students who or what monitors food safety in the United States. Where do the rules for food safety come from? Write their suggestions on the board.

Then have students read about the Food and Drug Administration (FDA) and chemical food additives on page 171.

Ask:

- **What does the FDA do?** (The FDA determines what information goes on food labels. It also determines which foods can be sold and which claims food makers can put on their labels. The FDA also makes sure that chemicals put into foods are safe.)

Have students read about other government agencies that control food safety and how to handle foods safely on page 172.

Ask:

- What is the fortification of food? (Fortification adds nutrients to foods that are naturally low in those nutrients.)

- What other agencies, in addition to the FDA, help to control food safety? (The U.S. Department of Agriculture and local and state Public Health departments also control food safety.)

- How does the USDA help make the foods we eat safe? (The USDA grades foods such as meat so that people will know their quality. It inspects meat-packing plants and food processors to make sure that foods are packaged and stored safely.)

- How do local and state public health departments monitor food safety? (Local public health departments inspect restaurants to make sure they are clean and that equipment that heats and cools food is working properly.)

- How can food become contaminated? (Food can become contaminated by contact with germs or toxins that cause food poisoning.)

## BACKGROUND INFORMATION

For more information on government agencies that deal with food safety, students with access to a computer and the Internet can look at their web sites. The Food and Drug Administration can be found at www.fda.gov. The United States Department of Agriculture's web site is www.usda.gov.

---

**Contaminate**
*Infect by contact with germs or toxins*

Fortification means certain nutrients are added because the food is naturally low in those nutrients. Milk is fortified with vitamin D. Some brands of orange juice are fortified with calcium. Sometimes foods that are low in all nutrients are fortified to make them healthier. Punch is often fortified with vitamins. Some sugared breakfast cereals are also fortified with nutrients. Without fortification, punch and some breakfast cereals would provide calories but few nutrients.

### Which Other Agencies Control Food Safety?
The U.S. Department of Agriculture (USDA) and the Public Health Department are two other agencies that work to keep food safe. The USDA is a federal agency. The Public Health Department is a state or local agency.

The USDA grades foods for quality so that buyers know what they are buying. Meat is an example of a food that receives grades from the USDA. The USDA also makes sure that meat-packaging plants are clean. They carry out inspections to make sure that the foods are packaged and stored properly.

The Public Health Department inspects restaurants. They make sure that restaurants are clean. They make sure that safe practices are used when food is handled. A health inspector might check the temperature of refrigerators and steam tables at a restaurant. Inspectors want to make sure cold foods are kept cold enough and hot foods are kept hot enough.

### Why Should You Learn to Handle Food Properly?
There are two main reasons why you should learn how to handle foods properly. First, you want to make sure nutrients are not lost when you store and cook foods. Second, you want to make sure that foods do not make you sick. Foods can become infected, or **contaminated** with germs or toxins that cause food poisoning. Handling foods properly prevents this.

Wash fruits and vegetables before eating or cooking them.

### How Can You Keep Nutrients in Your Foods?

One way to keep nutrients from being lost is to use fresh foods within days after buying them. When preparing foods, cook vegetables as little as possible. Remember that most vitamins and some minerals dissolve in water. If foods are cooked in water, you may be throwing away vitamins and minerals with the water. You can steam vegetables or quickly stir-fry them instead.

### How Can You Keep Foods Safe to Eat?

Cold foods should be kept cold—at 40 degrees Fahrenheit or below. Hot foods should be cooked until they reach 140 degrees Fahrenheit. Germs grow quickly at room temperature. Foods left at room temperature for even twenty minutes can spoil and can cause illness. Therefore, leftovers should be refrigerated right after you eat a meal.

*Making Healthy Food Choices*    *Chapter 8*    **173**

Have students read about how to keep nutrients in food and maintain food safety on page 173.

Ask:

- Name two ways to keep nutrients in foods. (Nutrients can be kept in foods by using fresh foods quickly after they are purchased and by cooking vegetables as little as possible.)

- Why is it dangerous to leave foods at room temperature? (Foods that are left at room temperature can spoil.)

- Why is it important to wash fruits and vegetables before eating or cooking them? (Fruits and vegetables can have germs on them that could make you sick if they are not washed off.)

### APPLICATION

**Environment**
Some people think that eating organic foods is a good way to keep toxins out of food and out of the environment. Instruct students to look at sources in the library and on the Internet to find out what organic produce is and why it might be safer to eat. If possible, have students interview an organic farmer or a grocer who sells organic foods. After students do their research, have the class split into two groups to debate the pros and cons of organic food.

Have students read the information on keeping food safe on page 174.

Ask:

- What are the four main rules for keeping food safe? (The rules for keeping food safe are the following: keep cold foods cold and hot foods hot; always wash hands with warm, soapy water before touching food or utensils; wash surfaces and utensils before using them; do not handle food if you have an open wound on your hand.)

- Why is it necessary to wash countertops carefully after preparing raw meat on them? (Countertops must be washed carefully after meat preparation because the meat can leave germs on the surface that could contaminate other foods.)

## Lesson 4 Review Answers

1) Answers may include any two of the following: FDA, USDA, Public Health Department.
2) Fortified food has nutrients added because the food is naturally low in those nutrients. Enriched food has added nutrients because they have been lost during processing.
3) Answers include any two of the following: use fresh foods within days after buying them; when preparing foods, cook vegetables as little as possible; steam or quickly stir fry vegetables instead of cooking them in lots of water.
4) Answers include any three of the following: keep cold foods cold and hot foods hot; always wash hands with warm, soapy water before touching food or utensils; wash surfaces and utensils before using them; do not handle foods if you have an open wound on your hand.
5) Answers will vary and may include washing the cutting board, utensils, your hands, and the kitchen countertops.

---

Food can be contaminated with germs when people who are sick handle it. Do not handle foods if you have an open wound on your hands. You should also always wash your hands with warm, soapy water before handling any foods or utensils. Foods can be contaminated if the countertop or your utensils have germs on them. Always cook with clean utensils and in areas that have been cleaned properly.

Always clean up carefully and quickly after cooking with meat. If you put raw chicken on a cutting surface, clean the surface with hot, soapy water before putting any other ingredients on it. Otherwise, those ingredients could become contaminated with germs. Use the rules below to help you remember these safe practices.

> **Rules for Keeping Food Safe**
> - Keep cold foods cold and hot foods hot.
> - Always wash your hands with warm, soapy water before touching food or utensils.
> - Wash surfaces and utensils before using them.
> - Do not handle foods if you have an open wound on your hands.

**LESSON 4 REVIEW** Write the answers to these questions on a separate sheet of paper. Use complete sentences.

1) What are the names of two agencies that help keep food in the United States safe?
2) What is the difference between fortified food and enriched food?
3) What are two things you can do to make sure the foods you prepare do not lose their nutrients?
4) What are three things you can do to keep the foods you cook at home safe?
5) You have just cut up raw chicken on a cutting board. What should you do next?

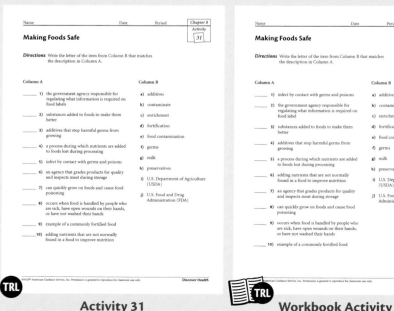

**Activity 31**        **Workbook Activity 31**

■ The amount of energy you need will change over the course of your life. A person's energy needs depend on his or her height, weight, activity level, and stage of growth.

■ Teenagers may get as much as one-third of their daily calories from snacks. Choosing healthy snacks is one way for teenagers to get the extra nutrients and calories that are needed for growth.

■ Anorexia and bulimia are life-threatening eating disorders. By eating too little or too much, a person can harm his or her body.

■ Malnutrition results from lack of calories or nutrients.

■ Feelings, environment, people, culture, and advertising can all affect your food choices. It is important to know what these things are so you can make healthy food choices.

■ If only unhealthy foods are available, you will have limited healthy choices. You may choose to eat some foods because others like them, rather than because you like them.

■ Advertisers use different techniques to get people to buy certain foods. Foods are advertised in ways that will make you notice them and want to buy them.

■ Food labels include information about the food inside. Labels include Nutrition Facts, Daily Values information, and a list of ingredients.

■ Nutrition Facts tell serving size, number of servings in the package, and number of calories per serving.

■ Daily Values show the percentage of nutrients in a 2,000-calorie diet.

■ The U.S. government has set up agencies to make sure foods are labeled correctly and are safe to eat.

■ Different chemicals are added to foods. Additives are used to improve flavor or some other characteristic of food. Preservatives are used to prevent spoiling.

■ By handling foods safely, you can prevent food poisoning and keep foods nutritious.

*Making Healthy Food Choices* Chapter 8 **175**

## ■ Using the Chapter Summary

To further reinforce the facts and concepts presented in the chapter, read and discuss with students the questions that follow.

### Ask:

- On what do a person's energy needs depend? (Energy needs depend on a person's height, weight, activity level, and stage of growth.)

- Why is it important for teenagers to choose healthy snacks? (Teenagers need to choose healthy snacks because they get as much as one-third of their daily calories from snacks.)

- Why are anorexia and bulimia dangerous eating disorders? (These are dangerous eating disorders because eating too little, too much, or artificially purging your body of food can be life threatening.)

- List some influences on food choices. (Influences on food choices include feelings, environment, other people, advertising, and culture.)

- How does advertising affect your choice of foods? (Foods are advertised in a way that makes them appealing so you will notice them and want to buy them.)

- What information is included on food labels? (Information on food labels includes a list of ingredients, serving size, number of servings, calories per serving, number of calories from fat, major nutrients, and the percentage of your daily requirements of certain nutrients that you can get from the food.)

- Why are additives put into foods? (Additives are used to improve flavor, texture, or nutritional content of foods.)

- How can you prevent food from getting contaminated? (You can prevent food from getting contaminated by keeping cold foods cold and hot foods hot, washing hands before handling food, keeping countertops and utensils clean, and avoiding handling food when you have an open wound on your hand.)

The Teacher's Resource Library includes two parallel forms of the Chapter 8 Mastery Test. The difficulty level of the two forms is equivalent. You may wish to use one form as a pretest and the other form as a posttest.

### Review Answers

**Comprehension: Identifying Facts**

1) fortification  2) enrichment  3) weight
4) Snacks  5) chemicals  6) nutrients
7) food poisoning  8) diet  9) serving size

## Chapter 8 Review

### Comprehension: Identifying Facts

On a separate sheet of paper, write the correct word or words from the Word Bank to complete each sentence.

| WORD BANK | |
|---|---|
| fortification | serving size |
| Public Health Department | weight |
| diet | USDA |
| food poisoning | wash |
| chemicals | room temperature |
| nutrients | snacks |
| enrichment | |

1) Adding calcium to orange juice is an example of _____.

2) Adding nutrients to punch is an example of _____.

3) Energy needs vary depending on your height, _____, activity level, and stage of growth.

4) _____ are an important part of a healthy diet.

5) Preservatives are _____ that are added to foods to prevent spoiling.

6) If foods are not handled properly, they can lose their _____.

7) When left at room temperature, some foods can become contaminated and can cause _____.

8) Daily Values are based on a 2,000-calorie _____ per day.

9) The _____ on a food label tells you how much of the food is used for the Nutrition Facts.

### Chapter 8 Mastery Test A

**Chapter 8 Mastery Test A** — Chapter 8 Mastery Test A page 1

**Directions** Circle the letter of the answer that *best* completes each sentence.

1) A person's energy needs depend on his or her height, weight, _____, and state of growth.
 a) interests
 b) hair color
 c) activity level
 d) shoe size

2) An example of a healthy snack is _____
 a) raw vegetables.
 b) candy.
 c) cake.
 d) potato chips.

3) Anorexia and _____ are life-threatening eating disorders.
 a) balotia
 b) bulimia
 c) additives
 d) contamination

4) _____ are added to a food to make it better.
 a) Fortifications
 b) Additives
 c) Contaminations
 d) Malnutrition

5) To allow food to travel long distances without spoiling, _____ are added.
 a) preservatives
 b) additives
 c) nutrients
 d) enrichments

6) Adding minerals to cereal is an example of _____
 a) contamination.
 b) obesity.
 c) enrichment.
 d) bulimia.

7) Taste, _____, friends, and family all influence the foods you eat.
 a) refrigeration
 b) lot numbers
 c) snacks
 d) advertising

**Chapter 8 Mastery Test A, continued** — Chapter 8 Mastery Test A page 2

8) Daily values are based on a 2,000-calorie _____ per day.
 a) weight
 b) nutrients
 c) diet
 d) serving size

9) Foods can become infected, or contaminated, with _____ that cause food poisoning.
 a) fiber
 b) vitamins
 c) ingredients
 d) germs

10) The _____ inspects meat-packaging plants and grades meat products.
 a) Public Health Department
 b) U.S. Department of Agriculture (USDA)
 c) Food and Drug Administration (FDA)
 d) restaurant

11) Germs can grow quickly at _____
 a) contamination.
 b) night.
 c) room temperature.
 d) refrigerated spaces.

12) _____ results from lack of calories or nutrients.
 a) Malnutrition
 b) Obesity
 c) Bloated
 d) Weight

13) Food labels include Nutrition Facts, Daily Values information, and a list of _____
 a) diets.
 b) chemicals.
 c) advertisements.
 d) ingredients.

14) If foods are not handled properly, they can lose their _____
 a) taste.
 b) nutrients.
 c) contamination.
 d) fortification.

15) All of the information on the _____ can be helpful in making healthy food choices.
 a) USDA
 b) lot number
 c) food label
 d) FDA

**10)** The _____ inspects restaurants.

**11)** The _____ inspects meat-packaging plants and grades meat products.

**12)** Before handling food, you should always _____ your hands with warm, soapy water.

**13)** Germs can grow quickly at _____.

### Comprehension: Understanding Main Ideas

Write the answers to these questions on a separate sheet of paper. Use complete sentences.

**14)** If you think that you are overweight, what should you do?

**15)** How might a food advertiser try to convince a young child that its product is good?

**16)** List three things that affect your food choices.

**17)** What are some reasons additives are added to foods?

**18)** List three things you can do to handle food properly.

### Critical Thinking: Write Your Opinion

**19)** Why do you think the U.S. government has agencies to help keep our food safe?

**20)** Before you studied this chapter, did you regularly use safe food-handling practices? Explain your answer.

---

**Test Taking Tip** | When you read test directions, try to restate them in your own words.

---

*Making Healthy Food Choices* Chapter 8 **177**

---

**10)** Public Health Department **11)** USDA
**12)** wash **13)** room temperature

### Comprehension: Understanding Main Ideas

**14)** If you think you are overweight, talk to a doctor or dietitian before changing your diet.

**15)** Answers will vary. Answers include making the food package colorful, making the food look fun, and placing the package at a child's eye level in the store.

**16)** Answers include any three of the following: feelings, environment, culture, people, advertising.

**17)** Additives are added to foods to extend shelf life and to improve texture, appearance, and taste.

**18)** Answers can include any three of the following: keep cold foods cold and hot foods hot; always wash hands with warm, soapy water before touching food or utensils; wash surfaces and utensils before using them; do not handle foods if you have an open wound on your hand.

### Critical Thinking: Write Your Opinion

**19)** Answers will vary. Students should back up their opinion with information about what types of practices keep foods safe and the roles of different agencies in maintaining food safety.

**20)** Answers will vary. Students should back up their opinion with information about safe food handling practices and their past behaviors.

---

**Chapter 8 Mastery Test B**

## Deciding for Yourself

Have students read "Words Used in Advertising Foods" in the Deciding for Yourself lesson on page 178.

### Ask:

- Do you look for words such as "light" and "low fat" on packages? (Answers will vary. Some students may look for such words, while others do not.)

- Why do you look for these words? (Answers will vary. Students who say they look for them may say they want to lose weight or they think low-fat foods are healthier.)

- Does advertising have an effect on your food choices? (Answers will vary. Some students might be influenced by ads, while others pay no attention to them.)

- Is an ad misleading if it makes you think that all fats are bad? (Yes, this would be misleading.)

### Deciding for Yourself Answers

1) Answers will vary. Students should find a variety of food ads, depending on where they look. Ads may be for chips, cereals, fast foods, and many new products.

2) Answers will vary. Words that connote health include the following: low-fat, fat free, high in fiber, low calorie, fresh, no cholesterol, all natural.

3) Answers will vary. Words that may make people think other foods are harmful include higher in fat, salt, cholesterol, or other substances.

4) Answers will vary. Students' answers should include the fact that reading the food label is an objective way to find out about the contents of a food product and that food labels are standardized to help people compare different products. Students may also point out that the food label is not an advertisement and its not intended to persuade a consumer to buy the product.

### ■ Deciding for Yourself Activity

Have students complete the Unit 3 Deciding for Yourself Activity.

---

## Words Used in Advertising Foods

Think about some of the words you see in food ads and on food packages. Have you ever seen the words *light, low fat, nonfat,* or *fat free*? These words are common. They seem to say that any fat in foods is bad.

Advertisers use these and other words to make us think that their foods are healthy. They want us to think that eating their foods will make us healthy. Many people think they are making healthy food choices when they buy these foods.

It is true that eating too much fat is not healthy. But the body needs some fat to function properly. It's important to read all the information on a food label. Don't just read the advertised words. For example, notice how many calories the food has. The amount of salt or sugar is also important.

The best way to stay healthy is to eat foods from all six food groups and to exercise regularly.

### Questions

1) Look for food ads. You can find them in newspapers or magazines. Cut out the ads. What kind of ads did you find?

2) List the words that might make someone think the foods are healthy. Then write down how you feel when you hear these words.

3) List any negative words that hint that you could harm your health by choosing other foods.

4) Why is reading the food label the best way to tell how healthy a food is?

---

Name _____ Date _____ Period _____ | Unit 3 Deciding for Yourself Activity 3

**Food Advertising Words and Questions**

1) Bring examples of food advertisements to class. Identify any examples of words that make you think the foods are healthy.

2) If questions are used in the advertisements, explain how they cause you to think you can improve your health if you use the product.

3) Rewrite each question in a way that encourages you to use the product but is not misleading.

TRL

**Deciding for Yourself Master 3**

■ The body needs six essential nutrients. These are carbohydrates, proteins, fats, vitamins, minerals, and water.

■ Carbohydrates, proteins, and fats give the body energy.

■ Vitamins, minerals, and water help the body to use other nutrients and to function properly.

■ Carbohydrates are found in grains, fruits, and vegetables.

■ Protein gives the body energy. Proteins are important for building and repairing tissue. Meat, cheese, eggs, and beans are good sources of protein.

■ The body needs fats. Saturated fats are less healthy than polyunsaturated fats. Too much fat can lead to heart disease.

■ The body also needs cholesterol. Too much cholesterol can build up in the blood vessels and prevent proper blood flow.

■ The Food Guide Pyramid can help you make healthy food choices.

■ The amount of energy you need depends on your height, weight, activity level, and stage of growth.

■ Feelings, environment, people, culture, and advertising can affect your food choices.

■ Advertisers use different techniques to get people to buy foods.

■ Food advertising is intended to affect your food choices. Foods are advertised in ways that will make you notice them and want to buy them.

■ Food labels include Nutrition Facts, Daily Value information, and a list of ingredients. Food labels can help you know how healthy the food is.

■ The U.S. government has set up agencies to make sure foods are labeled correctly and are safe to eat.

## Unit Summary

Read and discuss the Unit Summary statements on page 179 with students.

### Ask:

• Your body needs six essential nutrients. What are they? (carbohydrates, proteins, fats, vitamins, minerals, water)

• Which foods contain carbohydrates? (Carbohydrates are found in grains, fruits, and vegetables.)

• Why do you need to eat protein? (Protein gives the body energy and is important for building and repairing tissue.)

• Which foods contain protein? (meat, cheese, eggs, beans)

• Why is too much cholesterol bad for the body? (Too much cholesterol prevents proper blood flow.)

• What is the Food Guide Pyramid? (The Food Guide Pyramid is a diagram that shows which foods should be eaten each day and in what amounts.)

• What things affect your food choices? (feelings, environment, people, culture, advertising)

• What can you find out by reading a food label? (A food label can tell you the ingredients in the food, nutritional content in Nutrition Facts, Daily Value information, number of servings, and list of ingredients.)

• What agencies monitor food safety and labeling in the United States? (Food safety and labeling are monitored by the Food and Drug Administration and the U.S. Department of Agriculture on the federal level. Food safety is monitored by health departments on the state and local levels.)

# Unit 3 Review

The Teacher's Resource Library includes a two-page Unit Mastery Test pictured on this page. Answers are in the Answer Keys beginning on page 433 of this Teacher's Edition.

## Review Answers

### Comprehension: Identifying Facts

1) weight  2) Preservatives  3) nutrients
4) Daily Values  5) wash  6) Calories
7) carbohydrates  8) complete  9) water

## Comprehension: Identifying Facts

On a separate sheet of paper, write the correct word or words from the Word Bank to complete each sentence.

### WORD BANK

| | | |
|---|---|---|
| calories | Daily Values | water |
| USDA | wash | vitamins |
| Food Guide Pyramid | carbohydrates | complete |
| | serving size | nutrients |
| weight | preservatives | |

1) Your energy needs depend on your _____, height, activity level, and stage of growth.

2) _____ are added to foods to prevent spoiling.

3) If foods are cooked in lots of water, you may be throwing away _____ with the water.

4) _____ are based on a 2,000 calorie diet per day.

5) Before handling food, you should always _____ your hands with warm, soapy water.

6) _____ are used to measure the amount of energy in foods.

7) Simple _____ are sometimes called "empty calories."

8) A _____ protein is one that contains all nine amino acids that the body cannot make on its own.

9) You need to replace all the _____ that your body loses each day.

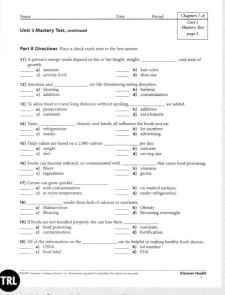

**Unit 3 Mastery Test, page 1**

**Unit 3 Mastery Test, page 2**

10) The _____ can help you determine how much and what kind of foods to eat.

11) _____ and minerals do not give the body energy.

12) The _____ inspects meat-packaging plants and grades meat products.

13) _____ is a way to measure the amount of different foods that you should eat.

## Comprehension: Understanding Main Ideas

Write the answers to these questions on a separate sheet of paper. Use complete sentences.

14) What is the Food Guide Pyramid?

15) List the six essential nutrients you should eat each day.

16) What are three things you can do to handle food safely?

17) What are two pieces of information you can find on a food label?

18) Describe three things that affect your food choices every day.

## Critical Thinking: Write Your Opinion

19) Why do you think it is important to make healthy food choices every day?

20) What can you do to improve your food choices?

10) Food Guide Pyramid  11) Vitamins
12) USDA7  13) Serving size

## Comprehension: Understanding Main Ideas

14) The Food Guide Pyramid is an aid provided by the U.S. government to help people choose a healthy diet.

15) The six essential nutrients you should eat each day are carbohydrates, proteins, fats, vitamins, minerals, and water.

16) Answers will vary. Accept any three of the following: keep cold foods cold and hot foods hot; always wash hands with warm, soapy water before touching food or utensils; wash surfaces and utensils before use; do not handle foods if you have an open wound on your hands.

17) Answers will vary. Accept any two of the following: name of the product, serving size, total calories in the food, product's weight, list of the product's ingredients, the product's Nutrition Facts, information comparing the product's nutrients to Daily Values.

18) Answers will vary. Accept any three of the following: feelings, environment, people, culture, advertising.

## Critical Thinking: Write Your Opinion

19) Answers will vary. Students should back up their opinion with information on the effects of food choices on their health.

20) Answers will vary. Students should back up their answers with information about the factors that affect food choices and behaviors that are conducive to healthy food choices.

# Unit 4 Planning Guide

## Use and Misuse of Substances

| | Student Lesson | | | |
|---|---|---|---|---|
| | Student Pages | Vocabulary | Lesson Review | Writing About Health |
| ***Chapter 9 Medicines and Drugs*** | 185–211 | | | |
| Lesson 1 Prescription and Over-the-Counter Medicines | 186–189 | • | • | |
| Lesson 2 The Effect of Medicines and Drugs on the Body | 190–193 | • | • | • |
| Lesson 3 Tobacco | 194–197 | • | • | |
| Lesson 4 Alcohol | 198–201 | • | • | |
| Lesson 5 Narcotics, Depressants, Stimulants, and Hallucinogens | 202–205 | • | • | |
| Lesson 6 Other Dangerous Drugs | 206–208 | • | • | |
| ***Chapter 10 Drug Dependence—Problems and Solutions*** | 212–223 | | | |
| Lesson 1 The Problem of Drug Dependence | 213–216 | • | • | |
| Lesson 2 Solutions to Drug Dependence | 217–220 | • | • | • |

### Unit Activities

**Home Connection**
**What Do You Think?**
**Deciding for Yourself**

### AGS-Related Resources

**Discover Life Skills Handbook**
**Discover Healthy Sexual Development**

### Assessment Options

**Student Text**
- **Lesson Reviews**
- **Chapter Reviews**
- **Unit Review**

**Teacher's Resource Library**
- **Chapter Mastery Tests**
- **Unit Mastery Test**

| Student Text Features | | | | | | Teaching Strategies | | | | | | | Learning Styles | | | | | Teacher's Resource Library | | | |
|---|---|---|---|---|---|---|---|---|---|---|---|---|---|---|---|---|---|---|---|---|---|
| Action for Health | Careers | Health, Fitness, and Nutrition Tips | Healthy Subjects | Then and Now | Technology | Background Information | Career Application | Community Application | Environment Application | Global Connection | Home Application | Multicultural Connection | Auditory | Group Learning | LEP/ESL | Tactile/Kinesthetic | Visual | Activities | Mastery Tests | Student Study Guide | Workbook Activities |
| | | | | | | | | | | | | | | | | | | | • | • | |
| 187 | | | | 189 | | 189 | | | | 188 | | | | | | | | 32 | | | 32 |
| | 190 | 191 | 192 | | | | | | | | | 193 | | 191 | 190 | | | 33 | | | 33 |
| | | | | | | 195 | | | 196 | 196 | | | | | | | 197 | 34 | | | 34 |
| | | | | | 200 | 199 | | 199 | | | | | | | | | | 35 | | | 35 |
| | | 203 | | | | | | | | | | | | 203 | | 204 | | 36 | | | 36 |
| | | 208 | | | | | | | | | | | 207 | | | | | 37 | | | 37 |
| | | | | | | | | | | | | | | | | | | | • | • | |
| 216 | | | | | | 215 | | | 216 | 214 | 214 | | 215 | | | | | 38 | | | 38 |
| | 220 | 217, 219 | 219 | | | 218 | | 218 | | | | 218 | | 220 | 219 | 219 | | 39 | | | 39 |

## Block Scheduling

Here is a suggested teaching activity if you have extended instructional time, such as a block schedule.

**Drug Laws** *To increase your understanding of drug-related issues, problems, consequences, and solutions.*

You have become the mayor of a small city. Your first duty is to develop the city's drug laws. Prepare a threefold brochure or large poster that clearly explains to all citizens your drug policies, consequences, and prevention strategies. Your brochure or poster information should include:

(1) the name and location of your city, (2) laws pertaining to all the drugs identified in Chapter 9, (3) a list of possible offenses for each drug category or type, (4) the penalties or consequences for each offense, (5) your plan for helping your citizens avoid drug-related problems, (6) whether there is a difference between the first and subsequent offenses, and (7) whether offenses for some drugs are treated more seriously than for others. Provide a reason why or why not and examples for items 6 and 7.

**Unit 4:**

**Use and Misuse of Substances**
pages 182–227

**Chapters**

**Audiocassette**

**Teacher's Resource Library** (TRL)

Unit 4 Home Connection Master 4

Unit 4 What Do You Think?
Activity Master 4

Unit 4 Deciding for Yourself
Activity Master 4

Unit 4 Mastery Test

(Answer Keys for the Teacher's
Resource Library begin on page 433
of this Teacher's Edition.)

## Other Resources

### Books for Teachers

*Drugs and Beyond: A Family Approach to
Abused and Misused Drugs.* Tofield, Alberta,
Canada: Global Health Research, 1995.

*Helping Teens Stop Using Tobacco.*
Minneapolis: Community Intervention,
Inc. (1-800-328-0417), 1996.

McCuen, Gary E., ed. *Born Hooked:
Poisoned in the Womb.* Hudson, WI:
McCuen Publishing, 1994.

### Books for Students

Folkers, Gladys, and Jeanne Engelmann.
*Taking Charge of My Mind & Body.*
Minneapolis: Community Intervention,
Inc. (1-800-328-0417). (This guide provides
stories and tips from people who have
been addicted, sick, and scared. Provides
young people with ways to develop skills
that empower them to make healthy
choices.)

*Drug misuse is not a disease.
It is a decision, like the decision to
step out in front of a moving car.
You would call that not a disease
but an error of judgment.*

—Phillip K. Dick, *A Scanner Darkly*

### Videos

*Keep Off the Grass.* (27 minutes). Waco,
TX: Health EDCO (1-800-299-3366),
1997. (Helps students understand the
harmful effects of marijuana and drug
use.)

*Alcohol and Your Body.* (30 minutes). Waco,
TX: Health EDCO (1-800-299-3366),
1996. (Traces the effects of alcohol on
various body systems.)

**Home Connection Master 4**

# Use and Misuse of Substances

W hat do you think of when you hear the word *drug*? You might think of a medicine you took for a cold or other illness. Or, you might be reminded of a tragedy you have read about that resulted from using an illegal drug.

Medicines are drugs used to cure and treat disease. They are wonderful and important scientific tools that benefit people. In this unit, you will learn to use medicines safely. You will also learn the dangers of illegal drugs and of misusing legal drugs.

▶ Chapter 9 Medicines and Drugs

▶ Chapter 10 Drug Dependence—Problems and Solutions

## Introducing the Unit

Have students look at the picture and think about what it shows. While they are doing this, read aloud the quotation on page 182. Then have volunteers read the introductory material on page 183.

Ask:

- The quotation says that "Drug misuse is not a disease. It is a decision." What do you think that means? (Accept all reasonable answers. Students should express the idea that no one is forced to use drugs. The first use of a drug starts with a decision made by an individual.)

- What do you think of when you hear the word *drug*? (Answers will vary, depending on students' prior knowledge.)

- Medicines are useful drugs, so it's easy to understand why people use them. But why would people use illegal drugs that are harmful? (Accept all reasonable answers. Students might say that people are curious about illegal drugs or they think the drugs will make them feel better.)

- What are some ways medicines might be misused? (Answers will vary, depending on students' prior knowledge.)

- What does the picture show and how can you relate it to drug misuse? (Answers will vary. Students may suggest that playing a computer game may involve decisions or errors in judgment like drug misuse.)

## What Do You Think?

Have volunteers read aloud the story on page 184.

### Ask:

- Is Tony too young to have a drinking problem? (No, Tony is not too young to have a drinking problem.)

- Why do you think Sharon is worried? (Sharon is worried because Tony appears to be drinking a lot, although he denies it. She is also worried that he is drinking while driving.)

- What are some actions Sharon might take? (Answers will vary. Students may suggest that Sharon talk with her parents. The parents can then talk with Tony about his behavior.)

- What do you think you would have done in this situation? (Answers will vary. Accept all reasonable answers, but have students explain their reasoning.)

Have students complete the Unit 4 What Do You Think? Activity sheet.

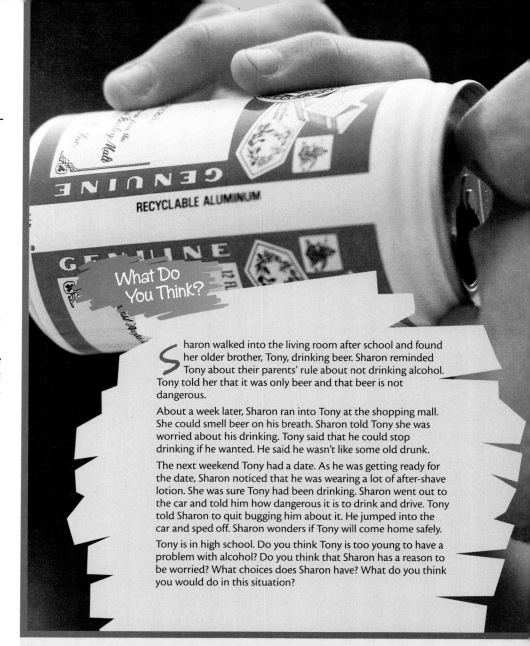

### What Do You Think?

Sharon walked into the living room after school and found her older brother, Tony, drinking beer. Sharon reminded Tony about their parents' rule about not drinking alcohol. Tony told her that it was only beer and that beer is not dangerous.

About a week later, Sharon ran into Tony at the shopping mall. She could smell beer on his breath. Sharon told Tony she was worried about his drinking. Tony said that he could stop drinking if he wanted. He said he wasn't like some old drunk.

The next weekend Tony had a date. As he was getting ready for the date, Sharon noticed that he was wearing a lot of after-shave lotion. She was sure Tony had been drinking. Sharon went out to the car and told him how dangerous it is to drink and drive. Tony told Sharon to quit bugging him about it. He jumped into the car and sped off. Sharon wonders if Tony will come home safely.

Tony is in high school. Do you think Tony is too young to have a problem with alcohol? Do you think that Sharon has a reason to be worried? What choices does Sharon have? What do you think you would do in this situation?

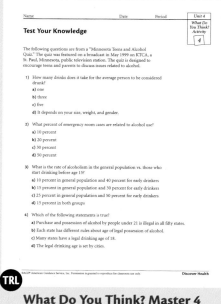

**What Do You Think? Master 4**

# Medicines and Drugs

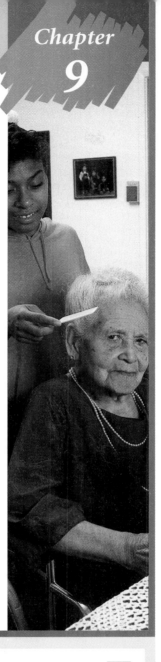

Have you recently taken a medicine? Did it help you feel better if you were sick? Did it help make you well? Did it help you avoid becoming sick? What do medicines do? How do they work? Why are there so many different kinds? How do they differ from drugs?

In this chapter, you will learn about medicines. You will learn how they can improve and save lives. You will also learn about harmful drugs.

## Goals for Learning

▶ To define the terms *drug* and *medicine*

▶ To explain the difference between prescription medicines and over-the-counter medicines

▶ To describe how medicines and drugs affect the body

▶ To identify the health risks associated with tobacco use

▶ To describe the effects that alcohol has on the brain and the body

▶ To list some often-abused drugs and describe dangers associated with each

## Chapter at a Glance

### Chapter 9:
**Medicines and Drugs**
pages 185–211

### Lessons

### Audiocassette

### Teacher's Resource Library

Activities 32–37

Workbook Activities 32–37

Student Study Guide 15  pages 1–2

Chapter 9 Mastery Tests A and B

(Answer Keys for the Teacher's Resource Library begin on page 433 of this Teacher's Edition.)

---

**Student Study Guide 15, page 1**

**Student Study Guide 15, page 2**

## Introducing the Chapter

To evaluate what students already know about medicines and drugs, lead a discussion asking students what they think the difference is between a medicine and a drug.

Have a volunteer read the introduction and the Goals for Learning.

### Ask:

• **What is the difference between medicines and drugs?** (Accept all reasonable answers as a basis for discussion. Write students' responses on the chalkboard. Refer back to these initial responses as students read the chapter to see how their responses change.)

# Lesson at a Glance

## Chapter 9 Lesson 1

**Overview** In this lesson, students learn the difference between drugs and medicines and about prescription and over-the-counter medicines.

## Objectives

■ To distinguish between drug and medicine.

■ To explain the difference between prescription medicines and over-the-counter medicines.

**Student Pages** 186–189

**Audiocassette**

**Teacher's Resource Library** **TRL**

Activity 32

Workbook Activity 32

# Teaching Suggestions

## ■ Vocabulary

*drug, medicine, pharmacist, prescription, over-the-counter medicine, antibiotic, antihistamine, decongestant, ointment, antibody, cardiovascular, cardiovascular medicine, diabetes, psychoactive medicine, vaccine, Food and Drug Administration (FDA)*

Ask students which of the vocabulary words they have heard before and how they have heard it. Then read and review each definition with students.

## ■ Teaching the Lesson

Ask students if they have ever taken a medicine. Talk about why they took the medicine and where they got it. List on the chalkboard as many reasons students can think of why people take medicines.

Have students read about the different types of medicines and what they do on page 186.

---

## Prescription and Over-the-Counter Medicines

**Drug**
*A substance that changes the way the mind or body works*

**Medicine**
*A drug used to treat or prevent a disease or health problem*

**Pharmacist**
*A person trained and licensed to prepare and sell prescription drugs*

**Prescription**
*A written order from a doctor for a medicine*

**Over-the-counter medicine**
*A medicine that can be bought without a doctor's written order*

People can use **drugs** or **medicines** to relieve pain or restore health. A drug is a substance that changes the way the body or mind works. A medical drug, also called a medicine, is used to treat or prevent disease, or to relieve discomfort. Medicines can be classified by how they are bought.

### What Are Prescription Medicines?

Some medicines are sold by **prescription** only. You must have a written order from a doctor to buy a prescription medicine. A **pharmacist** can fill a prescription. A pharmacist is a trained and licensed professional who fills prescription medicines.

### What Are Over-the-Counter Medicines?

Some medicines are sold without a doctor's prescription. These are called **over-the-counter medicines**. You probably are familiar with many kinds of over-the-counter medicines. There are medicines for minor pain and fever, for colds, and for minor skin problems. There are so many similar over-the-counter medicines that it is hard to choose among them. It is a good idea to let your doctor or pharmacist suggest one for your needs.

Read the labels on prescription drugs carefully.

### What Do Different Medicines Do?

Thousands of different prescription and over-the-counter medicines are available in the United States. These medicines can be grouped by the purpose for which they are used.

**Over-the-counter medicines are usually not as strong as prescription medicines. Why do you think this is so?**

### Pain Relievers

Mild pain relievers are available over the counter. You may have taken aspirin or other remedies for a headache or muscle pain. These medicines also reduce fever. For severe pain, doctors prescribe stronger pain relievers. Strong pain relievers are sold by prescription only. A doctor must supervise their use because they can be dangerous in large doses.

---

**186** *Chapter 9 Medicines and Drugs*

---

Ask:

• What is a drug? (A drug is a substance that changes the way the body or mind works.)

• What is a medicine? (A medicine is a drug that is used to treat or prevent a disease or health problem.)

• What is the difference between a prescription medicine and an over-the-counter medicine? (You must have a prescription from a doctor to get a prescription medicine. An over-the-counter medicine is sold without a doctor's prescription.)

---

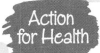

## BEING PREPARED FOR DRUG REACTIONS

There is some risk in using any kind of drug or medicine. Occasionally, people have a dangerous reaction to a drug. They may be allergic to the drug, take too much of it, or combine it with other drugs. A serious drug reaction can cause permanent damage to a person's health.

You can be prepared for a drug reaction. Think about what you would do in a drug reaction emergency. Talk with your family members and friends to make a list of actions you could take. Find telephone numbers for a poison control center and the nearest hospital emergency room. Keep these numbers next to your telephone in case a drug reaction emergency should ever happen in your home.

**Antibiotic**
*A drug used to fight bacterial infections*

**Antihistamine**
*A medicine used for treating allergy symptoms*

**Decongestant**
*A medicine that opens lung and nasal passages*

**Ointment**
*A medicine for minor skin infections*

### Antibiotics

**Antibiotics** are medicines that stop the growth of germs that cause disease. You might have taken an antibiotic for a sore throat or other infection. Most antibiotics are prescription medicines. Antibiotics, however, do not stop the growth of all germs. Antibiotics do not affect germs that cause colds and flu. The only antibiotics sold over the counter are found in **ointments**, or medicines for minor skin infections.

### Symptom Relievers

Many medicines relieve the symptoms of diseases. For example, **decongestants** open lung and nasal passages. **Antihistamines**, medicines used for treating allergy symptoms, dry up a runny nose. Cough medicine quiets coughing. Some of these medicines are sold over the counter. Other stronger medicines of this kind are prescription medicines.

Consult an adult before using over-the-counter medicines.

*Medicines and Drugs* Chapter 9 **187**

## Action for Health

Encourage students to follow the information in the Action for Health section to make a "What to Do When Someone Has a Drug Reaction" poster for hanging on the wall at home. Students can find resources at a local library or on the Internet. Students can also interview people at a hospital emergency room, health department, police department, or fire department for additional information.

Have students read about different types of medicines on page 187.

Ask:

- **What is an antibiotic?** (An antibiotic is a medicine that stops the growth of germs that cause disease.)

- **What is a decongestant?** (A decongestant is a medicine that opens lung and nasal passages.)

- **What is an antihistamine?** (An antihistamine is a medicine used for treating allergy symptoms.)

### BACKGROUND INFORMATION

Tell students that there are generic prescription and over-the-counter drugs. Generic drugs are chemically the same as brand-name medicines, but they are cheaper. The difference in price is due in large part to simple packaging and lack of advertising. Often the same manufacturer makes the brand name and the generic drug, but there are some companies that make only generic drugs. Although generic drugs are chemically identical, studies have found that some do not work the same in everyone's body as their brand-name equivalents.

Have students read about different types of medicines on page 188.

Ask:

- Why is it dangerous to overuse medicines that relieve symptoms? (Overusing medicines that relieve symptoms can be dangerous because the symptoms may mask a serious underlying disease.)

- What are cardiovascular medicines? (Cardiovascular medicines are drugs used for the heart and blood vessels.)

- What causes diabetes, and how can it be treated? (Diabetes results when the body cannot make enough insulin. People with this disease get insulin by giving themselves a shot, changing their diet, or taking medication.)

- What is a vaccine? (A vaccine is a prescription medicine that prevents diseases by stimulating the immune system to produce antibodies that fight diseases.)

- What does a psychoactive medicine do? (A psychoactive medicine changes the function of the brain.)

## APPLICATION

**At Home**
Suggest that students look in their medicines cabinets at home. Can they tell the difference between prescription and over-the-counter medicines? Have students find examples of generic medicines. Encourage students to write a paragraph about the ways the labels on these three types of medicines differ.

**Antibody**
*A protein that is stimulated by the immune system to fight disease*

**Cardiovascular**
*Relating to the heart and blood vessels*

**Cardiovascular medicine**
*A drug used for the heart and blood vessels*

**Diabetes**
*A disease in which the body does not make enough insulin*

**Psychoactive medicine**
*A medicine that changes the function of the brain*

**Vaccine**
*A medicine that stimulates the immune system to fight off a disease*

Are all medicines drugs? Why or why not?

It is important that symptom relievers, as well as pain medicines, are not overused. Pain or a cough might be a symptom of a serious disease. Relieving the symptoms does not cure the disease. Rather, it may mask the disease. All symptoms are important clues to a doctor. Your doctor may have diagnosed the cause of your symptoms. In that case, he or she may allow you to use symptom relievers to be more comfortable.

### Cardiovascular Medicines
**Cardiovascular** diseases affect the heart and blood vessels. These diseases are major health problems for adults in this country. Some **cardiovascular medicines** improve the function of the heart and blood vessels. Others lower blood pressure or reduce fats in the blood. These medicines are sold by prescription only. One over-the-counter medicine, however, may help the heart. Aspirin may help prevent heart attacks in some adults.

### Chemical Replacements
Some diseases are caused by the lack of a certain chemical in the body. An example is the disease **diabetes**. The body cannot make enough of a chemical, insulin, that controls the amount of sugar in the blood. People with this disease get insulin by giving themselves a shot. This helps make their blood sugar level normal. Some people can control the disease by changing their diet and taking medication.

### Vaccines
Some medicines prevent disease. A **vaccine** is a prescription medicine that can prevent diseases, such as measles, mumps, and chicken pox. The vaccine stimulates the immune system to produce **antibodies** to a possible disease. Antibodies are proteins that fight diseases. Vaccines are prescription medicines that you can get in a doctor's office or a health clinic.

### Psychoactive Medicines
Some medicines help the brain function normally. A medicine that affects thoughts and emotions is called a **psychoactive medicine**. Some psychoactive medicines help people with depression, and others reduce anxiety.

**Food and Drug Administration (FDA)**
*A government agency that oversees the testing and sale of medicines*

All psychoactive medicines are prescription medicines. A doctor must supervise the use of psychoactive medicines.

## How Do We Know Medicines Are Safe?

In the United States, the **Food and Drug Administration (FDA)** oversees the testing and sale of medicines. New medicines must go through many tests before they can be sold. Medicines are carefully tested before the FDA approves their use. The FDA determines whether a medicine will be sold over the counter or by prescription. The FDA also tells the maker what the medicine's label should say. Labels must state the purpose of the medicine, the recommended dosage, possible side effects, and other cautions. Always read and follow the directions on medicines. If you need help reading a label, ask an adult for assistance.

**LESSON 1 REVIEW** Write the answers to these questions on a separate sheet of paper. Use complete sentences.

1) What is the difference between a medicine and a drug?

2) What is the difference between an over-the-counter drug and a prescription drug?

3) Describe what a pharmacist does.

4) List four purposes of medicines.

5) How do you know if it is safe for you to take a medicine?

### PATENT MEDICINES

Around 1900, newspapers were full of ads for "patent medicines." These medicines were said to cure one or more illnesses or problems. But the medicines were often fifty percent or more alcohol. Manufacturers never tested them for safety or the accuracy of the claims. People wanted to feel better. So they believed the claims and ordered the medicines. Sellers became rich, but the medicines didn't help the buyers. Today the Food and Drug Administration (FDA) regulates medicines. Researchers must prove a medicine does what it claims. No medicine can be sold without FDA approval.

*Medicines and Drugs* Chapter 9 **189**

---

Have students read about the ways we know that medicines are safe on page 189.

Ask:

- What information must a medicine label include? (the purpose of the medicine, the recommended dosage, possible side effects, and other cautions)

## Lesson 1 Review Answers

1) A drug is a substance other than food that changes the way the body works. A medicine is used to relieve pain or restore health.

2) A prescription drug must have a prescription from a doctor. An over-the-counter drug is sold without a doctor's prescription.

3) A pharmacist fills prescriptions.

4) Answers will vary. Accept any four of the following: to relieve pain, to treat or prevent disease, to stop the growth of germs that cause disease, to relieve symptoms of diseases, to improve the function of the heart and blood vessels, to help the brain function normally.

5) You know if it is safe for you to take a medicine by asking a doctor or pharmacist and by reading the directions on the label.

## Then and Now

Challenge students to find out about the drug approval process in the United States. Encourage students to work alone or in pairs to write reports on the topic. Students can find resources at the library and on the FDA's web site at www.fda.gov.

### APPLICATION

**Career Connection**
Every drug sold in the United States has to be approved for use by the FDA. The process starts when a drug company creates a drug and tests it. These tests are overseen by medical doctors and pharmacists who specialize in this type of drug research. Encourage students to give short oral reports about what doctors who monitor clinical trials of new drugs do and what kind of training they need.

---

# Lesson at a Glance

## Chapter 9 Lesson 2

**Overview** In this lesson, students learn how medicines and other drugs affect the body. Students also learn that factors such as age, weight, gender, and body chemistry can affect how medicines act in the body.

## Objectives

■ To describe how medicines and drugs affect the body.

**Student Pages** 190–193

**Audiocassette** 🎧

**Teacher's Resource Library** TRL

  Activity 33
  Workbook Activity 33

---

# Teaching Suggestions

## ■ Vocabulary

*inject, suppository, codeine, side effect, therapeutic effect*

Write the vocabulary words on the chalkboard and ask students to provide definitions based on prior knowledge. Then read the definitions aloud from the text. Have students compare their previous ideas with the actual definitions.

## ■ Teaching the Lesson

Have students brainstorm ways that medicines can be taken. Write their answers on the chalkboard. (Answers can include injected, orally, and absorbed through the skin).

Have students read about ways that medicines are taken on page 190.

## Careers

Have students interview a pharmacy clerk, then write an article about what this job is like. Encourage students to supplement the information they get from the pharmacy clerk with information from library books. Make time for students to share and compare their articles.

---

## Lesson 2 · The Effect of Medicines and Drugs on the Body

**Inject**
*Use a needle to take medicine into the body*

**Suppository**
*A cylinder containing medicine to be inserted into the rectum*

Do medicines that are taken orally begin to work right away? Why or why not?

*T*o affect the body, a medicine must be taken into the body and enter the bloodstream. After a drug enters the bloodstream, it is carried to all parts of the body.

**How Are Medicines Taken?**
Medicines can be taken in several different ways. You probably have taken medicine by mouth. The way a medicine is given is based on the nature of the medicine.

• Some medicines can be taken by mouth, or orally—in liquid, pill, or capsule form.

• Some medicines are **injected**—either under the skin, into a muscle, or into a vein. Injection is the fastest way to get medicine into the body. Most injections use a metal needle that makes a hole in the skin.

• Some medicines can be absorbed through the skin. The body slowly absorbs medicine from a special patch. Some heart medicines and antismoking medicines are given this way.

• Some medicines are given in a **suppository**. A suppository is inserted into the rectum. The medicine is absorbed through the thin mucous membranes.

**Careers**

**PHARMACY CLERK**

Pharmacy clerks usually work in hospitals or drug stores. Under a pharmacist's direction, they measure out or mix prescriptions. They deliver prescriptions to nursing units in the hospital. They may be responsible for figuring out the cost of medicines. They also check the pharmacy's stock of medicines. They order and keep records of medicines and supplies. They also may type and file reports and answer phones.

Most states require pharmacy clerks to be licensed. A clerk may take a five- to ten-month program or a two-year program at a community college.

**190** *Chapter 9 Medicines and Drugs*

---

**Ask:**

· What are four ways that medicines can be taken? (orally, injected, absorbed through the skin, in a suppository)

· Which way of taking medicine gets it into your body the fastest? (injection)

## LEARNING STYLES

 **LEP/ESL** While reading the section How Are Medicines Taken? on page 190, pantomime the methods described. For example, pantomime taking a pill, giving an injection, using an inhaler, and rubbing a lotion on your arm.

---

**Codeine**
*A prescription medicine that relieves severe pain*

**Side effect**
*An unexpected and often harmful result of taking medicine*

**Therapeutic effect**
*A helpful result of taking medicine*

### How Does a Medicine Affect the Body?

When a medicine has spread throughout the body, it begins to affect certain parts of the body. A **therapeutic effect** is the helpful effect the medicine provides. For example, **codeine** is a prescription medicine. Its therapeutic effect is relief of severe pain. But codeine, like some medicines, has unwanted effects, called **side effects**. Side effects can be as minor as an uncomfortable feeling or a dry mouth. Some side effects are dangerous or can be life threatening. A doctor must weigh the therapeutic effects against the side effects. For some patients, some side effects are too severe to deal with. In this case, the doctor must try a different medicine.

Mixing one or more medicines can cause problems. For example, a person who takes one medicine may also need to take another medicine. Sometimes two different medicines cause a bad chemical reaction in the body.

A person can become dependent on a medicine. For example, someone might take a medicine to help sleep. If the person takes the medicine too frequently, he or she may not be able to sleep without it. This is one reason it is important not to take more of a medicine than your doctor prescribes.

### Why Do Medicines Affect Different People Differently?

Many things influence how a medicine affects a person. A person's sex, age, weight, or amount of body fat all affect how medicines act in the body. A doctor considers these things when he or she decides the dose you need. A heavy adult male may need more of the same medicine than a thin, young female.

Another important thing that influences how a medicine affects a person is body chemistry. Some kinds of medicine have possible side effects. One person might have no side effects from a medicine. Another person might have serious side effects. Side effects are difficult to predict. It is important to ask your doctor or pharmacist about side effects for each medicine you take.

*Health Tip*

Some drugs have side effects. Discuss with your doctor alternatives to treatment with medicines.

Have students read about how medicines affect the body on page 191.

Ask:

- What is a therapeutic effect? (A therapeutic effect is the helpful effect that medicines provide.)

- What is the therapeutic effect of a medicine such as codeine? (relief of severe pain)

- Why can mixing one or more medicines cause problems? (Sometimes two different medicines cause a bad chemical reaction in the body.)

- Why is it important to avoid taking medicines too frequently? (It is important to avoid taking medicines too frequently because you could become dependent on them.)

**LEARNING STYLES**

**Auditory** Bring in several over-the-counter medicines. Have student volunteers read the "Possible Side Effects" section of the labels aloud to the class. Encourage students to take notes on the types of side effects that are possible as a result of taking these medicines. Discuss with students the idea that all medicines can have possible side effects.

Have students read about how medicines can affect an unborn baby on page 192.

Ask:

• Why should a pregnant woman be careful about the medicines she takes? (The medicines might be harmful for a developing baby.)

• What should a woman who is pregnant or who thinks she might be pregnant do before taking any medicine? (She should ask her doctor before she takes any medicine.)

## Healthy Subjects

Discuss with students whether they would want to be tested to find out if their baby could have a birth defect. Emphasize the importance of proper nutrition, exercise, sleep, and health care during pregnancy in contributing to a healthy baby.

An unborn baby is much smaller than the woman. Any drug has a greater effect on the baby than on the woman.

## How Can Taking Medicines Affect an Unborn Baby?

A pregnant woman must be careful about the medicines she takes. Many medicines can enter her unborn baby's body. Many medicines that are safe for adults are harmful for a developing baby. Unborn babies who are exposed to medicines or drugs can be smaller than normal. They may have damaged internal organs or other permanent disabilities. These children may need special care throughout their lives.

A woman who is pregnant or who might be pregnant should ask her doctor before she takes any medicine. Even over-the-counter medicines can harm unborn babies. Medicines and drugs most easily hurt a developing baby during early pregnancy. Of course, a pregnant woman's use of tobacco, alcohol, or any drug is dangerous for her baby. Some unborn babies are exposed to medicines and drugs before their mothers know they are pregnant. Any woman who might be pregnant should understand the risks of medicine use.

**PREVENTING DISEASE AND BIRTH DEFECTS**

Scientists working in biological and genetic sciences continue to find better ways to prevent disease and birth defects in unborn babies. Women who are pregnant can now be tested early enough in their pregnancy to detect the possibility of a serious disease.

**192** *Chapter 9 Medicines and Drugs*

## What Should You Think About When Taking a Medicine?

Medicines contain powerful chemicals. Medicine can help you if you are sick. If used in the wrong way, however, medicine can make you sick. It is important to follow safety rules for taking medicine.

- Let your doctor know about all of the medicines that you take, even vitamins.
- Carefully follow the directions for taking the medicine. Ask your doctor if you should take all of the prescription medicine in a container.
- Read and follow all warnings on the medicine container. For example, some medicines might make you sleepy. A label might warn you not to drive or use machinery.
- Tell your doctor immediately about any side effects.
- For both prescription and over-the-counter medicine, take only medicine given to you by a trusted adult. *Never* accept medicine from anyone else.
- Store medicines properly. Do not take prescription medicine unless it was prescribed for your current illness.
- Do not mix medicines unless your doctor has told you to do so. *Never* mix medicines and alcohol.

### Writing About Health

Some people take medicines that aren't necessary and may be harmful. Write why you think it is important to take only necessary medicines.

**LESSON 2 REVIEW** Write the answers to these questions on a separate sheet of paper. Use complete sentences.

1) What are two ways drugs are taken into the body?
2) Why do some drugs have bad side effects?
3) Why can two people react differently to the same drug?
4) Why must a pregnant woman be careful about taking drugs?
5) Write a list of five safety tips for using drugs wisely.

*Medicines and Drugs* *Chapter 9* **193**

---

Have students read about rules for taking medicines on page 193.

**Ask:**

- Why is it important to read all the warnings on the medicine container? (so you know how the drug might affect you, such as becoming sleepy, or to know what behavior to avoid after taking the drug, such as driving)

### Lesson 2 Review Answers

1) Answers will vary. Accept any two of the following: orally, injected, absorbed through the skin, in a suppository.
2) Some drugs have bad side effects because the person may be allergic to the drug or be taking other drugs.
3) Factors that influence how a drug affects a person are the person's sex, age, weight, or amount of body fat.
4) A pregnant woman must be careful about taking drugs because drugs can enter her unborn baby's body.
5) Answers will vary. Accept any five of the following: let your doctor know about all the medicines you take, even vitamins; follow the directions for taking the medicine; read and follow all warnings on the medicine container; tell your doctor about any side effects; never take medicine that belongs to someone else; store medicines properly; do not mix medicines unless directed to do so by a doctor; never mix medicines and alcohol.

### MULTICULTURAL CONNECTION

Tell students that most of the medicines we take today are made by large drug companies, but a large percentage have their origins in plant remedies that have been around for many years. Knowledge of plant medicines was passed down from generation to generation by Native Americans. Challenge students to research plant remedies used by Native Americans as well as other cultures. Invite students to report their findings to the class.

---

**Activity 33**

Name _____ Date _____ Period _____ | Chapter 9 Activity 33

**The Effect of Medicines and Drugs on the Body**

*Part A Directions* Complete each sentence by writing the letter of the *best* word or words in the space on the left-hand side of the page.

_____ 1) Never use a medicine without the knowledge and supervision of a _____ adult.

_____ 2) When using an over-the-counter medicine, read the _____ carefully and follow them exactly as they are stated.

_____ 3) Never mix _____ types of medicines at the same time unless the doctor has prescribed them for you.

_____ 4) _____ and other drugs should never be mixed.

_____ 5) Drugs can enter the body of an unborn _____.

a) alcohol
b) baby
c) different
d) directions
e) trusted

*Part B Directions* Write the letter of the item from Column B that matches the description in Column A.

Column A

_____ 6) used to administer drugs through the rectum
_____ 7) fastest way to get drugs into the body
_____ 8) an unexpected result of taking medicine
_____ 9) a helpful result of taking medicine
_____ 10) a way to absorb medicines through the skin

Column B

f) injection
g) patch
h) suppositories
i) side effect
j) therapeutic effect

©AGS® American Guidance Service, Inc. Permission is granted to reproduce for classroom use only. Discover Health

---

**Workbook Activity 33**

Name _____ Date _____ Period _____ | Chapter 9 Workbook Activity 33

**The Effect of Medicines and Drugs on the Body**

*Part A Directions* Write the letter of the item from Column B that matches the description in Column A.

Column A

_____ 1) a way to absorb medicines through the skin
_____ 2) used to administer drugs through the rectum
_____ 3) fastest way to get drugs into the body
_____ 4) an unexpected result of taking medicine
_____ 5) a helpful result of taking medicine

Column B

a) injection
b) patch
c) suppositories
d) side effect
e) therapeutic effect

*Part B Directions* Complete each sentence by writing the letter of the *best* word or words in the space on the left-hand side of the page.

_____ 6) Never use a medicine without the knowledge and supervision of a _____ adult.

_____ 7) When using an over-the-counter medicine, read the _____ carefully and follow them exactly as they are stated.

_____ 8) Never mix _____ types of medicines at the same time unless the doctor has prescribed them for you.

_____ 9) _____ and other drugs should never be mixed.

_____ 10) Drugs can enter the body of an unborn _____.

f) alcohol
g) baby
h) different
i) directions
j) trusted

©AGS® American Guidance Service, Inc. Permission is granted to reproduce for classroom use only. Discover Health

## Lesson at a Glance

### Chapter 9 Lesson 3

**Overview** This lesson looks at the use of tobacco products and their negative effects on health. The lesson also contains information on how people who use tobacco can quit.

### Objectives

■ To identify the health risks associated with tobacco use.

**Student Pages** 194–197

**Audiocassette**

**Teacher's Resource Library** **TRL**

   Activity 34

   Workbook Activity 34

## Teaching Suggestions

### ■ Vocabulary

*nicotine, stimulant, emphysema, lung cancer, secondhand smoke, smokeless tobacco, tar, withdrawal*

Review the vocabulary words and definitions with students. Ask them whether they have known anyone who suffers from emphysema or lung cancer.

After reading the lesson and learning the vocabulary words, have students use as many of the words as possible to write a Public Service Announcement (PSA) warning other students about the dangers of smoking. Have students put their PSAs on tape and play them in class.

### ■ Teaching the Lesson

Ask students if they have ever seen ads for tobacco products on billboards or in magazines or newspapers. Discuss what the ads show and what the people in the ads seem to be like. Students might suggest that the people in the ads seem young and healthy and appear to be having fun. Ask students how the image compares to the reality of using tobacco products. Return to this question again at the end of the lesson.

Have students read about the reasons people use tobacco and what tobacco does to the body on page 194.

---

**Nicotine**
*A chemical in tobacco to which people become addicted*

**Stimulant**
*A drug that speeds up the central nervous system*

Why do some young people think smoking tobacco makes them seem older?

A drug is a chemical substance other than food that changes the way the mind or body works. The main reason people continue to smoke is because of **nicotine**, a chemical in tobacco. Tobacco use is legal for adults over 18 years of age. Using tobacco, however, has been proved to be harmful to a person's health. Today, the majority of people in the United States do not smoke or use other tobacco products. Many people who used to smoke have quit as they learned the possible harm that tobacco can do.

Cigarettes, cigars, chewing tobacco, pipe tobacco, and snuff all contain tobacco. Many people who use tobacco began when they were teens. Choosing to start using tobacco may not seem harmful at the time. But tobacco users quickly become dependent on the powerful drug in tobacco.

**Why Do People Use Tobacco?**
Many older people began to smoke before the harmful effects of tobacco were known. They may believe that smoking helps them relax or concentrate better.

Younger people may begin to smoke cigarettes because of peer pressure. Smoking may make them feel more comfortable in social settings.

**What Does Tobacco Do to the Body?**
Tobacco has many harmful effects on the body. Tobacco use is linked to cancer, cardiovascular disease, and lung disease. A 30-year-old person who smokes two packages of cigarettes a day might shorten his or her life by about eight years.

How can tobacco shorten someone's life? As mentioned above, tobacco contains the chemical nicotine. Nicotine is a **stimulant**. Nicotine raises the heart rate and blood pressure. It narrows blood vessels. This reduces the amount of blood that reaches some parts of the body. These actions are hard on the heart and can cause someone's early death.

**194**  *Chapter 9   Medicines and Drugs*

---

Ask:

· List three products that contain tobacco.
(Accept any three of the following: cigarettes, cigars, chewing tobacco, pipe tobacco, snuff.)

· List two health problems that are linked to tobacco. (Accept any two of the following: cancer, cardiovascular disease, lung disease, shorter life span.)

**Emphysema**
*A serious disease of the lungs that causes difficulty in breathing*

**Lung cancer**
*A disease of the lungs caused primarily by smoking tobacco*

**Secondhand smoke**
*Tobacco smoke breathed by nonsmokers*

**Smokeless tobacco**
*Tobacco that is chewed*

**Tar**
*A substance in tobacco that can form a thick, brown, sticky substance in the lungs*

**Cigar smokers do not inhale. Does this make cigar smoking a safe thing to do?**

### What Are the Harmful Effects of Cigarette Smoke?

Burning tobacco produces more than two thousand harmful chemicals. These include **tars**. Tars are dark-colored, sticky substances. Tars contain smoke particles and many different chemicals. Tars damage the interior surface of lung passages. A lung damaged by tars cannot clean itself. This can lead to a serious lung disease called **emphysema**. People with emphysema have difficulty breathing. They cannot push air out of their lungs.

**Lung cancer**, one of the most deadly cancers, is linked to smoking. Smoking causes more than 90 percent of lung cancer cases. Most people who get lung cancer will die from it. But lung cancer is not the only cancer linked to smoking. Smokers have high rates of mouth and throat cancer, bladder cancer, and cancer of the pancreas.

### How Does Smoking Affect Other People?

Being near a smoker can harm your health. **Secondhand smoke** is cigarette smoke that pollutes the air. Secondhand smoke can cause disease in nonsmokers. Breathing secondhand smoke causes the heart to beat faster. It also causes blood pressure to rise.

Adults who smoke may put their families at risk. Children of smokers have more respiratory illnesses than children of nonsmokers. Babies of smoking mothers are born smaller than other babies. These babies are more likely to die before birth or in the first months of their life.

### Are There Safe Forms of Tobacco?

There is no safe way to use tobacco. Some people smoke cigarettes that have less tar and nicotine than regular ones. These people, however, may smoke more often. They may inhale smoke more deeply. They probably do this to get the same amount of nicotine as from a regular cigarette.

Some people use **smokeless tobacco**. Smokeless tobacco is put between the cheeks and gums and chewed. In the past, people believed that it was safe to use smokeless tobacco.

*Medicines and Drugs* Chapter 9 **195**

Have students read about the harmful effects of smoking on page 195.

Ask:

- What are tars and how do tars harm the body? (Tars are dark-colored, sticky substances. Tars contain smoke particles and many different chemicals. Tars damage the interior surface of lung passages.)

- What is emphysema? (Emphysema is a lung disease that causes difficulty in breathing.)

- What is secondhand smoke? (Secondhand smoke is tobacco smoke breathed by nonsmokers.)

- How is secondhand smoke harmful to nonsmokers? (Secondhand smoke can cause disease in nonsmokers. Breathing secondhand smoke causes the heart to beat faster and blood pressure to rise.)

### BACKGROUND INFORMATION

Tell students that in 1965, 42 percent of Americans smoked. By the late 1990s, that percentage had fallen to 25 percent. Considering the health risks, this is still too large a percentage. Smoking accounts for more than 400,000 premature deaths a year in the United States—people who die earlier than they would have if they had not smoked. Another 53,000 deaths each year are due to secondhand smoke. The Environmental Protection Agency (EPA) has classified secondhand smoke as a cancer-causing chemical in the same category as asbestos and radon.

Have students read about smokeless tobacco, how to stop using tobacco, and the rights of nonsmokers on pages 195 and 196.

Ask:

- What health problems can using smokeless tobacco cause? (damage to the teeth and gums, cancer in the mouth)

- What is withdrawal? (Withdrawal is a physical reaction to the absence of a drug in the body.)

- What are some methods that people can use to try to quit smoking? (People can get skin patches or special gum.)

## GLOBAL CONNECTION

In the United States and many other countries, smoking is considered an unhealthy habit. But in some countries, smoking is more acceptable. Encourage students to research why smoking is increasing in some countries. Have students also report on the resulting health effects. For example, the incidence of smoking-related disease, such as lung cancer, is increasing in China. Invite students to make oral reports to share their findings with the class.

## APPLICATION

### Environment
Have students research information on lawsuits against tobacco companies and new restrictions on tobacco advertising. Encourage students to share their findings with the class.

**Withdrawal**
*A physical reaction to the absence of a drug*

Although users of smokeless tobacco do not get lung damage from smoke, they absorb many poisons from tobacco. They become dependent on nicotine, as smokers do. The use of smokeless tobacco can cause the gums to pull away from the teeth so that the teeth become loose and fall out. Smokeless tobacco can also cause cancer in the mouth. Using smokeless tobacco is not safer than smoking tobacco. It is not safe at all.

### How Can People Stop Using Tobacco?

Many people who use tobacco realize that they should quit. They are addicted, however, to nicotine. People who try to stop using tobacco may go through a period of **withdrawal**. This is a physical reaction to the absence of a drug in the body. They may have headaches, be unable to sleep, or have a hard time concentrating. People who choose to stop using tobacco can get help. They can get skin patches or special gum. These patches and gum have a small amount of nicotine. This helps a person slowly stop using nicotine.

### What Are the Rights of Nonsmokers?

People have begun to learn how harmful secondhand smoke can be. As they have, steps have been taken to protect the health of nonsmokers. First, restaurants began to have nonsmoking sections. Many restaurants now do not allow smoking at all. You may have seen signs on restaurants telling customers the restaurant is smoke free.

All tobacco products contain nicotine and can cause health problems.

People used to be able to smoke on airplane flights. The smoke stayed in the cabin during the flight so that everyone had to breathe it. Now all airplane flights within the United States are nonsmoking. This rule protects both the passengers and the people who work for the airlines.

**What do the warnings printed on tobacco products say?**

Because of the harm that secondhand smoke can do, many laws now forbid smoking in public places. These laws protect the rights of nonsmokers. Today there are fewer places where it is legal to smoke. This may help people decide that it is worth the effort for them to quit.

### How Can You Avoid Secondhand Smoke?

Breathing cigarette smoke is dangerous to your health. Nonsmokers can get some of the same physical effects that smokers get. Stay away from areas in which people are smoking. Look for no-smoking signs in restaurants and other buildings. Better yet, try to stay in areas that are posted as smoke-free environments. In most places today, it is easy to avoid breathing cigarette smoke.

**LESSON 3 REVIEW** Write the answers to these questions on a separate sheet of paper. Use complete sentences.

1) Why do people become addicted to smoking tobacco?

2) What is smokeless tobacco?

3) What diseases can be caused by smoking tobacco?

4) How does smoking tobacco endanger the health of nonsmokers?

5) Why are smoke-free buildings good for people's health?

Have students read about the rights of nonsmokers and ways to avoid secondhand smoke on page 197.

### Ask:

• Why do many laws now prohibit smoking in public places? (to protect the rights of nonsmokers)

• How can you avoid secondhand smoke? (Stay away from areas in which people are smoking. Look for no-smoking signs in restaurants and other buildings. Try to stay in areas that are posted as smoke-free environments.)

## Lesson 3 Review Answers

1) People become addicted to smoking tobacco because tobacco contains the drug nicotine, which is addictive.

2) Smokeless tobacco is tobacco that is put between the cheeks and gums and chewed.

3) Diseases that can be caused by smoking tobacco are emphysema and cancers of the lungs, mouth, throat, bladder, and pancreas.

4) Smoking tobacco endangers the health of nonsmokers because nonsmokers breathe the secondhand smoke and are at risk of getting diseases.

5) Smoke-free buildings are good for people's health because they protect nonsmokers from secondhand smoke.

## LEARNING STYLES

**Visual** Write the warnings printed on packs of cigarettes on the chalkboard. Discuss them with students. Challenge students to use what they know about the health effects of cigarette smoke to make their own warning labels for cigarette packs. Encourage students to put the labels on poster board. Display them in the classroom.

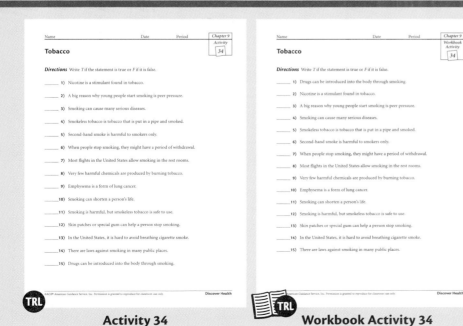

**Activity 34**                **Workbook Activity 34**

# Lesson at a Glance

## Chapter 9 Lesson 4

**Overview** In this lesson, students learn about the effects of alcohol and ways that people with an alcohol abuse problem can get help.

### Objectives

- To identify the effects that alcohol has on the body.

**Student Pages** 198–201

**Audiocassette**

**Teacher's Resource Library**

Activity 35

Workbook Activity 35

## Teaching Suggestions

### ■ Vocabulary

*alcohol, alcoholic beverage, depressant, disinfectant, alcohol abuse, intoxicated, alcoholism, designated driver, ethyl alcohol, Alcoholics Anonymous (AA)*

Have students study the meanings of the vocabulary words. Then tell each student to write a sentence using one of the words, leaving a blank where the vocabulary word should be. Have pairs of students exchange papers and fill in the sentences with the correct words. Have students check each other's work.

### ■ Teaching the Lesson

Ask students to think about instances when they have seen people drink alcoholic beverages on TV shows and in movies. How is this portrayed? In what situations do people drink? (Students might mention that people drink at parties or when they are upset.) Then ask if drinking is portrayed as harmful or helpful to the people involved. Return to the topic after students have read the lesson.

Have students read about the reasons people use alcohol on page 198.

---

**Alcohol**
*A chemical that depresses the central nervous system*

**Alcoholic beverage**
*A drink that contains alcohol*

**Depressant**
*A drug that slows down the central nervous system*

**Disinfectant**
*A chemical used to prevent the spread of disease*

**A**lcohol is a substance that has many uses. You might have used alcohol to clean a computer keyboard. Alcohol works better than other cleaners because it evaporates so quickly. Alcohol is also used as a **disinfectant**, or a chemical to prevent the spread of disease. Many medicines, both prescription and over-the-counter, contain alcohol. You might have taken a medicine for a cold that contained alcohol as one of the ingredients.

But the most common use of alcohol is as a drug. Drinks that are partly alcohol include wine, beer, and liquors. Any drink that is part alcohol is called an **alcoholic beverage**.

Drinking alcoholic beverages is legal for adults over 21 years of age. In some states, it is legal for people over 18 years of age to drink beer or other liquor. There are reasons, however, why some people should never drink alcohol at all. No one should abuse alcohol.

### Why Do People Use Alcohol?

People use alcohol to feel comfortable in social situations, to give themselves more self-confidence, or to relax. Some people use alcohol for the wrong reasons. They may be trying to escape uncomfortable emotions. Using alcohol for this reason may have a bad effect. The alcohol may temporarily cover up the bad emotions, but it doesn't change them. Then the effects of the alcohol wear off. The emotions—and the problems that are causing them—are still there.

Many teens may try alcohol because of peer pressure. This is not a good reason to use alcohol. First, alcohol is probably illegal for teens in your state. And, alcohol use by teens can cause serious physical, mental, and social problems.

### What Does Alcohol Do to the Body?

Alcohol is a central nervous system **depressant**. It slows the activity of the brain and decreases muscle control and coordination. When people use alcohol, they will not be able

**198**    *Chapter 9    Medicines and Drugs*

---

**Ask:**

- **What is alcohol?** (Alcohol is a chemical that depresses the central nervous system.)

- **What are some reasons people use alcohol?** (People use alcohol to feel comfortable in social situations, to give them more self-confidence, and to relax. Some people may be trying to escape uncomfortable emotions. Some teens use alcohol because of peer pressure.)

**Alcohol abuse**
*Drinking too much alcohol or drinking too frequently*

**Intoxicated**
*Excited or stimulated by a drug*

to hear, see, or think as well as they ordinarily would. The effects of using alcohol happen quickly after the drug is used. The more alcohol that is taken, the greater the effects will be.

Alcohol is taken into the stomach. Then it is absorbed into the bloodstream and taken to various parts of the body. Too much alcohol can be harmful. The body cannot absorb the drug quickly enough, so the person becomes **intoxicated**, or drunk.

### What Happens If Too Much Alcohol Is Used?

An intoxicated person experiences major changes in body functions. These include confused thinking, loss of motor control, difficulty walking, and slurred speech. Alcohol is a psychoactive drug. It affects the mind or mental processes and can interfere with a person's ability to think. A person who drinks too much alcohol may become emotional or violent.

Extreme amounts of alcohol can make you sick. Large amounts can cause unconsciousness and sometimes death. Drinking too much alcohol, drinking alcohol too frequently, or combining alcohol with other drugs is called **alcohol abuse**.

### What Are the Harmful Effects of Alcohol?

Drinking too much alcohol over a long period of time can permanently damage the body. The brain, heart, kidneys, stomach, intestines, and liver can all be harmed by alcohol abuse.

### When Is It Dangerous to Use Alcohol?

It is always dangerous to drink too much alcohol. Combining alcohol with medicine can be unsafe also. A person should never use alcohol before driving a car or using dangerous machinery such as an electric drill.

### How Does Society Encourage the Safe Use of Alcohol?

Every year hundreds of people are killed in car accidents caused by someone driving while intoxicated. Many of the people killed are children or teenagers—innocent victims

All of these drinks contain about the same amount of pure alcohol.

*Medicines and Drugs    Chapter 9    **199***

---

Have students read about how alcohol affects the body and dangers of alcohol use on pages 198 and 199.

Ask:

- What does it mean when we say that alcohol depresses the central nervous system? (It means that alcohol slows the activity of the brain and decreases muscle control and coordination.)

- How does alcohol spread throughout the body after you drink it? (Alcohol is absorbed into the bloodstream and taken to various parts of the body.)

- What is the result of drinking too much alcohol? (If too much alcohol is drunk, the body cannot absorb the drug quickly enough, so the person becomes intoxicated.)

- What is alcohol abuse? (drinking too much alcohol, drinking alcohol too frequently, or combining alcohol with other drugs)

**BACKGROUND INFORMATION**

Alcohol abuse has damaging effects on not only the abuser but on the abuser's family, friends, and community. For additional information on alcohol abuse and its effects, students with access to computers can take a look at the following web sites: Mothers Against Drunk Driving at www.madd.org and Students Against Destructive Decisions (formerly Students Against Driving Drunk) at www.saddonline.com.

**APPLICATION**

**In the Community**
What resources are available in your community for people—especially teens—who think they might have a drinking problem? Have students find out and make a brochure that contains information parents and teens might need if they want to get help. Ask the school administration if the class can make the information available to other students at school.

Have students read about using alcohol safely and the problems of alcoholism on pages 199 and 200.

## Ask:

- What tragic situations often result when people drive cars while drunk? (Drunk drivers often kill or injure others.)

- What is a designated driver, and how can using one reduce deaths from drunk driving? (A designated driver is the person in a group who will not drink alcohol and will drive the group home. Choosing a designated driver protects the lives of the people drinking as well as the lives of people in other cars.)

- What is alcoholism? (Alcoholism is a severe mental and physical dependence on alcohol.)

- What are some of the possible effects of alcoholism? (Alcoholics can hurt themselves and their families and lose their jobs or quit school. They may also have major health problems.)

## Technology

Discuss the technology highlighted in the book. Ask students whether it seems like a good solution to drunk driving. Also discuss other methods of deterring drunk drivers. Tell students about laws in some places that require those arrested for drunk driving to put a sign on their cars announcing that they were arrested for driving drunk. The idea is to deter people who would be ashamed to drive around with such signs. Discuss whether this is an adequate punishment. New York City has a law that allows police to take the cars of people arrested for drunk driving. Ask students if they think this would be a deterrent to people.

**Alcoholism**
*A disease in which a person is dependent on the use of alcohol*

**Designated driver**
*The person in a group who will not drink alcohol and will drive the group home*

**Ethyl alcohol**
*A kind of alcohol found in beer, wine, and hard liquors*

of alcohol abuse. Many people are working to change this situation. Two such groups are Mothers Against Drunk Driving (MADD) and Students Against Drunk Driving (SADD). There may be groups such as these in your community.

One idea that can help reduce deaths from drunk drivers is the **designated driver**. In a group that will be drinking, the designated driver is chosen ahead of time. He or she drives the group home. The designated driver does not drink. Choosing a designated driver protects the lives of the people drinking as well as the lives of people in other cars.

### What Is Alcoholism?

People can become both physically and psychologically addicted to **ethyl alcohol**. Ethyl alcohol is found in beer, wine, and hard liquors. **Alcoholism** is a severe mental and physical dependence on alcohol. People with the disease of alcoholism cannot control their drinking. They can hurt themselves and their families and lose their jobs or quit school. They may also begin having major health problems.

technology

### SOFTWARE FOR ALCOHOL TESTING

People who drink and drive are dangerous to themselves and others. Breath analyzers help police keep drunk drivers off the roads. These analyzers measure blood alcohol levels. One analyzer is called "ignition interlock." It is put on the cars of people who have had problems with drinking and driving. The device is wired to the car's starter. Before starting the car, the driver blows into the device. Sensors check for alcohol in the breath. If they sense alcohol, the car will not start. The computer records the number of failed tests. It can even tell if the system has been tampered with. Such technology keeps everyone safer.

Drunk drivers kill hundreds of people each year. Students Against Drunk Driving (SADD) works to stop people from driving after drinking.

---

**Alcoholics Anonymous (AA)**
*An organization that helps people live alcohol-free lives*

## How Can People With Alcoholism Get Help?

The disease of alcoholism has no cure. People with alcoholism must stop drinking and never drink again. Many community mental health centers offer alcohol treatment programs at low cost. A nationwide group helping people with alcoholism is **Alcoholics Anonymous (AA)**. AA groups help people lead alcohol-free lives.

## Are Some Kinds of Alcoholic Drinks Safer Than Others?

**What are some ways to recognize a driver who has been drinking?**

Some people believe that drinking wine or beer is safer than using "hard liquors" such as whiskey, vodka, or gin. This is not true. One serving of each type of alcoholic beverage contains about the same amount of alcohol. Drinking too much of any kind of alcohol can damage the body.

**LESSON 4 REVIEW** Write the answers to these questions on a separate sheet of paper. Use complete sentences.

1) Name three uses of alcohol.
2) How does alcohol affect the body?
3) What are some health effects caused by drinking too much alcohol?
4) Why is it dangerous to drive a car after using alcohol?
5) What can people in your community do to prevent or reduce alcohol abuse?

*Medicines and Drugs* Chapter 9 **201**

---

Have students read about places where alcoholics can get help and different kinds of alcoholic drinks on page 201.

### Ask:

- Can alcoholism be cured? (No, alcoholism has no cure.) How do alcoholics deal with their disease? (Alcoholics must never drink again.)

- What are some places where alcoholics can get help? (community mental health centers, nationwide groups such as Alcoholics Anonymous.)

- Why is drinking wine or beer not safer than drinking hard liquor? (Drinking wine or beer is not safer than drinking hard liquor because one serving of wine or beer contains about the same amount of alcohol as one serving of hard liquor.)

## Lesson 4 Review Answers

1) Alcohol is used as a drug, as a cleaner, as a disinfectant, and as an ingredient in medicines.
2) Alcohol slows the activity of the brain and decreases muscle control and coordination.
3) Drinking too much alcohol can damage the brain, heart, kidneys, stomach, intestines, and liver.
4) It is dangerous to drive a car after using alcohol because a person's physical abilities are slowed down. He or she will not be able to react quickly in an emergency.
5) Answers will vary and may include the following: join or support groups such as Mothers Against Driving Drunk, encourage campaigns on designated drivers.

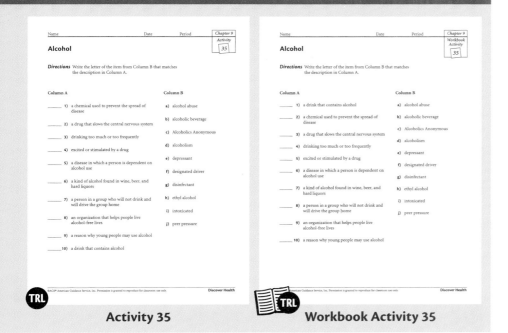

**Activity 35**          **Workbook Activity 35**

# Lesson at a Glance

## Chapter 9 Lesson 5

**Overview** In this lesson, students learn about narcotics, depressants, stimulants, and hallucinogens.

### Objectives

■ To describe the dangers associated with narcotics, depressants, stimulants, and hallucinogens.

**Student Pages** 202–205

**Audiocassette**

**Teacher's Resource Library**

Activity 36

Workbook Activity 36

## Teaching Suggestions

### ■ Vocabulary

*hallucinogen, heroin, narcotic, opiate, synthetic, tolerance, convulsion, tremor, amphetamine, caffeine, cocaine, crack cocaine, ice, hallucination, psychedelic drug*

Tell students to read the words and definitions. List the four types of drugs: narcotics, depressants, stimulants, and hallucinogens. Then have students begin a chart with each of the types of drugs in a separate column. Encourage students to add information to the chart as they proceed through the chapter.

### ■ Teaching the Lesson

Discuss the way narcotics, depressants, stimulants, and hallucinogens might affect someone's ability to study in school, play sports, or enjoy activities with friends. Have students read about narcotics on page 202.

---

## Lesson 5

## Narcotics, Depressants, Stimulants, and Hallucinogens

**Hallucinogen**
*A drug that confuses the way the brain processes information*

**Heroin**
*A dangerous and illegal narcotic drug*

**Narcotic**
*A drug that dulls the senses or relieves pain*

**Opiate**
*A drug made from opium poppy plants; another name for narcotic*

**Synthetic**
*A narcotic drug that is manufactured in laboratories*

**Tolerance**
*A condition in which a person must take more and more of a drug to get the same effect*

You might have heard the term *narcotic* used to describe all illegal drugs. As you will learn, **narcotics** are just one group of often-abused drugs. Three other groups are depressants, stimulants, and **hallucinogens**.

### What Are Narcotics?

Narcotics are a group of drugs that have a true medical use. Morphine and codeine are used for severe pain, such as pain after surgery or in late stages of cancer. Narcotics are also called **opiates** because many of them are produced from the opium poppy plant. Other narcotics are **synthetic**. They are manufactured in laboratories.

Narcotic drugs can cause unpleasant side effects. They slow breathing, cause sleepiness, confuse thinking, and cause nervousness. No one should ever take narcotic drugs without the advice and supervision of a doctor.

Narcotics can produce a powerful physical and mental dependence. So, these drugs are very habit forming. A person taking the drug builds up a **tolerance** to it. More and more of the drug is needed to get the same result. As the person takes more of the drug, an overdose may occur. This could cause unconsciousness or even death.

**Heroin** is a dangerous and illegal narcotic drug. Heroin has no legal or medical use in the United States. Any person who buys or sells heroin is breaking the law. Heroin is usually injected into a vein with a needle. This means that heroin users also risk diseases, such as AIDS, from using contaminated needles.

### What Are Depressants?

A depressant is a drug that slows the activity of the brain. You have read about alcohol, which is a depressant. Tranquilizers, barbiturates, and nonbarbiturate sleeping drugs are also

---

Ask:

· **What are narcotics?** (Narcotics are drugs that dull the senses or relieve pain.)

· **What is heroin?** (Heroin is a dangerous and illegal narcotic drug.) **How can the way heroin is usually used expose a person to other diseases?** (Heroin is usually injected into a vein with a needle. This means that heroin users risk diseases, such as AIDS, from using contaminated needles.)

· **Why do people build up a tolerance to narcotics?** (Narcotics are habit forming, and so more and more of the drug is needed to get the same results.)

**Convulsion**
*A drawing tightly together and relaxing of a muscle*

**Tremor**
*Severe shaking*

depressant drugs. Most depressants are prescription medicines. Doctors may prescribe tranquilizers for anxiety or barbiturates to help people sleep.

Depressants produce a calming effect because they slow down the central nervous system. They lower blood pressure and heart rate. Using a depressant drug can cause sleepiness or confused thinking. It may be dangerous to drive a car or operate machinery while taking depressant drugs.

Depressants are often abused. A user can quickly become dependent on the drug. Then, more and more of the drug must be taken to get the same result. Sometimes a person cannot get a doctor's prescription for more of the drug. Then he or she may begin buying it illegally. Because depressants affect the brain centers that control breathing, an overdose can cause respiratory failure.

*Health Tip*

Use physical exercise instead of drugs to relax your body and relieve anxiety or stress.

A person who is dependent on a depressant may not be able to stop using the drug suddenly. In users, the brain has changed physically. It has "learned" to operate with the drug. When a depressant is stopped suddenly, the user may have **tremors**. The person may shake severely or have his or her muscles drawn tight in **convulsions**. Suddenly stopping a depressant can be life threatening. A person who is trying to stop using alcohol or any other depressant should be under a doctor's care.

The table below lists some types of commonly abused drugs.

| Narcotics (opiates) | Depressants | Stimulants | Hallucinogens |
|---|---|---|---|
| Codeine | Alcohol | Nicotine | LSD |
| Morphine | Tranquilizers | Amphetamines | PCP |
| Heroin | Barbiturates | Cocaine | MDMA (Ecstasy) |
| Synthetic opiates | Nonbarbiturate sleeping drugs | Crack cocaine | Mescaline |
| | | | Psilocybin |

Why would a person misuse both depressants and stimulants?

Have students read about depressants on pages 202 and 203.

**Ask:**

- What is a depressant? (A depressant is a drug that slows the activity of the brain.)

- What types of medical uses do depressants have? (Doctors may prescribe tranquilizers for anxiety or barbiturates to help people sleep.)

- How can abusing depressants cause harm? (A user can quickly become dependent on the drug. Because depressants affect the brain centers that control breathing, an overdose can cause respiratory failure.)

- What happens when someone who is dependent on a depressant stops using it? (The user may have tremors.)

**LEARNING STYLES**

**Group Learning** Encourage groups of students to pick one of the categories of drugs at the bottom of page 203. Students should make a presentation on that group of drugs, including the history of their use, how the drugs are made, where the drugs come from, effects on the body, and dangers to users and others. Students can include photos, short films, posters, or other visual or audio aids in their presentations.

Have students read about stimulants on page 204.

Ask:

- What are stimulants? (Stimulants are drugs that increase the activity of the brain.)

- Name two stimulants. (Accept any two of the following: caffeine, cocaine, crack cocaine, amphetamines, nicotine.)

- What are cocaine and crack cocaine? (Cocaine is an illegal stimulant drug made from the coca plant. It is white powder that is sniffed through the nose or injected into a vein. Crack cocaine is a powerful form of cocaine that is smoked.)

- What are amphetamines? (Amphetamines are synthetic stimulants.)

- What is ice, and why is it dangerous? (Ice is a form of amphetamine that is smoked. Ice can cause permanent mental disability.)

- Some diet drugs are amphetamines, but they are not prescribed by doctors often. Why is this the case? (Diet drugs that are amphetamines are not prescribed often because there is too much risk that a person can become dependent upon them.)

## LEARNING STYLES

**Tactile/Kinesthetic** Encourage students to make a list of foods that contain caffeine and compare their caffeine content. At the end of the activity, ask students to state which foods contain the most caffeine and which contain the least. Invite students to discuss in class which of these foods they eat and the amount of caffeine in these foods.

---

**Amphetamine**
*A synthetic stimulant*

**Caffeine**
*A stimulant found in coffee, tea, chocolate, and some soft drinks*

**Cocaine**
*A dangerous and illegal stimulant drug made from the coca plant*

**Crack cocaine**
*A form of cocaine that is smoked*

**Ice**
*A form of an amphetamine that is smoked*

**Suggest some better ways to lose weight other than taking amphetamine drugs.**

## What Are Stimulants?

A stimulant is a drug that increases the activity of the brain. You have read about the stimulant nicotine. **Caffeine** is the mild stimulant found in coffee, tea, soft drinks, and chocolate.

The other stimulants in this group are dangerous drugs. **Cocaine** is an illegal drug made from the coca plant. It is a white powder that is sniffed through the nose. It can also be injected into a vein. **Crack cocaine** is a powerful form of cocaine that is smoked. Dependence on cocaine can occur rapidly—sometimes with the first use. People who use cocaine stop eating properly, and malnutrition may result.

**Amphetamines** are synthetic stimulants. Some amphetamines are prescription medicines. For example, a doctor might prescribe an amphetamine drug to help someone lose weight. But, doctors do not prescribe these drugs as often as they once did. There is too much of a risk that a person will become dependent on the drug. There are several different kinds of illegal amphetamines. **Ice** is a form of amphetamine that is smoked. Ice can cause permanent mental disability.

Stimulant drugs speed up the heart and breathing. At first, they cause a user to feel clearheaded and not tired. Later, users feel nervous, anxious, and irritable. A user may become confused, fearful, and violent. Users may go for long periods without food or sleep while under the effects of the drug. Stimulants are habit-forming. Some users switch between a stimulant and a depressant so they can sleep. A large dose of amphetamine or cocaine can cause the user's heart to stop beating.

**Hallucination**
*A distortion of the senses caused by mental disease or drugs*

**Psychedelic drug**
*Another term for hallucinogen*

## What Are Hallucinogens?

Hallucinogens confuse the central nervous system. They change the way the brain processes information from the senses. A person who uses a hallucinogen senses the world in a distorted way. These distortions of the senses are called **hallucinations**. The user might think that he or she hears voices. The user might become frightened of something that does not exist. Or the user might think that people are plotting against him or her.

Hallucinogens are also called **psychedelic drugs**. They are illegal and have no current accepted medical uses. Two hallucinogens, mescaline and psilocybin, grow naturally. LSD, phencyclidine (PCP), and MDMA (Ecstasy) are synthetic. A great danger of hallucinogens is that the user will hurt himself or herself or someone else. Users of PCP often become violent. A large dose of PCP can cause convulsions, coma, and death. Some hallucinogens cause flashbacks. The user experiences a hallucination. But it occurs months or years after the drug is taken.

**LESSON 5 REVIEW** Write the answers to these questions on a separate sheet of paper. Use complete sentences.

1) List three reasons why narcotics are dangerous.
2) Name two depressants and their effect on the body.
3) Name two stimulants and their effect on the body.
4) What kinds of drugs can cause hallucinations?
5) What is a synthetic drug?

*Medicines and Drugs* Chapter 9 **205**

Have students read about the dangers of hallucinogens on page 205.

**Ask:**

• What is a hallucinogen? (A hallucinogen is a drug that changes the way the brain processes information from the senses, causing a user to sense the world in a distorted way.)

• What is a great danger of hallucinogens? (The user will hurt himself or herself or someone else.)

• What are the dangers of the hallucinogen PCP? (PCP can cause users to become violent. A large dose of PCP can cause convulsions, coma, and death.)

### Lesson 5 Review Answers

1) Narcotics are dangerous because they cause unpleasant side effects, they produce a powerful physical and mental dependence, and users risk diseases such as AIDS.
2) Answers will vary. Accept any two of the following: alcohol, tranquilizers, barbiturates, nonbarbiturate sleeping drugs. Depressants produce a calming effect. They lower blood pressure and heart rate and can cause sleepiness or confused thinking. An overdose can cause respiratory failure.
3) Answers will vary. Accept any two of the following: caffeine, nicotine, amphetamines, cocaine, crack cocaine. Stimulants can cause permanent mental disability, nervousness, anxiety, irritability, confusion, fear, and violent behavior.
4) Hallucinogens such as LSD, PCP, mescaline, and psilocybin can cause hallucinations.
5) A synthetic drug is a narcotic that is manufactured in a laboratory.

---

**Activity 36**

Name ___ Date ___ Period ___ 

Chapter 9 Activity 36

**Narcotics, Depressants, Stimulants, and Hallucinogens**

**Directions** Write the letter of the item from Column B that matches the description in Column A.

**Column A**

___ 1) a synthetic stimulant
___ 2) a dangerous and illegal narcotic
___ 3) a stimulant found in coffee, tea, chocolate, and some soft drinks
___ 4) a drug that dulls the senses or relieves pain
___ 5) a dangerous and illegal stimulant made from the coca plant
___ 6) a drug made from the opium poppy
___ 7) a form of cocaine that is smoked
___ 8) a narcotic made in laboratories
___ 9) a form of an amphetamine that is smoked
___ 10) a condition in which a person needs more and more of a drug for the same effect
___ 11) a distortion of the senses caused by mental disease or drugs
___ 12) a drawing tightly together and relaxing of a muscle
___ 13) another term for hallucinogen
___ 14) severe shaking
___ 15) a drug that confuses the way the brain processes information

**Column B**

a) amphetamine
b) caffeine
c) cocaine
d) convulsion
e) crack cocaine
f) hallucination
g) hallucinogen
h) heroin
i) ice
j) narcotic
k) opiate
l) psychedelic drug
m) synthetic drug
n) tolerance
o) tremor

**Workbook Activity 36**

Name ___ Date ___ Period ___

Chapter 9 Workbook Activity 36

**Narcotics, Depressants, Stimulants, and Hallucinogens**

**Directions** Write the letter of the item from Column B that matches the description in Column A.

**Column A**

___ 1) a drug that confuses the way the brain processes information
___ 2) a synthetic stimulant
___ 3) a dangerous and illegal narcotic
___ 4) a stimulant found in coffee, tea, chocolate, and some soft drinks
___ 5) a drug that dulls the senses or relieves pain
___ 6) a dangerous and illegal stimulant made from the coca plant
___ 7) a drug made from the opium poppy
___ 8) a form of cocaine that is smoked
___ 9) a narcotic made in laboratories
___ 10) a form of an amphetamine that is smoked
___ 11) a condition in which a person needs more and more of a drug for the same effect
___ 12) a distortion of the senses caused by mental disease or drugs
___ 13) a drawing tightly together and relaxing of a muscle
___ 14) another term for hallucinogen
___ 15) severe shaking

**Column B**

a) amphetamine
b) caffeine
c) cocaine
d) convulsion
e) crack cocaine
f) hallucination
g) hallucinogen
h) heroin
i) ice
j) narcotic
k) opiate
l) psychedelic drug
m) synthetic drug
n) tolerance
o) tremor

*Medicines and Drugs* Chapter 9 **205**

### Chapter 9 Lesson 6

**Overview** In this lesson, students learn about several other dangerous drugs, including inhalants, steroids, marijuana, designer drugs, and look-alike drugs.

### Objectives

■ To describe the dangers associated with dangerous drugs.

**Student Pages** 206–208

**Audiocassette** ∩

**Teacher's Resource Library** **TRL**

Activity 37

Workbook Activity 37

## Teaching Suggestions

### ■ Vocabulary

*inhalant, anabolic steroid, marijuana, sterile, steroid, testosterone, designer drug, look-alike drug*

Have students review the vocabulary words and their definitions. Then have students add the drug types to the chart they started at the beginning of the previous lesson. The completed chart can be used as a study sheet at the end of the unit or as a reference sheet to take home.

### ■ Teaching the Lesson

Have students explain what they have heard about inhalants, steroids, and marijuana. Write their statements on the chalkboard. After finishing the lesson, have students return to these statements. How would they revise them based on their new knowledge of these substances?

Have students read about inhalants on page 206.

---

## Lesson 6   Other Dangerous Drugs

| Inhalant
A substance that
is breathed |

$I$n Lesson 5, you learned about four groups of drugs. Narcotics, depressants, and stimulants can be helpful when used for proper medical purposes. They are dangerous, however, when abused or used illegally. Hallucinogens are always dangerous and always illegal. This lesson describes the properties and effects of some other dangerous substances.

### What Are Inhalants?

Breathable substances are called **inhalants**. You breathe, or inhale, the substance, which enters your body through your lungs. Some people use inhalants that contain medicine for asthma, severe allergies, or pain.

Some substances that are inhaled were never intended as medicines. These dangerous inhalants include household products such as glue, cleaners, paint removers, correction fluid, and gasoline. The labels on these products have warnings telling people not to breathe them.

People who ignore the warnings and breathe the products are abusing the products. In many places, this misuse of these products is illegal. People use these dangerous substances to get a hallucinogenic effect. Some people may simply be "experimenting."

Using illegal inhalants is extremely dangerous. They depress the central nervous system and can cause slurred speech, poor judgment, confusion, dizziness, and headaches. Some illegal inhalants make people violent. Others can cause permanent brain damage. None of them are safe to use.

Dangerous and illegal inhalants include paint thinner, polish remover, glue, and spray paint.

**206**   *Chapter 9   Medicines and Drugs*

---

**Ask:**

• What is an inhalant? (An inhalant is a substance that is breathed.)

• What types of substances are used as illegal inhalants? (glue, cleaners, paint removers, correction fluid, gasoline)

• What are the effects of illegal inhalants on the body? (They depress the central nervous system and can cause slurred speech, poor judgment, confusion, dizziness, and headaches. Illegal inhalants make people violent and can cause permanent brain damage.)

## Glossary (sidebar)

**Anabolic steroid**
*A synthetic drug that resembles the hormone testosterone*

**Marijuana**
*An illegal drug from the hemp plant that produces intoxication*

**Sterile**
*Unable to have children*

**Steroid**
*A chemical that occurs naturally in the body or is made in a laboratory*

**Testosterone**
*The male hormone that produces male characteristics, such as facial hair and a deep voice*

---

### What Are Anabolic Steroids?

**Steroids** are chemicals, such as hormones, that occur naturally in the body or are made in a laboratory. Some people's bodies do not make enough of these needed chemicals. Then, a doctor can prescribe medicine to make up for the lack of the chemical.

One group of steroids is called **anabolic steroids**. These mimic the effects of the male hormone **testosterone**. This hormone produces characteristics, such as facial hair and a deep voice. People soon realized that taking anabolic steroids also stimulates the body to produce muscle tissue. Some athletes began to take these drugs to try to improve their performance. Young boys sometimes took the steroids because they wanted to appear older and stronger.

Using anabolic steroids is dangerous and is illegal without a prescription. Starting in the 1960s, athletes have been tested to see if they use steroids. If they do, they are disqualified from competition.

Anabolic steroids have many side effects. The liver, heart, and reproductive systems can all be permanently damaged. Steroids can cause cancer, heart attacks, and strokes. Both males and females can become **sterile**, or unable to have children. Teenagers who use steroids may stop growing and never reach their normal adult height. Steroids also have mental side effects. They can cause anxiety, depression, and violent behavior known as "roid rages."

### What Is Marijuana?

Another illegal drug is **marijuana**. This drug comes from a hemp plant called Cannabis sativa. The leaves and buds of the plant have an intoxicating effect. To get this effect, some people smoke, eat, or make tea with this drug.

In the 1950s, some people believed that marijuana was safe to use. They were wrong. Marijuana depresses the central nervous system. It interferes with memory, concentration, and the ability to drive a car or do schoolwork. Marijuana smokers inhale deeply and hold the smoke in their lungs. This means that using marijuana can cause lung disease and cancer.

**Why do young people use inhalants more often than other illegal drugs?**

*Medicines and Drugs   Chapter 9   **207***

---

Have students read about anabolic steroids and marijuana on page 207.

### Ask:

- What are steroids? (Steroids are chemicals that occur naturally in the body or are made in a laboratory.)

- What is testosterone and what does it do? (Testosterone is the male hormone that produces characteristics such as facial hair and a deep voice.)

- Name two possible side effects of steroid use. (Accept any two of the following: permanent damage to the liver, heart, and reproductive system; cancer, heart attack, or stroke; sterility; stops teens from growing to normal adult height; causes anxiety, depression, and violent behavior.)

- What is marijuana? (Marijuana is an illegal drug from the hemp plant that produces intoxication.)

- Is marijuana safe to use? (No, marijuana is not safe.) Explain your answer. (Marijuana is not safe because it depresses the central nervous system. It interferes with memory, concentration, and the ability to drive or do schoolwork. Marijuana can also cause lung disease and cancer.)

### LEARNING STYLES

**Auditory** Read a newspaper article to students that recounts the problems encountered by an athlete who took steroids and had health problems, died, or was disqualified from participating in sports as a result. Encourage students to take notes and summarize the article in one or two paragraphs.

Have students read about designer drugs and look-alike drugs on page 208.

Ask:

- What are designer drugs? (Designer drugs are illegal manufactured drugs that are made from chemicals like those in a legal drug or medicine.)

- How do designer drugs differ from legal drugs? (Designer drugs can be made many times stronger and can imitate the effect of narcotics.)

- What are look-alike drugs? (Look-alike drugs are illegal manufactured drugs that imitate the effects of legal prescription drugs.)

- What is a problem with using look-alike drugs? (A user cannot be sure what substances are contained in the drug.)

## Lesson 6 Review Answers

1) Accept any three of the following: glue, cleaners, paints, correction fluid, gasoline.

2) Some athletes have used anabolic steroids to improve their performance.

3) The health risks of using anabolic steroids are permanent damage to the liver, heart, and reproductive system; cancer, heart attack, or stroke; stops teens from growing to normal adult height; and causes anxiety, depression, and violent behavior.

4) Smoking marijuana can cause lung disease and cancer. It also interferes with memory, concentration, and the ability to drive a care or do schoolwork.

5) Designer drugs can be many times stronger than legal drugs. Look-alike drugs are illegally produced, so a user cannot be sure what substances are contained in the drug.

**Designer drug**
*An illegal manufactured drug that is almost the same as a legal drug*

**Look-alike drug**
*An illegal manufactured drug that imitates the effect of other drugs*

### What Are Designer Drugs?

Criminals who make and sell illegal drugs try to avoid the law. One way they try is to create **designer drugs**. These are made from chemicals like those in a legal drug or medicine. The designer drugs, however, are different from legal drugs. They can be many times stronger and can imitate the effect of narcotics. Someone has created a designer drug called "China White." This drug has the same effect as heroin.

At one time, designer drugs were legal because the law had not described them as illegal. In 1986, a law called the Anti-Abuse Drug Act was passed. It made all designer drugs illegal. Designer drugs are dangerous because they often contain strong, poisonous chemicals.

### What Are Look-Alike Drugs?

Another group of drugs made from legal chemicals are the **look-alike drugs**. They may imitate the effects of legal prescription drugs. However, look-alike drugs are illegally produced. A user cannot be sure what substances are contained in the drug. For example, someone may think he or she is buying an amphetamine, but the drug is actually LSD.

Look-alike drugs often contain dangerously large amounts of caffeine. They can cause anxiety, restlessness, weakness, headaches, and rapid heartbeat. These drugs are especially dangerous. The user cannot know how strong they are or what their side effects may be. The risk of taking an overdose is very high.

**LESSON 6 REVIEW** Write the answers to these questions on a separate sheet of paper. Use complete sentences.

1) What are three products that are misused as inhalants?

2) Why have some athletes used anabolic steroids?

3) What are the health risks of using anabolic steroids?

4) How does smoking marijuana affect the body?

5) Why are designer and look-alike drugs particularly dangerous?

*Health Tip*

Use your refusal skills. Don't go to places where there will be drugs.

How can you use positive peer pressure to keep your friends from using drugs?

Activity 37

Workbook Activity 37

■ A drug changes the way the mind or body works. All medicines are drugs. Not all drugs are medicines.

■ Prescription medicines require a written note from a doctor. Over-the-counter drugs do not need a doctor's prescription.

■ The effects of medicines include relieving pain, preventing or curing disease, and helping the brain to function normally.

■ Medicines affect people in different ways. Body size, weight, and other factors may change the effects of a medicine.

■ Medicines may have side effects. Follow directions carefully when taking medicines.

■ Do not take someone else's medicine. Do not take prescription medicine unless it was prescribed for your current illness.

■ Tobacco is a stimulant. The nicotine in tobacco is addictive. The use of tobacco can result in life-threatening diseases involving the lungs, heart, and other organs.

■ People who breathe secondhand tobacco smoke can have the same health problems that smokers have.

■ Alcohol is a depressant. Misusing alcohol can result in the disease of alcoholism and cause permanent health and family problems.

■ It is always dangerous to drive a car after drinking alcohol.

■ Narcotics, depressants, and stimulants can all be addictive drugs. Illegal drugs in these groups are dangerous. They can cause permanent health damage and sometimes death.

■ Hallucinogens change the way the brain processes information. All hallucinogens are illegal and dangerous.

■ Inhalants, anabolic steroids, marijuana, designer drugs, and look-alike drugs are dangerous and addictive.

*Medicines and Drugs* *Chapter 9* **209**

---

### ■ Using the Chapter Summary

To further reinforce the facts and concepts presented in the chapter, read and discuss with students the questions that follow.

Ask:

• **What is a drug?** (A drug is a substance that changes the way the mind or body works.)

• **What are the two main types of medicines?** (prescription and over-the-counter)

• **What are the effects of medicines?** (Medicines relieve pain, prevent or cure disease, and help the brain to function normally.)

• **What does using tobacco do to the body?** (Using tobacco can result in life-threatening diseases involving the lungs, heart, and other organs.)

• **Why is secondhand smoke dangerous for nonsmokers?** (Breathing secondhand smoke can cause nonsmokers some of the same health problems that smokers have.)

• **Why is illegal use of narcotics, depressants, and stimulants dangerous?** (Illegal use of narcotics, depressants, and stimulants can cause permanent health damage and sometimes death.)

• **What do hallucinogens do?** (Hallucinogens change the way the brain processes information.)

# Chapter 9 Review

The Teacher's Resource Library includes two parallel forms of the Chapter 9 Mastery Test. The difficulty level of the two forms is equivalent. You may wish to use one form as a pretest and the other form as a posttest.

## Review Answers

### Comprehension: Identifying Facts
1) stimulant  2) nicotine  3) depressant
4) tolerance  5) Prescription  6) withdrawal
7) narcotic  8) hallucinogenic  9) pregnant

## Comprehension: Identifying Facts
On a separate sheet of paper, write the correct word from the Word Bank to complete each sentence.

| WORD BANK | | |
| --- | --- | --- |
| alcoholism | nicotine | stimulant |
| depressant | pain | tolerance |
| hallucinogenics | pregnant | tremors |
| inhalants | prescription | |
| narcotic | steroids | |

1) A _____ is a drug that speeds up the central nervous system.

2) All forms of tobacco contain the addictive drug _____.

3) Alcohol is a central nervous system _____.

4) A drug user builds up _____ to a drug and needs more and more to get the same effect.

5) _____ drugs require a written note from a doctor.

6) People who stop using addictive drugs experience _____.

7) Morphine, cocaine, and heroin are _____.

8) All _____ drugs are illegal.

9) Women who are _____ must be particularly careful about using drugs.

---

**Name** _____  **Date** _____  **Period** _____  Chapter 9 Mastery Test A page 1

### Chapter 9 Mastery Test A

*Directions* Read the words in the Word Bank. Choose the item that *best* completes each sentence. On the blank before each number, write the letter for that item.

**Word Bank**

| | | |
| --- | --- | --- |
| a) antibiotics | f) inhalants | k) secondhand smoke |
| b) cocaine | g) narcotics | l) steroids |
| c) designated driver | h) nicotine | m) stimulant |
| d) designer drugs | i) over-the-counter medicines | n) testing |
| e) hallucinogen | j) pregnant | o) withdrawal |

____ 1) Medicines for minor pain and fever, for colds, and for minor skin problems are all _____.

____ 2) _____ are medicines that stop the growth of germs that cause disease.

____ 3) In the United States, the Food and Drug Administration (FDA) oversees the _____ and sale of medicines.

____ 4) A woman who is _____ should ask her doctor before she takes any medicine.

____ 5) The main reason people continue to smoke is because of _____ an addictive chemical in tobacco.

____ 6) A _____ is a drug that speeds up the central nervous system.

____ 7) Because of the harm _____ can do, many laws now forbid smoking in public places.

____ 8) People who try to stop using a drug may go through a period of _____.

____ 9) A _____ is the person in a group who will not drink alcohol and will drive the group home.

**TRL** ©AGS® American Guidance Service, Inc. Permission is granted to reproduce for classroom use only.  **Discover Health**

---

**Name** _____  **Date** _____  **Period** _____  Chapter 9 Mastery Test A page 2

### Chapter 9 Mastery Test A, continued

____ 10) Legal _____, such as morphine and codeine, are used for severe pain.

____ 11) _____ is a dangerous and illegal stimulant drug.

____ 12) A person who uses a _____ senses the world in a distorted way.

____ 13) Gasoline, paint remover, and glue are dangerous _____.

____ 14) Some athletes abuse _____.

____ 15) A _____ is an illegal manufactured drug that is almost the same as a legal drug.

**TRL** ©AGS® American Guidance Service, Inc. Permission is granted to reproduce for classroom use only.  **Discover Health**

## Chapter 9 Mastery Test A

**10)** The disease of _____ has no known cure.

**11)** One beneficial use of drugs is to prevent _____.

**12)** Paint thinner and glue are dangerous _____.

**13)** Some athletes abuse _____ to try to perform better.

## Comprehension: Understanding Main Ideas

Write the answers to these questions on a separate sheet of paper. Use complete sentences.

**14)** List four safety tips for taking medicines.

**15)** What are two ways to decide which over-the-counter medicine to buy?

**16)** List drugs that can interfere with a person's ability to drive a car.

**17)** Why are tobacco and alcohol legal if they can cause harm to a person's health?

**18)** Name two narcotic drugs and two stimulant drugs that are illegal.

## Critical Thinking: Write Your Opinion

**19)** Suppose you have a bad cold. Should you take medicine or just wait for the cold to go away? Explain your answer.

**20)** Why do you think alcoholism or any drug dependence could be considered a family disease?

**Test Taking Tip** Read test questions carefully to identify those questions that require more than one answer.

---

**10)** alcoholism **11)** pain **12)** inhalants **13)** steroids

## Comprehension: Understanding Main Ideas

**14)** Answers will vary. Accept any four of the following: let your doctor know about all the medicines you take, even vitamins; follow the directions for taking the medicine; read and follow all warnings on the medicine container; tell your doctor about any side effects; never take medicine that belongs to someone else; store medicines properly; do not mix medicines unless directed to do so by a doctor; never mix medicines and alcohol.

**15)** To decide which over-the-counter medicine to buy, you can ask your doctor or pharmacist, or you can consult an adult.

**16)** Drugs that can interfere with a person's ability to drive a car include alcohol, all narcotics and depressants, and all illegal drugs.

**17)** Tobacco and alcohol are legal because the dangers of tobacco and alcohol were not known in the past and many people have become addicted.

**18)** Two narcotic drugs that are illegal are heroin and opium. Two stimulant drugs that are illegal are cocaine and crack cocaine.

## Critical Thinking: Write Your Opinion

**19)** Answers will vary. Possible answer: If you have a bad cold, you might try drinking orange juice and other liquids for a few days to see if the cold gets better.

**20)** Alcoholism and any drug dependence could be considered a family disease because the drug user's behaviors affect all family members. For example, the drug user needs money for the drugs and may take money from the family, or the drug user may become violent and hurt other family members.

---

Chapter 9 Mastery Test B

Name _____ Date _____ Period _____ | Chapter 9 Mastery Test B page 1

**Chapter 9 Mastery Test B**

**Directions** Read the words in the Word Bank. Choose the item that *best* completes each sentence. On the blank before each number, write the letter for that item.

**Word Bank**

a) antibiotics    f) inhalants    k) secondhand smoke
b) cocaine    g) narcotics    l) steroids
c) designated driver    h) nicotine    m) stimulant
d) designer drugs    i) over-the-counter medicines    n) testing
e) hallucinogen    j) pregnant    o) withdrawal

____ 1) Some athletes abuse _____.

____ 2) A _____ is an illegal manufactured drug that is almost the same as a legal drug.

____ 3) A _____ is the person in a group who will not drink alcohol and will drive the group home.

____ 4) Legal _____, such as morphine and codeine, are used for severe pain.

____ 5) Medicines for minor pain and fever, for colds, and for minor skin problems are all _____.

____ 6) _____ are medicines that stop the growth of germs that cause disease.

____ 7) In the United States, the Food and Drug Administration (FDA) oversees the _____ and sale of medicines.

____ 8) _____ is a dangerous and illegal stimulant drug.

____ 9) A person who uses a _____ senses the world in a distorted way.

Name _____ Date _____ Period _____ | Chapter 9 Mastery Test B page 2

**Chapter 9 Mastery Test B, continued**

____ 10) Gasoline, paint remover, and glue are dangerous _____.

____ 11) Because of the harm _____ can do, many laws now forbid smoking in public places.

____ 12) People who try to stop using a drug may go through a period of _____.

____ 13) A woman who is _____ should ask her doctor before she takes any medicine.

____ 14) The main reason people continue to smoke is because of _____, an addictive chemical in tobacco.

____ 15) A _____ is a drug that speeds up the central nervous system.

Discover Health

Discover Health

## Introducing the Chapter

In Chapter 9, students learned about the effects of medicines and drugs. Before beginning this chapter, briefly review the positive uses of medicines, such as the treatment of disease or the relief of pain. Then ask students to think about the way medicines and drugs can be misused. List student responses on the board. At the end of the chapter, have students look at the list again. Have them revise the list based on what they have learned.

Have a volunteer read page 212 aloud, including the Goals for Learning.

## Ask:

• What does it mean to become dependent on a drug? (Accept all reasonable answers. Possible answers include becoming physically ill if your body doesn't get the drug or thinking you need the drug to function.)

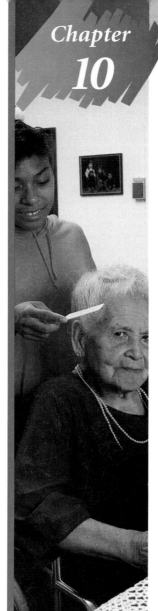

# Drug Dependence— Problems and Solutions

*A*s you grow older, you will be faced with many choices. The more you know about something, the better your choices will be. An important choice that you must make concerns the use of drugs. Both adults and teenagers are learning more about drugs. People now know how much damage drugs can do.

In this chapter, you will learn about drug dependence. Drug dependence causes problems with health. It causes problems with life. You will learn ways that drug users can get help. You will also learn about healthy alternatives to drug use.

> ### Goals for Learning
> ▶ To explain the term *drug dependence*
> ▶ To describe how drug dependence affects a person's life
> ▶ To identify different ways that drug users can be helped
> ▶ To identify healthy activities to take the place of drug use

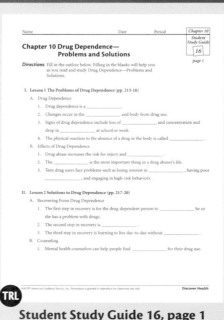

Student Study Guide 16, page 1

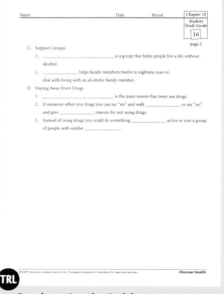

Student Study Guide 16, page 2

**Drug abuse**
*The improper use of legal or illegal drugs*

**Drug dependence**
*The need for a drug that results from frequent use of that drug*

*H*ave you ever taken aspirin for a headache? When your pain stopped, did you want to continue taking aspirin? Probably not. People usually do not become dependent on aspirin. People can, however, become dependent on other kinds of drugs.

Dependence on alcohol and other drugs is a serious problem. It is a problem not only for individuals but for families and society.

**Drug abuse** includes the misuse or overuse of a medical drug. Drug abuse also includes use of *any* illegal drug.

### What Is Drug Dependence?

**Drug dependence** is a need for a drug that results from frequent use of that drug. Sometimes, people become dependent on prescribed medicine. Most drug dependence, however, involves nicotine, alcohol, or other nonmedical drugs. Drug dependence often has three stages. In the first stage, the drug is used once in a while. In the second stage, the drug is used often. In the third stage, use of the drug takes over a person's life. Drug dependence is a disease. The only treatment is to stop using the drug.

A drug-dependent person may

• Use a drug often

• Use a drug in large amounts

• Use a drug although it causes serious problems

Drugs cause changes in the brain and body. A drug-dependent person builds tolerance. This means that the brain and body have gotten used to the drug. The user must take more of the drug to get the desired effect. As a user builds tolerance for a drug, he or she may take too much of the drug.

---

## Chapter 10 Lesson 1

**Overview** This lesson defines drug dependence and teaches students to recognize signs that could indicate someone is dependent on drugs. Students learn about the body's physical reactions to drug dependence and the health problems dependence can cause. Students also find out about the negative effects a drug-dependent person can have on his or her family and community.

## Objectives

■ To explain the term *drug dependence*.

■ To describe how drug dependence affects a person's life.

**Student Pages** 213–216

**Audiocassette**

**Teacher's Resource Library**

**Activity** 38
**Workbook Activity** 38

## Teaching Suggestions

### ■ Vocabulary

*drug abuse, drug dependence, tolerance, withdrawal symptoms, sexually transmitted disease*

As students read the chapter, challenge them to write an original sentence containing each vocabulary word they come across.

### ■ Teaching the Lesson

Have students think about the reasons that people begin to use drugs and how someone might become dependent on them. Write each student response on the board and use it as a springboard for prereading discussion.

### Ask:

• What is drug dependence? (It is the need for a drug that results from frequent use of the drug. Students might also mention that the use of a drug in large amounts can also lead to dependence.)

---

• What types of drugs do people become dependent on? (Most drug dependence involves nicotine, alcohol, or other nonmedical drugs. People can also become dependent on prescription medicines.)

• What does it mean that a drug-dependent person has developed tolerance for a drug? (Tolerance indicates that the brain and body have gotten so used to the drug that the user must take more of the drug to get the desired effect.)

• To what dangerous situation can tolerance lead? (Tolerance might lead to taking too much of the drug.)

## Healthy Subjects

Lead a discussion in which students talk about the way a person's experiences as a young child might affect decisions that person makes about drugs as a teen or an adult. Ask students to suggest how family, friends, or others in a child's life might help the child to have positive experiences that would help develop self-esteem and resist drug use.

Ask:

- What are some of the signs that someone might be dependent on drugs? (Possible answers include: major changes in appearance or behavior; loss of memory or concentration; lying, stealing, or borrowing money; reduced energy; loss of interest in activities or hobbies; drop in performance at school or work; lateness or absences from school or work; trouble with police; anger when discussing his or her drug use.)

- What is withdrawal? (Withdrawal is the physical reaction to the absence of a drug in the body.)

### APPLICATION

**At Home**
Discuss how talking about important personal issues with family members might help a person stay emotionally healthy. Have students write four issues that are important to them. Suggest that they share this information with family members through a family discussion.

### GLOBAL CONNECTION

The problem of drug use in the United States has global dimensions because the sources of many illegal drugs are outside the United States. For example, the opium poppy, which is the basis of heroin, is grown primarily in Asia. Coca leaves, which are the source of cocaine, come largely from the Andes Mountains of South America. Have students research and find statistics for the amount the government spends in attempting to keep these drugs from entering the country. Encourage students to present their findings in a report.

**Literature**

**"JUNIOR ADDICT"**

The African-American writer Langston Hughes wrote many poems and stories about drug dependence. His poem "Junior Addict" describes an African-American boy. The boy is sad because of his drug use. His problem may be linked to the way his people have been treated in America. If only he can live to see "the sunrise" far away. The poet calls to the African sunrise to "come, quickly, come." The boy may find strength and hope if he can feel pride in his heritage.

**Withdrawal**
*The body's physical reaction to the absence of a drug*

## What Are Some Signs of Drug Dependence?

If someone shows several of the following signs, they may have a problem with drugs.

- Major changes in appearance or behavior
- Loss of memory and concentration
- Lying, stealing, or borrowing money
- Reduced energy
- Loss of interest in favorite activities or hobbies
- Drop in performance at school or work
- Lateness and absences from school or work
- Trouble with the police
- Anger when discussing his or her drug use

### What Is Withdrawal?

Another problem of drug dependence is **withdrawal**. Withdrawal is a physical reaction to the absence of a drug in the body. Withdrawal symptoms depend upon the kind of drug taken. If a person stops taking a stimulant, he or she might feel tired or sad. A person who stops taking a depressant might feel nervous. He or she might not be able to sleep. A person who is trying to stop using a drug should be under a doctor's care.

## What Are the Effects of Drug Dependence?

Drug dependence causes many problems. Drug users often have problems with their family and friends. School and work suffer. The drug user's health becomes poor. He or she may have money problems. A user may even be arrested for having a drug or for crimes linked to drugs.

### Health and Safety Problems

Many drugs damage the body. Different drugs can affect different parts of the body. Some drugs damage the major body systems. This damage can cause long-term health problems or even death.

Drug abuse increases the risk for injury and death. Alcohol and other drugs are related to more than 50 percent of traffic accidents in which someone dies. More than 69 percent of drownings involve use of alcohol or other drugs.

### Family Problems

Drug abusers have problems with everyday life. Between 20 and 35 percent of all suicides are linked to drug abuse. Drug dependence damages families. To a drug abuser, the drug becomes the most important thing in his or her life. Drug-dependent parents may not be able to provide for their families. Families may not have enough money for food and a home.

A trained professional uses a combination of approaches that may best help each individual.

Drug-dependent people sometimes are violent. Almost one-half of all cases of wife abuse or husband abuse are linked to alcohol or other drugs. Likewise, drugs are linked to more than one-third of child abuse cases. The whole family suffers when one member is drug dependent.

*Drug Dependence—Problems and Solutions   Chapter 10*   **215**

Have students brainstorm about the effect a person who is dependent on drugs might have on themselves, their families, and others.

Then have students read about the effects of drug dependence on page 215.

Ask:

- How can drug abuse affect a person's health? (Drugs can damage the body, causing long-term health problems. Drug abuse can also lead to death.)

- How can drug abuse affect someone's safety? (Drugs, including alcohol, are related to a large number of fatal traffic accidents and drownings.)

- How can drug abuse cause problems for families? (Students should understand that drugs can cause problems when taking the drug becomes the most important activity in a drug abuser's life. Parents may not be able to provide for their families. Drug abusers can become violent and abuse children or spouses. Accept any other reasonable answers.)

### APPLICATION

**Career Connection**
Ask students to research and write a report about educational requirements and job opportunities for pharmacists. Then have students interview a pharmacist about the precautions and guidelines that are followed to identify and prevent abuse of legal drugs by customers.

### LEARNING STYLES

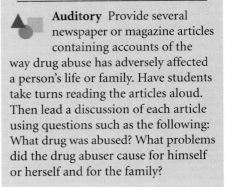

**Auditory** Provide several newspaper or magazine articles containing accounts of the way drug abuse has adversely affected a person's life or family. Have students take turns reading the articles aloud. Then lead a discussion of each article using questions such as the following: What drug was abused? What problems did the drug abuser cause for himself or herself and for the family?

## Action for Health

Have students figure out what other community needs might have been met with the money spent to combat drug abuse or deal with the effects of drug abusers on the community. Have students research the cost of these other community needs compared with the money spent as the result of drug abuse. Encourage students to provide the comparative information visually, using bar graphs or pie charts.

## Lesson 1 Review Answers

1) Drug abuse is the misuse or overuse of a medical drug.
2) Drug dependence is a need for a drug that results from frequent use of the drug.
3) Three tragedies often linked to drug use are traffic accidents, drownings, and suicides.
4) Some dangers that teen drug users may face are high-risk behaviors, unwanted pregnancies, drug-related diseases, long-term health problems, and death.
5) Drug-dependent parents may not be able to provide for their families. Families may not have enough money for basic needs. Drug-dependent people are sometimes violent. Wife, husband, or child abuse are often linked to alcohol or other drugs.

## APPLICATION

### Environment
Ask students to discuss the various ways they have seen smokers dispose of cigarette butts. Have students explain how improper disposal of cigarettes and cigarette butts has a negative effect on the environment.

### Action for Health

## LEARNING ABOUT THE COSTS OF DRUG USE

Find out how much drug abuse costs your community. Contact your county or state health department. Many cities and counties have mental health agencies and drug education agencies. Ask for information about drug abuse in your community.

Contact law enforcement agencies for information about crimes linked to drugs. Look in the city, county, and state government pages in the telephone book to find the phone numbers you need. You might call your local library for help.

> **Sexually transmitted disease**
> *A disease spread by sexual contact*

## Problems for Society

Every year, drug abuse costs our country billions of dollars. Taxpayers pay more than $16 million a year to treat and support drug abusers. Businesses lose more than $98 million a year because of drug abuse by workers. The cost of crime linked to drugs is $25 million each year. These dollar costs are high. But they do not include the value of lives lost to drugs.

## What Problems Are Linked to Drug Use by Teens?

For young people, drug use can cause problems that follow them through their whole life. Many teen drug users lose interest in school. They may not learn the basic thinking skills they need for life. Teen drug users often do not form normal relationships with people. Drug users have poor judgment. They often engage in high-risk behavior. As a result, the teen user may face an unwanted pregnancy. He or she may get a **sexually transmitted disease** or other diseases linked to drug use.

**LESSON 1 REVIEW** Write the answers to these questions on a separate sheet of paper. Use complete sentences.

1) What is drug abuse?
2) What is drug dependence?
3) What three tragedies are often linked to drug use?
4) What dangers do teen drug users face?
5) How does drug dependence affect family life?

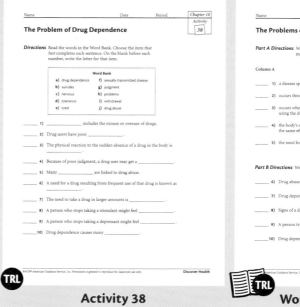

**Activity 38**

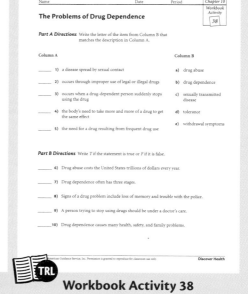

**Workbook Activity 38**

## Solutions to Drug Dependence

**Detoxification**
*The removal of a drug from the body*

Drug dependence is not a life sentence. People who are close to drug abusers can help them. Recovery from drug dependence is the first step.

### How Can People Recover From Drug Dependence?

Recovery from drug dependence has three main steps. First, the drug-dependent person must admit that he or she has a problem with drugs. This seems easy, but it often is not. A drug user may deny that he or she is dependent on a drug. Friends and family members may have to confront the drug user.

The second step in recovery is **detoxification**. Detoxification is the removal of drugs from the body. To avoid serious problems, detoxification should take place in a hospital.

The third step in recovery is learning to live day-to-day without drugs. This is the longest process of recovery. The person in recovery learns skills to cope with life without drugs. He or she becomes emotionally and physically healthy. The process of recovery never stops. Drug dependence cannot truly be cured. Drug dependence can, however, be treated. The goal of recovery is never to use drugs again. Sometimes, people go back to using drugs. In this case, the process of recovery must begin again. With help, the recovering user still can reach the goal of a life without drugs.

*Nutrition Tip*

Take time to eat well when you're under stress.

### How Can a Person Get Help?

There are several places to begin looking for help. If you or someone you are close to abuses drugs, ask for help.

### Counseling

Most schools have counselors or a program to help students with problems. Students can discuss their concerns about drug use in their family or among their friends. Community mental health centers also can help. Mental health counselors can help people find treatment for their drug use. They can help people in recovery and help the families of recovering users.

*Drug Dependence—Problems and Solutions    Chapter 10*    **217**

• Detoxification is the second step in recovery from drug dependence. What is detoxification? (Detoxification is treatment that removes a drug from the body.)

• What is the third step in recovery? (The third step in recovery is learning to cope with life without the drug.)

• How can community mental health counselors help drug-dependent people? (Counselors can direct a drug-dependent person to treatment centers. Counselors can also help support or advise recovering drug-dependent people and their families.)

Before reading about support groups, ask students how a group of people who abuse drugs might be able to help one another during the recovery process.

Then have students continue reading about support groups on page 218.

## Ask:

- What is a support group? (A support group is a group of people with similar problems who help one another.)

- What is Alcoholics Anonymous (AA)? (AA is a support group for people who abuse alcohol.)

- What is the purpose of a sponsor in a support group such as AA? (In AA, the sponsor helps the newly-recovering alcoholic deal with the urge to drink.)

### APPLICATION

**In the Community**
Have students research, design, and compile a booklet that lists major organizations in their community that help people recover from drug dependence.

### MULTICULTURAL CONNECTION

Have students interview people who were born in or have lived in other countries to find out how health or law enforcement authorities in those countries deal with people with drug-dependence problems. Use the information gathered to start a class discussion.

### BACKGROUND INFORMATION

Students can find out more about alcohol and other drugs by taking a look at the National Council on Alcoholism and Drug Dependence web site at www.ncadd.org.

---

**Alateen**
*A support group for teens*

**Sponsor**
*A recovering alcoholic who helps a new AA member*

**Support group**
*A group of people with similar problems who help one another*

## Support Groups

A **support group** is a group of people with similar problems. The people in the group help and encourage one another. Alcoholics Anonymous (AA) was the first organization of support groups. The goal of AA members is to live a life without alcohol. Alcoholics must live day-to-day, choosing not to drink. In AA, each person has a **sponsor**. A sponsor is another recovering alcoholic. The sponsor usually has not used alcohol for several years. He or she helps the newly recovered alcoholic deal with the urge to drink.

You can talk about drug use with a frien

AA has three other groups for family members of alcoholics. Al-Anon is a support group for adults, such as the husband or wife of an alcoholic. **Alateen** is for 12- to 18-year-olds. Alatot is for 6- to 12-year-olds. Members of these groups help one another deal with living with an alcoholic family member. Alateen also helps teens deal with alcoholic family members who don't live with them.

Other support groups help people deal with other kinds of drug dependencies. Two examples are Cocaine Anonymous and Narcotics Anonymous. The National Council on Alcoholism and Drug Dependence also can give information and help with problems linked to drugs.

### Writing About Health

Think about some healthy choices you have made that kept you from drug use. Write about the choices. Did they have long-term physical health benefits? Did they benefit your mental health?

**SMOKE ALARM**

In the 1880s, a manufacturer used the first cigarette-making machine. Cigarette smoking spread. During and after World War II, advertising glamorized smoking.

Today, research shows that smoking contributes to heart and lung disease and cancer. Health warnings are now on advertisements and cigarette packages. Some states forbid smoking in public places. Airlines have banned smoking on U.S. flights.

## Residential and Outpatient Treatment Centers

A residential treatment center is a place where recovering drug users live for a time. Some centers treat only teens. Others may treat all age groups. Some people get treatment from an outpatient center. In this case, recovering drug users live at home. They go to the center each day for treatment.

## How Can a Person Stay Away From Drugs?

The main reason that teens use drugs is peer pressure. Sometimes it helps to practice saying "no" in a safe setting. Practice in a safe setting can help a person say "no" in a real setting. For example, a person may need to say "no" and leave a party where drugs are being used.

## Refusing Drugs

If someone offers you drugs or pressures you to use drugs:

• Say "no," and walk away.

• Say "no," and change the subject.

• Say "no," and give honest reasons for not using drugs.

• Say "no," and keep repeating that you don't use drugs.

## Getting Help

Getting help for problems can help a person avoid drug use. This is very important for someone from a home where drugs are used. Everyone is responsible for his or her own behavior. Family members are not to blame for the drug user's behavior.

*Fitness Tip*

Get regular exercise. You will be better able to cope with stress.

*Drug Dependence—Problems and Solutions* *Chapter 10* **219**

## Then and Now

Discuss why teens and others begin to smoke, even though the health risks are known. If possible, obtain a tape of an antismoking Public Service Announcement (PSA). You might have students recall one announcement that all students have heard or seen. Have students evaluate it. Would the PSA prevent the students from smoking? Why or why not?

Discuss with students why staying away from drugs altogether is a better strategy than trying to recover once drug use has begun. Then have students read about drug treatment and drug refusal skills on page 219.

Ask:

• What is the difference between residential and outpatient treatment centers? (Residential treatment centers are places where recovering drug users live while they are getting treatment. Outpatient treatment centers are places where recovering drug users receive daily treatment while continuing to live at home.)

• Identify two ways that you can refuse drugs if you are pressured to use them by someone you know. (Possible answers include: Say "no," and walk away. Say "no," and change the subject. Say "no," and give honest reasons for not wanting to use drugs. Say "no," and keep repeating that you don't use drugs.)

**LEARNING STYLES**

 **Tactile/Kinesthetic** Have students break into groups to write skits that show them using one of the refusal strategies on page 219. Have students perform the skits for their classmates.

**LEARNING STYLES**

 **LEP/ESL** Have students list people that someone with drug problems might turn for help. With the aid of an English proficient student volunteer, have the LEP/ESL student write simple sentences that describe the characteristics of the people listed.

*Drug Dependence—Problems and Solutions* *Chapter 10* **219**

## Careers

To give students a better understanding of this career, invite a drug abuse counselor from a local hospital, clinic, or treatment center to visit your class. Ask the counselor to talk about the job, the training needed for it, and how he or she feels about being a drug abuse counselor. Have your guest discuss how he or she became a counselor and what a typical day is like.

Have students read about some better choices other than drugs on page 220.

### Ask:

- Name two better choices to drug use that can increase fitness and energy. (Possible answers include: Do something physically active such as dancing, biking, or swimming. Volunteer at a community service organization. Join a group of people with similar interests, such as a school-sponsored club or the school newspaper.)

## Lesson 2 Review Answers

1) The three steps in recovery from drug dependence are: The user must admit that he or she has a problem with drug use. The user must go through detoxification. The user must live day-to-day without drugs.
2) Drug dependence cannot be cured, but it can be treated.
3) Support groups help people to know that they are not alone in having a certain problem.
4) A person can go to a residential or outpatient treatment center to get treatment for drug dependence.
5) A person can avoid people who use drugs and say "no" to offers of drugs.

### DRUG ABUSE COUNSELOR

Drug abuse counselors work with people who are dependent on drugs. Some counselors are recovering drug users themselves. This helps the counselor understand the people they are helping. Counselors, together with other health professionals, develop treatment plans. Some counselors may work only with alcoholics. Others work with people addicted to other drugs. Some work only with children, teenagers, pregnant women, or other groups. Preparation may include a one-year certification program, two-year associate's degree, or four-year college degree.

### What Are Some Better Choices Than Drugs?

Using drugs to deal with problems only makes the problems worse. Activities that help you feel better about yourself can help you. Here are some activities that can increase fitness and energy.

- Do something physically active. Try a dance class. Go mountain biking with a group. Join a swim team.
- Find a cause that is important to you and give your time to it. For example, volunteer at a hospital. Attend a beach cleanup day. Tutor a younger child in reading.
- Join a group of people with similar interests. For example, you could work on the school newspaper or join a school-sponsored club.

**LESSON 2 REVIEW** Write the answers to these questions on a separate sheet of paper. Use complete sentences.

1) What are the three steps in recovery from drug dependence?
2) Can drug dependence ever be cured?
3) How do support groups help people?
4) Where can a person go to get treatment for drug dependence?
5) How can you stay away from drugs?

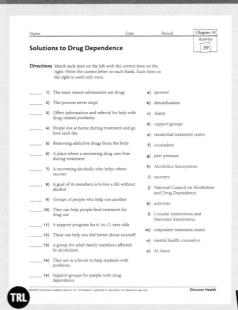

**Activity 39**

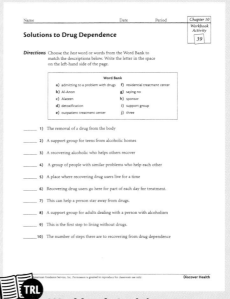

**Workbook Activity 39**

■ Drug dependence is a need for a drug resulting from frequent use of that drug. Most drug dependence involves nicotine, alcohol, or other nonmedical drug.

■ Drug abuse includes the misuse or overuse of a medical drug. It also includes use of any illegal drug. Tolerance to a drug develops when the brain and body become used to the drug. Then the user must take more of the drug to get the desired effect.

■ When the drug is stopped, withdrawal symptoms occur. Withdrawal is a physical reaction to the absence of a drug.

■ Signs of drug dependence include changes in behavior or appearance, lying or stealing, loss of interest in old activities, and/or poor work habits.

■ Drugs damage the body. Drugs can cause long-term health problems or death.

■ Drugs play a part in many traffic accidents, drownings, and suicides. Many cases of abuse are linked to drug use.

■ Drug users often engage in high-risk behavior. Unwanted pregnancy and getting sexually transmitted diseases are sometimes linked to drug use.

■ People can recover from drug dependence. The first step is admitting that they have a problem with drug use.

■ The second step in recovery is detoxification, which is removal of drugs from the body. The third and longest step is learning to live without drugs.

■ There are several ways a drug-dependent person can get help. Mental health counselors can help people find treatment.

■ Support groups can help drug-dependent people realize that they are not alone. Support groups for families of drug users help members deal with living with a drug-dependent person.

■ The best way to avoid drug problems is never to use drugs. You can avoid people who use drugs. You can say "no" to an offer of drugs and mean it.

*Drug Dependence—Problems and Solutions* *Chapter 10* **221**

## ■ Using the Chapter Summary

To further reinforce the facts and concepts presented in the chapter, read and discuss with students the questions that follow.

### Ask:

• How does drug dependence develop? (Drug dependence develops primarily from frequent use of a drug.)

• How does tolerance to a drug develop? (Tolerance develops when frequent use of a drug causes the brain and body to become so accustomed to it that the user must take increasing amounts of the drug to get the desired effect.)

• List three signs of drug dependence. (Possible answers include: major changes in appearance or behavior; loss of memory and concentration; lying, stealing, or borrowing money; reduced energy; loss of interest in favorite activities or hobbies; drop in school or work performance; lateness or absence from school or work; trouble with police; anger when discussing his or her drug use.)

• What are some problems of drug abuse? (Students should understand that drug abuse impairs judgment and physical ability that could lead to traffic accidents, drownings, suicides, abuse, unwanted pregnancy, and sexually-transmitted disease.)

• What is the first thing a drug user must do before he or she can recover? (The drug user must admit that he or she has a problem with drugs.)

• What are the three steps in recovery from drug abuse? (admitting the problem, detoxification, learning to live without drugs)

• How can support groups help someone who is a family member or friend of a drug abuser? (The support group can help a family member or friend deal with living with a drug-dependent person.)

• What is the best way to avoid the problems that drug use can cause? (Students should recognize that saying "no" to drug use altogether is the best way to avoid problems.)

## Chapter 10 Review

The Teacher's Resource Library includes two parallel forms of the Chapter 10 Mastery Test. The difficulty level of the two forms is equivalent. You may wish to use one form as a pretest and the other form as a posttest.

### Review Answers

#### Comprehension: Identifying Facts

**1)** drug dependence **2)** drug abuse **3)** Alcohol **4)** tolerance **5)** withdrawal symptoms **6)** behavior **7)** teen drug users **8)** brain **9)** sexually transmitted disease **10)** Teen

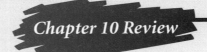

## Chapter 10 Review

### Comprehension: Identifying Facts

On a separate sheet of paper, write the correct word or words from the Word Bank to complete each sentence.

| WORD BANK | |
|---|---|
| Alateen | sexually transmitted disease |
| alcohol | support group |
| behavior | teen |
| brain | teen drug users |
| detoxification | tolerance |
| drug abuse | withdrawal |
| drug dependence | |

1) Frequent use of a drug is called _____.

2) Misuse or overuse of a medical drug, or any use of an illegal drug, is called _____.

3) _____ and other drugs are related to more than 50 percent of traffic accidents in which someone dies.

4) The buildup of _____ means that a drug user must use more and more of the drug.

5) When a drug-dependent person stops a drug, he or she may go through _____.

6) A major change in appearance or _____ may signal drug dependence.

7) Many _____ lose interest in school.

8) Drugs often damage the _____.

9) Drug abusers may engage in high-risk behavior. Therefore, some may get a _____.

10) _____ drug users are more likely to use many drugs later in life.

---

**Chapter 10 Mastery Test A**

*Name_____ Date_____ Period_____* | Chapter 10 Mastery Test A page 1

**Directions** Read the words in the Word Bank. Choose the item that best completes each sentence. On the blank before each number, write the letter for that item.

| Word Bank | | |
|---|---|---|
| a) Alateen | f) drug dependence | k) teen |
| b) Alcoholics Anonymous | g) health problems | l) tolerance |
| c) appearance | h) peer pressure | m) traffic accidents |
| d) detoxification | i) sexually transmitted disease | n) volunteering |
| e) drug abuse | j) sponsor | o) walk away |

____ 1) Alcohol and drugs play a part in over 50 percent of _____ and drownings.

____ 2) _____ includes the misuse or overuse of a medical drug or any use of an illegal drug.

____ 3) Signs of drug dependence include major changes in _____ and behavior.

____ 4) The need for a drug resulting from frequent use is called _____.

____ 5) Drugs can cause long-term _____ or death.

____ 6) The buildup of _____ happens when the brain and body become used to the drug.

____ 7) Drug users often engage in high-risk behavior, which may lead to an unwanted pregnancy or a _____.

____ 8) The second step in recovery is _____, which is the removal of drugs from the body.

____ 9) _____ was the first organization of support groups.

---

**Chapter 10 Mastery Test A,** continued

*Name_____ Date_____ Period_____* | Chapter 10 Mastery Test A page 2

____ 10) A support group for teenagers who have an alcoholic family member is _____.

____ 11) A _____ is a recovering alcoholic who helps a new AA member.

____ 12) The main reasons that teens use drugs is _____.

____ 13) Mountain biking, joining a school-sponsored club, and _____ are better choices than using drugs.

____ 14) If someone offers you drugs you could say "no" and then _____.

____ 15) _____ drug users are more likely to use many drugs later in life.

**Chapter 10 Mastery Test A**

11) The second step of recovery from drug dependence is
_____.

12) Members of a _____ help one another with
problems.

13) A support group for teens is called _____.

## Comprehension: Understanding Main Ideas

Write the answers to these questions on a separate sheet of
paper. Use complete sentences.

14) On what kinds of drugs do people usually become
dependent?

15) What are three signs of drug dependence?

16) Why is drug abuse particularly harmful to teens?

17) What is the first step of recovery, and why is it sometimes
difficult?

18) If you live with a person, is it your fault that they are
drug-dependent? Why or why not?

## Critical Thinking: Write Your Opinion

19) Why do you think finding positive activities helps people
stay away from drugs?

20) What could you do to help a drug-dependent friend or
family member?

**Test Taking Tip** Make a short outline of the main ideas of the chapter using
the paragraph headings that appear in the text.

*Drug Dependence—Problems and Solutions* *Chapter 10* **223**

---

11) detoxification  12) support group
13) Alateen

## Comprehension: Understanding Main Ideas

14) People usually become dependent on
nicotine, alcohol, or other nonmedical
drugs.

15) Accept any three of the following:
major changes in appearance or
behavior; loss of memory and
concentration; lying, stealing, or
borrowing money; reduced energy;
loss of interest in favorite activities or
hobbies; drop in performance at
school or work; lateness and absences
from school or work; trouble with
police; anger when discussing his
or her drug use.

16) Drug use can cause problems that
follow teens through their whole life.

17) In the first step of recovery, a person
must admit that he or she has a
problem with drugs. This first step
is sometimes difficult because the
drug user may deny that he or she
is dependent on a drug.

18) Everyone is responsible for his or her
own behavior. It is not your fault if
someone else is dependent on drugs.

## Critical Thinking: Write Your Opinion

19) Positive activities make people feel
better and relieve stress.

20) Answers will vary. Possible answers:
confront the drug user and ask him
or her to admit that drugs are a
problem, help that person find
treatment for the drug problem.

---

**Chapter 10 Mastery Test B**

## Deciding for Yourself

Have students read "Using Drugs to Change Emotions" in the Deciding for Yourself lesson on page 224.

Ask:

- How can drugs that change emotions be helpful? (Drugs that change emotions can be helpful because they allow a person who takes them to function more normally.)

- How can someone become addicted to drugs that affect emotions? (People can become addicted to drugs that affect emotions if they think they need the feelings the drugs provide and begin to take the drugs regularly and in large amounts.)

- Besides taking drugs, what are some positive methods someone might use to change emotions? (A person can use positive actions and positive thinking to fight depression. Physical activity can reduce stress. Talking about feelings and emotions with others can also help a person deal with them.)

## Deciding for Yourself Answers

1) Drugs that are used to change emotions include tranquilizers such as Valium and Librium. These drugs make a person more calm. Stimulants can help a depressed person feel better.

2) Taking drugs for emotional problems is not a good idea because doing so can prevent a person from finding the cause of the problem. People can become dependent on drugs.

3) It is better to find out what is causing the emotional or mental problem and deal with that. Talking with friends, family members, or mental health professionals about negative emotions is always a good idea.

4) Answers will vary. People might use drugs rather than other solutions for mental and emotional problems because it is the easier solution or because they are not able to discuss their feelings with others. Accept all reasonable answers.

## ■ Deciding for Yourself Activity

Have students complete the Unit 4 Deciding for Yourself Activity.

### Using Drugs to Change Emotions

There are many drugs that can change how a person feels. Some of these are tranquilizers such as Valium and Librium. These drugs calm a person down. Other drugs are stimulants. They can help a depressed person feel more hopeful. Drugs that change emotions and mental states can be helpful when used correctly.

Drugs are one way to change emotions. Taking a drug may sound like an easy solution to someone who is suffering mental or emotional pain. But drugs may not be the best answer.

People can become dependent on taking drugs. They may come to believe they need the feelings and emotions the drugs provide. Then they take the drug more and more frequently. They may become addicted to the drug.

Taking drugs to change emotions can prevent someone from finding the cause of those emotions. If you felt anxious, you could take a drug. But the drug is only a temporary solution. When the drug wears off, the problems causing the anxiety come back. Rather than taking drugs, it is better to find out what is causing the depressed emotions and deal with the underlying problem.

There are other ways to change emotions. Positive action and positive thinking can help with depression. Physical activity can reduce stress. Talking with someone about your feelings and emotions can help you deal with them.

### Questions

1) What kinds of drugs are used to change emotions?

2) Why might it be a bad idea to take drugs for emotional problems?

3) What should someone do before taking a drug to help with an emotional or mental problem?

4) Why do you think some people use drugs rather than other solutions for mental and emotional problems?

---

Name _____ Date _____ Period _____

Unit 4
Deciding for Yourself Activity
4

### Skills for Handling Stress

Sometimes stress causes emotional problems. Following is a list of skills for handling stress. Read the list and answer the questions below.

**How to Handle Stress**

1) Learn to relax.
2) Make exercise a routine in your life.
3) Don't try to do more than there is time for.
4) Slow down.
5) Be good to your body.
6) Talk with someone about your problems.

**Questions**

1) Which of the skills on the list do you think you do well? Describe what you do.

2) Choose a skill that you would like to develop. Write a plan for ways you can develop that skill.

3) Rank the list of skills in order of their importance. Number the skill you think is most important "1," and the one you think is least important "6." Write a reason why you think the number 1 skill is most important.

©AGS® American Guidance Service, Inc. Permission is granted to reproduce for classroom use only.          **Discover Health**

**TRL**

**Deciding for Yourself Master 4**

■ Medicines are drugs used to treat, cure, or prevent disease.

■ Medicines affect different people differently because of body size, weight, or other factors.

■ All medicines can have side effects. Following directions on the label carefully will usually prevent problems.

■ Tobacco is a stimulant drug that can cause life-threatening diseases. The nicotine in tobacco is addictive. Secondhand tobacco smoke is also dangerous to people's health.

■ Alcohol is a depressant drug that can be addictive and is often misused. Alcohol abuse can cause serious diseases and contributes to many traffic fatalities.

■ Most narcotics, depressants, and stimulants are legal drugs, but they can be misused or bought illegally.

■ Hallucinogens are particularly dangerous drugs that change the way the mind processes information.

■ Inhalants, anabolic steroids, marijuana, designer drugs, and look-alike drugs are dangerous and addictive.

■ A person dependent on drugs must take more and more of the drug to get the same effect. Signs of drug dependence include changes in behavior, lying or stealing, and poor work habits.

■ Drug users often engage in high-risk behavior. For example, injecting drugs with used needles can lead to diseases such as AIDS.

■ People can recover from drug dependence. They must admit they have a problem, go through detoxification, and then learn to live without drugs.

■ Support groups for drug users and their families can help people change to drug-free lives.

■ The best way to avoid drug problems is never to use drugs. Avoiding people who use drugs and saying "no" to drugs are ways to stay drug free.

*Unit 4 Summary* **225**

## Unit Summary

To further reinforce the facts and concepts presented in the unit, read and discuss with students the questions that follow.

### Ask:

- What are medicines? (Medicines are drugs used to treat, cure, or prevent disease.)

- All medicines have side effects. What can you do to prevent problems? (Follow the directions on the label carefully.)

- What is the drug in tobacco that causes addiction? (nicotine)

- Why is alcohol a dangerous drug when it is misused? (Alcohol abuse can cause serious diseases and contributes to many traffic accidents.)

- What are hallucinogens? (Hallucinogens are particularly dangerous drugs that change the way the mind processes information.)

- What are signs of drug dependence? (Signs of drug dependence include changes in behavior, lying or stealing, and poor work habits.)

- What are the three steps that a drug-dependent person must go through to recover? (The person must admit that he or she has a problem, go through detoxification, and then learn to live without drugs.)

- What is the best way to avoid drug problems? (never use drugs, avoid people who use drugs, and say "no" to drugs)

# Unit 4 Review

The Teacher's Resource Library includes a two-page Unit Mastery Test pictured on this page. Answers are in the Answer Keys beginning on page 433 of this Teacher's Edition.

## Review Answers

### Comprehension: Identifying Facts

**1)** side effects **2)** prescription
**3)** stimulant **4)** depressant **5)** narcotic
**6)** abuse **7)** heroin **8)** inhalants
**9)** tolerance

## Comprehension: Identifying Facts

On a separate sheet of paper, write the correct word or words from the Word Bank to complete each sentence.

### WORD BANK

| | | |
|---|---|---|
| abuse | inhalants | stimulant |
| depressant | narcotic | support group |
| detoxification | prescription | tolerance |
| hallucinogens | recovery | withdrawal |
| heroin | side effects | |

**1)** Following the directions on medicines carefully will usually help prevent _____.

**2)** A doctor's written order for a drug is a _____.

**3)** Tobacco is a _____ that speeds up the central nervous system.

**4)** Alcohol is a _____ that slows down the central nervous system, making it dangerous to drive.

**5)** Morphine is a _____ drug used to relieve pain.

**6)** Misuse or overuse of a medical drug is called drug _____.

**7)** There are no legal uses for the narcotic drug _____.

**8)** Dangerous _____ include paint thinner and glue.

**9)** Drug users can build up _____ so that they need more and more of the drug.

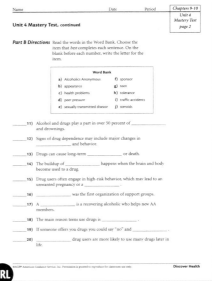

**Unit 4 Mastery Test, page 1**          **Unit 4 Mastery Test, page 2**

10) When a drug user stops taking a drug, he or she can have _____ symptoms.

11) A drug user going through recovery experiences _____, the removal of the drugs from the body.

12) Dangerous, illegal drugs that change the way the brain processes information are _____.

13) Drug users can live drug-free lives by going into _____ programs.

14) Treatment in a _____ involves drug users helping one another to stay drug free.

## Comprehension: Understanding Main Ideas

Write the answers to these questions on a separate sheet of paper. Use complete sentences.

15) Why is it dangerous to ignore the directions on prescription medicine?

16) Make a list of legal drugs that are often misused.

17) What are some signs of drug dependence?

18) Describe the three stages of drug recovery.

## Critical Thinking: Write Your Opinion

19) When is it safe to take drugs?

20) What kinds of refusal skills can help you avoid using dangerous drugs?

10) withdrawal 11) detoxification
12) hallucinogens 13) recovery
14) support group

## Comprehension: Understanding Main Ideas

15) It is dangerous to ignore the directions on prescription medicine because the medicine may not work as intended if not taken correctly.

16) Misused legal drugs include tobacco, alcohol, caffeine, morphine, tranquilizers, barbiturates, and anabolic steroids.

17) Signs of drug dependence include changes in behavior or appearance, loss of memory or concentration, lying, stealing, reduced energy, loss of interest in familiar activities, poor performance at school or work, and lateness or absences from school or work.

18) Drug recovery includes admitting there is a problem, going through detoxification, and learning to live a drug-free life.

## Critical Thinking: Write Your Opinion

19) It is safe to take drugs when they are recommended by a doctor or pharmacist and when all directions are followed properly.

20) Refusal skills include avoiding situations where drugs will be used, walking away from an offer of drugs, and practicing different ways of saying "no."

## Midterm Mastery Test

The Teacher's Resource Library includes the Midterm Mastery Test. The Midterm Mastery Test assesses the major learning objectives for Chapters 1–10.

**Midterm Mastery Test, pages 1–4**

# Unit 5 Planning Guide

## Preventing and Controlling Diseases and Disorders

| | Student Lesson | | | |
|---|---|---|---|---|
| | Student Pages | Vocabulary | Lesson Review | Writing About Health |
| ***Chapter 11 Disease—Causes and Prevention*** | 231–241 | | | |
| Lesson 1 Causes of Disease | 232–234 | • | • | • |
| Lesson 2 The Body's Protection From Disease | 235–238 | • | • | |
| ***Chapter 12 Preventing AIDS and Sexually Transmitted Diseases*** | 242–253 | | | |
| Lesson 1 AIDS | 243–246 | • | • | |
| Lesson 2 Sexually Transmitted Diseases | 247–250 | • | • | • |
| ***Chapter 13 Common Diseases*** | 254–275 | | | |
| Lesson 1 Cardiovascular Disease | 255–258 | • | • | |
| Lesson 2 Cancer | 259–262 | • | • | |
| Lesson 3 Asthma | 263–264 | • | • | |
| Lesson 4 Diabetes | 265–267 | • | • | |
| Lesson 5 Arthritis | 268–269 | • | • | • |
| Lesson 6 Epilepsy | 270–272 | • | • | |

### Unit Activities

**Home Connection**
**What Do You Think?**
**Deciding for Yourself**

### AGS-Related Resources

**Discover Life Skills Handbook**
**Discover Healthy Sexual Development**

### Assessment Options

**Student Text**
- **Lesson Reviews**
- **Chapter Reviews**
- **Unit Review**

**Teacher's Resource Library**
- **Chapter Mastery Tests**
- **Unit Mastery Test**

**Student Text Features | Teaching Strategies | Learning Styles | Teacher's Resource Library**

| Action for Health | Careers | Health, Fitness, and Nutrition Tips | Healthy Subjects | Then and Now | Technology | Background Information | Career Application | Community Application | Environment Application | Global Connection | Home Application | Multicultural Connection | Auditory | Group Learning | LEP/ESL | Tactile/Kinesthetic | Visual | Activities | Mastery Tests | Student Study Guide | Workbook Activities |
|---|---|---|---|---|---|---|---|---|---|---|---|---|---|---|---|---|---|---|---|---|---|
| | | | | | | | | | | | | | | | | | | | • | • | |
| | 234 | 234 | | | | 233 | | | | | 234 | | | 234 | | | 233 | | | | |
| 238 | | 235 | | 236 | | | 238 | 237 | 236 | 236 | 237 | | 238 | | | | | | | | |
| | | | | | | | | | | | | | | | | | | | • | • | |
| | | 245 | 245 | 244 | | | | 246 | 246 | 244 | 245 | | | | | 245 | 244 | | | | |
| 248 | 250 | | | | | 250 | 249 | | | | 248 | | | 249 | | | | | | | |
| | | | | | | | | | | | | | | | | | | | | | |
| | 257 | 255, 258 | | | | | | 257 | | 256 | 258 | | | 258 | | | | | • | • | |
| | | | | 261 | | | | | | 260 | | | 262 | 261 | | | | | | | |
| | | | | | | | | | 264 | | | | | | | | | | | | |
| | | | | | | 266 | | | | | | | | | | | | | | | |
| | | | | | | | 269 | | | | | | | | | | | | | | |
| | | | | | | 271 | | | | | | | | | | | | | | | |

## Block Scheduling

Here is a suggested teaching activity if you have extended instructional time, such as a block schedule.

**Family Tree** *To create a family tree that shows diseases that run in the family, and to make a plan to help promote health and prevent the disease.*

Create a family tree going back as many generations as you can. In a data notebook, record the diseases for each person. Your data notebook should include: (1) the name, age, and sex of the person, (2) the name of the disease and how old the person was when he or she got the disease, (3) if a person has died, note the cause of death. Finally, make a family tree showing diseases that run in your family. Then create a plan to help your generation to stay healthy. For example, if cardiovascular disease runs in your family, make a plan for regular exercise and a low-fat diet. Last, write a 50- to 100-word summary of your most important findings.

*Diseases have no eyes.
They pick with a dizzy finger
anyone, just anyone.*

—Sandra Cisneros, *The House on
Mango Street*

## Unit 5:

### Preventing and Controlling Diseases and Disorders
pages 228–279

### Chapters

**Audiocassette**

**Teacher's Resource Library** **TRL**

- **Unit 5 Home Connection Master 5**

  **Unit 5 What Do You Think?
  Activity Master 5**

  **Unit 5 Deciding for Yourself
  Activity Master 5**

  **Unit 5 Mastery Test**

  (Answer Keys for the Teacher's
  Resource Library begin on page 433
  of this Teacher's Edition.)

## Other Resources

### Books for Teachers

*The Mayo Clinic Family Health Book*
(second edition). New York: William
Morrow and Company, Inc., 1996.

*The PDR Family Guide to Women's
Health.* Montvale, NJ: Medical
Economics, 1994.

Phelan, Glen, and Susan Phelan. *Health—
Walch Science Literacy Series.* J. Weston
Walch: Portland, ME, 1997.

### Books for Students

*The American Heart Association Family
Guide to Stroke.* Times Books: New York,
1994. (Looks at the treatment and
prevention of strokes.)

Bess, Clayton. *The Mayday Rampage.*
Lookout Press: Sacramento, CA, 1993.
(Relates the story of high school students
who wanted to write frank articles about
AIDS for the school paper and the
resistance they met.)

### Videos

*A Million Teenagers.* (27 minutes) Santa
Cruz, CA: ETR Associates (1-800-321-
4407), 1995. (Dispels myths about the
sexually transmitted diseases that one
million teens contract each year.)

*Time-Life Medical Series.* (30 minutes
each tape) Time-Life, 1996. (A series of
eighteen tapes on various diseases and
disorders from headaches to cancers.)

| Name | Date | Period | Unit 5 |
|---|---|---|---|

**Family AIDS Awareness Assessment**

AIDS is a topic that is in the news almost daily. Unfortunately, there is a
great deal of confusion about this disease. This activity will give you an
opportunity to test your family's awareness about AIDS and to share
what you have learned.

**Step 1** The true-or-false quiz below will reveal some common misconceptions
about AIDS. Make sure you have the correct answers before giving
family members the quiz.

1. AIDS is a disease that never affects teenagers. True or false?

2. There is no known cure for AIDS at this time. True or false?

3. Sneezing, coughing, crying, and mosquito bites are all ways that AIDS
can be transmitted. True or false?

4. A person can get AIDS while donating blood. True or false?

**Step 2** After the quiz, use your text to share with your family information on
AIDS and other sexually transmitted diseases.

List three ways AIDS is acquired.

List three ways AIDS is not acquired.

How are sexually transmitted diseases prevented?

**TRL**

**Home Connection Master 5**

# Preventing and Controlling Diseases and Disorders

*I*f you are rarely sick, you are fortunate. You may occasionally have a cold or a headache. If this is true for you, you may have made smart decisions about your health. Developing good health habits can prevent some diseases. It helps you recover more quickly when you do get sick.

Diseases are caused in different ways. In this unit, you will learn about the causes of different types of diseases. You will read about ways these diseases can be cured or prevented. You will also find out things you can do right now to decrease your chances of getting serious diseases.

*Ryan White, 1972–1990*

## Introducing the Unit

Direct the attention of students to the picture and the quote on page 228. Ask a volunteer to read the quote.

Explain to students that the people in the picture are Ryan White and his mother. Ryan White contracted HIV from transfusions to treat hemophilia, a blood disease. Ryan White died of AIDS in 1990. During his life, he fought for the rights of people with HIV/AIDS. Students may want to find more information about Ryan White on the Internet.

### Ask:

- What does the quotation "Diseases have no eyes . . ." mean? (The quotation means that diseases strike all people, regardless of their age, gender, or race.)

- Think back to the last time you had a cold or the flu. How did you get it? (Answers will vary. Students might suggest that they caught it from someone else.)

- Are there ways that people can prevent the occurrence of diseases? (Answers will vary. Students might suggest vaccinations, changes in eating habits, or lifestyle changes such as exercising and reducing stress.)

## What Do You Think?

Have volunteers read the story on page 230 to the class.

### Ask:

- Why did Margie probably get sick just before her ballet tryout? (Margie probably got sick because she was run-down. She was doing a lot of things each day and not getting enough rest. She probably wasn't eating well. Her body was weaker and more likely to be affected by an illness.)

- How could stress have played a part in Margie's illness? (Margie could have been worried about the audition, causing stress that made her even more tired, tense, and run-down. This made it easier for her to get sick.)

- How did Margie prevent an asthma attack? (Margie used medicine breathed in through an inhaler to prevent the asthma attack.)

- What can Margie do from now on to prevent becoming tired? (Accept all reasonable answers. Students might suggest that Margie could get more sleep, eat healthy meals, cut back on the extra ballet classes, relax, or do something fun with friends to relieve stress.)

- What are some things that you do to stay in good health? (Answers will vary, according to the personal habits of students. Students might say they stay in good health by eating healthy foods, getting regular exercise, and getting regular medical and dental check-ups.)

Have students complete the Unit 5 What Do You Think? Activity sheet.

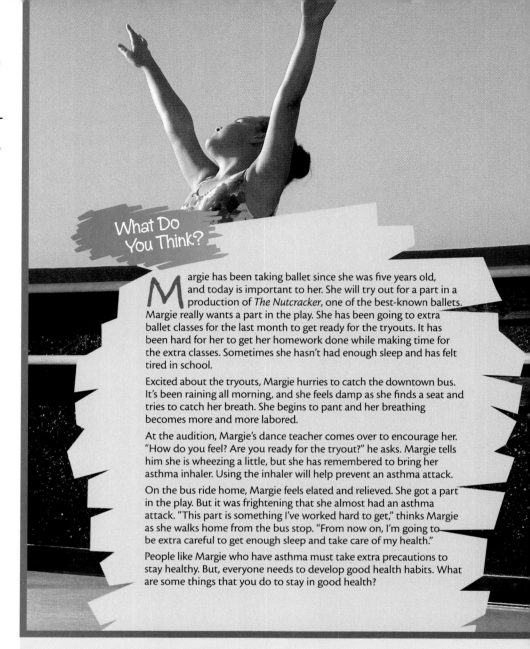

### What Do You Think?

Margie has been taking ballet since she was five years old, and today is important to her. She will try out for a part in a production of *The Nutcracker*, one of the best-known ballets. Margie really wants a part in the play. She has been going to extra ballet classes for the last month to get ready for the tryouts. It has been hard for her to get her homework done while making time for the extra classes. Sometimes she hasn't had enough sleep and has felt tired in school.

Excited about the tryouts, Margie hurries to catch the downtown bus. It's been raining all morning, and she feels damp as she finds a seat and tries to catch her breath. She begins to pant and her breathing becomes more and more labored.

At the audition, Margie's dance teacher comes over to encourage her. "How do you feel? Are you ready for the tryout?" he asks. Margie tells him she is wheezing a little, but she has remembered to bring her asthma inhaler. Using the inhaler will help prevent an asthma attack.

On the bus ride home, Margie feels elated and relieved. She got a part in the play. But it was frightening that she almost had an asthma attack. "This part is something I've worked hard to get," thinks Margie as she walks home from the bus stop. "From now on, I'm going to be extra careful to get enough sleep and take care of my health."

People like Margie who have asthma must take extra precautions to stay healthy. But, everyone needs to develop good health habits. What are some things that you do to stay in good health?

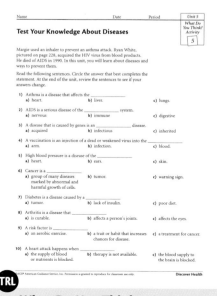

**What Do You Think? Master 5**

# Disease—Causes and Prevention

*I*f you are healthy, you probably don't think much about your health. But when you are sick, health seems precious. And it is. Many of the things you do affect your health. Healthy habits can improve your life by guarding your health.

In this chapter, you will learn about the causes of some common diseases. You will learn how your body fights disease. You will also learn how to prevent many diseases. Forming good habits at a young age will affect your health for years to come.

## Goals for Learning

▶ To explain the difference between inherited and acquired diseases

▶ To describe how pathogens cause disease

▶ To explain how the inflammatory and immune responses protect the body

▶ To explain how immunizations prevent diseases

## Introducing the Chapter

Ask a volunteer to read the information on page 231.

To reinforce the importance of maintaining health, discuss the limitations that even ordinary illnesses place on the body. Discuss the Goals for Learning.

Ask:

- Who has ever had a cold or the flu? What did the illness prevent you from doing? (Accept all reasonable answers: Possible answers include: It was difficult to breathe because of a stuffy nose. It was difficult to swallow because of a sore throat. It was hard to get comfortable because of a fever.)

---

Name _____ Date _____ Period _____ | Chapter 11 Student Study Guide 17 page 1

**Chapter 11 Disease—Causes and Prevention**

**Directions** Fill in the outline below. Filling in the blanks will help you as you read and study Disease—Causes and Protection.

I. Lesson 1 Causes of Disease (pp. 232-34)
   A. Inherited and Acquired Diseases
      1. Genes that are passed from parent to child are _____ diseases.
      2. Contact with germs, human behaviors, or the environment are _____ diseases.
      3. The germs that cause acquired diseases are called _____ .
   B. Stopping Pathogens
      1. Mucous membranes make a sticky liquid called _____ .
      2. _____ in the nose trap pathogens.
      3. A _____ in the skin is a way for pathogens to get into the body.
      4. Pathogens that enter your body might _____ .
      5. AIDS is an example of an _____ disease.
   C. Avoiding Infectious Diseases
      1. _____ your hands often to avoid getting an infectious disease.
      2. Some pathogens live in uncooked meat and _____ .

II. Lesson 2 The Body's Protection From Disease (pp. 235-38)
   A. Invading Pathogens
      1. The first thing to happen when pathogens enter the body is called the _____ response.

©AGS® American Guidance Service, Inc. Permission is granted to reproduce for classroom use only.  Discover Health

**Student Study Guide 17, page 1**

---

Name _____ Date _____ Period _____ | Chapter 11 Student Study Guide 17 page 2

   B. Immune System
      1. Blood makes _____ when a foreign substance enters the bloodstream.
      2. When an antibody stays in the body after a disease is over, you become _____ to that disease.
   C. Vaccinations
      1. A vaccination is an injection of dead or weakened _____ into your body.
      2. Babies that drink breast milk are protected from certain diseases from the _____ in the breast milk.

©AGS® American Guidance Service, Inc. Permission is granted to reproduce for classroom use only.  Discover Health

**Student Study Guide 17, page 2**

# Lesson at a Glance

## Chapter 11 Lesson 1

**Overview** This lesson teaches students the difference between inherited and acquired diseases. Students learn about the body's defenses against disease. Students also learn the simple things they can do to avoid getting infectious diseases.

- ■ To explain the difference between inherited and acquired diseases.

- ■ To describe how pathogens cause disease.

**Student Pages** 232–234

**Audiocassette** 🎧

**Teacher's Resource Library** 🅣🅡🅛

Activity 40

Workbook Activity 40

## Teaching Suggestions

### ■ Vocabulary

*acquired disease, disease, gene, inherited disease, muscular dystrophy, pathogen, infection, infectious disease, mucous membrane, mucus, multiply*

Before beginning the lesson, tell students to make two columns on a sheet of paper, with the titles "Prereading Definition" and "Actual Definition." Tell students to write each vocabulary word in the first column, along with what they think the word means. As students encounter the vocabulary words in the text, have them write the actual definition in the second column. Have students evaluate how closely their prereading definitions match the actual definitions of the words.

### ■ Teaching the Lesson

Discuss with students the fact that some diseases can be acquired, or caught, while others are inherited. Colds and flu are mentioned in the introduction in the text. Ask students whether they think these diseases are caught or inherited, and why.

After the discussion, have students read about the sources of inherited and acquired diseases on page 232.

---

## Lesson 1

### Causes of Disease

**Acquired disease**
*A disease caused by infection or human behavior*

**Disease**
*A disorder of normal body function*

**Gene**
*Parts of a cell that are passed from parent to child*

**Inherited disease**
*A disease passed through genes*

**Muscular dystrophy**
*An inherited disease in which the muscles do not develop normally*

**Pathogen**
*A disease-causing germ*

*T*hink back to the last time you were sick. Perhaps you had a cold or the flu. You might have diabetes or asthma, **diseases** that do not go away. Disease is the interruption or disorder of normal body operations. A person can either inherit or acquire diseases.

#### What Are Inherited Diseases?

**Inherited diseases** run in families. They are caused by **genes** that are passed from parent to child. A gene is like a recipe for making part of the body. If the recipe is wrong, the body will not behave normally. You might have heard of some inherited diseases. **Muscular dystrophy** is an inherited disease. In a person with muscular dystrophy, the muscles do not develop normally.

#### What Are Acquired Diseases?

An **acquired disease** is not caused by genes. Acquired diseases are caused by contact with germs, human behaviors, or the environment. For example, lung cancer is an acquired disease. Most lung cancer is caused by smoking. In some cases, the environment can affect health and cause acquired diseases. Some diseases, such as heart disease, are partly inherited and partly acquired. The tendency for heart disease is inherited. However, a person's lifestyle can prevent the disease from developing.

Germs that cause acquired diseases are called **pathogens**. Think back to that cold you had. You might have said, "I caught a cold." In a sense, this is true. You probably picked up cold germs on your hands. You might have breathed them in from the air. Pathogens are everywhere. However, you can lower your chances of getting a cold by using healthy habits.

**Writing About Health**

Think about your personal health practices. List the things you could do to prevent getting an infectious disease such as a cold. Then list the things you could do when you have a cold to avoid spreading it to others.

**232** *Chapter 11 Disease—Causes and Protection*

---

**Ask:**

- · **What is an inherited disease?** (An inherited disease is a disease that is passed from one person to another through genes.)

- · **What is an acquired disease?** (An acquired disease is a disease that is caused by contact with germs, by human behaviors, or picked up from the environment.)

- · **How can pathogens get into your body to cause disease?** (Possible answers include: A person can pick pathogens up on their hands by touching objects that are contaminated with them. A person can breathe in pathogens from the air.)

## How Does the Body Stop Pathogens?

Your body has several roadblocks for pathogens. **Mucous membranes** are the moist surfaces that line your mouth, nose, and other body openings. Mucous membranes make a sticky liquid, **mucus**. Mucus traps pathogens before they enter the body. Hairs in the nose trap pathogens. Acid in the stomach kills many pathogens. Coughing, sneezing, and even vomiting remove pathogens from the body.

Some pathogens do, however, enter the body. A cut in the skin is a way in. Pathogens can also enter your body in food. If pathogens do enter your body, they may **multiply**. This process is called **infection**. Diseases caused by pathogens are called **infectious diseases**. Some infectious diseases, such as a cold, are not serious. Others, such as AIDS, are deadly. Figure 11.1 shows the stages of an infectious disease.

**Infection**
*A sickness caused by a pathogen in the body*

**Infectious disease**
*A disease caused by a pathogen*

**Mucous membrane**
*The thin, moist tissue that lines body openings*

**Mucus**
*The sticky fluid produced by mucous membranes*

**Multiply**
*Increase in number*

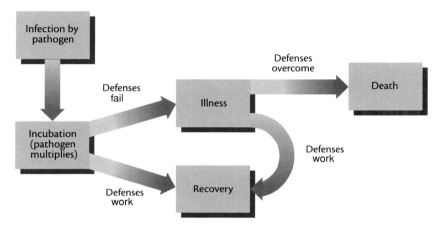

**Figure 11.1.** Stages of infectious disease

*Disease—Causes and Protection   Chapter 11*   **233**

---

Tell students that people can go to doctors to get medical treatment for a disease. But the body also has its own defenses that sometimes prevent pathogens from causing disease. Challenge students to think about what these defenses might be. Write their suggestions on the board.

Then have students read about the body's defenses against pathogens on page 233.

### Ask:

- What do mucous membranes do to fight disease? (Mucous membranes make a sticky liquid called mucus that traps pathogens before they can enter the body.)

- What are some of the body's other defenses against pathogens? (Other defenses against pathogens include hairs in the nose that trap pathogens; acid in the stomach that kills pathogens; coughing, sneezing, and vomiting that can remove pathogens.)

- What is an infectious disease? (An infectious disease is a sickness caused by a pathogen in the body.) **Give an example.** (Accept all reasonable answers: Possible answers include: a cold, AIDS)

## LEARNING STYLES

**Visual** Direct students' attention to the diagram showing the stages of infectious disease at the bottom of page 233. Using the diagram as a reference, have students write a short paragraph t*.

## BACKGROUND INFORMATION

One of the most common infectious diseases is the common cold. More than 100 different viruses can cause colds. Most of them are members of the rhinovirus family. The viruses often enter the body after being released into the air by a person with a cold who sneezes, coughs, or speaks.

## Careers

Discuss with students the kinds of qualities someone would need to do this job. Qualities suggested by students might include the ability to organize, good communications skills, dependability, and the ability to work well with people.

Have students read the section on avoiding infectious diseases on page 234.

## Lesson 1 Review Answers

**1)** An inherited disease is a disease caused by genes that are passed from parent to child.

**2)** An acquired disease is a disease caused by infection or human behavior.

**3)** Pathogens multiply when they enter your body.

**4)** Mucous membranes make mucus, which traps pathogens before they enter the body. Hairs in the nose trap pathogens. Acid in the stomach kills pathogens. Coughing, sneezing, and vomiting remove pathogens from the body.

**5)** Because pathogens are passed from person to person on the hands, washing the hands decreases the number of pathogens on the hands.

### APPLICATION

**At Home**
Have students observe the hand-washing habits of family members for one day. Encourage students to discuss any needed changes in hand-washing habits with their families.

### LEARNING STYLES

**Group Learning** Discuss with students the ways to educate others about the need to wash hands to prevent infectious diseases. Divide students into groups to plan public education campaigns on the subject. Have each group report on what methods and materials they would use to get this information to others.

---

**Careers**

## HEALTH SERVICE COORDINATOR

Health service coordinators work in doctors' offices, clinics, and hospitals. They keep information about patients. They give information to nurses, doctors, and other health care workers. They order special diets, drugs, equipment, supplies, laboratory tests, and X-ray exams. Health service coordinators may have different job titles depending on their specific job. Two to four years of training are required. Health service coordinators also must know basic medical terms and nursing and testing procedures.

**Fitness Tip**

Exercise will increase your resistance to infectious diseases.

**Health Tip**

Wash your hands often to prevent some infectious diseases.

### How Can I Avoid Getting an Infectious Disease?

Many pathogens are passed from person to person on the hands. Wash your hands often. Always wash your hands before you eat or prepare food. Wash your hands after you use the bathroom or take out the garbage. Pathogens live by the millions on doorknobs, telephone receivers, and stair rails. In public places such as airports, there are more pathogens than there are in your home. Assume that you have pathogens on your hands unless you have just washed them. Avoid rubbing your eyes or touching your lips with unwashed hands.

Some pathogens live in uncooked meat and eggs. When you prepare food, cook meats until they are well done. Do not eat food containing raw eggs. Clean kitchen surfaces and utensils with detergent and hot water before you use them again. Once you have learned how infectious diseases are spread, it becomes easy to avoid many of them.

**LESSON 1 REVIEW** Write the answers to these questions on a separate sheet of paper. Use complete sentences.

**1)** What is an inherited disease?

**2)** What is an acquired disease?

**3)** What do pathogens do when they enter your body?

**4)** Describe some ways the body blocks pathogens.

**5)** How can washing your hands reduce your chances of getting an infectious disease?

---

Name _____ Date _____ Period _____ | Chapter 11 Activity 40

**Causes of Disease**

**Directions** Match each item on the left with the correct item on the right. Write the correct letter on each blank. Each item on the right may be used once, more than once, or not at all.

_____ **1)** An infectious disease that is not serious
_____ **2)** Passed only by parents
_____ **3)** An inherited disease
_____ **4)** An acquired disease
_____ **5)** A deadly infectious disease
_____ **6)** Caused by pathogens
_____ **7)** An acquired disease can come from this
_____ **8)** Causes lung cancer
_____ **9)** A sticky liquid that traps germs
_____ **10)** It can pass a cold or flu
_____ **11)** A "recipe" for making part of the body
_____ **12)** May be partly acquired and partly inherited
_____ **13)** The process of germs entering the body and multiplying
_____ **14)** A germ that causes disease
_____ **15)** These make a sticky liquid that traps pathogens

a) infectious disease
b) germ
c) environment
d) pathogen
e) gene
f) mucous membranes
g) smoking
h) AIDS
i) lung cancer
j) cold
k) mucus
l) heart disease
m) muscular dystrophy
n) infection
o) inherited disease

TRL | **Activity 40**

---

Name _____ Date _____ Period _____ | Chapter 11 Workbook Activity 40

**Causes of Disease**

**Directions** Write the letter of the item from Column B that matches the description in Column A.

**Column A**

_____ **1)** disease is caused by infection
_____ **2)** disorder of normal body function
_____ **3)** sticky fluid produced by mucous membranes
_____ **4)** disease caused by a pathogen
_____ **5)** sickness caused by a pathogen in the body
_____ **6)** parts of a cell passed from parent to child
_____ **7)** disease passed through genes
_____ **8)** inherited disease in which the muscles do not develop normally
_____ **9)** a disease-causing germ
_____ **10)** thin, moist tissue that lines body openings

**Column B**

a) acquired disease
b) disease
c) gene
d) infection
e) infectious disease
f) inherited disease
g) muscular dystrophy
h) mucus
i) mucous membrane
j) pathogen

TRL | **Workbook Activity 40**

## Lesson 2

### The Body's Protection From Disease

**Immune system**
*A system of organs, tissues, and cells that fight infection*

**Inflammatory response**
*The body's first response to a pathogen*

Some pathogens get through the body's protection from infection. A healthy body is ready, however, to fight pathogens in several ways.

#### What Happens When Pathogens Invade?

When you are infected by pathogens, the body tries to fight the infection. If you have ever cut your finger, you are familiar with some of the ways the body fights. The area around the cut swells. Blood vessels become larger. The body sends special blood cells to the injured area. These blood cells kill pathogens. The injured area becomes hotter than the rest of the body. The heat slows the multiplication of the pathogens. These events are called the **inflammatory response**. They are the first things that happen when pathogens enter.

The inflammatory response may not stop the pathogens. They may still multiply and start an infection. The body, however, does not give up. A special system of organs, tissues, and cells begins to fight pathogens. This system is called the **immune system**.

### Healthy Subjects

#### Social Studies

**THE BUBONIC PLAGUE**

An *epidemic* is a widespread disease. Some of the world's worst epidemics were of bubonic plague. Bubonic plague is caused by a pathogen carried by fleas. The fleas move from place to place on the bodies of rats. Bubonic plague causes fever, pain, and open sores. Before modern medicine, the plague was usually deadly. The first recorded plague was in 435 B.C. The worst known outbreak occurred in Europe from 1347 to 1351. Known as the Black Death, it killed millions of people. In the early 1900s, over ten million people in India died of the plague. Today, there are medicines to fight this disease. Over the years, a few cases of plague have appeared in the United States. When this happens, the U.S. Public Health Service isolates victims and cleans up infected areas. This stops the spread of the disease.

*Disease—Causes and Protection*    *Chapter 11*    **235**

---

**Ask:**

- Give an example of how the inflammatory response works when you get a cut. (When you get a cut, the area around the cut swells as blood vessels there become larger and blood cells that kill pathogens move to the injured area. The injured area also becomes hotter than the rest of the body, which slows the multiplication of pathogens.)

- What is the immune system? (The immune system is a system of organs, tissue, and cells that fight infection.)

Have students read about the way antibodies work as part of the immune system on page 236.

**Ask:**

- How does a vaccination help a person fight off disease? (A vaccination is an injection of a dead or weakened virus into the bloodstream. The virus is strong enough to cause the body to make antibodies to the disease, but not strong enough to make the person sick.)

## Then and Now

Have students do research to find out how the treatment for some medical ailments has changed over the last few decades. They can choose illnesses that were once deadly and can now be cured or have been largely wiped out. Students can also choose a method of treatment that has changed because the illness is now treated by drugs rather than surgery or is now treated with a newer type of surgery. Have students share their findings with the class.

## GLOBAL CONNECTION

Have students contact the World Health Organization (WHO) to get information on current epidemics in the United States and elsewhere.

## APPLICATION

**Environment**
Have students find out how pollution causes or worsens disease. For example, air pollution worsens respiratory diseases such as asthma and bronchitis. Encourage students to present their information on a poster.

**Immune**
*Resistant to infection*

**Immunization**
*Means of making a body immune from a disease*

**Vaccination**
*An injection of dead or weakened viruses to make the body immune to the virus*

### How Does the Immune System Work?

The immune system is the body's final line of defense against infection. When a foreign substance enters the bloodstream, the blood make antibodies. Antibodies are proteins that kill specific pathogens. If the correct antibodies are in the blood when an infection occurs, they begin to fight it. They may knock out the infection early enough so that you don't become sick.

Antibodies form in the blood in a number of ways. If you do become sick, antibodies to a pathogen develop during the course of the illness. Then the antibodies help to fight the illness so that recovery is speeded up.

Some antibodies remain in the body after a disease is over. These antibodies give you immunity so you won't get the disease again. You are **immune**.

### How Does a Vaccination Work?

Antibodies may also be in the blood as a result of **vaccination** or **immunization**. A vaccination is an injection, a shot, or oral medication of dead or weakened viruses into your body. Enough virus is injected to make you immune to but not sick from the disease. For example, when you get a measles vaccination, your body makes antibodies to the measles virus. Then you are immune to measles.

**Then and Now**

### TONSILS

Tonsils are pieces of tissue that lie on either side of the back of the throat. Sometimes tonsils become infected. This disease is called *tonsillitis*. Tonsillitis can cause a sore throat, fever, and difficulty swallowing. For many years, doctors simply removed diseased tonsils.

In recent years, however, researchers have learned that tonsils are useful. Tonsils are part of the body's immune system. They trap pathogens entering the body. Also, the tonsils produce chemicals that help fight infections. Today the common treatment for tonsillitis is medicine. Tonsils are sometimes still removed. But that happens only when the infection doesn't go away with medical treatment.

You already have antibodies when you are born. You are born immune to some diseases. For example, humans cannot get certain diseases that animals get. Humans are naturally immune to such diseases.

**Why might a person in poor general health get several different diseases?**

Some immunities are acquired naturally. Babies are protected from certain diseases because of antibodies in their mother's milk. This immunity works in babies until their own immune system takes over. Without the immune system, people would have many more diseases and infections. Your immune system is an important defense against disease.

The table on the next page shows some of the vaccines that are given to people.

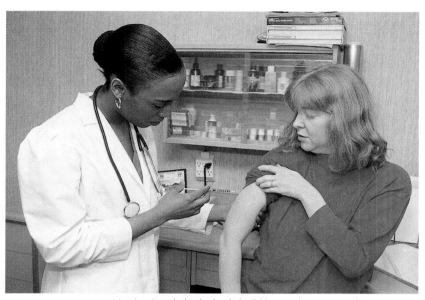

Vaccinations help the body build immunity to some diseases.

*Disease—Causes and Protection* *Chapter 11* **237**

Have students read about natural immunity on page 237.

Ask:

- How do the antibodies you are born with affect your ability to fight disease? (The antibodies you are born with make you naturally immune to some diseases.)

- How do babies acquire some immunities naturally? (Babies can acquire some immunities as a result of antibodies in their mother's milk.)

- How does the immunity acquired from a baby's mother help protect the baby? (The immunity acquired from the mother works in babies until his or her own immune system takes over.)

**APPLICATION**

**In the Community**
Have students do research to find out which vaccinations are required to attend school in your community. Have them make a chart showing those vaccinations and when your community requires them to be received.

**MULTICULTURAL CONNECTION**

Ethnobotonists are scientists who visit remote parts of the world to gather the medicinal plant knowledge of native peoples. Such plants have often been used as the basis for new medicines. Ethnobotonists visit areas such as the Amazon rain forest, where many useful plants that could provide cures for diseases are still unknown to people in the outside world. The Amazon rain forest is being cut down at a rapid rate. Discuss with students how this could affect the work of ethnobotonists.

## Action for Health

Have students choose one of the diseases for which a vaccine is listed on page 238. Ask them to research the cause and symptoms of that disease. Also have students find out how vaccinations have affected the rate of occurrence of the disease. Give students the opportunity to share their findings with the class.

## Lesson 2 Review Answers

1) During the inflammatory response, the area of injury becomes hot and its blood vessels enlarge. This brings many special blood cells to the area to attack the invading pathogens.
2) The immune response begins when certain cells in the body detect invading pathogens.
3) Antibodies are made in the blood.
4) Antibodies to pathogens develop during the course of the illness. Antibodies may also be in the blood as a result of a vaccination.
5) A vaccination is a harmless form of a pathogen. It causes the body to make antibodies to the pathogen.

## LEARNING STYLES

**Auditory** Have students use audiocassettes to create radio Public Service Announcement (PSAs) to encourage parents to get their children vaccinated. Students can use their own research and material in the text to give reasons in the PSA for vaccinations. Allow students to work alone or in pairs. Have them play their completed PSAs in class.

## APPLICATION

**Career Connection**
Tell students that they are going to role-play a scenario in which they are a doctor for a patient who needs a vaccination. The patient can be a child, an adult, or an older person. Have the doctor explain to the patient why he or she needs the vaccination. Then have students switch roles.

---

Action for Health

### KEEPING TRACK OF YOUR VACCINATIONS

Ask your family to help you make a list of all your vaccinations and the dates when you had them. This chart shows some usual types of vaccinations and the ages when they are recommended. If your vaccinations are not up-to-date, see your doctor.

| Vaccine | Recommended Age |
| --- | --- |
| Diphtheria, whooping cough, tetanus | 2, 3, 6, and 15 months; 4 to 6 years |
| Oral polio vaccine | 15 months; 4 to 6 years |
| Measles | 15 months; 4 to 6 years |
| Mumps | 15 months; 4 to 6 years |
| German measles | 15 months; 4 to 6 years |
| Tetanus, diphtheria | 14 to 16 years; every 10 years thereafter |
| Chicken pox | 12 to 18 months; adults who have never had the disease |
| Hepatitis B | three injection series; birth through adults; usually by age 11 |

**LESSON 2 REVIEW** Write the answers to these questions on a separate sheet of paper. Use complete sentences.

1) What happens during the inflammatory response?
2) How does the immune system work?
3) Where are antibodies made?
4) How do we build antibodies to pathogens?
5) What is a vaccination, and what does it do in the body?

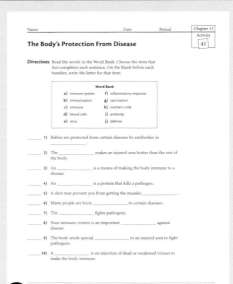

**Activity 41**                    **Workbook Activity 41**

■ Diseases can be either acquired or inherited.

■ A person gets an inherited disease through genes.

■ Infection, human behaviors, or environmental conditions cause acquired diseases. An acquired disease can be picked up from contact with germs.

■ Some diseases are partly inherited and partly acquired.

■ Pathogens are germs that cause acquired diseases. Pathogens can enter the body through a cut in the skin or in food. Once in the body, they multiply and cause infection.

■ The body has several protections from infections. The skin, mucous membranes, stomach acids, coughing, sneezing, and vomiting help prevent infection.

■ The inflammatory response stops infections by some pathogens.

■ Good health habits can help avoid infection. Washing hands, cleaning kitchen surfaces, and cooking food well help to prevent infectious diseases.

■ The immune system fights foreign substances in the bloodstream by producing antibodies.

■ Antibodies get in the blood in a number of ways. Earlier infections or vaccinations build antibodies in the blood to fight infections. You are born with certain antibodies. A baby gets them through its mother's milk.

■ **Using the Chapter Summary**

To further reinforce the facts and concepts presented in the chapter, read and discuss with students the questions that follow.

Ask:

• **What is the difference between acquired and inherited diseases?** (Acquired diseases are caused by infection and human behavior. Inherited diseases are passed from parent to child through genes.)

• **What are pathogens?** (Pathogens are disease-causing germs.)

• **Name two ways that pathogens can enter the body.** (Pathogens can enter the body through cuts in the skin or through eating contaminated food. Accept any other reasonable answers.)

• **How do mucous membranes prevent infections?** (Mucous membranes produce a sticky liquid called mucus that traps pathogens before they enter the body.)

• **Give an example of the inflammatory response.** (Possible answers include: At the site of a cut, swelling occurs as enlarged blood vessels bring pathogen-killing cells to the area. The area around the cut gets warmer than the rest of the body to slow down the multiplication of pathogens.)

• **How can washing hands help prevent disease?** (Washing hands can remove pathogens that can enter the body when you touch openings such as the mouth and eyes.)

• **What does your immune system do?** (The immune system fights foreign substances in the bloodstream by producing antibodies.)

• **How do vaccinations work?** (During vaccinations, dead or weakened viruses are injected into the bloodstream to cause the body to make antibodies to the virus. The antibodies give the vaccinated person future immunity to the disease.)

# Chapter 11 Review

The Teacher's Resource Library includes two parallel forms of the Chapter 11 Mastery Test. The difficulty level of the two forms is equivalent. You may wish to use one form as a pretest and the other form as a posttest.

## Review Answers

### Comprehension: Identifying Facts

1) disease  2) Inherited diseases  3) gene
4) pathogens  5) mucous membranes
6) Mucus  7) infection  8) infectious disease  9) inflammatory response

## Comprehension: Identifying Facts

On a separate sheet of paper, write the correct word or words from the Word Bank to complete each sentence.

### WORD BANK

| | |
|---|---|
| acquired disease | infectious disease |
| antibodies | inflammatory response |
| blood | inherited diseases |
| disease | mucous membranes |
| gene | mucus |
| immune system | pathogens |
| immunization | vaccination |
| infection | |

1) When you have a _____, the body does not work normally.

2) _____ run in families.

3) A _____ causes an inherited disease.

4) Germs that cause acquired diseases are called _____.

5) The moist surfaces that line the mouth and other body openings are _____.

6) _____ is a sticky fluid that traps pathogens.

7) Multiplication of pathogens in the body is called _____.

8) An _____ is a disease caused by pathogens.

9) During the _____, blood vessels get larger and the area gets hot.

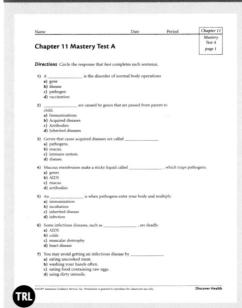
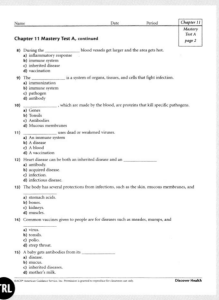

**Chapter 11 Mastery Test A**

10) The _____ is a system of special organs, tissues, and cells that fights disease.

11) Lung cancer is an _____.

12) Heart disease is an _____ and an _____.

13) _____ makes antibodies.

14) _____ fight diseases by killing specific pathogens.

15) _____ is a way to prevent people from getting infectious diseases.

16) _____ uses dead or weakened viruses.

## Comprehension: Understanding Main Ideas

Write the answers to these questions on a separate sheet of paper. Use complete sentences.

17) Do you have more control over getting an inherited disease or an acquired disease?

18) How do people get antibodies from immunizations?

## Critical Thinking: Write Your Opinion

19) What might happen if the body made a mistake and attacked its own cells?

20) Do you think immunizations should be required of people living in society? Why or why not?

**Test Taking Tip**  Be sure you understand what the test question is asking. Reread it if necessary.

*Disease—Causes and Protection*  *Chapter 11*  **241**

---

10) immune system  11) acquired disease
12) acquired disease, inherited disease
13) Blood  14) Antibodies
15) Immunization  16) vaccination

## Comprehension: Understanding Main Ideas

17) You have more control over getting an acquired disease. (You have no control over getting an inherited disease.)

18) The harmless form of the pathogen used in an immunization causes the production of antibodies to the pathogen.

## Critical Thinking: Write Your Opinion

19) If the body made a mistake and attacked its own cells, the body might destroy part of itself.

20) Answers will vary. Either viewpoint should be well supported.

---

**Chapter 11 Mastery Test B**

# Chapter at a Glance

## Chapter 12:
**Preventing AIDS and Sexually Transmitted Diseases**
pages 242–253

### Lessons

1) **AIDS pages** 243–246

2) **Sexually Transmitted Diseases** pages 247–250

**Chapter Summary and Review** pages 251–253

**Audiocassette**

**Teacher's Resource Library** (TRL)

Activities 42–43

Workbook Activities 42–43

Student Study Guide 18 pages 1–2

Chapter 12 Mastery Tests A and B

(Answer Keys for the Teacher's Resource Library begin on page 433 of this Teacher's Edition.)

## Introducing the Chapter

Talk with students about the way relationships are portrayed in movies and on TV. When two people are attracted to each other, they may decide to become closer and engage in a sexual relationship. But this also leaves each person open to the risk of sexually transmitted diseases. Encourage students to discuss what they know about AIDS and other sexually transmitted diseases before beginning the chapter.

Have students read the chapter introduction and Goals for Learning on page 242.

### Ask:

• How do you think a sexually transmitted disease differs from a disease such as measles, in terms of how it spreads? (Students should express the idea that a sexually transmitted disease can only be passed to another person through sexual contact.)

• What do you know about AIDS and other sexually transmitted diseases? (Answers will vary. Students may say they are aware that many people die of AIDS.)

## Chapter 12

# Preventing AIDS and Sexually Transmitted Diseases

Some diseases are spread by contact during sexual activity. A pregnant woman with a sexual disease can give it to her baby. Some of these diseases can be cured, but others cannot. All sexually transmitted diseases can cause serious health problems.

In this chapter, you will learn about what causes some sexually transmitted diseases. You will read about the life-threatening disease AIDS. The lessons in the chapter will describe the symptoms and treatments for these diseases. You will also learn how sexually transmitted diseases can be prevented.

### Goals for Learning

▶ To describe the causes and symptoms of AIDS

▶ To identify the ways that AIDS is transmitted

▶ To describe the symptoms and treatment of four other sexually transmitted diseases

▶ To learn how sexually transmitted diseases can be prevented

**Student Study Guide 18, page 1**

**Student Study Guide 18, page 2**

## AIDS

**AIDS**
*Acquired immunodeficiency syndrome, a disorder of the immune system*

**HIV**
*Human immunodeficiency virus, the virus that causes AIDS*

**A**IDS is a serious disease of the immune system. The letters in AIDS stand for acquired immunodeficiency syndrome. The disease is acquired because one person can acquire it, or catch it, from someone else.

The immune system is what the body uses to fight off infections and diseases. If a person has AIDS, the immune system is damaged or weakened. So, the person is at risk of getting many serious diseases. Nearly all people with AIDS will die from one of these diseases. Right now, there is no cure for AIDS.

### What Causes AIDS?

AIDS is caused by a virus called the human immunodeficiency virus, or **HIV** for short. HIV invades the body through the bloodstream. It infects body cells and cripples the human immune system. People who have HIV in their blood do not always have AIDS. But most people with the virus will eventually get AIDS.

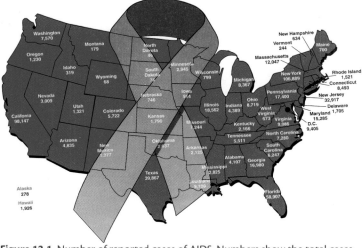

**Figure 12.1** Number of reported cases of AIDS. Numbers show the total cases through December of 1996.

*Preventing AIDS and Sexually Transmitted Diseases* Chapter 12 **243**

---

---

## Then and Now

Allow interested students to research the progress that has been made in the attempt to find treatments for AIDS, and ultimately, a cure. The Centers for Disease Control and Prevention (CDC) is a good source for up-to-date information. Have students report their findings to the class.

Have students read about how AIDS is detected and the symptoms of AIDS on page 244.

Ask:

- A person who is HIV positive may stay healthy for many years, but eventually he or she will develop the symptoms of AIDS. Name two symptoms of AIDS.
  (Accept any two of the following: swollen lymph nodes, weight loss, skin rashes, diarrhea, fever, night sweats, memory loss, personality changes, paralysis.)

 **GLOBAL CONNECTION**

AIDS has been known in Africa much longer than in other parts of the world. Challenge students to research the AIDS epidemic in Africa. Have them find out which countries are most severely affected, what percentage of the population has the disease, and what is being done to prevent its spread. Encourage volunteers to give oral reports to the class.

 **LEARNING STYLES**

**Visual** Have students look at the map of the United States on page 243 that shows the number of AIDS cases per state. Photocopy a table from an almanac or encyclopedia with the population of each state. Give a copy to each student. Then have each student find the actual percentage of the population with AIDS in one or two of the states. Have students use the formula Number of AIDS cases ÷ Total Population × 100. Have students pool their data to compare the percentage of AIDS cases per state.

**THE SPREAD OF AIDS**

In 1984, about 3,450 people died from AIDS. The number of deaths increased each year. In 1996, there were 50,140 deaths. Then, new drugs and prevention programs began to work. In 1997, the number of deaths was down to 38,780.

Many scientists are working to find treatments and cures for AIDS. Because of research and greater health precautions, people who now have AIDS are living longer and have fewer painful symptoms. But AIDS is still a disease with no cure. Until scientists find a cure, the only protection against AIDS is not to get the disease.

**HIV negative**
*Not having HIV in the blood*

**HIV positive**
*Having HIV in the blood*

**Kaposi's sarcoma**
*A rare type of cancer affecting the skin or internal organs*

### How Is AIDS detected?

If a doctor suspects that someone has AIDS, the doctor orders a blood test. The test can find out if HIV is in the person's blood. A person with HIV is **HIV positive**. This means that the test was positive. It showed that the blood has HIV. If someone does not have the virus, the person is **HIV negative**.

### What Are the Symptoms of AIDS?

AIDS is an illness that can have a long incubation period. This means a person with HIV may not show signs of AIDS for six to ten years. During all that time, the person appears healthy. But the disease is weakening the person's immune system.

Eventually, the symptoms of AIDS will appear. These symptoms include swollen lymph nodes, weight loss, skin rashes, diarrhea, fever, and night sweats. As the disease gets worse, people with AIDS can develop memory loss, personality changes, and paralysis.

Because HIV weakens the immune system, people with AIDS can have serious diseases. For example, they may get a lung infection called pneumonia. They may get a rare type of cancer called **Kaposi's sarcoma**. It affects the skin or internal organs.

**244** *Chapter 12 Preventing AIDS and Sexually Transmitted Diseases*

## How Do People Get AIDS?

Like all illnesses caused by a virus, AIDS is a **communicable** disease. This means that one person can get the disease from another. HIV, which causes AIDS, is in the blood and other body fluids of the sick person. These fluids can carry the disease to another person. There are several ways that someone can get HIV.

### Sexual Contact

AIDS is spread through sexual activity. During sexual activity, body fluids, such as semen and vaginal secretions, are passed from one person to the other. If one person has HIV, the partner can get it during sex.

### Infected Blood and Needles

Any needle used for injecting a drug or medicine gets blood on it. If a person with HIV is injected, then afterwards, that needle can carry HIV. Sometimes drug addicts share needles. In this way, HIV is passed from one person to another.

Sometimes a sick or an injured person needs more blood. The person receives a **transfusion** in which blood is transferred from one person to another. Before it was known how HIV spread, some infected people donated blood for use in transfusions. The infected blood carried HIV to new victims. A blood test for AIDS was developed in 1985. Now the American blood supply is almost always safe.

### Healthy Subjects

**Social Studies**

A hospice is a nontraditional setting for health care. People dying with diseases such as AIDS can choose to live in a hospice to get the care they need. Some patients in hospices can no longer be helped in a hospital.

A hospice has a homelike setting. Family, friends, and volunteers assist those with medical training in a hospice. The volunteers may feed or dress patients. They may read and talk to them.

Have students read about the ways that people can get AIDS on page 245.

Ask:

- What is a communicable disease?
  (A communicable disease is one that can be passed from one person to another.)

- How does HIV pass from person to person during sexual activity? (During sexual activity, body fluids, such as semen and vaginal secretions, pass from one person to another.)

- How are people protected from getting HIV through blood transfusions?
  (Blood is now tested for HIV.)

## Healthy Subjects

Ask students if they have ever had the experience of knowing a friend or family member in hospice care. Discuss what such an experience would be like and how hospice care might be different from care in a hospital. If there is a hospice nearby, try to arrange for a hospice care worker to visit the class to talk about how these institutions help the families of terminally ill people.

### APPLICATION

**At Home**
Hospice programs allow patients to be cared for in a homelike setting. Have students discuss with members of their family feelings about hospice programs that care for people with terminal illnesses. Encourage students to express their wishes, fears, and concerns about this type of medical care.

### LEARNING STYLES

**Tactile/Kinesthetic** Have groups of students role-play a situation in which one teen is pressuring another teen to have sex. The person being pressured is refusing because he or she wants to be safe from sexually transmitted diseases such as AIDS. Have the class discuss the role-playing skits.

Have students read about mother-to-child transmission of AIDS and some myths about AIDS on page 246.

- When can a woman pass HIV to her baby? (before, during, or after birth)
- Can you eat from dishes used by someone with AIDS? (Yes, you cannot get AIDS by eating from dishes used by someone with AIDS.)

## Lesson 1 Review Answers

1) AIDS is a disease of the immune system. HIV is the virus that causes AIDS.
2) The first symptoms of AIDS are swollen lymph nodes, weight loss, skin rashes, diarrhea, fever, and night sweats. As the disease gets worse, people can develop memory loss, personality changes, and paralysis.
3) Some ways of transmitting AIDS include sexual activity, drug users sharing infected needles, and blood transfusions with infected blood.
4) Avoiding sexual contact is the best way to prevent AIDS.
5) Yes, it is safe to be around someone with AIDS. Casual contact does not spread the disease.

## APPLICATION

### In the Community
Have students find out if your community organizes an annual AIDS walk to raise money for research and treatment programs. Encourage students to participate in such a walk.

## APPLICATION

### Environment
To prevent the spread of diseases such as AIDS, medical personnel dispose of hazardous biochemical waste (needles, bandages, urine/stool containers) in safe ways. Encourage students to find out what happens to hazardous biochemical waste in the hospitals in your community. Invite students to report their findings to the class.

Children with AIDS are the innocent victims of this deadly disease.

**If a student in your school has AIDS, do the other students need to be tested? Why or why not?**

## Mother to Child
A woman can pass HIV to her baby before, during, or after birth. The virus can also be passed to the baby while the baby drinks the mother's milk. Pregnant women can be tested for HIV. There are now ways to prevent the transfer of the disease to the unborn baby.

## What Are Some Myths About AIDS?
AIDS is a serious disease that cannot be cured. Because of this, some people are afraid to be around a person who has AIDS. It is important to understand that AIDS is not acquired by breathing the air people with AIDS breathe. Touching, holding, hugging, or shaking hands with a person with AIDS will not spread the disease. Sharing dishes or swimming in a pool with an AIDS victim will not spread the disease either. It is safe for children with AIDS to go to school with other children. The other children are not at risk of catching the disease.

**LESSON 1 REVIEW** Write the answers to these questions on a separate sheet of paper. Use complete sentences.

1) What is the difference between HIV and AIDS?
2) What are the symptoms of AIDS?
3) How is AIDS passed from one person to another?
4) How can AIDS be prevented?
5) Is it safe to be around a person with AIDS? Explain your answer.

---

Name _____ Date _____ Period _____  Chapter 12 Activity 42

**AIDS**

**Directions** Match each item on the left with the correct item on the right. Write the correct letter on each blank. Each item on the right may be used once, more than once, or not at all.

_____ 1) A rare type of cancer affecting the skin or internal organs
_____ 2) Causes AIDS
_____ 3) The transfer of blood from one person to another
_____ 4) A disorder of the immune system
_____ 5) A liquid that can pass the AIDS virus
_____ 6) A way that AIDS cannot be spread
_____ 7) One way to detect HIV
_____ 8) Acquired immunodeficiency syndrome
_____ 9) A lung infection
_____ 10) May not appear for six to ten years
_____ 11) A way that drug users pass AIDS
_____ 12) AIDS may cause it
_____ 13) Scientists are researching them
_____ 14) AIDS weakens it
_____ 15) There are none for AIDS

a) pneumonia
b) heart disease
c) AIDS
d) transfusion
e) preventative measures
f) HIV
g) Kaposi's sarcoma
h) immune system
i) mother's milk
j) touching
k) cures
l) vaccine
m) needle sharing
n) blood test
o) memory loss

©AGS® American Guidance Service, Inc. Permission is granted to reproduce for classroom use only.  Discover Health

**Activity 42**

---

Name _____ Date _____ Period _____  Chapter 12 Workbook Activity 42

**AIDS**

**Directions** Match each item on the left with the correct item on the right. Write the correct letter on each blank. Each item on the right may be used once, more than once, or not at all.

_____ 1) Body system that fights disease
_____ 2) Rare type of cancer of the skin or internal organs
_____ 3) Having HIV in the blood
_____ 4) Virus that causes AIDS
_____ 5) Not having HIV in the blood
_____ 6) Transfer of blood from one to another
_____ 7) Able to be passed from one person to another
_____ 8) Acquired immunodeficiency syndrome
_____ 9) One way AIDS is spread
_____ 10) How AIDS is detected

a) AIDS
b) blood test
c) communicable
d) HIV
e) HIV-negative
f) HIV-positive
g) immune system
h) Kaposi's sarcoma
i) sexual contact
j) transfusion

American Guidance Service, Inc. Permission is granted to reproduce for classroom use only.  Discover Health

**Workbook Activity 42**

## Sexually Transmitted Diseases

**Chronic**
*Lasting*

**Genital herpes**
*A sexually transmitted chronic infection*

**Sexually transmitted disease**
*A disease passed from one person to another through sexual contact*

Any disease that can be spread through sexual activity is a **sexually transmitted disease**. One example is AIDS. Other diseases pass from one person to another through sexual contact. Most sexually transmitted diseases can be cured if they are discovered early.

### Which Sexually Transmitted Diseases Have No Cure?

Two sexually transmitted diseases have no cure. There are no vaccines to prevent these diseases. Once a person has the disease, there is no way to eliminate it from the body.

### AIDS

You read about the AIDS disease in Lesson 1. AIDS has no cure. Almost all people who get HIV, which causes AIDS, will die from the disease. AIDS passes from one person to another through sexual contact or through needles used by infected people.

### Genital Herpes

A less serious incurable disease is **genital herpes**. This is a **chronic**, or lasting, infection. The main symptom of genital herpes is clusters of painful, small blisters in the genital area. The blisters break, heal, and come back.

Genital herpes is spread by contact with the broken blisters. Avoiding sexual contact with an infected person can prevent someone from getting this disease.

**Why is it difficult to prevent the spread of sexually transmitted diseases?**

Genital herpes can lead to other health problems. Women may get repeated infections involving the cervix. This can lead to cancer of the cervix. A pregnant woman can pass genital herpes to her baby. During birth, the baby passes through the birth canal. The baby then becomes infected with the disease. Genital herpes can cause brain damage in babies.

Genital herpes has no known cure. A pill can speed up healing but does not get rid of the infection. Over time, the infections tend to be less severe. But genital herpes never goes away.

*Preventing AIDS and Sexually Transmitted Diseases   Chapter 12*   **247**

---

- What is the main symptom of genital herpes? (The main symptom of genital herpes is clusters of painful, small blisters in the genital area.)

- How is genital herpes spread? (Genital herpes spreads through contact with the broken blisters.)

---

## Lesson at a Glance

### Chapter 12  Lesson 2

**Overview** In this lesson, students learn about other sexually transmitted diseases such as genital herpes, gonorrhea, chlamydia, and syphilis. Students also learn how these diseases can be prevented.

### Objectives

- To describe the symptoms and treatment of other sexually transmitted diseases.

- To learn how sexually transmitted diseases can be prevented.

**Student Pages** 247–250

**Audiocassette**

**Teacher's Resource Library**

Activity 43
Workbook Activity 43

## Teaching Suggestions

### ■ Vocabulary

*chronic, genital herpes, gonorrhea, penicillin, chlamydia, syphilis*

Write the vocabulary words on the chalkboard and ask students to write definitions based on their prior knowledge. Then review the actual definitions with the class. Have volunteers read their definitions aloud.

### ■ Teaching the Lesson

Have students discuss what they already know about sexually transmitted diseases other than AIDS. Are they aware of people who have had such diseases and the effect it has had on them? After the discussion, have students read about sexually transmitted diseases that have no cure on page 247.

Ask:

- Which sexually transmitted diseases have no cure? (AIDS, genital herpes)

- What is genital herpes? (Genital herpes is a sexually transmitted disease that is a chronic infection.)

## Action for Health

Encourage each student to write on a sheet of paper a way for communicating "no." Have students fold the papers. Collect the papers. Read each way aloud one by one. Then have the class evaluate and discuss each way of communicating "no."

Have students read about gonorrhea on page 248.

Ask:

· **What is gonorrhea?** (Gonorrhea is a sexually transmitted disease that often has no symptoms.)

· **When symptoms do appear in males, what are they?** (Symptoms are a white discharge from the urethra and burning while urinating.)

· **When symptoms appear in females, what are they?** (Symptoms are a vaginal discharge and some swelling and redness in the genital area.)

· **Why is gonorrhea dangerous?** (Gonorrhea is dangerous because many infected people have no symptoms. Untreated gonorrhea can cause sterility.)

## MULTICULTURAL CONNECTION

Native Americans first caught sexually transmitted diseases from European explorers, starting from the time of Columbus's first voyages to the Caribbean. Challenge groups of students to research diseases transmitted during Columbus's time. Invite students to present their research in a report.

---

### Action for Health

**PRACTICE SAYING "NO"**

Some teenagers experience peer pressure to have sexual activity. But it is a smart decision to decide not to have sex. If you decide to abstain from sex, you may need to tell others of your decision. You will need to express yourself in ways that are very clear to others so that they understand your wishes. Make a list of different ways you can communicate "no" to someone who thinks you should have sexual relations.

**Gonorrhea**
*A sexually transmitted disease that often has no symptoms*

**Penicillin**
*An antibiotic used to treat diseases such as gonorrhea*

**Native Americans often contracted sexually transmitted diseases from Europeans. Why were the diseases particularly harmful to Native Americans?**

### What are Other Sexually Transmitted Diseases?

Other sexually transmitted diseases can be cured if they are discovered early. But if these diseases are not treated, they can lead to other serious health problems.

**Gonorrhea**

The most commonly reported infectious disease in the United States is **gonorrhea**. At least two million cases occur each year. Gonorrhea is sexually transmitted. It can also be passed to babies of infected women as the babies pass through the birth canal. Gonorrhea can cause an eye infection in babies that may lead to blindness.

In males, the symptoms are a white discharge from the urethra and burning while urinating. Females may have a vaginal discharge and some swelling and redness in the genital area.

Gonorrhea is dangerous because many infected people have no symptoms. Most females have no symptoms. From 20 to 40 percent of males have no symptoms either. If gonorrhea is not treated, it can cause sterility. Sterility is the inability to have children.

Gonorrhea can be treated successfully with the antibiotic **penicillin**. Penicillin destroys the bacteria that cause the disease. If a person thinks he or she may have gonorrhea, many health clinics can diagnose and treat the disease.

**248**    *Chapter 12   Preventing AIDS and Sexually Transmitted Diseases*

Chlamydia
*A sexually transmitted disease that often has no symptoms*

Syphilis
*A sexually transmitted disease that has three stages*

## Chlamydia

The symptoms of **chlamydia** are like those of gonorrhea. There may be a discharge from the urethra in males or from the vagina in females. Usually, however, females have no symptoms. Like gonorrhea, this disease can pass from a mother to her baby during birth. Chlamydia can cause an eye infection in babies that leads to blindness. Chlamydia can be treated with an antibiotic.

## Syphilis

If **syphilis** is not treated, it passes through three stages. In the first stage, there is a small, painless, hard sore with a small amount of yellow discharge. The sore appears on the penis, anus, or rectum in men; on the cervix and genital areas in women. In the second stage, there is a rash and sometimes headache, loss of appetite, and other symptoms. During the third stage, the symptoms disappear for many years. But the disease is still there. It can damage the heart and brain.

Syphilis is passed from one person to another through sexual contact. It can pass from a woman to her baby before the baby is born. Syphilis is easily diagnosed by a blood test. A medical professional can also look through a microscope at a sample taken from a sore. Syphilis can be treated with antibiotics.

*Health Tip*

If you avoid sexual contact, you have almost no chance of getting a sexually transmitted disease.

Talk to a medical professional immediately if you think you have a sexually transmitted disease.

### How Are Sexually Transmitted Diseases Prevented?

All newborns are given eye medicine after birth to prevent eye infections that might be caused by sexually transmitted diseases.

Most states require people to have blood tests before they can get a marriage license. The test identifies diseases such as syphilis. Then the diseases can be treated with antibiotics such as penicillin.

*Preventing AIDS and Sexually Transmitted Diseases   Chapter 12*   **249**

Have students read about chlamydia and syphilis on page 249.

Ask:

- What is chlamydia? (Chlamydia is a sexually transmitted disease that often has no symptoms.)

- If there are symptoms of chlamydia, what are they likely to be? (There may be a discharge from the urethra in males or from the vagina in females.)

- What is syphilis? (Syphilis is a sexually transmitted disease that has three stages.)

- How can chlamydia and syphilis be treated? (Chlamydia and syphilis can be treated with antibiotics.)

## APPLICATION

**Career Connection** Inform students about the role of the Centers for Disease Control and Prevention (CDC) in helping to prevent and control communicable diseases in the United States. Have students research the CDC in the library and by visiting their web site at www.cdc.gov. Encourage students to describe the various branches of the CDC.

## LEARNING STYLES

**Group Learning** Divide the class into groups. Assign each group a different sexually transmitted disease to research. Include syphilis, gonorrhea, genital herpes, chlamydia, vaginitis, scabies, and pubic lice. Encourage students to create a Public Service Announcement (PSA) for the prevention of the disease they choose, based on their research. PSAs can be done on videotape. Invite students to present their PSAs to the class.

## Careers

Invite a laboratory assistant from a local hospital, clinic, diagnostic laboratory, or pharmaceutical company to speak to the class about what he or she does and the training needed for the job. Invite students to prepare questions that they would like answered in advance of the guest's visit.

Have students read about how sexually transmitted diseases are prevented on page 250.

## Lesson 2 Review Answers

1) AIDS and genital herpes have no cure.
2) AIDS, genital herpes, gonorrhea, chlamydia, and syphilis can be passed from a woman to her baby.
3) It is important to diagnose sexually transmitted diseases quickly because some of the diseases can be cured if they are detected early.
4) AIDS, gonorrhea, and chlamydia may have no symptoms in the early stages. Gonorrhea and chlamydia may never show symptoms.
5) The spread of sexually transmitted diseases can be stopped by avoiding sexual contact.

## BACKGROUND INFORMATION

Research shows that 25 percent of the population has some type of sexually transmitted disease. Some sexually transmitted diseases are caused by viruses, such as human papilloma virus (HPV), which causes genital warts and is a precursor of cervical cancer. HPV is a cauliflower-like growth that occurs on the cervix, vagina, mouth, rectum, or penis. The warts can be treated with an acid called TCA, removed with laser surgery, or frozen (cryotherapy). Despite these treatments, the virus stays in a person's body for life.

---

**Careers**

### LABORATORY ASSISTANT

Do you like to look through microscopes at tiny organisms? Then you might want to be a laboratory assistant. Laboratory assistants work with medical technicians. They look at samples of human fluids and tissues for organisms that cause disease. They report all situations that do not appear normal so that doctors can treat diseases. Laboratory assistants also help to keep medical equipment working properly. They must also protect themselves from disease. They wear disposable gloves and other protective clothing. You need one or two years of college to become a laboratory assistant.

Many health clinics emphasize the diagnosis and treatment of sexually transmitted diseases. The people who work at these clinics know that the possibility of having such a disease can be embarrassing. They protect the identity of their patients.

**LESSON 2 REVIEW** Write the answers to these questions on a separate sheet of paper. Use complete sentences.

1) Which sexually transmitted diseases have no cure?
2) Which sexually transmitted diseases can be passed from a woman to her baby?

### Writing About Health

What would you say to a friend who is thinking about starting a sexual relationship? Write how you could warn your friend about the dangers of this activity.

3) Why is it important to diagnose sexually transmitted diseases quickly?
4) Which diseases mentioned in this lesson often have no symptoms?
5) How can the spread of sexually transmitted disease be stopped?

---

Name _____ Date _____ Period _____    Chapter 12 Activity 43

**Sexually Transmitted Diseases**

**Directions** Match each item on the left with the correct item on the right. Write the correct letter on each blank. Each item on the right may be used once, more than once, or not at all.

_____ 1) Chlamydia is one example
_____ 2) Antibiotic that kills gonorrhea germs
_____ 3) Inability to have children
_____ 4) Passed from mother to baby before birth
_____ 5) This disease is similar to gonorrhea
_____ 6) Can cause an eye infection in babies
_____ 7) A painless, hard sore is one symptom
_____ 8) Lasting
_____ 9) Any diseases spread through sexual activity
_____ 10) Two million cases per year
_____ 11) Blisters in the genital area are a symptom
_____ 12) Symptoms of gonorrhea
_____ 13) May be identified by a blood test
_____ 14) May lead to cancer of the cervix
_____ 15) A disease that progresses in three stages

a) chancre
b) chronic
c) gonorrhea
d) mumps
e) sexually transmitted diseases
f) sterility
g) penicillin
h) discharge
i) treatment
j) syphilis
k) measles
l) herpes
m) chlamydia
n) stomach
o) influenza

**Activity 43**

---

Name _____ Date _____ Period _____    Chapter 12 Workbook Activity 43

**Sexually Transmitted Diseases**

**Part A Directions** Place a check mark beside all answers that apply.

1) Which are sexually transmitted diseases?
   a) herpes, AIDS, gonorrhea, syphilis, chlamydia
   b) gonorrhea, syphilis, chlamydia, chancre, penicillin
   c) syphilis, chlamydia, trachoma, AIDS, chancre
   d) trachoma, chancre, penicillin, herpes, AIDS

2) Gonorrhea:
   a) is the most commonly reported infectious disease in the U.S.
   b) if left untreated, progresses to three stages.
   c) can cause swelling and redness in the genitals.
   d) is slow to develop and difficult to diagnose.

3) Syphilis:
   a) is the most commonly reported infectious disease in the U.S.
   b) if left untreated, progresses to three stages.
   c) can be spread from pregnant woman to fetus.
   d) is slow to develop and difficult to diagnose.

4) STDs that are easily cured are:
   a) chlamydia, herpes, gonorrhea.
   b) chlamydia, gonorrhea, syphilis.
   c) AIDS, gonorrhea, syphilis.
   d) herpes, AIDS, syphilis.

**Part B Directions** Write T if the statement is true or F if it is false.

_____ 5) Genital herpes is a chronic disease.
_____ 6) AIDS is a sexually transmitted disease.
_____ 7) Herpes is easily cured with penicillin.
_____ 8) A small, painless, hard sore that appears on a person infected with syphilis.
_____ 9) Painful blisters on a person's genitals may indicate an active case of herpes.
_____ 10) Males infected with gonorrhea can become sterile if the disease is not treated promptly.
_____ 11) Gonorrhea can cause an eye infection in babies.
_____ 12) If a person acquires one STD, he or she is immune to other STDs.
_____ 13) Physicians have no treatment to offer patients with AIDS or herpes.
_____ 14) Chlamydia and gonorrhea have similar symptoms.
_____ 15) Blood tests before marriage can help detect STDs.

**Workbook Activity 43**

■ AIDS (acquired immunodeficiency syndrome) is a communicable and life-threatening disease. It is caused by HIV (human immunodeficiency virus).

■ HIV, which causes AIDS, is spread through certain body fluids.

■ A person can contract AIDS during sexual activity or by using an infected needle.

■ A woman with AIDS can pass the disease to her baby.

■ People previously got AIDS through blood transfusions. Now the U.S. blood supply is safer because blood can be tested for HIV.

■ The first symptoms of AIDS are minor. As the disease progresses, the person can get serious diseases such as pneumonia and Kaposi's sarcoma.

■ A person with HIV may not show any symptoms for six to ten years.

■ There is no cure for AIDS. It can be prevented by avoiding contact with body fluids that may be infected with HIV.

■ A sexually transmitted disease is spread through sexual contact.

■ Two sexually transmitted diseases that are not curable are AIDS and genital herpes.

■ The symptoms of genital herpes are painful blisters in the genital area.

■ Gonorrhea often has no symptoms. It can be treated with the antibiotic penicillin. If not treated, it can cause sterility in adults or blindness in babies.

■ Chlamydia often has no symptoms and is treated with antibiotics. It can cause blindness in babies.

■ An infected woman can pass a sexually transmitted disease to her baby.

■ People who suspect they may have sexually transmitted diseases can be tested at health clinics. They can also receive treatment at health clinics.

*Preventing AIDS and Sexually Transmitted Diseases* Chapter 12 **251**

■ **Using the Chapter Summary**
To further reinforce the facts and concepts presented in the chapter, read and discuss with students the questions that follow.

Ask:

• What is AIDS? (AIDS is a communicable and life-threatening disease caused by HIV.)

• How can a person contract AIDS? (A person can contract AIDS during sexual activity or by using an infected needle.)

• How can AIDS be prevented? (AIDS can be prevented by avoiding contact with body fluids that may be infected with HIV.)

• How does a sexually transmitted disease spread? (through sexual contact)

• What are the symptoms of genital herpes? (A person with genital herpes has painful blisters in the genital area.)

• Why is it sometimes difficult for people to know they have gonorrhea or chlamydia? (Gonorrhea and chlamydia often have no symptoms.)

• Why is it important for people with gonorrhea to receive treatment? (It is important for people with gonorrhea to receive treatment because gonorrhea can lead to sterility in adults or blindness in babies.)

• What can happen to people who have sexual contact with others who have sexually transmitted diseases? (People who have sexual contact with those who have sexually transmitted diseases can get the diseases themselves.)

• What should people do if they suspect they may have a sexually transmitted disease? (People should be tested and receive treatment.)

# Chapter 12 Review

The Teacher's Resource Library includes two parallel forms of the Chapter 12 Mastery Test. The difficulty level of the two forms is equivalent. You may wish to use one form as a pretest and the other form as a posttest.

## Review Answers

### Comprehension: Identifying Facts

**1)** immune **2)** virus **3)** cancer
**4)** HIV positive **5)** Kaposi's sarcoma
**6)** transfusion **7)** Sterility **8)** discharge
**9)** herpes **10)** gonorrhea **11)** Chlamydia

---

## Comprehension: Identifying Facts

On a separate sheet of paper, write the correct word or words from the Word Bank to complete each sentence.

| WORD BANK | |
|---|---|
| abstinence | HIV positive |
| antibiotics | immune |
| cancer | Kaposi's sarcoma |
| chlamydia | sterility |
| discharge | syphilis |
| gonorrhea | transfusion |
| herpes | virus |

**1)** AIDS is a disease of the _____ system.

**2)** AIDS is caused by a _____ called HIV.

**3)** A person with AIDS may get a kind of _____ called Kaposi's sarcoma.

**4)** If a person has AIDS, a blood test will show that the person is _____.

**5)** _____ is a rare type of cancer that affects the skin or internal organs.

**6)** A person can receive a _____, in which blood is transferred from one person to another.

**7)** _____ is the inability to have children.

**8)** The first symptom of gonorrhea may be a _____.

**9)** The first symptoms of genital _____ are painful blisters.

**10)** The disease of _____ can lead to sterility.

**11)** _____ can cause an eye infection in babies that leads to blindness.

---

Name _____ Date _____ Period _____ | Chapter 12 Mastery Test A page 1

**Chapter 12 Mastery Test A**

***Directions*** Circle the response that *best* completes each sentence.

**1)** AIDS is a serious disease of the _____
a) digestive system.
b) immune system.
c) cardiovascular system.
d) endocrine system.

**2)** AIDS is caused by the HIV virus, which invades the body through the _____
a) bloodstream.
b) nose.
c) hands.
d) central nervous system.

**3)** A person with AIDS can have many _____, such as cancer or pneumonia.
a) activities
b) fluids
c) signals
d) diseases

**4)** Avoiding sexual contact is the best way to prevent _____
a) cancer.
b) abstinence.
c) sexually transmitted diseases.
d) transfusions.

**5)** There is no _____ for AIDS.
a) cure
b) reason
c) blood
d) contact

**6)** _____ is the inability to have children.
a) Chlamydia
b) Discharge
c) Syphilis
d) Sterility

**7)** One symptom of genital _____ is painful blisters.
a) gonorrhea
b) herpes
c) HIV
d) pneumonia

TRL ©AGS® American Guidance Service, Inc. Permission is granted to reproduce for classroom use only. | Discover Health

---

Name _____ Date _____ Period _____ | Chapter 12 Mastery Test A page 2

**Chapter 12 Mastery Test A, continued**

**8)** Gonorrhea, chlamydia, and syphilis can be treated with _____
a) sterility.
b) abstinence.
c) antibiotics.
d) transfusions.

**9)** An infected woman can pass a sexually transmitted disease to her _____
a) baby.
b) cat.
c) dog.
d) clinic.

**10)** Chlamydia and gonorrhea often have no _____
a) treatment.
b) cause.
c) symptoms.
d) transmission.

**11)** In the second state of _____, there is a rash, headache, and loss of appetite.
a) AIDS
b) syphilis
c) chlamydia
d) genital herpes

**12)** If not treated, the disease of _____ can cause sterility in adults.
a) herpes
b) pneumonia
c) virus
d) gonorrhea

**13)** _____ can cause an eye infection in babies that leads to blindness.
a) HIV
b) Genital herpes
c) Chlamydia
d) Sterility

**14)** People who suspect they may have sexually transmitted diseases can be treated at _____
a) health clinics.
b) home.
c) school.
d) diagnosis.

**15)** Now the _____ in the United States is safer because it can be tested for HIV.
a) chlamydia
b) number of health clinics
c) rate of sexually transmitted diseases
d) blood supply

TRL ©AGS® American Guidance Service, Inc. Permission is granted to reproduce for classroom use only. | Discover Health

**Chapter 12 Mastery Test A**

**12)** In the second stage of _____, there is a rash, headache, and loss of appetite.

**13)** Gonorrhea, chlamydia, and syphilis can be treated with _____.

**14)** Sexually transmitted diseases can be prevented by _____.

## Comprehension: Understanding Main Ideas

Write the answers to these questions on a separate sheet of paper. Use complete sentences.

**15)** List some ways that a person can get AIDS.

**16)** If someone contracts HIV, how quickly will symptoms of AIDS appear?

**17)** How are the symptoms of gonorrhea and chlamydia similar?

**18)** How do health clinics help people who think they may have a sexually transmitted disease?

## Critical Thinking: Write Your Opinion

**19)** How could you show caring and concern for a person who has AIDS?

**20)** Do you think all pregnant women should be tested for sexually transmitted diseases?

**Test Taking Tip** If you don't know the answer to a question, put a check beside it and go on. When you have finished the other questions, go back and try the questions with checks again.

---

*Preventing AIDS and Sexually Transmitted Diseases* Chapter 12 **253**

**12)** syphilis  **13)** antibiotics
**14)** abstinence

## Comprehension: Understanding Main Ideas

**15)** A person can get AIDS through sexual activity, using an infected needle, or through a blood transfusion with infected blood.

**16)** It may take six to ten years for AIDS symptoms to appear.

**17)** Both diseases have a discharge as a symptom. Both diseases may show no symptoms at all.

**18)** Health clinics can test for sexually transmitted diseases and provide treatment.

## Critical Thinking: Write Your Opinion

**19)** Answers will vary. Students may say you can show care and concern for a person who has AIDS by offering to help, by visiting or volunteering at hospices, or by contributing to campaigns to raise money for research.

**20)** Answers will vary. Students may say that all pregnant women should be tested for sexually transmitted diseases so that the baby can be protected. Other students may say that it would be very difficult to do so.

---

## Introducing the Chapter

Brainstorm the names of various famous
people who have been diagnosed with
diseases covered in this chapter, such as
cancer, cardiovascular disease, or diabetes.
Discuss with students the fact that these
diseases can strike anyone, regardless of
age, gender, or race.

Read the chapter opener with the class.
Then discuss the material, as well as the
Goals for Learning.

### Ask:

• What are some common diseases you
hear about on the news or among your
family and friends? (Answers will vary.
Students might mention cancer or heart
disease.)

• Do you think you can have an effect on
whether or not you get a disease such as
cancer or heart disease? (Answers will vary.
Accept all reasonable answers as a basis
for discussion.)

# Chapter 13

# Common Diseases

*I*f you are like most people your age, your health is
excellent. And, like most things that are worth doing,
keeping your body healthy will take some effort on your
part. The decisions you make now about the foods you eat
and the habits you form will influence your risk of developing
certain diseases.

In this chapter, you will learn about some noncontagious
diseases, what causes them, and how they are treated. You
will also find out how to reduce your risk of developing
some of these diseases.

### Goals for Learning

▶ To find out about cardiovascular diseases and what
causes them

▶ To identify certain types of cancer and how to
prevent them

▶ To explain how asthma affects the respiratory system

▶ To compare and contrast different types of diabetes

▶ To learn about arthritis

▶ To discover what causes epileptic seizures and what to
do if someone has a seizure in your presence

(TRL) **Student Study Guide 19, page 1**

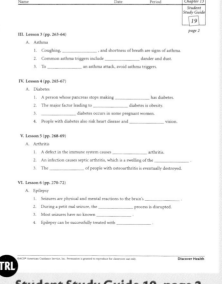

(TRL) **Student Study Guide 19, page 2**

## Cardiovascular Disease

Cardiovascular disease
*A disease of the heart and blood vessels*

Hypertension
*High blood pressure*

Diseases that affect the heart and blood vessels are called **cardiovascular diseases**. These diseases are common among people in the United States. In fact, they affect one in four people, or more than sixty-eight million Americans. These diseases of the circulatory system are the number one cause of death in the United States. Someone dies from these types of diseases every thirty-two seconds.

### What Is High Blood Pressure?

One common cardiovascular disease is high blood pressure, or **hypertension**. Blood presses against the walls of your arteries as your heart pumps blood throughout your body. This force is called blood pressure. Blood pressure usually increases when you exercise or are excited. Blood pressure normally goes down when you sleep or relax. When a person's blood pressure stays high, even at rest, the person has high blood pressure.

High blood pressure often leads to heart disease because it causes the heart to pump harder than it normally would. High blood pressure also causes the smooth artery walls to become rough. Thus, the heart has to work harder to move the blood through these thickened, irregular channels.

**Nutrition Tip**

Monitor your intake of salt (sodium). You only need 2,400 mg of this mineral each day.

Aerobic exercise and a healthy diet are two ways to reduce the risk of cardiovascular diseases.

*Common Diseases*   *Chapter 13*   **255**

---

• What is hypertension? (high blood pressure)

• How does high blood pressure lead to heart problems? (High blood pressure leads to heart problems because it causes the heart to pump harder than it normally would.)

---

**Lesson at a Glance**

## Chapter 13  Lesson 1

**Overview** In this lesson, students learn about cardiovascular diseases and the risk factors for developing them.

### Objectives

■ To find out about cardiovascular diseases and what causes them.

**Student Pages** 255–258

**Audiocassette**

**Human Body Transparency 7**

**Teacher's Resource Library**

    Activity 44

    Workbook Activity 44

## Teaching Suggestions

### ■ Vocabulary

*cardiovascular disease, hypertension, arteriosclerosis, atherosclerosis, heart attack, stroke, risk factor*

Write the vocabulary words on the chalkboard. Ask students which of the words they have heard. Have them explain what they think the words mean. Then read and review each definition with students.

### ■ Teaching the Lesson

Display a model or diagram that shows the human circulatory system. Ask students how the circulatory system works. (The heart pumps blood throughout the body. The blood carries oxygen and nutrients to certain parts of the body and removes wastes from others.) Ask students what would happen to the body if a disease caused this system to break down. (Students will probably say that this would be a serious problem that could cause illness or death.) Then tell students they are going to read about diseases that affect this system on page 255.

Ask:

• What is a cardiovascular disease? (A cardiovascular disease is a disease that affects the heart and blood vessels.)

*Common Diseases*   *Chapter 13*   **255**

Have students read about other diseases of the arteries on page 256.

Ask:

- What is arteriosclerosis? (Arteriosclerosis is a chronic disease in which the walls of the arteries thicken.)

- Arteriosclerosis can lead to another disease called atherosclerosis. What is atherosclerosis? (Atherosclerosis is a narrowing of the arteries due to a buildup of fat.)

- How can atherosclerosis be prevented ? (Atherosclerosis can often be prevented by eating a healthy diet low in fats.)

## APPLICATION

**At Home**
Encourage students to check the fat content of an evening meal with their families. Remind students that only 30 percent of their daily calories should come from fat. Have students use the knowledge of food labels and foods with high fat content gained from Unit 3 to estimate the percentage of calories in the evening meal that comes from fat. Ask students to bring the results of their meal reviews to class. Discuss whether the meal contains more fat than is healthy.

**Arteriosclerosis**
*A chronic disease in which the walls of the arteries thicken*

**Atherosclerosis**
*A narrowing of the arteries due to a buildup of fat*

## What Are Some Other Diseases of the Arteries?

At birth, the walls of the arteries are smooth. Over many years, however, fat can collect along these walls. This fat hardens and prevents blood from flowing normally through the arteries. **Arteriosclerosis** is a chronic disease in which the walls of the arteries thicken. The disease also causes the arteries to become rigid. This is why the process that leads to the disease is commonly called "hardening of the arteries."

Arteriosclerosis can cause other diseases. One of these is **atherosclerosis**, which causes large arteries to narrow because of fat buildup along their walls. The buildup narrows the pathway for blood. This, in turn, slows down the flow of blood to the heart. The blood then thickens and could cause blood clots to form. Blood clots block a vessel so much that the amount of oxygen flowing to the heart is greatly decreased. Atherosclerosis can often be prevented by eating a healthy diet low in fats. A blocked artery is shown in Figure 13.1.

**Research has shown that many children today have atherosclerosis. Why do you think this is so?**

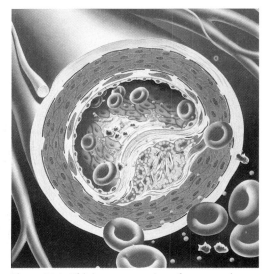

**Figure 13.1.** This is a cutaway view of an artery that has become blocked with fat.

**Why do you think heart transplants are rarely used to treat heart attack victims?**

## What Is a Heart Attack?

Like all the muscles in your body, your heart needs oxygen and other nutrients. A **heart attack** occurs when the supply of blood or other nutrients is greatly reduced or blocked. If a heart attack is mild, only a small amount of tissue is damaged.

People who survive heart attacks often have to take medicine to prevent other attacks. A change in diet, daily exercise, and regular checkups are important to heart attack survivors.

## What Is a Stroke?

Another cardiovascular disease is a **stroke**. A stroke occurs when the blood supply to a person's brain is suddenly blocked. Damaged arteries or blood clots can cause strokes. High blood pressure may also cause a stroke.

After a stroke, parts of the body may not be able to function as they once did. Some strokes are mild. In these situations, the victims will notice little change in body functions. Other strokes are severe and may prevent the person from doing certain activities. If the part of the brain that controls speech, for example, is damaged, the person might not be able to speak. Therapy is useful for people who have had strokes.

### Careers

### OCCUPATIONAL THERAPY ASSISTANT

Do you think you would like to help people who have lost some movement of their bodies due to strokes? If so, you might like a career as an occupational therapy assistant. You would work with other medical professionals to help patients perform everyday tasks. Some stroke victims must relearn how to dress themselves, cook, feed themselves, talk, or walk. An occupational therapy assistant also helps patients deal with stress. If the assistant sees that therapy is not helping the person, he or she must suggest ways to change the treatment. There are some one-year training programs for occupational therapy assistants. A two-year degree, or associate degree, however, is usually preferred.

Have students read about heart attack and stroke on page 257.

Ask:

- What is a heart attack? (A heart attack is a condition in which the blood supply to the heart is greatly reduced or stopped.)

- What can a person who has had a heart attack do to prevent having another one? (People who have had a heart attack often take medication to prevent additional attacks. They also try to eat a healthier diet, exercise, and see their doctors regularly.)

- What causes a stroke? (Damaged arteries, blood clots, or high blood pressure can cause a stroke.)

- How can severe strokes cause permanent disabilities? (Severe strokes prevent a person from doing certain activities. For example, if the part of the brain that controls speech is damaged, a person may not be able to speak after a stroke.)

## Careers

Discuss with students what it would be like to lose a bodily function that they take for granted, such as the ability to speak or to walk. Then discuss the types of qualities an occupational therapist would have to possess to help someone work through such problems. Also discuss the possible rewards of this kind of career. If possible, have an occupational therapist visit the class. Have students prepare questions in advance of the visit.

### APPLICATION

**In the Community**
People who have had heart attacks often go through a rehabilitation program that includes exercise. Suggest that students get brochures from a hospital, clinic, or doctor's office in the community that describes a rehabilitation program for people with heart disease. Encourage students to describe how the programs improve people's health.

Have students read about the risk factors for cardiovascular disease on page 258.

- **What is a risk factor?** (A risk factor is a trait or habit that increases a person's chances of having or getting a disease.)

## Lesson 1 Review Answers

1) Hypertension is high blood pressure. It can lead to a heart attack because it causes the heart to pump harder than it normally would.
2) Arteriosclerosis is a chronic disease in which the walls of the arteries thicken.
3) After a mild heart attack, only a small amount of the heart's tissue is damaged.
4) Risk factors that are inherited cannot be changed. Lifestyle risk factors are the result of choices that can be changed.
5) Accept all reasonable answers. Students might reason that stress could make a person eat or snack more, which could increase the amount of fat in their diet and cause them to gain weight to increase.

## LEARNING STYLES

**Group Learning** Have students send for pamphlets and other information from organizations that are concerned with decreasing the incidence of cardiovascular disease in the United States, such as the American Heart Association. When the materials come, encourage students to write a news letter explaining cardiovascular disease, reviewing its risk factors, and telling people what they can do about it.

## MULTICULTURAL CONNECTION

African-Americans have a higher incidence of high blood pressure than the American population in general. Tell students to review their own cultures and family backgrounds to discover any factors that might promote or prevent cardiovascular disease.

---

> **Risk factor**
> *A trait or habit that increases a person's chances of having or getting a disease*

### Fitness Tip

**Do some kind of aerobic exercise every day, especially if cardiovascular disease runs in your family.**

## What Are the Risk Factors for Cardiovascular Diseases?

A **risk factor** is a trait or a habit that is known to increase a person's chances of having a disease. Some risk factors are inherited and cannot be changed. These factors are called genetic factors. Other risk factors are related to lifestyle choices. These can be changed. The section below lists some genetic and lifestyle risk factors for cardiovascular diseases. Are you or anyone in your family at risk for these diseases?

### Some Cardiovascular Risk Factors

- Having family members with cardiovascular diseases increases your chances of having these diseases. Take the time to find out about your family's health history.
- Being male also increases your risk of a heart attack before you reach middle age. After middle age, a woman's risk of heart attacks also increases.
- Aging increases a person's risk of having a heart attack. More that half of all heart attacks occur in people who are 65 or older.
- Race can also increase a person's risk of cardiovascular diseases. African Americans, for example, have a greater rate of hypertension than Caucasians.

**LESSON 1 REVIEW** Write the answers to these questions on a separate sheet of paper. Use complete sentences.

1) What is hypertension and why can it lead to a heart attack?
2) What is arteriosclerosis?
3) What happens to a person's heart after a mild heart attack?
4) Compare and contrast risk factors that are inherited and those related to lifestyle.
5) How might stress influence risk factors that could lead to cardiovascular diseases?

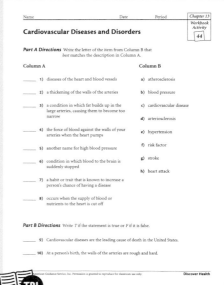

**Activity 44**          **Workbook Activity 44**

**Benign tumor**
*A mass of cells that are not harmful*

**Cancer**
*A group of diseases marked by the abnormal and harmful growth of cells*

**Malignant tumor**
*A mass of cells that are harmful*

**Metastasize**
*Spread cancer to distant tissues*

Cancer is a group of more than one hundred diseases marked by the abnormal and harmful growth of cells. Cancer is the second leading cause of death in the United States. Cancer can develop in any tissue in the body. Some types of cancer remain in the tissues where they started. Some cancers "travel" in the blood or lymph fluids. They move to other parts of the body that are far from the original site. When cancer spreads to distant tissues, it is said to have **metastasized**.

Some cancers grow and form masses of abnormal cells called tumors. **Benign tumors** are masses of cells that are not harmful. Over 90 percent of all tumors are benign. **Malignant tumors**, on the other hand, are harmful masses that invade normal tissue. They often spread to other organs in the body.

### What Are Some Symptoms and Warning Signs of Cancer?

The symptoms of cancer vary according to the type of tissue affected by the disease. A person with lung cancer, for example, might have a cough that doesn't get better with medical treatment. A woman with breast cancer might feel a lump in her breast. Blood in the stool may be a sign of cancer in the intestines or the colon.

A type of cancer might not have a particular symptom. But seven general warning signs could indicate cancer. These are listed in the chart at the left. Look at the letter that begins each phrase. What word do these letters spell?

---

**THE SEVEN WARNING SIGNS OF CANCER**

**C** hange in bowel or bladder habits

**A** sore that will not heal

**U** nusual bleeding or discharge

**T** hickening or lump in the breast or elsewhere

**I** ndigestion or difficulty in swallowing

**O** bvious change in a wart or mole

**N** agging cough or hoarseness

---

## Chapter 13  Lesson 2

**Overview** In this lesson, students learn about the symptoms of cancer, some common types of cancer, and treatments for cancer.

### Objectives

- To identify certain types of cancer.
- To identify the warning signs of cancer.
- To describe different ways cancer is treated.

**Student Pages** 259–262

**Audiocassette**

**Teacher's Resource Library**

Activity 45
Workbook Activity 45

## Teaching Suggestions

### ■ Vocabulary

*benign tumor, cancer, malignant tumor, metastasize, chemotherapy, radiation*

Write the vocabulary words on the chalkboard and ask students to provide definitions based on prior knowledge. Then read the definitions aloud from the text. Have students compare their previous ideas with the actual definitions.

### ■ Teaching the Lesson

Ask students what the following quotation means: "Violence is like a cancer in our society." (Students should reason that violence is spreading quickly throughout our society, but accept all reasonable answers.) Ask students to look at the way the word *cancer* is used in the sentence and try to relate the meaning of the sentence to the actual disease. (Students should suggest that the disease is destructive, deadly, and that is spreads quickly.)

Have students read about cancer and its warning signs on page 259.

**Ask:**

- What is cancer? (Cancer is a group of diseases marked by the abnormal and harmful growth of cells.)

- What are the seven warning signs of cancer? (The seven warning signs of cancer are change in bowel or bladder habits, a sore that will not heal, unusual bleeding or discharge, thickening or lump in the breast or elsewhere, indigestion or difficulty in swallowing, obvious change in a wart or mole, and nagging cough or hoarseness.)

Have students read about some common kinds of cancer on page 260.

Ask:
_____

Have students use the chart on page 260 to answer the following questions.

- What is the most common type of cancer in men? (prostate gland cancer)

- What is the most common type of cancer in women? (breast cancer)

- What is the second most common type of cancer in both men and women? (lung cancer)

- Name three factors that can increase a woman's chance of getting breast cancer. (having a female relative who has or had the disease, having no children, having children later in life)

- At what age do men usually develop prostate cancer? (over the age of 65)

**GLOBAL CONNECTION**

Tell students that different types of cancer are more common in some countries than in others. Encourage students to compare and contrast the types of cancer that are most common in the United States with those that are most common in several other countries. For example, in Asia the most common fatal form of cancer in the past was stomach cancer, but lung cancer has risen rapidly with the spread of cigarette smoking on that continent. Allow students to choose the countries with which to make comparisons. Challenge students to find out why the differences exist. Students can then share their findings by giving reports to the class.

## What Are Some Common Kinds of Cancer?

Chances are you or someone you know either has some type of cancer or will get it. In fact, according to the American Cancer Society, one in three persons has cancer or is at risk of developing the disease. While there are over one hundred different kinds of cancers, some types are common. The chart below shows the cancer incidence by site and sex.

### Breast Cancer

One in eight American females will develop breast cancer during her life. Women whose female relatives had or have the disease are at an increased risk of developing breast cancer. Also, women who have a child by age 30 are less likely to develop the disease than childless women. Having children later in life can increase a woman's chances of developing breast cancer.

### Prostate Cancer

Prostate cancer is the most common cancer in men. One in eleven American men will get the disease. Most cases of prostate cancer occur in men over the age of 65. In these situations, the disease often develops slowly. Men in their 40s and 50s also get the disease. But it grows more rapidly in men in this age group.

### Lung Cancer

The leading cause of death due to cancer in both males and females is lung cancer. What make this statistic so unfortunate is that lung cancer is one of the few cancers that can be prevented. Over 85 percent of people with lung cancer develop the disease because they smoke.

**Cancer Incidence by Site and Sex**

| Men | Women |
|---|---|
| Prostate Gland 184,500 | Breast 178,700 |
| Lung 91,400 | Lung 80,100 |
| Colon & Rectum 64,600 | Colon & Rectum 67,000 |
| Urinary Bladder 39,500 | Uterus 36,100 |
| Non-Hodgkin's Lymphoma 31,100 | Ovary 25,400 |
| Skin—Melanoma 24,300 | Non-Hodgkin's Lymphoma 24,300 |
| Mouth 20,600 | Skin—Melanoma 17,300 |
| Kidney 17,600 | Urinary Bladder 14,900 |
| Blood 16,100 | Pancreas 14,900 |
| Stomach 14,300 | Cervix 13,700 |
| All Sites 627,900 | All Sites 600,700 |

*Source: American Cancer Society, Inc., 1998.*

**Figure 13.2.** Different types of cancers are more common in women than in men and vice versa.

**Chemotherapy**
*A cancer treatment that uses drugs to kill cancer cells*

**Radiation**
*A type of treatment that uses energy waves to destroy cancer cells*

Smoking is a lifestyle choice. Don't give in to peer pressure and start smoking. If you do smoke, even occasionally, stop immediately. If people you know smoke, encourage them to get help to quit.

### Skin Cancer

Skin cancer is the most common type of cancer in the United States. About 600,000 new cases of this kind of cancer occur in the United States each year. Most skin cancer is caused by harmful radiation from the sun and the lights used in tanning booths.

### How Is Cancer Treated?

There are three basic kinds of treatment for cancer. One common method of cancer treatment is to use drugs that destroy cancer cells. This type of treatment is called **chemotherapy**.

Another form of cancer treatment is **radiation**, which uses energy waves to destroy cancerous tissue. Radiation is often used to treat some forms of thyroid cancer. It is also used to treat small cancerous masses that have not metastasized.

A third treatment for cancer is surgery. Surgery involves removing the cancer cells and any nearby tissue that the cancer may have affected. Surgery is commonly used to treat skin cancers.

**A sunburn you get as a child can cause problems when you become an adult. What does this tell you about the damage that the sun's rays do to skin?**

**Then and Now**

### CANCER SURVIVAL RATES

In the early 1900s, people with cancer almost always died from the disease or complications related to the disease. Today, however, almost 60 percent of all people under the age of 55 who have cancer will be alive five years after the diagnosis. Although there is no cure for cancer, this statistic is considered a cure. According to the American Cancer Society, more than five million people alive today have had cancer.

Have students read about other kinds of cancer and how cancer is treated on page 261.

Ask:

- What causes most skin cancer? (harmful radiation from the sun and the lights used in tanning booths)

- Name the three basic kinds of treatment for cancer. (chemotherapy, radiation, surgery)

- What is chemotherapy? (Chemotherapy is a cancer treatment that uses drugs to kill cancer cells.)

- What is radiation? (Radiation is a cancer treatment that uses energy waves to destroy cancer cells.)

- Why is it unnecessary for so many people to die of lung cancer? (It can easily be prevented by not smoking.)

### Then and Now

Do students know family members, friends, or acquaintances who have survived cancer? Have students conduct interviews with the cancer survivors to find out the type of cancer they had, how they found out they had it, and what treatment helped them recover. These should be positive stories with lessons for students about early detection and the fact that cancer can be overcome. Have students read their interviews in class.

### LEARNING STYLES

**Group Learning** Have groups of students visit drug stores and supermarkets to look at the labels on containers of sunburn protection products. Tell students to find out what ingredients are helpful in protecting the skin against harmful ultra violet (UV) radiation and which are not. Encourage students to report on whether any of the products are making false claims on their labels. Invite students to make presentations to the class. (Good sunscreens should have an SPF of at least 15. Cocoa butter, coconut oil, and baby oil offer no protection.)

## Lesson 2 Review Answers

1) Cancer is a group of diseases marked by the abnormal and harmful growth of cells.

2) A benign tumor is not harmful. A malignant tumor is a mass of cancerous cells that is harmful and invades normal tissue.

3) The seven warning signs of cancer are change in bowel or bladder habits, a sore that will not heal, unusual bleeding or discharge, thickening or lump in the breast or elsewhere, indigestion or difficulty in swallowing, obvious change in a wart or mole, and nagging cough or hoarseness.

4) Most cases of lung cancer are caused by smoking and can be prevented by not smoking.

5) The three basic kinds of treatment for cancer are the following: chemotherapy, which uses drugs to kill cancer cells; radiation, which uses energy waves to destroy cancerous tissue; and surgery, which involves removing the cancer cells and nearby tissue.)

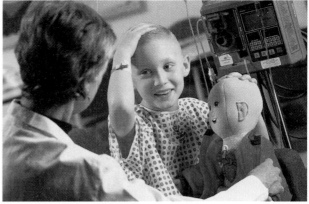

Why do you think it is necessary to wear sunscreen even on cloudy days?

People with cancer who have chemotherapy treatment can lose their hair. This hair loss is often just temporary.

**LESSON 2 REVIEW** Write the answers to these questions on a separate sheet of paper. Use complete sentences.

1) What is cancer?

2) What is the difference between benign and malignant tumors?

3) What are the seven warning signs of cancer?

4) What causes lung cancer and how can this disease be prevented?

5) Describe the three basic kinds of treatment for cancer.

Suppose a health care plan decides to charge double rates for smokers. Do you think this is fair? Explain your reasons.

**262** Chapter 13 Common Diseases

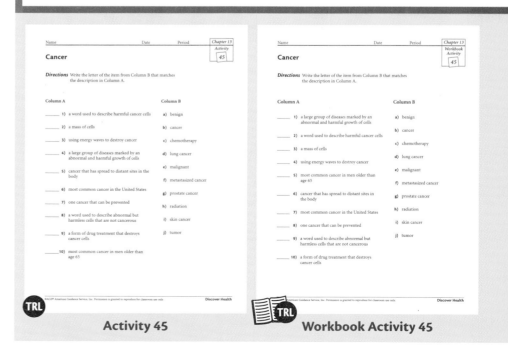

Activity 45          Workbook Activity 45

## Asthma

**Asthma**
*A disease that affects the lungs, making it difficult to breathe*

**A**sthma is a disease that affects the lungs, making it difficult to breathe. During an asthma attack, a person may cough, wheeze (make a whistle-like sound), and be short of breath. These reactions are due to the swelling and blockage of the airways that carry air from the nose and mouth to the lungs. Asthma attacks can occur as often as once every few hours. Some attacks happen only once every few years.

A person can develop asthma at any age, but the disease commonly affects children. Nearly 12.5 million Americans have asthma. Well over one-third of these people are under the age of 18.

### What Triggers Asthma?

*Why is exercise a common asthma trigger?*

Many things and situations trigger asthma. These triggers are different for different people. They also may affect the same people in different degrees at different times. The box below lists some of the most common asthma triggers.

---

**COMMON ASTHMA TRIGGERS**

- Pollen from flowers, trees, and grasses
- Paints and similar chemicals
- Mold spores
- Animal dander
- Household dust
- Cleaning products
- Dirty air filters in heating or cooling vents
- Perfumes, deodorants, cosmetics, and other scented toiletries
- Foods such as eggs, dairy products, fish, and peanuts
- Hard exercise
- Air pollutants
- Cigarette smoke

---

*Common Diseases* Chapter 13 **263**

---

## Chapter 13 Lesson 3

**Overview** In this lesson, students learn about the causes of asthma and things that can cause an asthma attack.

## Objectives

- To explain how asthma affects the lungs.
- To identify ways to prevent asthma attacks

**Student Pages** 263–264

**Audiocassette**

**Teacher's Resource Library**

   Activity 46
   Workbook Activity 46

## Teaching Suggestions

### ■ Vocabulary

*asthma*

Review the definition of the vocabulary word with students. Although asthma is a common disease, students may have misconceptions about it. Have students write down a question they would like to have answered about asthma. Tell students to look for the answer as they read the lesson.

### ■ Teaching the Lesson

Pass out two straws to each student— a thick straw and a thin straw or coffee stirrer. Tell students to first breathe through the thick straw, then try breathing through the thin straw. They should note that it is harder to breathe through the thin straw. Explain that this difficulty is similar to what a person with asthma would feel during an attack.

Have students read about the causes of asthma on page 263.

---

**Ask:**

- What is asthma? (Asthma is a disease that affects the lungs, making it hard to breathe.)

- What happens inside the body that makes it difficult for someone having an asthma attack to breathe? (During an asthma attack, the airways that carry air from the nose and mouth to the lungs swell and become partially blocked.)

Have students read about ways to prevent asthma attacks on page 264.

Ask:

- What is the best way for asthma sufferers to avoid an attack? (to avoid things and situations that trigger asthma)

- Why do you think asthma sufferers, such as the person in the picture, use inhalers to relieve their symptoms? (Students should reason that the medicine in the inhaler releases something into the air passages that helps to open them up and allow more air to pass through.)

## Lesson 3 Review Answers

1) Asthma is a disease that affects the lungs, making it hard to breathe.
2) During an asthma attack, the air passages that carry air from the nose and mouth to the lungs swell and become blocked.
3) Accept any five of the following: pollen; paints, mold spores; animal dander; dust; cleaning products; dirty air filters; perfumes, deodorants, cosmetics, and other scented toiletries; foods such as eggs, dairy products, fish, and peanuts; hard exercise; air pollutants; cigarette smoke.)
4) The best way to prevent an asthma attack is to avoid things and situations that trigger asthma.
5) To prevent asthma attacks, you can keep the sleeping area clean and dust-free, put pillows and mattresses in plastic, and wash linens in hot water every week.

## APPLICATION

### Environment
Inform students that recent research shows that asthma attacks are often caused by environmental air pollutants, such as particulates—commonly known as soot. The main sources of particulates are trucks, buses, and some factories. Encourage students to map the areas in your community where particulates are found. Discuss the implications for people who live, go to school, or play in these areas.

A person can get asthma at any age, but it often affects children.

## How Is Asthma Treated?

Without treatment, asthma can be life threatening. The best way to prevent an attack is to avoid things and situations that trigger asthma. It may be hard to avoid many of the common triggers. But keeping the sleeping area clean and dust-free is an important way to prevent attacks. Putting pillows and mattresses in plastic also helps to prevent severe attacks. Washing bed linens in hot water every week kills dust mites in the linens.

**LESSON 3 REVIEW** Write the answers to these questions on a separate sheet of paper. Use complete sentences.

1) What is asthma?
2) What happens during an asthma attack?
3) List five common asthma triggers.
4) What is the best way to prevent an asthma attack?
5) What are some things you can do to prevent asthma attacks?

---

| Name | | Date | Period | Chapter 13<br>Activity<br>46 |

**Asthma**

**Directions** Write *T* if the statement is true or *F* if it is false.

_____ 1) There are fewer than five triggers for asthma.

_____ 2) One trigger of asthma can be strenuous exercise.

_____ 3) During an asthma attack, the airways in the nose and mouth become swollen.

_____ 4) Asthma commonly affects adult over the age of 21.

_____ 5) Asthma is a disease that attacks the heart.

_____ 6) Asthma can be life threatening if left untreated.

_____ 7) Asthma causes mucus to be produced in the lungs.

_____ 8) People with asthma should avoid pollen and dust.

_____ 9) Asthma is caused only by nonfood items.

_____10) Asthma affects different people differently.

©AGS® American Guidance Service, Inc. Permission is granted to reproduce for classroom use only.                    Discover Health

**Activity 46**

---

| Name | | Date | Period | Chapter 13<br>Workbook<br>Activity<br>46 |

**Asthma**

**Directions** Write *T* if the statement is true or *F* if it is false.

_____ 1) Asthma is a disease that attacks the heart.

_____ 2) There are fewer than five triggers for asthma.

_____ 3) One trigger of asthma can be strenuous exercise.

_____ 4) During an asthma attack, the airways in the nose and mouth become swollen.

_____ 5) Asthma commonly affects adults over the age of 21.

_____ 6) Asthma affects different people differently.

_____ 7) Asthma can be life threatening if left untreated.

_____ 8) Asthma causes mucus to be produced in the lungs.

_____ 9) People with asthma should avoid pollen and dust.

_____10) Asthma is caused only by nonfood items.

American Guidance Service, Inc. Permission is granted to reproduce for classroom use only.                    Discover Health

**Workbook Activity 46**

Type I diabetes
*Insulin-dependent diabetes*

Diabetes is a group of conditions in which sugar levels are much higher than normal. A person develops diabetes when the pancreas stops producing insulin or doesn't produce enough. Insulin is a hormone that is used by the body to use digested food effectively. Without insulin, the body could not use glucose, a type of sugar, as a source of energy. Glucose would stay in the bloodstream and not be able to enter the cells where it is needed.

About sixteen million people in the United States are thought to have diabetes. Only about half of these people have actually been diagnosed with the condition.

People with diabetes can lead normal lives.

### What Is Type I Diabetes?

There are three types of diabetes. **Type I diabetes**, which is also known as insulin-dependent diabetes, is most common in children. The pancreas of a person with this type of diabetes produces little or no insulin. This happens because the body's immune system has destroyed all of the cells that produce this hormone.

One of the most common symptoms of type I diabetes is frequent urination. Other symptoms include increased thirst and hunger. Extreme tiredness and unexplained loss of weight are other symptoms of type I diabetes.

*Common Diseases    Chapter 13*    **265**

---

Ask:

• What is diabetes? (Diabetes is a group of conditions in which sugar levels are much higher than normal.)

• What role does insulin play in keeping sugar levels normal in your body? (Insulin is a hormone that is used by the body to use digested food effectively.)

• What is one of the most common symptoms of type I diabetes? (frequent urination)

---

Have students read about the other types of diabetes on page 266.

Ask:

- What is believed to be the major factor that leads to type II diabetes? (being grossly overweight)

- If a 12-year-old child has diabetes, which types is it likely to be? (A 12-year-old child probably has type I diabetes because this type begins in childhood.)

- If a pregnant woman develops diabetes, which type is it most likely to be? (A pregnant woman is most likely to have gestational diabetes because it develops during gestation, or pregnancy.)

## BACKGROUND INFORMATION

People who have diseases that could require special care in a medical emergency can wear ID bracelets or neck tags. Information about a person's medical condition and numbers to call in an emergency are engraved on the bracelet or tag. For more information, contact MedicAlert at 1-800-342-2383.

---

**Gestational diabetes** *Diabetes that develops during pregnancy*

**Type II diabetes** *Non-insulin-dependent diabetes*

### How Is Type I Diabetes Monitored?

People with diabetes must always balance their diets, exercise, and insulin to control their blood sugar levels. Blood glucose devices let a person know if his or her blood sugar level is too high or too low. A drop of blood is placed on a special strip. The strip can be read either visually or by a meter. Visual checking involves matching the color of the strip with a standard chart. A person can get a digital reading of his or her blood sugar level with a meter. This method is more accurate than the visual method.

### What Is Type II Diabetes?

The second type of diabetes is non-insulin-dependent, or **type II, diabetes**. Between 90 and 95 percent of all cases of the disease are of this type. It is currently not known what causes type II diabetes. But scientists believe that being grossly overweight is the major factor that leads to type II diabetes. Studies show that with this milder form of diabetes, cells "see" the insulin. However, they are unable to "read" its signal to break down the glucose.

When trying to diagnose type II diabetes, a doctor will look at a person's family history to see if diabetes runs in the family. A doctor will also determine if a person's weight might contribute to developing the disease. Thirst and frequent urination may be other symptoms of this type of diabetes. Blood and urine tests are also performed to determine if excess glucose is in these fluids.

### What Is Gestational Diabetes?

The third type of diabetes is called **gestational diabetes**. This is because the condition occurs during gestation, or pregnancy. Gestational diabetes often goes away when the pregnancy is finished. The cause of this type of diabetes is related to the nutritional needs of the developing baby. This type of diabetes usually develops about midway through pregnancy. Gestational diabetes is treated by changing the woman's diet. Some women, however, need to use insulin. Women who have had gestational diabetes can develop type II diabetes later in life.

## What Are Some Health Problems Associated With Diabetes?

Like many diseases, diabetes can cause other health problems. Heart disease is the most common life-threatening disease linked to diabetes. In fact, a person with diabetes has two to four times the risk of developing heart disease. People with diabetes also have a much higher risk of stroke and high blood pressure.

Nerve disease is another health problem common among people with diabetes. About 60 to 70 percent of people with diabetes have mild to severe forms of nerve damage. The damage can cause an impaired feeling in the feet or hands. Severe nerve disease related to diabetes can result in the amputation of the feet or legs.

Diabetes can affect the eyes in many ways. Blurred vision is a common problem among people with diabetes. **Cataracts** and **glaucoma** are eye diseases that occur more often in people with diabetes. Cataracts are a clouding of the lens of the eye. Glaucoma is a disease in which pressure can damage the main nerve of the eye. Blindness can be another complication due to diabetes. Between twelve and twenty-four thousand people with diabetes lose their vision each year in the United States.

**LESSON 4 REVIEW** Write the answers to these questions on a separate sheet of paper. Use complete sentences.

1) What is diabetes?

2) What causes type I diabetes?

3) What are some symptoms of diabetes?

4) Explain some of the health problems associated with diabetes.

5) What is gestational diabetes? How is it treated?

Have students read about health problems associated with diabetes on page 267.

Ask:

- List three health problems that can develop as the result of diabetes. (heart disease, nerve damage, vision problems such as cataracts and glaucoma)

- What are cataracts? (Cataracts are a clouding of the lens of the eye.)

- What is glaucoma? (Glaucoma is an eye disease in which pressure can damage the main nerve of the eye.)

## Lesson 4 Review Answers

1) Diabetes is a group of conditions in which blood sugar levels are much higher than normal.

2) Type I diabetes occurs because the body produces little or no insulin.

3) Symptoms of diabetes include frequent urination, excessive thirst or hunger, extreme tiredness, and unexplained weight loss.

4) Health problems associated with diabetes include a higher risk of developing cardiovascular problems such as heart disease, stroke, and high blood pressure. People with diabetes also risk nerve damage that can lead to loss of feeling in feet or hands, or amputation of feet or legs. People with diabetes can also develop eye problems such as cataracts and glaucoma.

5) Gestational diabetes is diabetes that develops during pregnancy. It is treated by changing the woman's diet. Some women need to use insulin.

---

**Activity 47**

Name _____ Date _____ Period _____  Chapter 13 Activity 47

**Diabetes**

*Directions* Write the letter of the item from Column B that matches the description in Column A.

Column A

____ 1) a group of conditions that cause a high level of sugar in the blood

____ 2) an important hormone, necessary to digest food

____ 3) the name for the chemical source of sugar your body uses to give you energy

____ 4) clouding of the lens of the eye

____ 5) first recognized during pregnancy and no longer present afterwards

____ 6) may cause amputation of hands or feet

____ 7) may be controlled by diet, exercise, and insulin

____ 8) may be caused by obesity and run in families

____ 9) diabetes results when this gland stops making insulin

____ 10) eye disease caused by pressure inside the eye

Column B

a) cataracts

b) diabetes

c) gestational diabetes

d) glaucoma

e) glucose

f) insulin

g) pancreas

h) severe nerve damage

i) Type I diabetes

j) Type II diabetes

---

**Workbook Activity 47**

Name _____ Date _____ Period _____  Chapter 13 Workbook Activity 47

**Diabetes**

*Directions* Write the letter of the item from Column B that matches the description in Column A.

Column A

____ 1) first recognized during pregnancy and no longer present afterwards

____ 2) a group of conditions that cause a high level of sugar in the blood

____ 3) an important hormone, necessary to digest food

____ 4) the name for the chemical source of sugar your body uses to give you energy

____ 5) clouding of the lens of the eye

____ 6) eye disease caused by pressure inside the eye

____ 7) may cause amputation of hands or feet

____ 8) may be controlled by diet, exercise, and insulin

____ 9) may be caused by obesity and run in families

____ 10) diabetes results when this gland stops making insulin

Column B

a) cataracts

b) diabetes

c) gestational diabetes

d) glaucoma

e) glucose

f) insulin

g) pancreas

h) severe nerve damage

i) Type I diabetes

j) Type II diabetes

## Lesson at a Glance

### Chapter 13 Lesson 5

**Overview** In this lesson, students learn about the various types of arthritis and how they affect the body.

### Objectives

- To describe arthritis and some of its treatments.

**Student Pages** 268–269

**Audiocassette**

**Teacher's Resource Library** **TRL**

Activity 48

Workbook Activity 48

---

## Teaching Suggestions

### ■ Vocabulary

*arthritis, chronic disease, rheumatoid arthritis, rheumatoid factor, osteoarthritis, septic arthritis*

Ask students to break into pairs. Have one student read a definition of a vocabulary word and a partner name the word that matches the definition. Have the pairs continue the process until all the words are reviewed. The students can then switch roles and repeat the activity.

### ■ Teaching the Lesson

Review the skeletal system and the function of joints with students. Ask them how the way they function would change if they felt pain in their joints whenever they moved. What things would they be unable to do or would they find difficulty doing? Then have students read about arthritis on page 268.

Ask:

- What is arthritis? (Arthritis is a group of diseases marked by swollen and painful joints.)

- What are some causes of arthritis? (Arthritis may be caused by aging, bacteria or viruses, or a defect in a person's immune system.)

---

**Arthritis**
*A group of diseases marked by swollen and painful joints*

**Chronic disease**
*A disease that lasts a long time*

**Rheumatoid arthritis**
*A type of arthritis caused by a defect in the immune system*

**Rheumatoid factor**
*The antibody associated with rheumatoid arthritis*

**What kind of treatment might be used to treat severe cases of arthritis?**

**A**rthritis is a group of diseases marked by swollen and painful joints. About forty million Americans have arthritis. Like diabetes and asthma, arthritis is a chronic disease. A **chronic disease** is a disease that lasts for a long time. Most chronic diseases have no cure. With medical care and treatment, however, chronic diseases can be managed.

There are three main types of arthritis. Each has a different cause. One type is thought to be a consequence of aging. Bacteria or viruses cause a second type of arthritis. A third type of arthritis is thought to result from a defect in a person's immune system.

### What Is Rheumatoid Arthritis?

**Rheumatoid arthritis** is a condition caused by a defect in the immune system. The immune system of the affected person reacts to the body's own tissues as if they were foreign. The antibody associated with rheumatoid arthritis is called the **rheumatoid factor**. Once it is activated, inflammation of the connective tissue between the joints occurs. The buildup of scar tissue that replaces the membranes and cartilage in the joints causes pain. The skin, bones, and muscles of the affected joints shrink and wither from disuse and destruction.

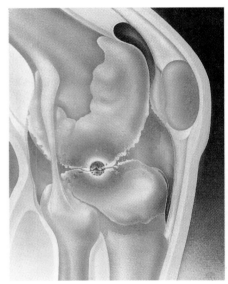

A human knee joint with osteoarthritis.

**268** *Chapter 13 Common Diseases*

**Osteoarthritis**
*A type of arthritis that causes a person's joints to get worse with age*

**Septic arthritis**
*A swelling of the joints caused by an infection*

Rheumatoid arthritis is three times more common in women than in men. The disease progresses gradually in most cases. Pain and stiffness in the joints are followed by swelling and muscle pain. Drugs are often prescribed to relieve pain and control the inflammation. Physical therapy and exercise can also relieve pain and swelling.

### What Is Septic Arthritis?

**Septic arthritis** is a swelling of the joints caused by an infection. Bacteria and viruses can cause joints to swell, feel sore, and fill with pus. Movement can be painful. Treatment of septic arthritis includes resting the affected joints, taking antibacterial and antiviral drugs, and therapy. If treatment is not provided in time, permanent damage to the joints occurs.

### What Is Osteoarthritis?

**Osteoarthritis** is a type of arthritis that causes a person's joints to get worse with age. Both posture and stress on the joints from weight play a major role in the start of the disease. Injury can also lead to this chronic disease.

In the first stages of osteoarthritis, the cartilage in the joints becomes soft. Over time, it is destroyed. Adjacent bones now have no protective covering. This makes the joints stiff, but moving the joints usually relieves the stiffness. Heat and medicines to relieve the inflammation and pain are used to treat this form of arthritis.

**Writing About Health**

Use what you have learned so far in this chapter to make a list of things to ask your doctor during your next checkup. Make sure you include at least two questions regarding each of these diseases: cardiovascular diseases, cancer, asthma, diabetes, and arthritis.

**LESSON 5 REVIEW** Write the answers to these questions on a separate sheet of paper. Use complete sentences.

1) What is arthritis?

2) Explain what happens to a person's joints when he or she develops rheumatoid arthritis.

3) What is septic arthritis?

4) What causes osteoarthritis?

5) Name the three types of arthritis and what causes them.

Have students read about the different types of arthritis on page 269.

**Ask:**

- What is the treatment for septic arthritis? (resting the affected joints, taking antibacterial and antiviral drugs, therapy)

## Lesson 5 Review Answers

1) Arthritis is a group of diseases marked by swollen and painful joints.

2) When someone develops rheumatoid arthritis, the connective tissue between the joints becomes inflamed. Gradually, the normal tissue in the joints is replaced by scar tissue.

3) Septic arthritis is a swelling of the joints caused by an infection.

4) Osteoarthritis develops from the long-term wear and tear on joints that causes their condition to worsen with age.

5) Rheumatoid arthritis is a condition caused by a defect in the immune system. Septic arthritis is a swelling of the joints caused by an infection. Osteoarthritis is a type of arthritis that causes a person's joints to get worse with age.

## APPLICATION

**Career Connection**
Have students find out how team coaches train the people on their teams to practice, exercise, and play sports without injuring their joints. Invite students to interview coaches and physical education teachers, or find information on the subject in the library or on the Internet.

---

**Arthritis**

Chapter 13 Activity 48

**Part A Directions** Write *T* if the statement is true or *F* if it is false.

_____ 1) Chronic diseases can be managed but not cured.

_____ 2) Rheumatoid arthritis occurs much more often in women than in men.

_____ 3) Bacteria and viruses can cause joints to swell and fill with pus.

_____ 4) In the first stage of osteoarthritis, the joints become soft.

_____ 5) Pain relievers and physical therapy can help in the treatment of rheumatoid arthritis.

**Part B Directions** Put a check mark next to the *best* answer.

6) Arthritis can be caused by _____
_____ a) aging.
_____ b) germs.
_____ c) a defect in the immune system.
_____ d) all of the above

7) A chronic disease _____
_____ a) lasts a long time.
_____ b) causes swelling of the joints.
_____ c) causes a person's joints to break down with old age.
_____ d) is caused by a defect in a person's immune system.

8) Septic arthritis _____
_____ a) lasts a long time.
_____ b) causes swelling of the joints.
_____ c) causes a person's joints to break down with old age.
_____ d) is caused by a defect in a person's immune system.

9) Rheumatoid arthritis _____
_____ a) lasts a long time.
_____ b) causes swelling of the joints.
_____ c) causes a person's joints to break down with old age.
_____ d) is caused by a defect in a person's immune system.

10) Osteoarthritis _____
_____ a) lasts a long time.
_____ b) causes swelling of the joints.
_____ c) causes a person's joints to break down with old age.
_____ d) is caused by a defect in a person's immune system.

**Activity 48**

---

**Arthritis**

Chapter 13 Workbook Activity 48

**Part A Directions** Put a check mark next to the *best* answer.

1) Arthritis can be caused by:
_____ a) aging.
_____ b) germs.
_____ c) a defect in the immune system.
_____ d) all of the above

2) A chronic disease:
_____ a) lasts a long time.
_____ b) causes swelling of the joints.
_____ c) causes a person's joints to break down with old age.
_____ d) is caused by a defect in a person's immune system.

3) Septic arthritis:
_____ a) lasts a long time.
_____ b) causes swelling of the joints.
_____ c) causes a person's joints to break down with old age.
_____ d) is caused by a defect in a person's immune system.

4) Rheumatoid arthritis:
_____ a) lasts a long time.
_____ b) causes swelling of the joints.
_____ c) causes a person's joints to break down with old age.
_____ d) is caused by a defect in a person's immune system.

5) Osteoarthritis:
_____ a) lasts a long time.
_____ b) causes swelling of the joints.
_____ c) causes a person's joints to break down with old age.
_____ d) is caused by a defect in a person's immune system.

**Part B Directions** Write *T* if the statement is true or *F* if it is false.

_____ 6) Chronic diseases can be managed but not cured.

_____ 7) Rheumatoid arthritis occurs much more often in women than in men.

_____ 8) Bacteria and viruses can cause joints to swell and fill with pus.

_____ 9) In the first stage of osteoarthritis, the joints become soft.

_____ 10) Pain relievers and physical therapy can help in the treatment of rheumatoid arthritis.

**Workbook Activity 48**

## Lesson at a Glance

### Chapter 13 Lesson 6

**Overview** In this lesson, students learn about epileptic seizures, what triggers them, and how epilepsy is diagnosed and treated. Students also learn how to help people who have seizures.

### Objectives

- To distinguish between the two types of epileptic seizures.
- To explain what causes epileptic seizures.

**Student Pages** 270–272

**Audiocassette**

**Teacher's Resource Library**

Activity 49

Workbook Activity 49

## Teaching Suggestions

### ■ Vocabulary

*epilepsy, grand mal seizure, seizure, petit mal seizure, febrile seizure*

Have students read the definitions of the vocabulary words. Then have students write an original paragraph containing all the words. Ask students to share their paragraphs by reading them aloud in class.

### ■ Teaching the Lesson

Ask students what they think of when someone says the word *epilepsy*. Write their statements on the board as they tell what they know about the disease. Leave the statements on the board as students read the lesson. Return to the statements after students have read the lesson to see how accurate students were in their ideas about epilepsy.

Have students read about epileptic seizures on page 270.

Ask:

- What is epilepsy? (Epilepsy is a chronic disease that is caused by disordered brain activity.)

---

## Lesson 6 — Epilepsy

**Epilepsy**
*A chronic disease that is caused by disordered brain activity*

**Grand mal seizure**
*A seizure that affects a person's motor skills*

**Seizure**
*A physical or mental reaction to disordered brain activity*

*E*pilepsy is a chronic disease that is caused by disordered brain activity. Epilepsy affects about 2.5 million people in the United States. The disease occurs more commonly in men than in women. Nearly three-fourths of affected people have their first attack before they are 20 years old.

### What Are Epileptic Seizures?

People with epilepsy have seizures. **Seizures** are physical or mental reactions to the brain's disordered activity. During a seizure, a person's mental functions can be disrupted. A person can become unconscious as a result of a seizure. During some seizures, parts of the person's body can move uncontrollably. Most epileptic seizures last fewer than several minutes. Contrary to popular belief, these seizures don't cause brain damage. Only seizures that last more than half an hour are considered dangerous.

There are different ways that epileptic seizures can be classified. One way is how a person reacts during the seizure. Other ways are where the seizure starts in the brain and the cause of the disordered brain function. There are two main types of epileptic seizures.

### What Is a Grand Mal Seizure?

The most common type of epileptic seizure is a **grand mal seizure**. During a typical grand mal, a person suddenly loses consciousness. If the person is standing or sitting, he or she will collapse and fall. The person's muscles will stiffen and relax in a repeating and uncontrollable manner. If the person's rib cage muscles are involved, air is forced from the person's lungs. This causes the person to make grunting sounds.

Sometimes, a person bites his or her tongue during a grand mal seizure because the jaw muscles might stiffen. However, a person cannot swallow his or her tongue during an epileptic seizure.

**270** Chapter 13 Common Diseases

---

- What happens to a person during a seizure? (During a seizure, a person can become unconscious, and parts of the person's body might move uncontrollably.)

- What is a grand mal seizure? (A grand mal seizure is a seizure that affects a person's motor skills.)

---

Petit mal seizure
A seizure that
affects a person's
mental functions

## What Is a Petit Mal Seizure?

A **petit mal seizure** is a less dramatic seizure than a grand mal seizure. Petit mal seizures generally last less than thirty seconds. In most cases, they aren't even noticeable to bystanders. The affected person may simply stare into space for a brief moment. He or she may drop an object that was being held. The person might seem momentarily confused or puzzled. Petit mal seizures originate in a part of the brain that controls thinking. Therefore, thought processes, not motor skills, are disrupted during these types of seizures.

---

### WHAT TO DO IF SOMEONE IS HAVING A GRAND MAL SEIZURE

- Move nearby objects to protect the person from getting hurt by the objects.
- Loosen the person's clothing.
- Place a cushion under the person's head.
- Turn the person's head to the side.
- *Do not* put any objects into the person's mouth.
- Call for help if the seizure lasts more than a few minutes.

---

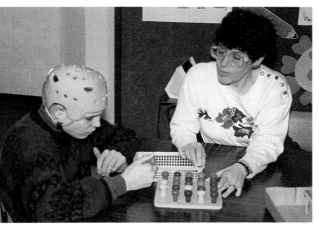

Children with epilepsy may wear protective equipment to avoid head injuries.

*Common Diseases* *Chapter 13* **271**

Have students read about petit mal seizure on page 271.

Ask:

- What is the difference between a grand mal seizure and a petit mal seizure? (Petit mal seizures disrupt thought processes rather than motor skills. Petit mal seizures are also less serious and last a shorter amount of time than grand mal seizures. In some very mild cases, petit mal seizures aren't even noticeable.)

- List six things you should do if someone near you is having a grand mal seizure. (Move nearby objects, loosen the person's clothing, place a cushion under the person's head, turn the person's head to the side, do not put any objects into the person's mouth, call for help if the seizure lasts more than a few minutes.)

### BACKGROUND INFORMATION

More than 90 percent of people who have seizures experience grand mal rather than petit mal seizures. A grand mal seizure begins with a loss of consciousness and falling to the ground. A rigid muscle period of fifteen to twenty seconds comes next, followed by a two-minute period of violent convulsions. When the seizure is over, the person slips into several minutes of calm sleep. When the person wakes up, he or she does not remember the seizure.

Have students read about the causes of seizures and the way epilepsy is diagnosed and treated on page 272.

Ask:

- What is a febrile seizure? (A febrile seizure is a seizure that is common in young children and results from a high fever.)

- How do doctors diagnose epilepsy? (To diagnose epilepsy, doctors examine medical history and conduct physical and neurological exams, including tests of blood and spinal fluid. The diagnosis often isn't made until after someone has had several seizures.)

- How do doctors treat epilepsy? (Epilepsy can be treated with medicines.)

- If a person's arms and legs are twitching while having a seizure, is the person having a grand mal or petit mal seizure? (The person is having a grand mal seizure.) How do you know? (The twitching of arms and legs involves the loss of motor control, which is the main characteristic of grand mal seizures.)

## Lesson 6 Review Answers

1) Epilepsy is a chronic disease caused by disordered brain activity.

2) During an epileptic seizure, a person's motor or mental functions are disrupted, resulting in loss of control of parts of the body, confusion, or unconsciousness.

3) Grand mal seizures involve the loss of motor control, while petit mal seizures involve a disruption of mental functions. Grand mal seizures are also more severe and last longer than petit mal seizures.

4) If a person is having a seizure, you should move nearby objects, loosen the person's clothing, place a cushion under the person's head, turn the person's head to the side, do not put objects into the person's mouth, and call for help if the seizures lasts more than a few minutes.

5) It is important to move nearby objects when a person is having a seizure to protect the person from getting hurt by the objects.

**Febrile seizure**
*A seizure that is common in young children*

## What Causes Seizures?

Seizures have many causes. Some well-known causes include tumors, injuries to the head, infections, and diseases that involve blood vessels in the brain. Most seizures, however, have no known cause.

In young children, the most common cause of a seizure is a high fever. Such a seizure is called a **febrile seizure**. These seizures decrease and eventually disappear with age. Febrile seizures are known to run in families. Children who have febrile seizures do not necessarily have epilepsy. A small fraction of these children do develop epilepsy later in life, however.

## How Is Epilepsy Diagnosed and Treated?

A diagnosis of epilepsy is often made when a person has had recurrent seizures. A doctor will also examine the person's medical history and conduct complete physical and neurological exams. Laboratory tests on the person's blood and spinal fluid are often used to confirm the disease.

Epilepsy can be successfully treated with medicines. Sometimes, a person will have seizures while taking the medication. Adjusting the amount of medicine usually will bring seizures under control. Once the proper amount of medicine is determined, seizures become less frequent.

Suppose a person is having an epileptic seizure. His legs and arms are twitching. Is he having a petit mal or grand mal seizure? Explain.

**LESSON 6 REVIEW** Write the answers to these questions on a separate sheet of paper. Use complete sentences.

1) What is epilepsy?

2) What happens during an epileptic seizure?

3) Explain the difference between grand mal and petit mal seizures.

4) What should you do to help a person who is having a seizure?

5) Why is it important to move nearby objects when a person is having a seizure?

Activity 49

Workbook Activity 49

■ Diseases that affect the heart and blood vessels are cardiovascular diseases.

■ High blood pressure, arteriosclerosis, and atherosclerosis are cardiovascular diseases.

■ A heart attack occurs when blood to the heart decreases or stops.

■ A stroke occurs when the blood supply to the brain is cut off.

■ Cancer is a group of about one hundred diseases marked by the abnormal and harmful growth of cells.

■ Benign tumors are masses of cells that are not harmful. Malignant tumors are harmful masses of cells that invade normal tissue.

■ Cancer is treated with radiation, chemotherapy, or surgery.

■ Asthma is a respiratory disease that makes it difficult to breathe.

■ Diabetes is a disease in which blood sugar levels are much higher than normal.

■ A person with type I diabetes must use insulin. This is because the pancreas produces little or none of this hormone.

■ In persons with type II diabetes, body cells "see" the insulin. But they are unable to "read" its signal to break down the glucose.

■ Gestational diabetes is a condition that occurs in some pregnant women.

■ Rheumatoid arthritis is a condition caused by a defect in the immune system. Septic arthritis is a swelling of the joints caused by an infection. Osteoarthritis causes a person's joints to get worse with age.

■ Epilepsy is caused by disordered brain activity.

■ During a grand mal seizure, a person loses control of motor skills. During a petit mal seizure, only a person's thought processes are disrupted.

■ Seizures can be caused by tumors, head injuries, infections, and diseases of the brain. Most seizures, however, have no known cause.

*Common Diseases    Chapter 13*    **273**

## ■ Using the Chapter Summary

To further reinforce the facts and concepts presented in the chapter, read and discuss with students the questions that follow.

### Ask:

• **What are cardiovascular diseases?** (Cardiovascular diseases are diseases that affect the heart and blood vessels.)

• **When does a heart attack occur?** (A heart attack occurs when blood to the heart decreases or stops.)

• **What are three methods of treating cancer?** (Chemotherapy, radiation, and surgery are three methods of treating cancer.)

• **What is asthma?** (Asthma is a respiratory disease that makes it difficult to breathe.)

• **What is diabetes?** (Diabetes is a disease in which blood sugar levels are much higher than normal.)

• **What is rheumatoid arthritis?** (Rheumatoid arthritis is a condition caused by a defect in the immune system.)

• **What things can cause seizures?** (Seizures can be caused by tumors, head injuries, infections, and diseases of the brain.)

## Chapter 13 Review

The Teacher's Resource Library includes two parallel forms of the Chapter 13 Mastery Test. The difficulty level of the two forms is equivalent. You may wish to use one form as a pretest and the other form as a posttest.

### Review Answers

#### Comprehension: Identifying Facts

**1)** type II diabetes **2)** arthritis **3)** type I diabetes **4)** Asthma **5)** stroke **6)** Atherosclerosis **7)** seizures **8)** Cancer **9)** Diabetes

---

### Comprehension: Identifying Facts

On a separate sheet of paper, write the correct word or words from the Word Bank to complete each sentence.

| WORD BANK | | |
|---|---|---|
| arthritis | grand mal seizure | stroke |
| asthma | | type I diabetes |
| atherosclerosis | petit mal seizure | type II diabetes |
| cancer | rheumatoid arthritis | |
| diabetes | | |
| epilepsy | seizures | |

1) A person with _____ is not dependent on insulin.

2) A group of diseases that cause joints to be stiff and painful is _____.

3) A person with _____ must take insulin.

4) _____ is a disease of the respiratory system.

5) A _____ occurs when blood to the brain is cut off.

6) _____ is a disease in which large arteries narrow because of fat buildup along their walls.

7) Disruptions in the body's physical or mental functions are called _____.

8) _____ is a group of diseases marked by the abnormal and harmful growth of cells.

9) _____ is a group of diseases in which the pancreas produces little or no insulin.

---

Name _____ Date _____ Period _____ | Chapter 13 Mastery Test A page 1

**Chapter 13 Mastery Test A**

**Directions** Circle the letter of the answer that *best* completes each sentence.

1) A common cardiovascular disease is high blood pressure, or _____
   a) arteriosclerosis.
   b) malignant tumor.
   c) hypertension.
   d) cancer.

2) _____ occurs when the supply of blood or other nutrients is greatly reduced or blocked.
   a) A heart attack
   b) Atherosclerosis
   c) A tumor
   d) Glaucoma

3) A stroke is a condition in which the blood supply to a person's _____ is suddenly blocked.
   a) heart
   b) lungs
   c) eyes
   d) brain

4) Risk factors that are inherited and cannot be changed are called _____ factors.
   a) lifestyle
   b) genetic
   c) race
   d) age

5) When cancer spreads to distant tissues, it is said to _____
   a) be benign.
   b) need chemotherapy.
   c) be malignant.
   d) have metastasized.

6) _____ is a cancer treatment that uses drugs to kill cancer cells.
   a) Chemotherapy
   b) Malignant therapy
   c) Radiation
   d) Surgery

7) A sore that will not heal and an _____ are among the seven warning signs of cancer.
   a) asthma attack
   b) interesting conversation
   c) obvious change in a wart or mole
   d) increase in exercise

©AGS® American Guidance Service, Inc. Permission is granted to reproduce for classroom use only.　Discover Health

---

Name _____ Date _____ Period _____ | Chapter 13 Mastery Test A page 2

**Chapter 13 Mastery Test A, continued**

8) _____ is a disease that affects the lungs, making it difficult to breathe.
   a) Diabetes
   b) Asthma
   c) Cataract syndrome
   d) Arthritis

9) A person with _____ must take insulin.
   a) epilepsy
   b) rheumatoid arthritis
   c) type 1 diabetes
   d) asthma

10) A group of diseases that cause joints to be stiff and painful is _____
   a) diabetes.
   b) epilepsy.
   c) cancer.
   d) arthritis.

11) Disruptions in the body's physical or mental functions are called _____
   a) strokes.
   b) seizures.
   c) diabetes.
   d) heart attacks.

12) _____ is a condition that occurs in some pregnant women.
   a) Gestational diabetes
   b) Asthma
   c) Epilepsy
   d) Stroke

13) A _____ seizure affects a person's muscles.
   a) petit-mal
   b) diabetes
   c) stroke
   d) grand-mal

14) Rheumatoid arthritis is a condition caused by a defect in the _____
   a) digestive system.
   b) endocrine system.
   c) immune system.
   d) nervous system.

15) Cataracts and _____ are eye diseases that occur more often in people with diabetes.
   a) glaucoma
   b) septic arthritis
   c) epilepsy
   d) asthma

©AGS® American Guidance Service, Inc. Permission is granted to reproduce for classroom use only.　Discover Health

**Chapter 13 Mastery Test A**

10) _____ is a type of arthritis caused by a defect in the immune system.

11) A disease caused by disordered brain activity is _____.

12) A _____ affects only the body's mental functions.

13) A _____ affects a person's muscles.

## Comprehension: Understanding Main Ideas

Write the answers to these questions on a separate sheet of paper. Use complete sentences.

14) How can you prevent cardiovascular diseases?

15) Compare and contrast some common cancers.

16) Distinguish among the three kinds of diabetes.

17) What are the causes of arthritis?

18) Explain the difference between grand mal and petit mal seizures.

## Critical Thinking: Write Your Opinion

19) What would you say to encourage someone to stop using tobacco?

20) Are you at risk for developing any of the diseases mentioned in this chapter? What can you do to reduce your risks?

**Test Taking Tip** Look for specifics in each question that tell you in what form your answer is to be. For example, some questions ask for a paragraph, and others may require only one sentence.

*Common Diseases* Chapter 13 **275**

10) Rheumatoid arthritis
11) epilepsy  12) petit mal seizure
13) grand mal seizure

## Comprehension: Understanding Main Ideas

14) Cardiovascular disease can be prevented by eating a healthy, low-fat diet, getting regular exercise, and seeing a doctor for regular check-ups.

15) Skin cancer and lung cancer are caused largely by lifestyle choices. Lung cancer is almost always the result of smoking, while skin cancer is caused by harmful rays from the sun and tanning lamps. Breast cancer is more likely for women whose relatives have had the disease. Prostate cancer often develops in men over the age of 65.

16) Type I diabetes results when the pancreas makes little or no insulin. In type II diabetes, the body makes insulin, but cells cannot recognize it and use it to break down glucose. Gestational diabetes is a type that occurs during pregnancy and is related to the nutritional needs of the growing baby.

17) The causes of arthritis are a defect in the immune system, bacteria and viruses, and wear and tear caused by aging.

18) Grand mal seizures affect a person's ability to control his or her muscles. A petit mal seizure affects a person's mental functions. Grand mal seizures are more intense and last longer than petit mal seizures.

## Critical Thinking: Write Your Opinion

19) Accept all reasonable answers. Students might suggest telling the person about the health problems tobacco can cause, such as lung cancer. Students might also mention that tobacco is addictive because it contains the drug nicotine.

20) Answers will vary, depending on the physical condition of students, their lifestyles, and their family medical histories.

**Chapter 13 Mastery Test B**

# Deciding for Yourself

Have students read "Applying Personal Health Habits" in the Deciding for Yourself lesson on page 276.

## Ask:

- How can infectious diseases be spread? (through direct contact with an infected person; by droplets coughed into air by an infected person; by contact with food or water that has been infected by a pathogen; through the bites of infected animals, such as insects)

- What are ways to avoid some contagious diseases? (Avoid close contact with people who have a cold or the flu. Keep your hands clean, and wash them before eating. Try not to put your fingers into your eyes or mouth. Do not borrow other people's utensils, dishes, toothbrushes, hairbrushes, or makeup.)

## Deciding for Yourself Answers

1) Flu can be spread from one person to another when people who have the flu come into contact with healthy people or release germs into the air by coughing.
2) Answers will vary, depending on the personal habits of students. Personal health habits students might mention include washing hands frequently, staying away from people who have colds or the flu, not touching eyes or mouth after touching objects in public places, and not using personal items of others.
3) People can avoid getting HIV by avoiding sexual contact.
4) Older people at nursing homes have a greater risk of getting infectious diseases because they live close together, sharing rooms as well as eating and recreational facilities.

## ■ Deciding for Yourself Activity

Have students complete the Unit 5 Deciding for Yourself Activity.

---

Deciding for Yourself

## Applying Personal Health Habits

You've read a great deal about how diseases are spread. Common infectious diseases may be spread in a number of different ways including:

- through direct physical contact with an infected person
- by droplets coughed into air by an infected person
- by contact with food or water that has been infected by a pathogen
- through the bites of infected animals, such as insects

You can cut down your chances of coming into contact with pathogens or passing them on to others. Of course, it is difficult to stay clear of certain pathogens, but the following steps will help you avoid some contagious diseases.

- Avoid close contact with people who have a cold or the flu.
- Keep your hands clean, and wash them before eating.
- Try not to put your fingers into your eyes or mouth.
- Do not borrow other people's utensils, dishes, toothbrushes, hairbrushes, or makeup.

## Questions

1) Why do you think the flu is so easily spread from one person to another?
2) What personal health habits do you do to avoid contagious diseases such as a cold or the flu?
3) Think about how HIV is spread. What can you do to avoid getting HIV?
4) Why do older people who are at nursing homes have a greater risk of getting infectious diseases?

**276** *Unit 5 Deciding for Yourself*

---

Name _____ Date _____ Period _____

Unit 5
Deciding for Yourself Activity
5

**Staying Healthy**

Think about your health habits. Put a check mark next to the things you do regularly. For each item you check, name a way that habit cuts down on your chances of getting sick. After finishing this unit, see if you are doing any other habits that you weren't at the beginning.

_____ Wash my hands before eating.

_____ Wash my hands after using the bathroom.

_____ Cover my mouth when I cough.

_____ Keep my hands away from my face.

_____ Avoid using other people's dishes, toothbrushes, hairbrushes, or makeup.

_____ Get eight hours of sleep each night.

_____ Exercise at least three times a week for twenty minutes.

_____ Use sun screen to protect myself from the sun's ultraviolet rays.

Think of other habits that would help you avoid disease or improve your overall physical fitness.

Do any hereditary diseases run in your family? If so, list some ways that you can improve your health to resist that disease. For example, what can you do to prevent heart disease if it runs in your family?

©AGS® American Guidance Service, Inc. Permission is granted to reproduce for classroom use only.                    Discover Health

**Deciding for Yourself Master 5**

■ Diseases can be acquired or inherited. Infection, human behaviors, or environmental conditions cause acquired diseases.

■ Diseases passed from one person to another are called infectious, contagious, or communicable.

■ The germs that cause acquired diseases are pathogens. The body is protected against pathogens through the skin, mucous membranes, stomach acids, coughing, and sneezing.

■ Acquired or inherited resistance to disease is called immunity. Vaccinations produce acquired immunity.

■ AIDS is a communicable disorder of the immune system caused by the HIV virus.

■ AIDS is spread through body fluids during sexual activity, by using infected needles, or from an infected mother to her baby.

■ Other sexually transmitted diseases are genital herpes, gonorrhea, chlamydia, and syphilis.

■ Cardiovascular diseases such as high blood pressure affect the heart and blood vessels. Heart attacks and strokes are the results of cardiovascular diseases.

■ Cancers are diseases marked by the abnormal and harmful growth of cells. Treatments for cancer include chemotherapy, radiation, and surgery.

■ Chronic disease affects a person for a long time. Examples of chronic diseases are asthma, diabetes, arthritis, and epilepsy.

■ Asthma is a respiratory disease. During an asthma attack, it is difficult to breathe.

■ In diabetes, sugar levels are much higher than normal. Some people with diabetes must use insulin because the pancreas doesn't produce enough of this hormone.

■ Arthritis results in swollen and painful joints. Rheumatoid arthritis is caused by a defect in the immune system. Septic arthritis is caused by an infection. Osteoarthritis is caused by loss of cartilage.

■ Epilepsy is caused by mental reactions to the brain's disordered activity. People with epilepsy have seizures in which they lose control of motor skills.

*Unit 5 Summary* **277**

## ■ Using the Unit Summary

To further reinforce the facts and concepts presented in the unit, read and discuss with students the questions that follow.

### Ask:

- **What causes acquired diseases?** (infection, human behaviors, environmental conditions)

- **How is the body protected against pathogens?** (through the skin, mucous membranes, stomach acids, coughing, sneezing)

- **What is AIDS and how does it spread?** (AIDS is a communicable disorder of the immune system caused by the HIV virus. AIDS is spread through body fluids during sexual activity, by using infected needles, or from an infected mother to her baby.)

- **What are cancers?** (Cancers are diseases marked by the abnormal and harmful growth of cells.)

- **What is asthma?** (Asthma is a respiratory disease that makes breathing difficult.)

- **What is diabetes?** (Diabetes is a condition in which sugar levels are much higher than normal.) **Why do some people with diabetes use insulin?** (Some people with diabetes use insulin because the pancreas doesn't produce enough of this hormone.)

- **What are the three causes of the swollen and painful joints that result from arthritis?** (a defect in the immune system, an infection, loss of cartilage)

- **What causes epilepsy?** (Epilepsy is caused by mental reactions to the brain's disordered activity.)

## Unit 5 Review

The Teacher's Resource Library includes a two-page Unit Mastery Test pictured on this page. Answers are in the Answer Keys beginning on page 433 of this Teacher's Edition.

### Review Answers

**Comprehension: Identifying Facts**

**1)** inherited **2)** pathogens **3)** antibodies
**4)** immunity **5)** infectious **6)** virus
**7)** sterility **8)** herpes **9)** gonorrhea

## Comprehension: Identifying Facts

On a separate sheet of paper, write the correct word or words from the Word Bank to complete each sentence.

| WORD BANK | | |
|---|---|---|
| antibodies | infectious | sterility |
| chemotherapy | inherited | stroke |
| gonorrhea | joints | tumors |
| herpes | pathogens | virus |
| immunity | pressure | |

**1)** Diseases can be either acquired or _____.

**2)** Germs called _____ cause acquired diseases.

**3)** The immune system produces _____ to fight infections.

**4)** A vaccination produces _____ by exposing the body to a dead or weakened virus.

**5)** Washing hands and cooking food properly can help prevent _____ diseases.

**6)** AIDS is caused by a _____ called HIV.

**7)** Some sexually transmitted diseases cause _____, the inability to have children.

**8)** Painful blisters in the genital area can be a symptom of _____.

**9)** Antibiotics can treat diseases such as _____ and syphilis.

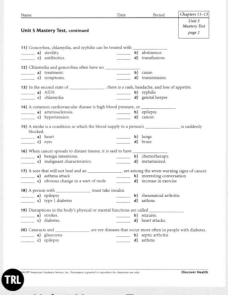

Unit 5 Mastery Test, page 1

Unit 5 Mastery Test, page 2

10) Hypertension is another name for high blood
_____.

11) When the blood to the brain is cut off, a person may have
a _____.

12) Arthritis causes stiff and painful _____.

13) Masses of cells that may be cancerous are
_____.

14) A person taking drugs for cancer is getting
_____.

## Comprehension: Understanding Main Ideas

Write the answers to these questions on a separate sheet of paper. Use complete sentences.

15) How does the body's immune system fight infection?

16) Name five sexually transmitted diseases. Explain which of these diseases are curable and which are not.

17) What are some risk factors for cancer?

18) How is a chronic disease like asthma different from a communicable disease?

## Critical Thinking: Write Your Opinion

19) Is it dangerous to be around someone who has AIDS? Explain why or why not.

20) How can someone reduce the risk of having a heart attack?

10) pressure  11) stroke  12) joints
13) tumors  14) chemotherapy

## Comprehension: Understanding Main Ideas

15) When a pathogen enters the bloodstream, the body produces antibodies, which are proteins that kill that particular pathogen. The antibodies help the body fight the illness. They then remain in the body to give immunity against the disease in the future.

16) AIDS, genital herpes, gonorrhea, chlamydia, and syphilis are sexually transmitted diseases. Gonorrhea, chlamydia, and syphilis can be treated with medicines and cured. AIDS and genital herpes have no cures.

17) Risk factors for breast cancer include having a close relative who has had the disease or being childless or having children later in life. Age is the main risk factor for prostate cancer because most men who get it are over 65. The main risk factor for lung cancer is smoking.

18) A chronic disease such as asthma lasts a very long time. Most chronic diseases have no cure and cannot be passed from person to person. A communicable disease is a disease that can be passed from person to person.

## Critical Thinking: Write Your Opinion

19) It is not dangerous to be around someone who has AIDS because AIDS can only be spread through direct contact with the body fluids of a person infected with HIV, such as by having sexual contact, sharing infected needles, or getting infected blood during a transfusion.

20) People can reduce the risk of having a heart attack by eating healthy diets that are low in fat, by getting regular exercise, and by seeing their doctor regularly for check-ups.

Unit 6

# Planning Guide

## Injury Prevention and Safety Promotion

| | Student Lesson: Student Pages | Vocabulary | Lesson Review | Writing About Health |
|---|---|---|---|---|
| ***Chapter 14 Preventing Injuries*** | 283–303 | | | |
| Lesson 1 Promoting Safety | 284–287 | • | • | • |
| Lesson 2 Reducing Risks of Fire | 288–290 | • | • | |
| Lesson 3 Safety for Teens | 291–294 | • | • | |
| Lesson 4 Emergency Equipment | 295–296 | • | • | |
| Lesson 5 Safety During Natural Disasters | 297–300 | • | • | |
| ***Chapter 15 First Aid for Injuries*** | 304–321 | | | |
| Lesson 1 What to Do First | 305–306 | • | • | |
| Lesson 2 Caring for Common Injuries | 307–310 | • | • | • |
| Lesson 3 First Aid for Bleeding, Shock, and Choking | 311–314 | • | • | |
| Lesson 4 First Aid for Heart Attacks and Poisoning | 315–318 | • | • | |
| ***Chapter 16 Preventing Violence*** | 322–337 | | | |
| Lesson 1 Defining Violence | 323–326 | • | • | |
| Lesson 2 Causes of Violence | 327–330 | • | • | |
| Lesson 3 Preventing Violence | 331–334 | • | • | • |

**Unit Activities**

**Home Connection**
**What Do You Think?**
**Deciding for Yourself**

**AGS-Related Resources**

**Discover Life Skills Handbook**
**Discover Healthy Sexual Development**

**Assessment Options**

**Student Text**
- **Lesson Reviews**
- **Chapter Reviews**
- **Unit Review**

**Teacher's Resource Library**
- **Chapter Mastery Tests**
- **Unit Mastery Test**

| | Student Text Features | | | | | | Teaching Strategies | | | | | | | Learning Styles | | | | | Teacher's Resource Library | | | |
|---|---|---|---|---|---|---|---|---|---|---|---|---|---|---|---|---|---|---|---|---|---|---|
| | Action for Health | Careers | Health, Fitness, and Nutrition Tips | Healthy Subjects | Then and Now | Technology | Background Information | Career Application | Community Application | Environment Application | Global Connection | Home Application | Multicultural Connection | Auditory | Group Learning | LEP/ESL | Tactile/Kinesthetic | Visual | Activities | Mastery Tests | Student Study Guide | Workbook Activities |
| | | | | | | | | | | | | | | | | | | | | • | • | |
| | | 287 | | 286 | | | 287 | | | | 285 | | 286 | 285 | | | | | | | | 50 |
| | 290 | | 289 | | | | | 289 | | | | | | | | | | | | | | 51 |
| | | | | | | | | | 292 | | | | | | | | 293 | | | | | 52 |
| | | | | | | | | | | | | | | | | | | 296 | | | | 53 |
| | | | 300 | | | | | | | | | 300 | | | | | 298 | | | | | 54 |
| | | | | | | | | | | | | | | | | | | | | • | • | |
| | | 305 | | | 306 | | | | | | | 306 | | | | | | | | | | |
| | 309 | 310 | 308 | | | | | | 308 | | 310 | | 309 | | | | 309 | | | | | |
| | | 314 | | | | | 313 | 312 | | | | | | 314 | | | 312 | 313 | | | | |
| | | | | 315 | | | 316 | | | 317 | | | | | | | | 316 | | | | |
| | | | | | | | | | | | | | | | | | | | | • | • | |
| | | | 325 | | | | | | | 324 | | 326 | | 325 | | | | | | | | |
| | | | 327 | 329 | 329 | | | | | | 328 | | | | | | 328 | | | | | |
| | 332 | 334 | | 331 | | | | 333 | 332 | | | 332 | | 333 | | | | | | | | |

## Block Scheduling

Here is a suggested teaching activity if you have extended instructional time, such as a block schedule.

**Gizmo Construction** *To invent and advertise an injury-reducing product.*

Consider all of the injuries and problems described in Chapters 14, 15, and 16. Invent a product not currently available that is designed to reduce the incidence of one or more injuries. Make a full-page newspaper advertisement promoting your product. Your advertisement must include: (1) product purpose, description, and use, (2) an illustration of your product, (3) a fictitious cost, and (4) a fictitious guarantee. If possible, actually construct your product and demonstrate it to the class.

### Unit 6:

### Injury Prevention and Safety Promotion
pages 280–341

### Chapters

### Audiocassette 🎧

### Teacher's Resource Library (TRL)

Unit 6 Home Connection
Master 6

Unit 6 What Do You Think?
Activity Master 6

Unit 6 Deciding for Yourself
Activity Master 6

Unit 6 Mastery Test

(Answer Keys for the Teacher's
Resource Library begin on page 433
of this Teacher's Edition.)

### Other Resources

#### Books for Teachers

Davis, Diane. *Working With Children
From Violent Homes.* Santa Cruz, CA:
ETR Associates (1-800-321-4407), 1986.

*Preventing Injuries and Violence Prevention,
Teenage Health Teaching Modules.* Waco,
TX: Health EDCO (1-800-299-3366).

#### Pamphlets for Students

*Dealing With Conflict, It's OK to Walk
Away.* Santa Cruz, CA: ETR Associates
(1-800-321-4407), 1994. (Shows how
young people can resolve conflict and
walk away from potential violence.)

*An ounce of prevention
is worth a pound of cure.*
—Proverb

#### Videos

*First Aid* (60 minutes). National Safety
Council, 1997. (Shows how to handle
real-life emergencies such as bleeding,
bone injuries, shock, and burns.)

*Kids Killing Kids/Kids Saving Kids*
(58 minutes). Minneapolis: Community
Intervention, Inc. (1-800-328-0417),
1994. (Award-winning drama shows the
consequences of using guns in response
to conflict and how young people use
programs to reduce violence and have
gun-free schools.)

### Home Connection Master 6

# Unit 6

# Injury Prevention and Safety Promotion

*A*re you prepared for an emergency? Do you know what to do if you or someone in your family has an accident? Knowing how to get help quickly in an emergency is a skill everyone needs. It's even better if you can prevent accidents from happening. But, accidents do happen. Most people have injuries due to accidents at some time.

Many accidents, particularly those in the home, can be prevented by simple safety precautions. In this unit, you will learn ways to help protect yourself and your family from accidental injury or injuries due to violence. You will read about ways to reduce the risk of injury and what you can do if an injury occurs.

## Introducing the Unit

Direct students' attention to the picture and the quotation on page 280. Read aloud the quotation.

Ask:

- What do you think the quote means? (that it is much better to prevent a problem from happening than to try to fix the results of the problem after it occurs)

- How does this idea relate to injuries or illnesses? (It is better to do something to prevent an injury or illness than to treat the injury or illness after it happens.)

- What safety equipment are the people in the canoes using? (life jackets) What are some other ways to stay safe in a canoe? (Answers might include not rocking the canoe, keeping the canoe in safe areas, and using the oars properly.)

- Have you ever had an injury that you could have prevented if you had taken certain precautions? If so, what could you have done to prevent it? (Answers will vary depending on students' experiences. Encourage students to tell the class about how they think they could have prevented certain injuries.)

## What Do You Think?

Have volunteers read the story on page 282 to the class.

### Ask:

- Why were Patrick and his father concerned about junk and hazardous materials in the garage? (They thought that Patrick's sisters might get hurt or poisoned.)

- Do you think Patrick and his father should have been concerned and cleaned out the garage right away? (Opinions will vary, but students should conclude that Patrick and his father should have been concerned to prevent any accidents.)

- Do you think there are any accidents waiting to happen in your home? If so, what are they? (Answers will vary, depending on students' homes.)

- What kinds of things could you and your family do to prevent the accidents that might happen in your home? (Answers will vary. Students might say their families can store dangerous products away from small children, check to see that electrical wires and appliances are working properly, avoid standing on unsteady chairs or tables to reach high areas, know how to use a fire extinguisher, and use safety glasses and gloves when needed.)

Have students complete the Unit 6 What Do You Think? Activity sheet.

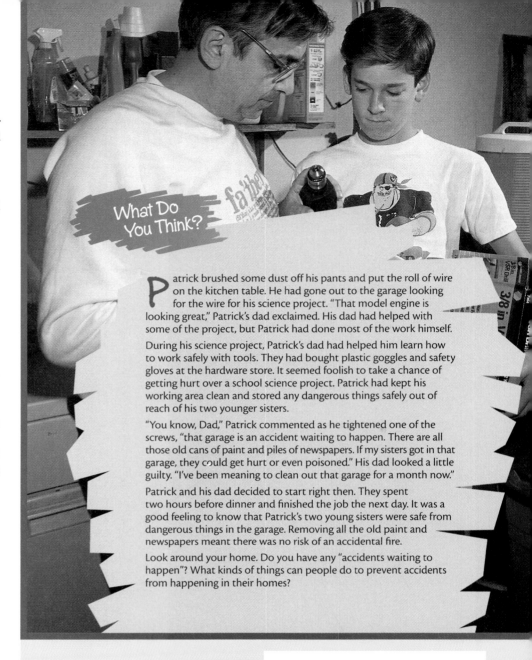

**What Do You Think?**

Patrick brushed some dust off his pants and put the roll of wire on the kitchen table. He had gone out to the garage looking for the wire for his science project. "That model engine is looking great," Patrick's dad exclaimed. His dad had helped with some of the project, but Patrick had done most of the work himself.

During his science project, Patrick's dad had helped him learn how to work safely with tools. They had bought plastic goggles and safety gloves at the hardware store. It seemed foolish to take a chance of getting hurt over a school science project. Patrick had kept his working area clean and stored any dangerous things safely out of reach of his two younger sisters.

"You know, Dad," Patrick commented as he tightened one of the screws, "that garage is an accident waiting to happen. There are all those old cans of paint and piles of newspapers. If my sisters got in that garage, they could get hurt or even poisoned." His dad looked a little guilty. "I've been meaning to clean out that garage for a month now."

Patrick and his dad decided to start right then. They spent two hours before dinner and finished the job the next day. It was a good feeling to know that Patrick's two young sisters were safe from dangerous things in the garage. Removing all the old paint and newspapers meant there was no risk of an accidental fire.

Look around your home. Do you have any "accidents waiting to happen"? What kinds of things can people do to prevent accidents from happening in their homes?

**What Do You Think? Master 6**

# Preventing Injuries

T hink about your daily life. On a typical day, you probably do many of the same things in pretty much the same order. You wake up. You take a shower, get dressed, and eat breakfast. On weekdays, you go to school, talk with friends, and do homework. Now think about a day that isn't typical. You stay up late to watch a movie and are tired the next day. You miss the bus. You have trouble concentrating. It is on these days that injuries often occur.

In this chapter, you will learn how to avoid injury in certain situations. You will find out what to do to minimize the risks associated with certain lifestyle choices, emergencies, accidents, fire, and some natural disasters.

---

### Goals for Learning

▶ To promote safety by thinking ahead to consider the risks and consequences of certain situations

▶ To learn how to prevent fires and how to react if a fire breaks out

▶ To identify safety rules that pertain to baby-sitting, emergency situations, and the Internet

▶ To identify items that should be in a basic emergency kit

▶ To learn how to prepare for and react during a natural disaster

---

## Introducing the Chapter

Ask students to describe a typical day. A typical day might include going to school, doing homework, spending time with a friend, and so on. Then have students describe a day that isn't typical. Try to elicit the response that injuries often occur on days that are not typical.

Have volunteers read the chapter opener on page 283 aloud, including the Goals for Learning.

### Ask:

- Have you recently had an injury? What kind of injury did you have? (Responses might include a sprained ankle, a broken finger or arm, or a bruised knee.)

- What could you have done to prevent the injury? (Responses might include slowing down or focusing on the task at hand.)

---

**Student Study Guide 20, page 1**

**Student Study Guide 20, page 2**

## Chapter 14 Lesson 1

**Overview** This lesson focuses on reducing the risk of injury, automobile safety, and preventing sports-related injuries.

### Objectives

- To explain how injuries can be reduced.

- To explain how vehicle crashes can be prevented.

- To explain how to prevent sports-related injuries.

**Student Pages** 284–287

**Audiocassette**

**Teacher's Resource Library**

Activity 50

Workbook Activity 50

## Teaching Suggestions

### ■ Vocabulary

*firearm*

Write the vocabulary word on the chalkboard. Ask students to provide a definition based on prior knowledge. Invite students to compare their definition to the definition in the textbook.

### ■ Teaching the Lesson

Ask students to think about different ways drugs, emotions, cars, sports, and firearms can affect their safety. Tell students that this lesson will point out ways people can act to stay safe.

Have students read about how drugs can affect safety on page 284.

Ask:

- How is safety affected by drugs? (Drugs can cause the user to take chances he or she wouldn't usually take. These chances often result in injury.)

---

## Promoting Safety

A re you familiar with the saying "always be prepared"? Simply knowing what to expect or how to react in a situation will prevent many injuries. Most injuries occur because people don't stop to think about the risks they or others might be taking. Too often, people don't think about what could happen in a given situation.

Teenagers are more at risk of injuring themselves than adults are. This is because teens often act suddenly when faced with certain decisions. And, unlike adults, teenagers are less likely to believe that risk is present in certain situations. Think about how your safety might be affected by:

- drugs
- your mood
- being in a moving car
- doing certain sports and activities
- being around firearms

### How Can Drugs Affect Safety?

The risk of injury increases when a person uses alcohol or other drugs. Drugs change how a person sees a situation. Drugs can cause the user to take chances that he or she wouldn't normally take. Taking such chances often results in injuries.

Drugs alter a person's reaction time, too. Stimulants, such as caffeine, speed up the function of brain cells. Depressants, such as alcohol and marijuana, decrease the brain's activity. Depressants greatly reduce a person's reaction time and coordination. The number of drug-related injuries in the United States is great. For example, over 50 percent of motor vehicle-related deaths in the United States involve drug-impaired drivers.

## What Are Some Motor Vehicle Safety Rules?

In 1998 alone, nearly 6,000 teenagers died from injuries suffered in motor vehicle crashes. In the same year, another 350,000 teenagers were injured in such collisions. As a passenger, you can reduce the chances of a collision by following these rules.

- Keep the noise levels down so that the driver can concentrate.
- Refuse to get into a car with a driver who has been drinking alcohol or taking other kinds of drugs.
- Ride only with drivers who obey all traffic laws.

If a crash does occur, injuries and deaths can be greatly reduced if you obey the rules below.

- Wear a seatbelt and remind others to wear theirs *at all times.*
- Keep your hands, head, legs, and feet inside the car while it is moving.
- Ride in the front seat of a car with air bags only if you meet the weight and height limit.

### Writing About Health

Although statistics show that seat belts save lives, many people refuse to wear them. Write a persuasive paragraph to convince people to wear seat belts.

**What are some other ways to prevent car accidents?**

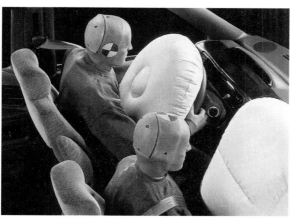

Air bags at work in an automobile.

*Preventing Injuries   Chapter 14*   **285**

Have students read about motor vehicle safety on page 285.

Ask:

- As a passenger, what are some unsafe driving behaviors you have noticed? (Students may say speeding, not signaling turns, not watching the road ahead, not slowing down when road conditions are dangerous, or talking on cell phones.)

### GLOBAL CONNECTION

 Show students examples of international road signs and discuss reasons for their use. Encourage students to evaluate whether the designs and symbols clearly show what they need to show. Then invite students to create their own road signs for road conditions, road safety hazards, or other information pertinent to drivers.

### LEARNING STYLES

 **Group Learning** Have students work in small groups to prepare and present a debate. Have each group prepare an argument for one side of the following topic: Drivers should receive traffic tickets if they and/or their passengers are not wearing seat belts. Have students present a realistic argument for their side.

Have students read about how to prevent sports-related injuries on page 286.

**Ask:**

- How might the season of the year affect the safety rules a person should follow for a sport? (Responses might include needing to drink more water in summer, needing to wear warmer clothing in winter, or needing to be careful of wet leaves on the ground in the fall.)

- How might sliding into a base during a softball game be dangerous for someone who has not practiced the necessary skills? (A person sliding into base might sprain an ankle, break a toe or leg, or damage a knee.)

## Then and Now

Ask students how they think cars have become safer during the last ten years. Then ask students what safety devices they think might be added to cars during the next ten years. For example, all cars might have front passenger and side air bags. Discuss ways to prevent children from being injured by air bags.

### MULTICULTURAL CONNECTION

Encourage students to research popular sports in other countries. Students should find out how such sports are played and what safety rules should be followed. Invite volunteers to report their research to the class.

### How Can You Prevent Certain Sports-Related Injuries?

As you probably know, sports and other forms of physical activity are good ways to stay healthy and fit. These activities also help you to relax and to relieve stress.

**What kinds of safety equipment should be worn to play soccer?**

There are many ways to prevent sports-related injuries. Some of these are listed below.

- Make sure you have the strength and endurance for a sport or an activity.
- Condition and warm up before participating in a game or an activity. Cool down after the game or activity.
- Wear proper safety equipment including a face mask, mouth guard, shin guards, goggles, and an appropriate helmet.

**How might you protect yourself from serious injury if you fall while skating?**

- Make sure your shoes and clothing fit properly. Check laces, buckles, and straps often for signs of wear.
- Play or carry out the activity at a well-maintained facility or in an area appropriate to the sport or activity.
- Always drink water before, during, and after the game or activity. This prevents heat exhaustion and dehydration.

**SAFER CARS**

The first automobiles had no doors, roofs, or windshields. They obviously weren't as safe as modern cars. Of course, they weren't as fast as today's vehicles, either. Traffic at that time doesn't compare to that on today's roads. Over the years, the number of cars has greatly increased. So have driving speed and concerns about safety. Seat belts, antilock brakes, safety glass, front-wheel drive, brake and signal lights, and shock-absorbing bumpers are just a few of the safety features of most cars on the road today. In the early 1990s, air bags became standard equipment in new cars. Air bags, when properly used, have reduced injuries from front-end collisions and have also reduced the number of traffic fatalities.

## INDUSTRIAL SAFETY SPECIALIST

A workplace should be safe for the people who work there. An industrial safety specialist is a person who works to make sure companies identify and correct unsafe working conditions. The duties and responsibilities of these specialists are to prevent work-related injuries and deaths and to protect the health of all workers. Industrial safety specialists must be concerned with waste disposal, environmental safety, pollution, and health hazards. Most industrial safety specialists have a college degree. Continuing education is also necessary to keep up with changes in laws that regulate workplace safety.

**Firearm**
*A handgun or rifle*

## What Can You Do to Be Safe Around Firearms?

**Firearms**, or handguns and rifles, are in about half of all homes in the United States. Most firearm injuries and deaths take place inside a house or an apartment or close to the buildings. The majority of firearm accidents among young people occur because children are curious about firearms. Another reason people are injured is that they don't realize the power of a handgun or rifle.

To reduce the risk of a firearm accident, handguns and rifles must be stored in locked containers or cabinets. The ammunition for the firearms must also be in a locked container that is separate from the firearms.

**LESSON 1 REVIEW** Write the answers to these questions on a separate sheet of paper. Use complete sentences.

1) Why are teenagers more at risk of injuring themselves than adults are?

2) What are two ways in which drugs affect safety?

3) Why is it important to drink water before, during, and after a game or an activity?

4) What are some rules to follow to reduce the chances of injury from a car crash?

5) How can you reduce the chances of injury from firearms?

*Preventing Injuries* Chapter 14 **287**

---

Have students read Careers and the section about firearms on page 287.

## Careers

Challenge students to brainstorm a list of unsafe or unhealthy conditions an industrial safety specialist might look for in different kinds of work situations. Examples include the leaking of dangerous gas in the workplace, objects strewn about, and rusted or broken pulleys and chains that could cause heavy loads to drop.

## Lesson 1 Review Answers

1) Teenagers are more at risk of injuring themselves than adults because teenagers often act suddenly when faced with certain decisions. Teenagers are less likely to perceive risk than adults are.

2) Drugs change a person's perception of a situation as well as alter a person's reaction time.

3) Drinking water prevents heat exhaustion and dehydration.

4) To reduce the chances of injury from a car crash, follow these rules: Wear a seat belt and remind others to wear theirs at all times. Keep your hands, head, legs, and feet inside the car while it is moving. Ride in the front seat of a car with air bags only if you meet the weight and height limit.

5) Always treat a firearm as if it were loaded.

## APPLICATION

**Environment**
Ask students what they think might be done to help prevent tragic shootings, such as those that have occurred in schools. Challenge the class to write a letter to their congressional representative telling him or her their ideas. Send a copy of the letter to your school's newspaper as well as your local newspaper.

---

Name _____ Date _____ Period _____ | Chapter 14
Activity **50**

### Promoting Safety

**Directions** Write *T* if the statement is true or *F* if it is false.

_____ 1) Stimulants speed up the function of brain cells.

_____ 2) When in a car, keep noise levels down so the driver can concentrate.

_____ 3) Wear a seat belt only if you are the driver of a car.

_____ 4) Avoiding sports-related injuries is impossible.

_____ 5) Always wear the right safety equipment when playing sports.

_____ 6) A firearm is a handgun or a rifle.

_____ 7) Most gun accidents among young people occur because of curiosity about firearms.

_____ 8) Be sure to keep guns and ammunition locked together in a safe cabinet.

_____ 9) Riding with a driver who has been drinking is dangerous.

_____ 10) When a person uses alcohol or other drugs, the risk of injury decreases.

© AGS® American Guidance Service, Inc. Permission is granted to reproduce for classroom use only.   Discover Health

**TRL**

**Activity 50**

---

Name _____ Date _____ Period _____ | Chapter 14
Workbook Activity **50**

### Promoting Safety

**Directions** Write *T* if the statement is true or *F* if it is false.

_____ 1) When a person uses alcohol or other drugs, the risk of injury decreases.

_____ 2) Stimulants speed up the function of brain cells.

_____ 3) When in a car, keep noise levels down so the driver can concentrate.

_____ 4) Wear a seat belt only if you are the driver of a car.

_____ 5) Avoiding sports-related injuries is impossible.

_____ 6) Always wear the right safety equipment when playing sports.

_____ 7) A firearm is a handgun or a rifle.

_____ 8) Most gun accidents among young people occur because of curiosity about firearms.

_____ 9) Be sure to keep guns and ammunition locked together in a safe cabinet.

_____ 10) Riding with a driver who has been drinking is dangerous.

© AGS® American Guidance Service, Inc. Permission is granted to reproduce for classroom use only.   Discover Health

**TRL**

**Workbook Activity 50**

## Chapter 14 Lesson 2

**Overview** This lesson discusses fire safety.

### Objectives

■ To explain how to reduce the risks of fire.

■ To describe what to do in case of a fire.

**Student Pages** 288–290

**Audiocassette**

**Teacher's Resource Library** **TRL**

    Activity 51

    Workbook Activity 51

## Teaching Suggestions

### ■ Vocabulary

*hazard*

Write the vocabulary word on the chalkboard. Read the definition from the textbook. Ask students for examples of fire hazards that may exist in a house or an apartment building.

### ■ Teaching the Lesson

Ask students to name ways a fire might start at home. Explain that to prevent fires, people need to take an active role in reducing risks.

Have students read about reducing risks of house fires on page 288.

Ask:

• What things can be done to reduce house fires? (taking care when cooking, smoking, or burning wood in fireplaces; checking for and fixing faulty wires and electrical cords; keeping matches, cigarette lighters, and fireworks out of children's reach)

• What are some safety tips you should follow if you burn candles? (Students might mention not burning candles close to curtains and not leaving burning candles unattended.)

---

## Reducing Risks of Fire

**Hazard**
*A danger*

House fires are among the leading causes of serious injuries and deaths in the United States. This is sad because over 90 percent of these fires are preventable. Most house fires are due to carelessness. The number of house fires could be greatly reduced. People only need to take care when they cook, smoke, or burn wood in their fireplaces. Checking for and fixing faulty wires and electrical cords can also help to reduce the risk of a house fire. Another way to prevent fires is to keep matches, cigarette lighters, and fireworks out of children's reach.

### How Can You Reduce the Risks of House Fires?

Take an active role in reducing the risk of fire in your house or apartment. With a responsible adult, look for possible fire dangers, or **hazards**. Use the list below as a guide. Can you think of any other possible hazards?

• Look for damaged wires and electrical cords.

• Don't overload electrical outlets or extension cords.

• Make sure all appliances are in good working order.

• Store flammable liquids and household cleaners away from all heat sources.

• Store gasoline only in an approved container.

• Make sure that matches and lighters are well out of reach of children.

• Place a fire screen in front of a fireplace when a fire is burning.

• Test smoke detectors twice a year to make sure they are working properly. Change the batteries two times a year.

• Turn pot and pan handles toward the center of the stove when cooking. Take care not to get cooking oil and grease too hot.

---

If a door is closed and you suspect a fire, feel the door and doorknob with the back of your hand to see if they are warm. A warm door or doorknob could signal fire on the other side. If the door or knob is warm, choose an alternate escape route.

Smoke detectors should be installed in hallways, bedrooms, the basement, and the kitchen.

## What Should You Do If a Fire Breaks Out?

Even if you have fireproofed your house or apartment, fires can happen. It is important to know that a fire will usually burn for two to four minutes before a smoke detector goes off. The size of a fire increases eight times every minute. That means you only have about a minute to get out of a burning structure. Therefore, it is important to get out quickly and then call 911. There are a few situations in which you might try to extinguish, or put out, the fire. First, if the fire is small and hasn't yet spread, you could try to put it out. Second, if a family member has his or her back to an escape route, an attempt to put the fire out could be made. Third, a family member could put out the fire if he or she uses a fire extinguisher correctly.

**Why should there be at least two neighbors that you can go to during a fire?**

Sometimes you know that the fire can't be extinguished. Then it is important that everyone leave the house or apartment building immediately. Make sure no one stops to take any belongings. Be sure that everyone follows one of the predetermined escape routes. Go directly to the meeting place. Check in with an adult in the group. Go to a neighbor who is not at risk from the fire and call the fire department or 911.

*Preventing Injuries* *Chapter 14* **289**

---

Have students read about what to do in case of a fire on page 289.

Ask:
_____

- What is the most important thing to do if a fire breaks out? (Get out quickly and then call 911.)

- In what situations might you try to put a fire out? (If the fire is small and hasn't spread, you can try to put it out. You need to have a fire extinguisher and know how to use it if you are going to try to put out the fire. It is important to have your back to an escape route when you try to put a fire out.)

- What should you do if a fire cannot be extinguished? (Leave the house or apartment building immediately. Do not take any belongings. Go directly to a meeting place and check in with an adult in the group. Then go to a neighbor's house and call the fire department or 911.)

## APPLICATION

**Career Connection**
Encourage students to investigate the roles of firefighters during emergencies. Students can talk to a firefighter at their local fire department to gather information. The information might focus on the qualifications for becoming a firefighter as well as areas in which firefighters can specialize (for example, water rescue, high-angle rescue, fire investigation). Invite students to share their information with the class.

Have students read about fire escape routes in Action for Health on page 290.

## Action for Health

Point out to students that making a plan of action in case of a fire can help save their life and the life of others in their family. Encourage students to follow the guidelines to make escape plans from their homes. Suggest that students share their plans with their family. Ask students what route they should follow from their bedroom out of their home in case of a fire. If the escape route is blocked, what alternate route would they follow? (Students should choose two routes that get them out of the building as quickly as possible. If their bedroom is on a first floor, the window might be the best option. Discuss students' plans.)

## Lesson 2 Review Answers

1) Most house fires are preventable because the majority of them are caused by carelessness.
2) A fire extinguisher can be used to put out small fires. An extinguisher won't help if one doesn't know how to operate it.
3) A fire drill plan should include a floor plan that shows escape routes from each room, an outside emergency meeting place, which family members will assist those with special needs, and the names and addresses of two trusted neighbors.
4) If you are in a building where a fire has started, get out quickly and then call 911.
5) You should *never* reenter a burning building because the building could collapse, you could get severely burned or injured, or the smoke could overcome you.

---

**Action for Health**

## PLAN FIRE ESCAPE ROUTES

Do you and other members of your family know how to get out of the house or apartment in case of a fire? Use these guidelines to make a plan of escape from *every* room in your home.

- Draw a floor plan of your house or apartment. Show at least two escape routes from each room, such as a door and a window.
- Practice crawling along the floor toward the escape exits.
- Make sure everyone knows where the outside emergency meeting place is.
- Decide who will help people in the family with special needs.
- Post the floor plan where everyone can review it once a month. Quiz family members to make sure everyone knows the escape routes and the location of the emergency meeting place.
- Beneath the floor plan, write the names and addresses of two neighbors to whom you can go in the event of any emergency.

**LESSON 2 REVIEW** Write the answers to these questions on a separate sheet of paper. Use complete sentences.

**Why should you crawl along the floor to escape a fire?**

1) Why are most house fires preventable?
2) Explain the importance of having a fire extinguisher and knowing how to use it.
3) What kinds of things should be included in a fire drill plan?
4) What should you do if you are in a building where a fire has started?
5) Why should you *never* reenter a burning building?

---

Name _____ Date _____ Period _____ | Chapter 14 Activity 51

**Reducing Risks of Fire**

*Directions* Write *T* if the statement is true or *F* if it is false.

_____ 1) Test smoke detectors at home twice a year.
_____ 2) Store flammable materials in the hottest part of your basement.
_____ 3) A fire increases five hundred times every minute.
_____ 4) When leaving a burning building, try to take as many belongings as possible.
_____ 5) Fires usually burn for two to four minutes before a smoke detector goes off.
_____ 6) To avoid fire, don't overload electrical outlets.
_____ 7) Only let children play with safety matches.
_____ 8) There are a few situations in which it is safe to try to put out a fire.
_____ 9) If your home is on fire, go to a neighbor and call 911.
_____ 10) Almost all house fires are preventable.

**Activity 51**

---

Name _____ Date _____ Period _____ | Chapter 14 Workbook Activity 51

**Reducing Risks of Fire**

*Directions* Write *T* if the statement is true or *F* if it is false.

_____ 1) Almost all house fires are preventable.
_____ 2) Test smoke detectors at home twice a year.
_____ 3) Store flammable materials in the hottest part of your basement.
_____ 4) A fire increases five hundred times every minute.
_____ 5) When leaving a burning building, try to take as many belongings as possible.
_____ 6) Fires usually burn for two to four minutes before a smoke detector goes off.
_____ 7) To avoid fire, don't overload electrical outlets.
_____ 8) Only let children play with safety matches.
_____ 9) There are a few situations in which it is safe to try to put out a fire.
_____ 10) If your home is on fire, go to a neighbor and call 911.

**Workbook Activity 51**

## Safety for Teens

**Internet**
*The worldwide computer network that provides information to users*

*I*n many situations, teens are more at risk of injuring themselves or causing others to become injured. This is because of their inexperience with the situations. You can learn ways to reduce and prevent injuries while baby-sitting. You can find out what to do in an emergency situation and how to protect yourself when you are walking alone or are at home by yourself. There are also safety rules to follow when using the **Internet**. The network of computers that provides information is the Internet.

### SAFETY FOR BABY-SITTERS

Baby-sitting or watching young children carries many responsibilities for safety. Here are some guidelines that can help avoid risks when you are watching young children.

- Know the number where parents can be reached and know when they will return.
- Have emergency and neighbors' phone numbers.
- Learn family rules for playing inside.
- Learn how to raise or lower the sides of a crib.
- Keep full attention on the children.
- Keep children away from appliances, matches, cleansers, soap, medicine, and bodies of water.

This chart lists some of the rules to follow when baby-sitting.

**What is the most important rule to follow when baby-sitting?**

### What Are Some Rules to Follow When Baby-sitting?

Baby-sitting can be fun and a good way to earn spending money. But because children are unaware of the consequences of many of their actions, watching them demands your full attention.

Choking, poisoning, and drowning are the three leading causes of death for children under age five. With this in mind, always keep the children you are watching away from small objects. Items like marbles, coins, and hard candy could cause choking. Cut their food into small bite-sized pieces. Don't let children run around while they are eating.

As a responsible baby-sitter, you must keep children away from bathtubs, toilets, buckets, and swimming pools. Children can drown in less than an inch of water. Supervise bath time for young children. Never leave them unattended for even a moment.

---

## Chapter 14 Lesson 3

**Overview** This lesson explains how to reduce and prevent injuries in an emergency.

### Objectives

- To explain how to reduce and prevent injuries when baby-sitting.
- To explain what to do in an emergency.
- To learn how to protect oneself on the Internet.

**Student Pages** 291–294

**Audiocassette**

**Teacher's Resource Library** **TRL**

Activity 52

Workbook Activity 52

## Teaching Suggestions

### ■ Vocabulary

*Internet, life-threatening emergency, e-mail*

Have students read the paragraphs in which each vocabulary word appears. Ask if students have any questions about the meanings of the words and discuss them.

### ■ Teaching the Lesson

Ask students if they baby-sit or if they use the Internet. Have them think about ways to prevent injuries while baby-sitting. Then ask them to describe any safety rules to follow when using the Internet.

Have students read about rules to follow when baby-sitting on page 291.

Ask:

- What are some ways that the children you baby-sit for can become injured if you do not watch them carefully? (Specific examples include falling down stairs, choking on small objects, eating poisonous objects, and so forth.)

Have students read page 292 to learn who to call in an emergency.

Ask:

- Other than 911, what other emergency numbers should you know? (telephone number of parent or guardian at work, neighbor, family doctor, poison control center, fire department, police department)

- Suppose you are baby-sitting and a young child falls down the stairs. What should you do? (Lead students to respond that they should call 911, the place where the parents are, and possibly their own parents for help.)

## APPLICATION

 **In the Community**
Have students find out the following telephone numbers for their community: emergency operator, police station, fire department, ambulance, hospital emergency room, poison control center. Invite students to prepare cards with the numbers that can be taped near their telephones at home. Encourage students to add telephone numbers of relatives, friends, and neighbors to contact in an emergency.

Life-threatening emergency
*Any situation in which a person might die if medical treatment isn't provided immediately*

## Who Should You Call in an Emergency?

In this chapter, you've learned about different kinds of injuries and how you might prevent them. In spite of precautions, however, injuries still occur. Thus, you should be aware of what to do when a person is injured.

Some injuries, as you might know from personal experience, are not serious. Minor burns, some insect and animal bites, and sprains are injuries that might require medical attention. But usually they are not **life-threatening emergencies**. A life-threatening emergency is a situation in which a person could die if treatment isn't immediately available. Shock, choking, stroke, heart attacks, poisoning, and severe bleeding are life-threatening emergencies.

Suppose you and a friend are riding your bikes. Your friend falls and scrapes her leg badly. Who should you call? Parents or other responsible adults, such as neighbors and relatives who live close by, can be contacted for help.

Now, suppose a passing car hits your friend. She is unable to move. In this situation, you or another person would call 911, a central emergency center. When you dial this number, people are immediately available to provide help. When calling 911, stay calm and talk slowly. Provide clear information about the situation. Answer all of the questions you are asked. Stay on the line until you are told to hang up. And remember, call 911 only if a real emergency exists.

### A CALL FOR HELP

The **911** telephone number is for emergencies. The system is available in about half of the United States. Where the system isn't available, calls can be made to an emergency operator, the police, or the fire department. The caller can help the 911 operator by providing information calmly, answering all questions, and following directions until instructed to hang up.

## How Can You Protect Yourself From Being Hurt by Others?

If you are like many teens today, you might be alone at home before or after school. You might have to walk or bike to and from school alone. If you are in these or similar situations, follow these rules to reduce your chances of being hurt by others.

- Find classmates to accompany you if you walk or ride your bike to and from school. If this isn't possible, walk or ride your bike only on well-traveled streets. Avoid shortcuts, small side streets, alleys, and wooded areas.

- Do not accept rides from strangers, even if they seem nice and appear to want to help you.

- If you are being followed by a stranger, quickly go to a crowded street, a public building, or some other active area.

- When you get home, call a parent or other adult immediately to say that you have arrived safely.

- When you are home alone, make sure you don't tell unknown phone callers that you are alone. Decide with the adults in your family what you should say if someone you don't know calls. Practice the script and keep a copy of it near the phone.

- Keep the door locked and do not open it. If someone comes to the door, speak through the closed, locked door—even if you know the person.

- Make sure a list of emergency numbers is by each phone in your house or apartment.

## How Can You Protect Yourself on the Internet?

You have probably discovered that the Internet is a great place to "hang out." You can do research on the Internet to help you complete school projects. You can use this powerful tool to visit sites to find books by a certain author.

Have students read page 293 to learn how to protect yourself from being hurt by others.

Ask:

- If a stranger offers you a ride, what should you do? (refuse rides from strangers even if they are offering to help you)

- What are some safety rules to follow when you are home alone? (don't tell unknown phone callers that you are home alone, keep the doors locked and do not open them)

### LEARNING STYLES

**Tactile/Kinesthetic** Have pairs of students role-play situations in which they protect themselves from being hurt by others. Situations might include a stranger coming to the door, a stranger following the student home, a stranger offering a ride, and so forth. Encourage each pair to write a script for their situation. Invite students to role-play more than one situation.

Have students read pages 293 and 294 to find out how to protect themselves on the Internet.

## Ask:

• What should you do if you are at a site and its activities make you uncomfortable? (You should leave the site immediately by clicking the Home icon.)

• What should you do if you get an e-mail from someone you do not know? (Do not respond to an e-mail from someone you do not know.)

• What rules should you follow about posting something at a site? (Never include your name, home address, or telephone number.)

• Suppose you are in a chat room and the person you are chatting with wants to meet you. What should you do? (Do not agree to meet face-to-face unless you have permission from a parent or guardian.)

## Lesson 3 Review Answers

1) Some important things to remember when baby-sitting are the following: never leave the children unattended; keep the children away from small items; cut food into small pieces; keep children away from bathtubs, toilets, buckets, and swimming pools; supervise bath time for young children.

2) Life-threatening emergencies are situations in which a person could die if treatment isn't immediately available.

3) When calling 911, stay calm and talk slowly. Provide clear information about the situation. Answer all of the questions you are asked. Stay on the line until you are told to hang up.

4) If you are being followed by a stranger, quickly go to a crowded street, public building, or some other active area.

5) Some rules to follow when using the Internet are the following: avoid any Internet sites that contain material that makes you uncomfortable; never give out information about yourself, your family, or where you live; don't go into chat rooms unless you have permission from a parent or guardian; never include your name, home address, or phone number when posting something at a site; accept other reasonable rules.

**E-mail**
*Messages sent and received over the Internet*

You can view online catalogs of your favorite clothes. You can listen to music and find tips and codes for video games. You can send electronic messages called **e-mail** to friends and family. You can even chat with people next door, across town, or in another country.

While the Internet is a useful tool, you must realize that some people can harm you. Follow these rules to make using the Internet a safe and enjoyable activity.

• Avoid any sites that contain material or activities that make you uncomfortable. If you accidentally go to such a site, leave it immediately by clicking on your Home icon.

• Never give out any information about yourself, your family, or where you live to people or sites without first talking to a parent or other responsible adult.

• Don't go into chat rooms unless you have permission from a parent or guardian.

**How is the Internet like a big city?**

• If you post something at a site, never include your name, home address, or phone number.

• Never respond to e-mail from people you don't know.

• Do not agree to meet face-to-face with someone you meet online unless you have permission from a parent or guardian.

**LESSON 3 REVIEW** Write the answers to these questions on a separate sheet of paper. Use complete sentences.

1) What are some important things to remember when you are baby-sitting?

2) What are life-threatening emergencies?

3) When calling 911, what should you do?

4) If you think a stranger is following you, what should you do?

5) What are some rules to follow when using the Internet?

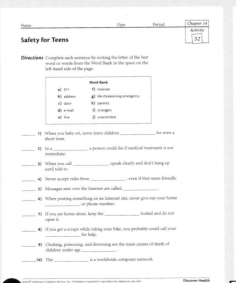

**Activity 52**

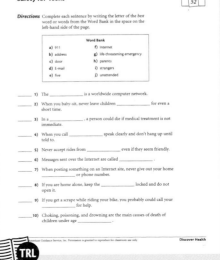

**Workbook Activity 52**

## Emergency Equipment

**Emergency kit**
*A collection of items that are useful in almost any kind of emergency*

Suppose you are baby-sitting and a bee stings one of the children. Do you know where to find the things you need to care for the bite? Suppose you are at home alone in the evening and the power goes out. Do you know where the flashlight is? You need to know about emergency equipment that should always be on hand in any house or apartment.

### What Kinds of Things Might You Need in an Emergency?

An **emergency kit** is a collection of items that can be used in almost any kind of emergency. Read about these different items.

### Radio

A battery-powered radio is an important item in an emergency kit. It could be your only source of information when the power in your area is out. Make sure your family's emergency kit contains a portable radio and the batteries to run it. In a citywide or statewide emergency, certain radio stations report and update people on the situation. They tell you how you and your family should respond.

### Sources of Light

During some emergencies, people can be without electricity for hours, days, or even weeks. At least two flashlights should be available for power outages. Packs of fresh batteries should be kept near the flashlights.

Candles are also good sources of light in an emergency. Make sure the candles are in sturdy candleholders so that they are not likely to tip over. Keep matches to light the candles in a heavy plastic bag near the candles. Never light a match, however, if you smell gas or suspect a gas leak.

*Preventing Injuries* *Chapter 14* **295**

---

## Lesson at a Glance

### Chapter 14  Lesson 4

**Overview** This lesson discusses emergency equipment and first aid kits.

### Objectives

■ To learn about what equipment is needed in an emergency.

■ To identify the basic materials in a first aid kit.

**Student Pages** 295–296

**Audiocassette**

**Teacher's Resource Library**

Activity 53
Workbook Activity 53

## Teaching Suggestions

### ■ Vocabulary

*emergency kit*

After discussing the meaning of *emergency kit*, have an emergency kit available for students to see. Ask volunteers to choose an item and give a short description of it.

### ■ Teaching the Lesson

Encourage students to bring in items they would put in an emergency kit or first aid kit. Have them share their items with the class and discuss why they have selected that particular item.

Have students read about things you might need in an emergency on page 295.

Ask:

· When might a battery-powered radio be needed? (If the power in your area goes out, it could be your only source of information.)

· What other supplies might you include in an emergency kit? (canned food, can opener, bottled water, wrenches to shut off gas and water, extra blankets, warm clothing)

Have students read about first aid kits on page 296.

Ask:

- Why is it important to check your first aid kit after it is used? (to replace items that were used or those that have expired)

- What are some personal items you would need in a first aid kit? (Answers will vary. Students may say they need an inhaler for allergies or medicine prescribed by a doctor.)

- Besides your home, where else might you keep an emergency kit? (in a car, in a garage, in a tool shed)

## Lesson 4 Review Answers

1) An emergency kit is a collection of items, such as a battery-powered radio and flashlights, that can be used in almost any kind of emergency.
2) A battery-powered radio is an important item in an emergency kit because it can be the only source of information when the power in the area is out.
3) You shouldn't light a match if you smell gas because there could be a gas leak, and a lighted match can cause a fire.
4) A first aid kit should contain bandages, ice packs, scissors, tweezers, gauze, tape, and medicines.
5) It is important to have both candles and flashlights in an emergency kit because during some emergencies, you might be without electricity for a long time.

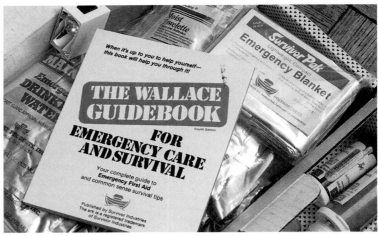

These are some of the emergency supplies that you should always have on hand.

### First Aid Kit

A good first aid kit contains bandages, ice packs, scissors, tweezers, gauze, tape, and medicines. These items can be used to treat simple injuries. They can also be used to treat serious injuries until professional help arrives. Check your first aid kit after each emergency. Replace items that were used or those that have expired.

**LESSON 4 REVIEW** Write the answers to these questions on a separate sheet of paper. Use complete sentences.

1) What is an emergency kit?
2) Why is a battery-powered radio an important item in an emergency kit?
3) Why shouldn't you light a match if you smell gas?
4) Name some items a first aid kit should contain.
5) Why is it important to have both candles and flashlights in an emergency kit?

**What are some items specific to your family that you would include in an emergency kit?**

**Emergency Equipment**

*Directions* Complete each sentence by writing the letter of the *best* word or words from the Word Bank in the space on the left-hand side of the page.

Word Bank
a) batteries    f) gas
b) candles      g) radio
c) emergency    h) respond
d) emergency kit  i) simple
e) first aid kit  j) two

1) A battery-powered _____ can give you information about what is happening during an emergency.
2) Radio reports tell people how to _____ in an emergency.
3) Always have at least _____ flashlights available.
4) A good source of light are _____ .
5) If you smell _____ or think there's a leak, never light a match.
6) Keep new _____ near your flashlights.
7) A _____ is necessary during an emergency.
8) Bandages, scissors, tweezers, and medicines can treat _____ injuries.
9) After every _____ , check your first aid kit.
10) A collection of things you might need in an emergency is an _____ .

**Activity 53**

**Emergency Equipment**

*Directions* Complete each sentence by writing the letter of the best word or words from the Word Bank in the space on the left-hand side of the page.

Word Bank
a) batteries    f) gas
b) candles      g) radio
c) emergency    h) respond
d) emergency kit  i) simple
e) first aid kit  j) two

1) A collection of things you might need in an emergency is an _____ .
2) A battery-powered _____ can give you information about what is happening during an emergency.
3) Radio reports tell people how to _____ in an emergency.
4) Always have at least _____ flashlights available.
5) A good source of light are _____ .
6) If you smell _____ or think there's a leak, never light a match.
7) Keep new _____ near your flashlights.
8) A _____ is necessary during an emergency.
9) Bandages, scissors, tweezers, and medicines can treat _____ injuries.
10) After every _____ check your first aid kit.

**Workbook Activity 53**

Natural disaster
*A destructive event that happens because of natural causes*

Earthquake
*A shaking of the rocks that make up the earth's crust*

**N**atural disasters are destructive events that happen because of natural causes. Some natural disasters, such as earthquakes and hurricanes, occur only in certain regions of the United States. Other disasters, such as floods and thunderstorms, can happen in all parts of the country. Do you know what to do to prepare for a natural disaster? What should you do during and after the disaster?

**How Should You Prepare for an Earthquake?**

An **earthquake** is a shaking of the rocks that make up the earth's crust, or outer layer. Earthquakes are caused when blocks of the earth's crust and middle layer shift. Most earthquakes in the United States occur along the west coast. However, the most destructive earthquake in the history of the United States took place in Missouri. Therefore, everyone should know how to prepare for an earthquake as well as how to react during this natural disaster.

If you live in a place that has earthquakes often, securely bolt heavy objects, like bookshelves, to a solid wall. Also make sure that heavy items are stored on shelves close to the floor. Don't hang heavy picture frames or mirrors above beds.

Locate the shutoff valves of the gas line and water main. Also know how to turn off the power in your house or apartment. Have a responsible adult show you how to turn off these valves.

Safety officials often stage natural disasters so that they can learn how to react to these events.

*Preventing Injuries* Chapter 14 **297**

---

## Lesson at a Glance

### Chapter 14 Lesson 5

**Overview** This lesson explains how to reduce the risks of injury from natural disasters.

### Objectives

- To explain how to prepare for natural disasters, such as earthquakes, thunderstorms, hurricanes, tornadoes, and floods.

**Student Pages** 297–300

**Audiocassette**

**Teacher's Resource Library**

Activity 54
Workbook Activity 54

## Teaching Suggestions

### ■ Vocabulary

*natural disaster, earthquake, hurricane, hurricane warning, hurricane watch, thunderstorm, flood, flood warning, flood watch, tornado, tornado warning, tornado watch*

Write the vocabulary words on the chalkboard and discuss their meanings. Invite students to write newspaper headlines using each of the words. Ask volunteers to read their headlines to the class.

### ■ Teaching the Lesson

Lead a class discussion about students' experiences with adverse weather conditions. Ask if their experiences posed a danger to them or to their family. Make a list of safety practices that students' families followed during these conditions. Save the list to compare with information students learn throughout the lesson.

Have students read about preparing for an earthquake on page 297.

---

Ask:

- What should you do if you live in an area that has earthquakes often? (securely bolt heavy objects to a solid wall, make sure heavy objects are stored on shelves close to the floor, don't hang picture frames or mirrors above beds)

Have students read about what to do during and after an earthquake on page 298.

Ask:

- What should you do if you are in school during an earthquake? (Students should suggest that they remain calm, stay away from windows, get under a sturdy desk or table, and cover their head and face with their arms.)

- What should you do if you are outdoors during an earthquake? (If outdoors, stay in an open area. Avoid buildings, power lines, trees, and other tall objects that could topple during the earthquake.)

## LEARNING STYLES

**Tactile/Kinesthetic** Present a model of how the earth's plates shift to produce an earthquake. Hold up two erasers side by side. Each eraser represents a plate. Press the erasers against each other. Let the erasers move suddenly a little past each other. This is the earthquake. Let students conduct their own demonstration by snapping their fingers. The thumb and finger represent two plates. As students press their thumb and finger, stress builds up. Enough stress builds up so that the thumb and finger slide past each other, releasing energy in the form of sound waves—a snap. These sound waves are like the waves that travel out from the origin of an earthquake and cause damage.

Earthquakes can cause buildings and highways to topple and crumble. Water lines and gas lines are also damaged during earthquakes. Broken gas lines are the most common cause of fires related to earthquakes.

### What Should You Do During and After an Earthquake?

During an earthquake, try to stay calm. If you are inside, get under a sturdy table or desk. Crouch down and cover your head and face with your arms. If the table or desk starts to move, hold onto it and move with it. Stay where you are until the shaking stops completely. Stay away from windows and glass doors. Don't try to run outside or use an elevator, an escalator, or the stairs.

If you are outdoors, stay in an open area. Avoid buildings, power lines, trees, or other objects that could topple during the earthquake. When it is safe to move about, make sure that you stay away from downed power lines. They could kill you if you touch them.

**Hurricane**
*A tropical storm that forms over the ocean*

**Hurricane warning**
*A situation in which a hurricane has reached land*

**Hurricane watch**
*A warning to prepare for a hurricane*

**Thunderstorm**
*A severe weather condition that produces thunder, lightning, and rain*

**If you are with a group of people outdoors during a thunderstorm, is it better to spread out or stay together? Explain your answer.**

Once the shaking stops, clean up any spills and broken glass. Have an adult check for gas and water leaks and for broken electrical wires. If damage is found, remind the adult to turn off the water, gas, or electricity at the source. Check the inside and outside of your house or apartment for cracks and other damage to walls.

## How Can You Stay Safe During a Thunderstorm?

A **thunderstorm** can form anywhere in the United States. It is a storm that produces thunder, lightning, and large amounts of rain. While thunder can be scary at times, it cannot harm you. Lightning, however, is dangerous. A single lightning bolt can discharge millions of volts of electricity. When indoors during a thunderstorm, stay away from open doors and windows. Don't use electrical appliances. Stay away from sinks and tubs that contain water. Do not use the phone except in an emergency.

If you are outdoors, avoid tall trees, hilltops, and isolated metal objects, such as fences and water towers. Crouch down and bend over to make yourself as small as possible. Do *not* lie flat on the ground and do *not* lie in a low spot where water can collect.

## What Dangers Are Associated With Hurricanes?

**Hurricanes** are tropical storms that form over the ocean. The winds generated by these storms blow at speeds of at least 75 miles per hour around a storm center called an eye. Hurricanes generally affect the eastern United States and states that border the Gulf of Mexico.

Hurricanes are storms that are easily tracked. If a hurricane is expected to reach land within a few days, a **hurricane watch** is issued. During a watch, people in the affected area should prepare for the heavy winds and rains produced by the storm. When a **hurricane warning** is issued, people should evacuate, or leave, the area. Before leaving, the gas and water mains should be closed. Electricity should also be turned off. Only necessities should be taken to the evacuation points. People should stay at the emergency shelters until officials tell them to leave.

*Preventing Injuries    Chapter 14*    **299**

Have students read about preparing for thunderstorms and hurricanes on page 299.

Ask:

Why is it unsafe to find shelter under a tree during a thunderstorm? (Lightning usually strikes tall objects such as trees.)

- What should you do if you are indoors during a thunderstorm? (Stay away from open doors and windows. Stay away from sinks and tubs that contain water. Don't use electrical appliances. Don't use the phone except in an emergency.)

- What is a hurricane? (A hurricane is a tropical storm that forms over the ocean and has winds of at least 75 miles per hour.)

- What is the difference between a hurricane watch and a hurricane warning? (A hurricane watch warns you to prepare for a hurricane. A hurricane warning tells you that a hurricane has reached land and that you should evacuate the area.)

Have students read about safety practices during a tornado and a flood on page 300.

Ask:

- What is a tornado? (A tornado is a whirling, funnel-shaped storm that forms and moves over land.)

- What is the difference between a tornado watch and a tornado warning? (A tornado watch means there is a possibility that a tornado will develop. A tornado warning means a tornado has been sighted in the area.)

- Why do you think it might be dangerous to drink water from a faucet during and after a flood? (The water supply might be contaminated by sewer water that has been backed up and flowed into the drinking source.)

## Lesson 5 Review Answers

1) If you are outdoors during an earthquake, stay in an open area. Avoid buildings, power lines, trees, or other objects that could topple during the earthquake.
2) If you are indoors during a thunderstorm, stay away from open doors and windows. Don't use electrical appliances. Stay away from sinks and tubs that contain water. Don't use the phone except in an emergency.
3) If a hurricane warning is issued, evacuate the area.
4) If you are outdoors during a flood, head for higher ground. Do not cross any streams in which water is at or above knee level.
5) If you are outside surrounded by tall trees during a thunderstorm, crouch down and bend over to make yourself as small as possible. Do *not* lie flat on the ground and do *not* lie in a low spot where water can collect.

### APPLICATION

**At Home**
With a parent or guardian, encourage students to make a safety plan for the disaster(s) that affect their area. Invite volunteers to share their plans with the class.

---

**Flood**
*A condition in which a body of water overflows and covers land that is not usually under water*

**Flood warning**
*A situation in which flooding has occurred*

**Flood watch**
*A situation in which flooding is possible*

**Tornado**
*A whirling, funnel-shaped storm that forms over land*

**Tornado warning**
*An alert issued when a tornado has been spotted in an area*

**Tornado watch**
*A situation in which a tornado may develop*

### Safety Tip

Find out what kinds of natural disasters are likely to affect your area. With an adult, make plans that you can follow during each type of disaster.

---

### How Can You Be Safe During a Tornado?

A **tornado** is a whirling, funnel-shaped storm that forms and moves over land. When a **tornado watch** is issued, there is a possibility that a tornado will develop. A **tornado warning** is issued when a tornado is spotted in an area.

When a tornado warning is issued in your area, follow these rules. If indoors, go to the basement and stay there. If the building you are in doesn't have a basement, go to the lowest floor. If you are outdoors during a tornado warning, lie flat in a low spot on the ground. If you are in a car, get out and go into a building if possible. If you are in the storm's path, move away from the funnel cloud at a right angle to its path.

### What Should You Do If Floods Affect Your Area?

A **flood** is a condition in which a body of water overflows and covers land that is not usually under water. If the possibility of flooding exists, a **flood watch** is issued. A **flood warning** is a situation in which you should head for higher ground because flooding has occurred.

During a flood, don't try to cross a stream in which water is at or above knee level. If you are a passenger in a car, make sure the driver does not drive through an underpass that is flooded. If the car stalls, make sure all the passengers get out and go to a safe place.

**LESSON 5 REVIEW** Write the answers to these questions on a separate sheet of paper. Use complete sentences.

1) If you are outdoors during an earthquake, what should you do?
2) If you are indoors during a thunderstorm, what should you do?
3) What should you do if a hurricane warning is issued?
4) If you are outdoors during a flood, what should you do?
5) Suppose that during a severe thunderstorm, you are outside surrounded by tall trees. How would you protect yourself?

**300** Chapter 14 *Preventing Injuries*

---

Name ___ Date ___ Period ___ | Chapter 14 Activity 54

**Safety During Natural Disasters**

**Directions** Write *T* if the statement is true or *F* if it is false.

___ 1) A natural gas line exploding is an example of a natural disaster.
___ 2) The largest earthquake in U.S. history occurred in California.
___ 3) If you are inside during an earthquake, take cover behind the curtains.
___ 4) If you are outside during an earthquake, avoid objects that could fall on you.
___ 5) Thunderstorms in the United States stay mainly on the Gulf Coast.
___ 6) An earthquake is a shaking of rocks in the earth's crust.
___ 7) A flood is safe to cross if the water reaches above your knees.
___ 8) During a tornado, do not go into the basement, and do avoid all windows.
___ 9) A tornado usually forms over land.
___ 10) If you are in a car during a tornado, try to stay ahead of the storm.
___ 11) A lightning bolt can discharge a million volts of electricity.
___ 12) The safest place to be in a thunderstorm is under a water tower.
___ 13) If you live in a place with earthquakes, be sure heavy objects are bolted down.
___ 14) Driving through floodwater is the safest way to cross it.
___ 15) A hurricane is a tropical storm that forms over the ocean.

**Activity 54**

---

Name ___ Date ___ Period ___ | Chapter 14 Workbook Activity 54

**Safety During Natural Disasters**

**Directions** Write *T* if the statement is true or *F* if it is false.

___ 1) An earthquake is a shaking of rocks in the earth's crust.
___ 2) A natural gas line exploding is an example of a natural disaster.
___ 3) The largest earthquake in U.S. history occurred in California.
___ 4) If you are inside during an earthquake, take cover behind the curtains.
___ 5) If you are outside during an earthquake, avoid objects that could fall on you.
___ 6) Thunderstorms in the United States stay mainly on the Gulf Coast.
___ 7) A hurricane is a tropical storm that forms over the ocean.
___ 8) A flood is safe to cross if the water reaches above your knees.
___ 9) During a tornado, do not go into the basement, and do avoid all windows.
___ 10) A tornado usually forms over land.
___ 11) If you are in a car during a tornado, try to stay ahead of the storm.
___ 12) A lightning bolt can discharge a million volts of electricity.
___ 13) The safest place to be in a thunderstorm is under a water tower.
___ 14) If you live in a place with earthquakes, be sure heavy objects are bolted down.
___ 15) Driving through floodwater is the safest way to cross it.

**Workbook Activity 54**

■ Teens are more at risk of injuries than adults. This is because teens often act suddenly when faced with certain situations.

■ Drugs increase a person's risk of injury because drugs change one's perception and alter reaction time.

■ Keeping noise levels down so that the driver can concentrate can reduce car collisions.

■ Warming up and cooling down before and after a game or an activity reduces your chances of injury.

■ To reduce firearm injuries, always treat a handgun or rifle as if it is loaded.

■ Nearly all house fires are preventable. Checking the house for fire hazards reduces the number of fires. Knowing what to do if a fire breaks out reduces your risk of injury.

■ A responsible baby-sitter keeps full attention on the children. A responsible sitter also knows what to do and who to contact in an emergency.

■ When calling 911, stay calm, talk slowly to the operator, and don't hang up until you are told to do so.

■ Use rules to make using the Internet a safe and enjoyable activity.

■ An emergency kit should include a battery-operated radio, flashlights, batteries, candles, matches, and a first aid kit.

■ Natural disasters can be caused by earthquakes, tornadoes, hurricanes, floods, and thunderstorms.

## ■ Using the Chapter Summary

To further reinforce the facts and concepts presented in the chapter, read and discuss with students the questions that follow.

### Ask:

- Why are teens more at risk of injuries than adults? (Teens often act suddenly when faced with certain situations.)

- How do drugs increase a person's risk of injury? (Drugs change one's perception and alter reaction time.)

- As a passenger in a car, what can you do to reduce car collisions? (Keep the noise level down. Refuse to get into a car with a driver who has been drinking alcohol or taking other drugs. Ride only with drivers who obey all traffic laws.)

- How can house fires be prevented? (Checking the house for fire hazards reduces the number of fires. Knowing what to do if a fire breaks out reduces one's risk of injury.)

- As a responsible baby-sitter, what should you do? (Keep full attention on the children, and know what to do and who to contact in an emergency.)

- What should you do when calling 911? (When calling 911, stay calm, talk slowly to the operator, and don't hang up until you are told to do so.)

- Name some items an emergency kit should contain. (a battery-operated radio, flashlights, batteries, candles, matches, and a first aid kit)

- What are some natural disasters that were discussed in this chapter? (earthquakes, tornadoes, hurricanes, floods, thunderstorms)

The Teacher's Resource Library includes two parallel forms of the Chapter 14 Mastery Test. The difficulty level of the two forms is equivalent. You may wish to use one form as a pretest and the other form as a posttest.

## Review Answers

### Comprehension: Identifying Facts

1) Hurricanes 2) Internet 3) earthquake 4) E-mail 5) thunderstorm 6) flood warning 7) firearms 8) flood 9) hurricane watch 10) life-threatening emergency

### Comprehension: Identifying Facts

On a separate sheet of paper, write the correct word or words from the Word Bank to complete each sentence.

| WORD BANK | | |
|---|---|---|
| earthquake | flood warning | thunderstorm |
| e-mail | hurricanes | tornado |
| emergency kit | hurricane watch | tornado watch |
| firearms | Internet | |
| flood | life-threatening emergency | |

1) _____ are storms that form over oceans.

2) You can use a computer to find information on the _____.

3) The shaking of the rocks that make up the earth's crust is an _____.

4) _____ is an electronic message sent over the Internet.

5) A severe storm that produces thunder, lightning, and lots of rain is a _____.

6) A _____ is issued when rivers overflow their banks and cover surrounding land.

7) Handguns and rifles are _____.

8) A _____ occurs when land that is normally dry is covered with water from a river or stream.

9) A _____ is issued when a tropical storm may hit nearby land.

10) A person having a heart attack is an example of a _____.

---

Name _____ Date _____ Period _____ | Chapter 14 Mastery Test A page 1

### Chapter 14 Mastery Test A

**Directions** Read each sentence. Write *T* if the statement is true or *F* if the statement is false.

_____ 1) Teens are more at risk of injuring themselves than adults are.

_____ 2) Drugs rarely change how a person sees a situation.

_____ 3) Keep the noise level down while you are a passenger in a vehicle so the driver can concentrate.

_____ 4) Wearing proper safety equipment is not necessary while playing sports.

_____ 5) Handguns and rifles are not dangerous, so you don't have to store them in a locked cabinet.

_____ 6) Over 90 percent of house fires are preventable.

_____ 7) To help reduce the risk of fire, don't overload electrical outlets or extension cords.

_____ 8) While baby-sitting, be sure to keep your full attention on the children.

_____ 9) Call 911 for every injury.

_____ 10) A life-threatening emergency is any situation in which a person might die if medical attention isn't provided immediately.

_____ 11) When walking, always go alone and take shortcuts through alleys and side streets.

©AGS® American Guidance Service, Inc. Permission is granted to reproduce for classroom use only.  Discover Health

---

Name _____ Date _____ Period _____ | Chapter 14 Mastery Test A page 2

### Chapter 14 Mastery Test A, continued

_____ 12) The Internet is a useful tool and is never harmful.

_____ 13) If you post something at a site on the Internet, never include your name, address, or phone number.

_____ 14) An emergency kit should include a radio and a first aid kit.

_____ 15) You do not need to prepare for natural disasters.

_____ 16) During an earthquake, try to stay calm.

_____ 17) During a storm, thunder is dangerous.

_____ 18) Hurricanes are tropical storms that form over the ocean.

_____ 19) If you are outdoors during a tornado warning, lie flat in a low spot on the ground.

_____ 20) During a flood, it is safe to cross a stream in which water is at or above knee level.

©AGS® American Guidance Service, Inc. Permission is granted to reproduce for classroom use only.  Discover Health

**Chapter 14 Mastery Test A**

11) Flashlights, a radio, and a first-aid kit are important items that should be in an _____.

12) When weather conditions are such that a funnel-shaped storm might form, a _____ is issued.

13) A _____ is a funnel-shaped cloud that forms on land and can cause much destruction as it moves in a narrow path.

## Comprehension: Understanding Main Ideas

Write the answers to these questions on a separate sheet of paper. Use complete sentences.

14) Why do most injuries occur?

15) What should be included in a fire escape plan?

16) How can you protect yourself from danger while walking home alone?

17) Name at least three things specific to your family that you would include in an emergency kit.

## Critical Thinking: Write Your Opinion

18) Why do you think everyone should be prepared for each kind of natural disaster?

19) How do you protect yourself against harm when using the Internet?

20) What would you do if a friend drank some alcohol and insisted on driving?

**Test Taking Tip** Avoid waiting until the night before a test to study. Plan your study time so that you can get a good night's sleep the night before a test.

---

11) emergency kit  12) tornado watch
13) tornado

## Comprehension: Understanding Main Ideas

14) Most injuries occur because people are careless or don't take the time to think about what might happen in a given situation. A lot of injuries also occur because people don't realize the risks involved in various situations.

15) Answers will vary. A fire escape plan might include a floor plan with escape routes shown from each room; where to meet outside the burning building; who will assist those needing help; who will call the fire department once the house or apartment has been evacuated, and so on.

16) Staying on well-lit and well-traveled streets, paying attention to the people and cars around you, and not talking to strangers are a few ways to stay safe while walking alone.

17) Answers will vary but might include medication and special foods for those with food allergies.

## Critical Thinking: Write Your Opinion

18) Even if a certain type of natural disaster isn't likely to strike your area, knowing what to do if such a disaster strikes in an area where you might be visiting is important because being prepared greatly reduces the injuries due to natural events.

19) Answers might include never giving out one's real name or address, going to sites that are appropriate for one's age and values, not responding to offers that sound "too good to be true," and so on.

20) Answers will vary but might include taking away the friend's keys and offering to drive, calling a cab, or calling a responsible adult to pick up the friend.

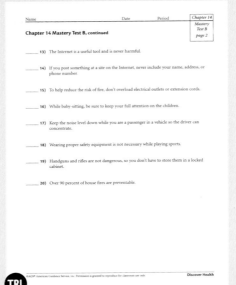

**Chapter 14 Mastery Test B**

## Introducing the Chapter

Ask students to think back to a time when they had a medical emergency that required first aid. Encourage volunteers to explain what first aid treatments, if any, were provided when the emergency happened. (Students might mention a bad cut, a broken bone, or a sprain.)

Ask a volunteer to read the introduction. Then discuss the Goals for Learning.

## Ask:

• How did the treatment you received keep the injury or other medical problem from getting worse? (Accept all reasonable answers, such as the fact that the treatment stopped bleeding or kept a break or sprain from getting worse.)

• Why is it important to know first aid? (It is important to know first aid so that you can help someone who has an injury in an emergency.)

# First Aid for Injuries

**H**ave you ever accidentally cut yourself? Did you ever take a bad fall off a bike or see a friend sprain an ankle? Each of these situations is an emergency—a sudden need for quick action. An emergency can happen at any time. Knowing how to handle it can keep a bad situation from getting worse. It might mean the difference between life and death.

In this chapter, you will learn how to provide basic first aid in emergencies. You will learn the signs of choking, respiratory failure, cardiovascular failure, severe bleeding, and shock. You will learn how to provide first aid for these and other life-threatening emergencies.

### Goals for Learning

▶ To list some of the guidelines for basic first aid

▶ To describe basic first aid techniques for common injuries

▶ To demonstrate the Heimlich maneuver and describe the universal sign for choking

▶ To explain the steps of rescue breathing and CPR

---

**Student Study Guide 21, page 1**

**Student Study Guide 21, page 2**

## Lesson 1

### What to Do First

Emergency
Medical Service
(EMS)
*An
intercommunity
emergency system
that sends out
fire, police, and
ambulances by
dialing 911 or 0
for operator*

First aid
*The immediate
care given to a
sick or an injured
person before
professional
help arrives*

**Keep a list of
emergency
numbers near
your phone.**

Emergency Medical Service staff provide first aid for
injured people before moving them to a medical facility.

**F**irst aid is the immediate emergency care given to a sick or an injured person before professional medical help arrives. The information in this chapter is only a first step toward first aid training. Classes offered by schools, fire departments, and park districts help you develop your first aid skills.

#### What Are the Basic Guidelines for First Aid?

The most important thing to do for a victim in an emergency is to remain calm. This helps you think clearly and provide the best care possible. Then follow these guidelines:

1. Look around the immediate area.
   Are you or the victim in any danger of fire, explosion, or drowning? If so, move the victim and yourself out of harm's way. If there is no danger, do not move the victim.

2. Find out if the victim is conscious by tapping the shoulder or loudly asking if he or she is all right. If the victim is not conscious, stay there and ask someone to call for help. If you are alone, quickly call 911 or 0 for the operator. This will put you in touch with the **Emergency Medical Service (EMS)** for your area. EMS personnel will ask you for your name, location, and details about the emergency.

3. Quickly return to the victim and check for breathing and a pulse. If the person is conscious, ask permission to provide care. Check for any injuries. See if the person has emergency medical identification, such as a tag, bracelet, or card. Cover the victim with a blanket or coat to prevent shock. Apply direct pressure to bleeding areas. Continue to provide care until help arrives.

*First Aid for Injuries    Chapter 15*    **305**

---

## Lesson at a Glance

### Chapter 15  Lesson 1

**Overview**  In this lesson, students learn how to give first aid to an injured person before professional help arrives on the scene.

### Objectives

■ To list the general guidelines for providing first aid.

**Student Pages** 305–306
**Audiocassette**
**Teacher's Resource Library**

Activity 55
Workbook Activity 55

## Teaching Suggestions

### ■ Vocabulary

*Emergency Medical Service (EMS), first aid, Good Samaritan Laws, infectious, Universal Precautions*

Write the vocabulary words on the chalkboard. Have students write definitions of the words, using their prior knowledge. Then read the definitions from the textbook. Have students compare their previous ideas with the definitions.

### ■ Teaching the Lesson

Before reading the lesson, have students brainstorm about what they would do if someone fainted near them. Then ask students to brainstorm about what they would not do. Write students' responses on the chalkboard. Return to the responses after the lesson to see how accurate students' original responses were.

Have students read about guidelines for first aid on pages 305.

---

Ask:

• What is first aid? (First aid is the immediate emergency care given to a sick or an injured person before professional help arrives.)

• Why is it important first to find out if there is danger of fire, explosion, or drowning when starting to give first aid? (It is important to look around for immediate dangers because you cannot help the victim if you are both in danger of more injuries.)

## Technology

Invite someone from the local 911 emergency services dispatching system to come to class to talk about how the system works, when it should be used, and how people can use the system most effectively. Encourage students to prepare questions in advance for the guest.

Have students read about Good Samaritan Laws and Universal Precautions on page 306.

### Ask:

- Why are Good Samaritan Laws necessary? (Good Samaritan Laws are necessary to protect people who assist victims in an emergency. If these laws did not exist, some people might be reluctant to help in an emergency.)

### Lesson 1 Review Answers

1) First aid is the immediate emergency care given to a sick or an injured person before professional help arrives.
2) It is important to remain calm so that you can think clearly and provide the best care possible.
3) Good Samaritan Laws are laws that protect people who provide first aid in an emergency.
4) Three examples of Universal Precautions are wearing latex gloves, wearing masks, and properly disposing of materials that have come into contact with body fluids.
5) You would first make sure there is no immediate danger in the area. Then you would find out if the person is conscious to ask if he or she is all right. If not, you would call 911 for help or send someone else to call. Then cover the victim with a blanket or coat and wait for help to arrive.

### APPLICATION

**At Home**
Encourage students to work with family members to make up a list of items that should be available in the home first aid kit. Items might include adhesive and cotton bandages in various sizes, antibiotic creams, ice packs, antibacterial sprays, and latex gloves. Tell students that they can add to the list as they read the chapter and find out more about the treatment for various injuries.

---

technology

## 911 SOFTWARE

Every day thousands of emergencies arise, and people dial 911 for fire, police, or EMS help. This life-saving emergency software has caller identification and a dispatch system that sends the appropriate emergency help quickly. The dispatcher's screen shows the caller's address and phone number before the call is answered. Computerized maps connect to the database to provide the quickest route to the caller. Deaf and hard-of-hearing people can call 911 by using a TDD (telecommunications device for the deaf). All calls are recorded.

> **Good Samaritan Laws** *The laws that protect people who assist victims in an emergency*
>
> **Infectious** *Contagious*
>
> **Universal Precautions** *The methods of self-protection that prevent contact with blood or other body fluids*

### What Are Good Samaritan Laws?

Many states have **Good Samaritan Laws**. These laws protect people who provide first aid in an emergency. These people must use common sense and the skills for which they are trained. The American Red Cross and the American Heart Association provide classes in basic first aid. Rescuers are not expected to risk their own lives in providing emergency care.

### What Are Universal Precautions?

A person who provides first aid should use **Universal Precautions**. These precautions protect rescuers or victims from **infectious**, or contagious, disease by preventing contact with blood or other body fluids. Universal Precautions include wearing latex gloves and masks whenever possible. Another Universal Precaution is disposing of materials like bandages that have come in contact with body fluids.

**LESSON 1 REVIEW** Write the answers to these questions on a separate sheet of paper. Use complete sentences.

> **How would you help a friend who broke an ankle while playing soccer?**

1) What is first aid?
2) Why is it important to remain calm in an emergency?
3) What are Good Samaritan Laws?
4) Provide three examples of Universal Precautions.
5) Suppose you see an older adult lying on the sidewalk. He had been shoveling snow. What would you do?

306   *Chapter 15   First Aid for Injuries*

---

| Name _____ Date _____ Period _____ | Chapter 15 Activity 55 |
|---|---|

**What to Do First**

**Directions** Write *T* if the statement is true or *F* if it is false.

_____ 1) Remaining calm in an emergency is the best thing to do.

_____ 2) Good Samaritan Laws protect people who provide first aid in emergencies.

_____ 3) Rescuers are expected to risk their own lives in providing first aid.

_____ 4) Universal Precautions include wearing rubber gloves and masks.

_____ 5) Bandages that have come into contact with body fluids should be disposed of.

_____ 6) Calling 911 will put you in touch with a hospital.

_____ 7) If you or a victim are in danger, move out of the way.

_____ 8) To prevent shock, cover an accident victim with a blanket or a coat.

_____ 9) Apply direct pressure to bleeding areas to prevent further bleeding.

_____ 10) First aid is emergency care given to an injured person before medical help arrives.

**Activity 55**

---

| Name _____ Date _____ Period _____ | Chapter 15 Workbook Activity 55 |
|---|---|

**What to Do First**

**Directions** Write *T* if the statement is true or *F* if it is false.

_____ 1) First aid is emergency care given to an injured person before medical help arrives.

_____ 2) Remaining calm in an emergency is the best thing to do.

_____ 3) Good Samaritan Laws protect people who provide first aid in emergencies.

_____ 4) Rescuers are expected to risk their own lives in providing first aid.

_____ 5) Universal Precautions include wearing rubber gloves and masks.

_____ 6) Bandages that have come into contact with body fluids should be disposed of.

_____ 7) If you or a victim are in danger, move out of the way.

_____ 8) To prevent shock, cover an accident victim with a blanket or a coat.

_____ 9) Apply direct pressure to bleeding areas to prevent further bleeding.

**Workbook Activity 55**

## Lesson 2 — Caring for Common Injuries

**Elevate**
*Raise*

**Fracture**
*A cracked or broken bone*

**Splint**
*A rigid object that keeps a broken limb in place*

**Sprain**
*The sudden tearing or stretching of tendons or ligaments*

Most situations that require first aid are slight to average emergencies. You have probably experienced some of the injuries described in this lesson. Were they treated correctly? Proper immediate care can prevent an injury from leading to other problems.

### What Is First Aid for Broken Bones and Sprains?

If the injured part of the body is swollen, crooked, or bruised, the person may have a **fracture**, or broken bone. He or she may be in severe pain or be unable to move that body part. Call EMS immediately. Keep the body part in the same position in which you found it and apply a **splint**. A splint is a rigid object that keeps a broken limb in place. It can be made of wooden sticks, rulers, pencils, or rolled up magazines. You should tie the splint above and below the fracture to keep that part of the body from moving.

A **sprain** is the sudden tearing or stretching of tendons or ligaments connecting joints. Sprains usually occur in ankles, wrists, or knees. Sprains often occur while playing sports but can also happen while walking. If you suspect a sprain or fracture, remember to ICE (immobilize, cold, elevate) it. First, immobilize the limb. Next, apply cold compresses to reduce swelling. Then, **elevate** the limb to reduce further swelling.

**What would you do if you are walking with a friend and your friend sprains an ankle?**

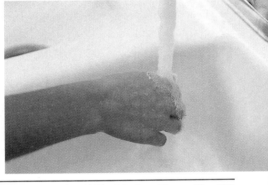
For first- and second-degree burns, run cold water to cool the burn.

*First Aid for Injuries   Chapter 15   307*

## Lesson at a Glance

### Chapter 15  Lesson 2

**Overview** In this lesson, students learn basic first aid techniques for some common injuries.

### Objectives

- To describe basic first aid techniques for common injuries.

**Student Pages** 307–310
**Audiocassette**
**Teacher's Resource Library**

Activity 56
Workbook Activity 56

## Teaching Suggestions

### ■ Vocabulary

*elevate, fracture, splint, sprain, heat exhaustion, heatstroke, hypothermia, frostbite, rabies, transmit*

Have students take turns reading the vocabulary words and definitions aloud. Discuss the words and have students use the words correctly in sentences. Invite students to share their sentences with the class.

### ■ Teaching the Lesson

Ask if there are any students who have taken first aid classes through a local community program or through an organization such as Girl Scouts, Campfire Inc., or Boy Scouts. If so, ask volunteers to share some aspects of this learning experience with the class.

Then have students read about first aid for broken bones and sprains on page 307.

Ask:

- How can you tell that an injury might be a fracture? (The victim might have a fracture if the injured part of the body is swollen, crooked, or bruised.)

- What is a sprain? (A sprain is the sudden tearing or stretching of tendons or ligaments connecting joints.)

## Healthy Subjects

Encourage students to contact the nearest office of the American Red Cross to find out how the organization works to help local communities during emergencies and natural disasters. Interested students might want to volunteer with the Red Cross if there are opportunities.

Have students read about first aid for burns and eye injuries on page 308.

### Ask:

- Describe the three types, or degrees, of burns. (A first-degree burn damages only the outer layer of skin. A second-degree burn affects the outer and underneath layers of skin. A third-degree burn extends through all layers of skin to the tissues underneath.)

- What is the first aid treatment for first- and second-degree burns? (First, remove the source of heat. Then cool the burn by applying large amounts of cool water. Last, cover the area loosely with clean bandages to prevent infection.)

- What is the first aid treatment for third-degree burns? (Get immediate professional attention.)

- What is the treatment for an object in the eye? (Flush the eye with lukewarm water, starting from the corner near the nose. If the object is not removed, then seek medical help.)

### APPLICATION

**In the Community**
Ask students if any of them baby-sit. Discuss why it would be good for baby-sitters to know first aid procedures. Mention that community organizations, such as libraries, hospitals, and fire departments, often offer first aid classes for teens. Encourage students to look into these classes. Have students compare the classes offered by each organization.

---

### Social Studies

### THE AMERICAN RED CROSS

The Red Cross began in Switzerland in 1863. A nurse named Clara Barton helped start the American Red Cross in the United States in 1881. The Red Cross helps people during wars, national disasters, or other serious needs. The Red Cross relies on volunteers to help with direct care, fund-raising, and disaster relief. They donate blood used by hospitals during national emergencies. Volunteers make the Red Cross work.

### What Other Problems Require First Aid?

**Burns**

There are three types, or degrees, of burns. A first-degree burn damages only the outer layer of skin. Most sunburns are first-degree burns. A second-degree burn affects the outer and underneath layers of skin. The area may swell and blister. A third-degree burn extends through all layers of skin to the tissues underneath.

For first- and second-degree burns, stop the burn by removing the source of heat. Then cool the burn by applying large amounts of cool water. Finally, cover the area loosely with clean bandages to prevent infection. Third-degree burns require immediate professional attention. Call EMS, stay with the victim, and watch closely for signs of shock. You will learn about shock later in this chapter.

### Writing About Health

Think about outdoor activities you enjoy throughout the year. Write about these activities. Tell the ways you can protect yourself from injuries related to temperature.

### Objects in the Eye

If there is an eye injury where you suspect an object is still in the eye, do not rub the eye. Flush it with lukewarm water starting from the corner near the nose. This may remove the object. If not, seek medical help.

### Nosebleeds

You or someone you know has probably had a nosebleed. For a minor nosebleed, sit down and lean forward. Hold the nostril with direct pressure for about ten minutes while breathing through your mouth. You can also apply a cold cloth across the forehead or bridge of the nose. If the bleeding doesn't stop, seek medical help.

### Exposure to Heat and Cold

**Heat exhaustion** occurs from too much activity or physical exercise in very hot temperatures. Signs of heat exhaustion include weakness, heavy sweating, muscle cramping, headaches, and dizziness. To give first aid for heat exhaustion, move the person out of the heat. Loosen the clothing, apply cool cloths to the forehead and neck, and offer water to sip.

**Heatstroke** may result when a person stays in the heat too long. The main sign of heatstroke is a lack of sweating. Other signs include red skin, vomiting, rapid pulse, confusion, very high body temperature, and sudden unconsciousness. Call EMS or 911 immediately and treat the same as for heat exhaustion.

The opposite of heatstroke is **hypothermia**, or being cold too long. This can occur if someone is not dressed properly in cold weather or if clothing becomes wet. Signs of hypothermia include shivering, slurred speech, and below-normal body temperature. A person can die from hypothermia. If the person isn't breathing, perform rescue breathing. Have someone call for help immediately.

**Action for Health**

### FIRST AID TRAINING

One of the best ways you can prepare for emergencies is to take a class in first aid training. Instructors will teach you the skills you need to give effective first aid. Through these classes, you will practice different first aid treatments on other members of the class and on life-size dolls. Check with your fire department, hospital, community center, park district, Red Cross, or American Heart Association for information about first aid classes.

Have students read about first aid for nosebleeds and exposure to heat and cold on page 309.

### Ask:

- What should you do if you get a nosebleed? (For a nosebleed, sit down and lean forward. Hold the nostril with direct pressure for about ten minutes while breathing through your mouth. You can also apply a cold cloth across the forehead or bridge of the nose.)

- What is the first aid treatment for heat exhaustion? (Move the person out of the heat. Loosen the clothing, apply cool cloths to the forehead and neck, and offer water to sip.)

- What is hypothermia and how does it occur? (Hypothermia is being cold too long. This can occur if someone is not dressed properly in cold weather or if clothing becomes wet.)

### Action for Health

Ask students who attend first aid classes to report back to their classmates on the experience. Invite students to share any useful information they learned in the classes by making an oral presentation. If the experience was a good one, other students might be encouraged to sign up for the classes as well.

### LEARNING STYLES

**Tactile/Kinesthetic** Invite groups of students to pantomime how they would give first aid in the various emergencies described in this lesson. Have the rest of the class rate each group on how well they follow the first aid guidelines in the textbook.

### MULTICULTURAL CONNECTION

Encourage students to research how people who live in extreme climates, such as the Arctic regions of North America, Europe, and Asia, or the deserts of Africa and the Middle East, have adapted to prevent heatstroke or hypothermia. Have students make oral reports to the class.

Have students read about first aid for frostbite and for bites on page 310.

Ask:

- How should you give first aid to someone with frostbite? (For frostbite victims, warm the affected area gradually. Bring the person into a warm place and put warm water on the site. Do not rub the area. Cover with clean, dry bandages and call for medical help.)

- Why should bites from animals be taken seriously? (Some bites can transmit rabies to humans.)

## Lesson 2 Review Answers

1) ICE stands for immobilize, cold, and elevate, the three things you do to the injured area when you suspect someone has a fracture or sprain.

2) The three types of burns are first-degree, second-degree, and third-degree burns.

3) Heatstroke is a condition that results from being in high heat too long. Victims of heatstroke do not sweat. They also can have red skin, vomiting, rapid pulse, confusion, very high body temperature, and sudden unconsciousness.

4) You should wash the area immediately with soap and water and apply a dressing. You should also seek medical care if the animal is not a family pet.

5) If the person was having heat exhaustion, you would see the following warning signs: weakness, heavy sweating, muscle cramping, headache, dizziness.

## GLOBAL CONNECTION

Three organizations that help train people in first aid techniques throughout the world are the World Health Organization (WHO), the United Nations Children's Emergency Fund (UNICEF), and the International Red Cross. Invite students to research one of the organizations to find out how they work, where they work, and how they have improved the health of people worldwide. Suggest that students report on one incident in which the organization gave emergency aid.

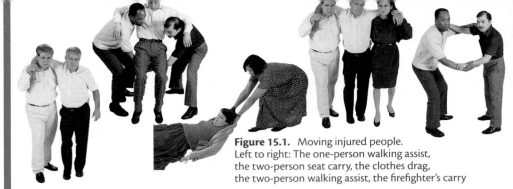

**Figure 15.1.** Moving injured people. Left to right: The one-person walking assist, the two-person seat carry, the clothes drag, the two-person walking assist, the firefighter's carry

**Frostbite**
*A tissue injury causing the tissue to freeze due to overexposure to cold temperatures*

**Rabies**
*A disease transmitted to humans through animal bites*

**Transmit**
*Spread*

**Frostbite** occurs when exposure to severe cold causes body tissue to freeze. Skin tissue will look gray or yellowish and feel numb, cold, and doughy. To treat frostbite, warm the affected area gradually. Bring the person into a warm place and put warm water on the site. Do not rub the area. Cover with clean, dry bandages and call for medical help.

**Bites**

Animal bites from dogs and other animals can **transmit**, or spread, diseases such as **rabies** to humans. If an animal bite occurs, wash the area immediately with soap and water and apply a dressing. Seek medical care if the animal is not a family pet.

Snakebites are serious if they come from one of the four poisonous snakes. These include the rattlesnake, copperhead, water moccasin, and coral snake. If a snakebite occurs, call for help.

*Health Tip*

Keep a first aid kit well stocked with bandages, antibiotic ointment, a chemical ice pack, latex gloves, scissors, and tweezers.

**LESSON 2 REVIEW** Write the answers to these questions on a separate piece of paper. Use complete sentences.

1) What does ICE mean?

2) What are the three types of burns?

3) Define and give the symptoms of heatstroke.

4) How should you treat an animal bite?

5) How would you know if a person was having heat exhaustion?

---

Name _____ Date _____ Period _____

| Chapter 15 |
| Activity |
| 56 |

**Caring for Common Injuries**

**Directions** Complete each sentence by writing the letter of the *best* word or words from the Word Bank in the space on the left-hand side of the page.

**Word Bank**

| | |
|---|---|
| a) animal bites | f) heat exhaustion | k) rabies |
| b) elevate | g) hypothermia | l) snakebite |
| c) first | h) ligaments | m) splint |
| d) fracture | i) lukewarm | n) third |
| e) frostbite | j) nosebleed | o) three |

____ 1) A cracked or broken bone is also called a _____.
____ 2) A _____ keeps a broken limb from moving.
____ 3) There are _____ types of burns.
____ 4) The worst kind of burn is a _____-degree burn.
____ 5) The best way to treat a _____ is to sit down and lean forward.
____ 6) The opposite of heatstroke is _____.
____ 7) A sprain is the sudden tearing of tendons or _____.
____ 8) A disease transmitted through animal bites is _____.
____ 9) To treat _____, warm the affected area of skin gradually.
____ 10) _____ from one of the four poisonous U.S. snakes is serious.
____ 11) ICE means immobilize, cold, and _____.
____ 12) If someone's eye has an object in it, flush the eye with _____ water.
____ 13) A sunburn is an example of a _____-degree burn.
____ 14) For all _____, wash the area with soap and warm water and apply a dressing.
____ 15) _____ results from physical exercise in very hot temperatures.

**TRL**

**Activity 56**

---

Name _____ Date _____ Period _____

| Chapter 15 |
| Workbook Activity |
| 56 |

**Caring for Common Injuries**

**Directions** Complete each sentence by writing the letter of the *best* word or words from the Word Bank in the space on the left-hand side of the page.

**Word Bank**

| | |
|---|---|
| a) animal bites | f) heat exhaustion | k) rabies |
| b) elevate | g) hypothermia | l) snakebite |
| c) first | h) ligaments | m) splint |
| d) fracture | i) lukewarm | n) third |
| e) frostbite | j) nosebleed | o) three |

____ 1) A sprain is the sudden tearing of tendons or _____.
____ 2) A cracked or broken bone is also called a _____.
____ 3) A _____ keeps a broken limb from moving.
____ 4) There are _____ types of burns.
____ 5) The worst kind of burn is a _____-degree burn.
____ 6) The best way to treat a _____ is to sit down and lean forward.
____ 7) The opposite of heatstroke is _____.
____ 8) _____ results from physical exercise in very hot temperatures.
____ 9) A disease transmitted through animal bites is _____.
____ 10) To treat _____, warm the affected area of skin gradually.
____ 11) _____ from one of the four poisonous U.S. snakes is serious.
____ 12) ICE means immobilize, cold, and _____.
____ 13) If someone's eye has an object in it, flush the eye with _____ water.
____ 14) A sunburn is an example of a _____-degree burn.
____ 15) For all _____, wash the area with soap and warm water and apply a dressing.

**TRL**

**Workbook Activity 56**

## First Aid for Bleeding, Shock, and Choking

**Shock**
*The physical reaction to injury in which the circulatory system fails to provide enough blood to the body*

Some emergencies can be life threatening if first aid is not provided before professional help arrives. Whether a victim lives may depend on the actions of helpful bystanders, such as yourself.

### What Is First Aid for Severe Bleeding?

Severe bleeding must be controlled quickly. A rescuer must do four things: (1) stop the bleeding, (2) protect the wound from infection, (3) treat the person for shock, and (4) get EMS help quickly.

If you are providing first aid for severe bleeding, you must protect yourself from possible infections. Use latex gloves if they are available. Cover the bleeding area with a clean cloth. Apply direct, even pressure with the palm of your hand. If blood soaks through the cloth, leave it in place and add more cloth or bandages. Try to elevate the wound above the heart to decrease the flow of blood to that area.

### What Is First Aid for Shock?

Severe bleeding, heart attack, and other serious injuries and illnesses can cause **shock**. Shock is a physical reaction to severe injury or illness. Shock can lead to death if not treated, even if the injury is not life threatening. Therefore, always treat for shock immediately, especially if you see the signs of shock. These signs may include a rapid or slow pulse, fast or slow breathing, pale skin, thirst, or confusion.

If a person is in shock, have someone call for EMS help immediately. Then use these first aid steps until help arrives:

1. Keep the person lying down. Elevate the legs higher than the heart to keep blood flowing to the heart. Do not elevate the legs, however, if you suspect there is a spine or neck injury.

---

*First Aid for Injuries    Chapter 15*    **311**

**Ask:**

- What is shock? (Shock is a physical reaction to severe injury or illness.)

- How should you treat someone in shock? (If someone is in shock, call EMS or 911 immediately. Then do the following until help arrives: Keep the person lying down. Elevate the legs higher than the heart unless there is a spinal or neck injury. Apply blankets or a coat around the victim. Do not give the victim any food or water.)

Have students read about first aid for choking and the Heimlich maneuver on page 312.

Ask:
_____

- What is the universal sign for choking? (clutching the throat between the thumb and index finger) What are some other signs of choking? (gasping, a weak cough, skin turning pale or blue, inability to speak, possible loss of consciousness)

- If you see a person grasping his or her throat, but the person can talk, what should you do? (Leave the person alone for the moment. Let the person try to cough up the object. Never pat the person's back.)

- What are the steps of the Heimlich maneuver? (1. Stand behind the choking victim. Wrap your arms around the person's waist. (2. Make a fist with one hand. (3. Place the thumb side of the fist against the middle of the victim's abdomen above the navel and below the ribs. (4. Use the other hand to grab the fist and give quick, upward thrusts into the abdomen. (5. Repeat step 4 until the object is forced out.)

**Heimlich maneuver**
*Firm, upward abdominal thrusts that force out foreign objects blocking an airway*

2. Maintain a constant body temperature by applying blankets or a coat around the victim.

3. Do not give the person any food or water. This can cause choking.

## What Is First Aid for Choking?

Have you ever had food go "down the wrong pipe"? Thousands of people choke to death each year because food or other objects block their airway. Knowing what to do in this emergency can truly be a lifesaver.

A person who is choking may clutch the throat between the thumb and index finger. This is the universal sign for choking. Other signs are gasping, a weak cough, skin turning pale or blue, inability to speak, and possible loss of consciousness. If a choking victim can still speak or cough, let the person try to cough up the object. Never pat the person's back. Doing so will cause the object to go farther down the windpipe and make matters worse.

If the choking victim cannot speak, cough, or breathe, you should do the **Heimlich maneuver**, using the following steps.

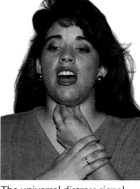

1. Stand behind the choking victim. Wrap your arms around the person's waist.

2. Make a fist with one hand.

3. Place the thumb side of the fist against the middle of the victim's abdomen above the navel and below the ribs.

4. Use the other hand to grab the fist and give quick, upward thrusts into the abdomen.

5. Repeat this action until the object is forced out.

The universal distress signal for choking.

**Figure 15.2.** First aid for choking

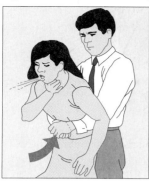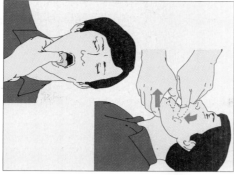

A. The Heimlich maneuver    B. The finger sweep

If the blockage is not removed and the person becomes unconscious, gently lower the victim to the floor. Have someone call 911. Open the victim's mouth and check the throat for the blockage, using the finger sweep. Use the following steps for the finger sweep.

1. Grasp the tongue and lower jaw between your thumb and fingers and lift the jaw.
2. Use your other index finger to sweep the back of the throat in a hooking action, trying to grasp the object.
3. If this doesn't work, begin rescue breathing, which will be described in Lesson 4.

Have students read about the finger sweep on page 313.

Ask:

- If the Heimlich maneuver does not remove the object blocking the victim's airway, what should you do? (Gently lower the victim to the floor and call 911. The finger sweep might then be tried.)

- What are the steps for the finger sweep? (1. Grasp the tongue and lower jaw between your thumb and fingers and lift the jaw. 2. Use your other index finger to sweep the back of the throat in a hooking action, trying to grasp the object. 3. If step 2 doesn't work, begin rescue breathing.)

 **BACKGROUND INFORMATION**

Inform students that their throats are designed for two functions—swallowing food and breathing. However, the throat is not used for both at the same time. Usually, when you swallow, the larynx moves up a bit, causing a piece of cartilage called the epiglottis to cover the windpipe. If, on occasion, the larynx doesn't move the epiglottis over the windpipe in time, food being swallowed can go down the wrong way into the windpipe instead of down the esophagus to the stomach. Coughing is usually enough to solve the problem. But if coughing doesn't dislodge the food, a person will start to choke.

**LEARNING STYLES**

 **Visual** Encourage students to make first aid posters that show the steps and procedures for any of the first aid techniques covered so far in the chapter. Display the posters on a bulletin board.

## Careers

Nurses do many types of jobs in hospitals, doctors' offices, home care facilities, and schools. Have a nurse come to class to discuss with students the many types of health care settings in which nurses work and the many types of duties they perform. Have the guest also discuss the difference between the duties of registered nurses and licensed practical nurses.

Have students read about first aid techniques for choking if you are alone on page 314.

### Ask:

- If you are alone and you start to choke, how can you help yourself? (Give yourself abdominal thrusts. Hold your hands together as in the Heimlich maneuver and thrust upward against your abdomen. You can also thrust your abdomen against the back of a chair.)

### Lesson 3 Review Answers

1) When providing first aid for severe bleeding, stop the bleeding, protect the wound from infection, treat the person for shock, and get EMS help quickly.
2) Elevating the legs of someone in shock keeps blood flowing to the heart.
3) The universal sign for choking is using the thumb and index finger to clutch the throat.
4) Patting a choking person's back is dangerous because it could cause the object to go farther down the windpipe and make matters worse.
5) If you are unable to remove the foreign object, you should try the finger sweep.

## Careers

### REGISTERED NURSE

Caring for sick and injured people is just one of the responsibilities of today's nurses. Nurses also teach patients how to care for themselves at home. Some nurses practice law. Others work with state legislatures and government agencies to develop laws that deal with health issues. There are different levels in nursing. To become a licensed practical nurse (LPN) requires one year in nursing school. To become a registered nurse (RN) requires two to four years in nursing school. Other advanced degrees in nursing can also be obtained.

If you are alone and are choking, you can give yourself abdominal thrusts. Hold your hands together as in the Heimlich maneuver and thrust upward against your abdomen. You can also thrust your abdomen against the back of a chair.

**LESSON 3 REVIEW** Write the answers to these questions on a separate sheet of paper. Use complete sentences.

1) What are four things that must be done when providing first aid for severe bleeding?
2) Why is it important to elevate the legs of someone in shock?
3) Describe the universal sign for choking.
4) Why is it important not to pat a choking person's back while he or she is coughing?
5) If a choking person has lost consciousness and you were able to remove the foreign object, what would you do next?

---

Name _____ Date _____ Period _____ | Chapter 15 Activity 57

**First Aid for Bleeding, Shock, and Choking**

**Directions** Complete each sentence by writing the letter of the *best* word or words from the Word Bank in the space on the left-hand side of the page.

**Word Bank**
a) decrease        f) physical
b) four            g) pressure
c) finger sweep    h) rubber gloves
d) Heimlich maneuver i) shock
e) patting         j) spine

_____ 1) To _____ blood flow to a wound, elevate the wound above the heart.
_____ 2) Slow pulse, slow or fast breathing, pale skin, thirst, or confusion are signs of _____.
_____ 3) Upward abdominal thrusts are part of the _____.
_____ 4) _____ the back of a person who is choking may make the object go farther down the throat.
_____ 5) Use a _____ to check if something is blocking a choking victim's throat.
_____ 6) In treating severe bleeding, always protect yourself with _____, if they are available.
_____ 7) Shock is a _____ reaction to injury.
_____ 8) If you think an injured person may have a neck or _____ injury, do not move the person.
_____ 9) To help stop severe bleeding, apply direct _____ with the palm of your hand.
_____ 10) A rescuer needs to do _____ things to control severe bleeding.

©AGS® American Guidance Service, Inc. Permission is granted to reproduce for classroom use only.        Discover Health

**Activity 57**

---

Name _____ Date _____ Period _____ | Chapter 15 Workbook Activity 57

**First Aid for Bleeding, Shock, and Choking**

**Directions** Complete each sentence by writing the letter of the *best* word or words from the Word Bank in the space on the left-hand side of the page.

**Word Bank**
a) decrease        f) physical
b) four            g) pressure
c) finger sweep    h) rubber gloves
d) Heimlich maneuver i) shock
e) patting         j) spine

_____ 1) A rescuer needs to do _____ things to control severe bleeding.
_____ 2) To _____ blood flow to a wound, elevate the wound above the heart.
_____ 3) Slow pulse, slow or fast breathing, pale skin, thirst, or confusion are signs of _____.
_____ 4) Upward abdominal thrusts are part of the _____.
_____ 5) _____ the back of a person who is choking may make the object go farther down the throat.
_____ 6) Use a _____ to check if something is blocking a choking victim's throat.
_____ 7) In treating severe bleeding, always protect yourself with _____, if they are available.
_____ 8) Shock is a _____ reaction to injury.
_____ 9) If you think an injured person may have a neck or _____ injury, do not move the person.
_____ 10) To help stop severe bleeding, apply direct _____ with the palm of your hand.

©AGS® American Guidance Service, Inc. Permission is granted to reproduce for classroom use only.        Discover Health

**Workbook Activity 57**

## First Aid for Heart Attacks and Poisoning

**Cardiac arrest**
*A condition in which the heart has stopped beating and there is no pulse*

**Cardiopulmonary resuscitation (CPR)**
*An emergency procedure for cardiac arrest*

**Irregular**
*Not normal*

As you have read, choking causes someone to stop breathing. Heart attack, drowning, and electrical shock are also causes of stopped breathing. Each of these emergencies requires immediate action.

### What Is First Aid for Heart Attacks?

If a blood vessel that supplies blood to the heart becomes blocked, part of the heart becomes damaged. This damage is a heart attack. Signs of a heart attack may include difficulty breathing, **irregular**, or not normal, heartbeat, nausea, or pain in the arm or jaw. Sometimes a person can stop breathing altogether. If a person's heart stops beating, the person is then in **cardiac arrest** and has no pulse. If a person has signs of cardiac arrest, call EMS or 911 immediately.

While waiting for EMS to arrive, you can help the victim by starting **cardiopulmonary resuscitation (CPR)**. This procedure uses both pressure against the chest and rescue breathing. Pressing the chest helps pump the blood from the heart to the body. Rescue breathing provides oxygen to the lungs so the vessels can transport the blood.

### RESUSCI-ANNIE

Cardiopulmonary resuscitation (CPR) was first introduced in the mid 1970s. Prior to this, people would often die while waiting for medical help. What made this profound impact in saving lives was the invention of the Resusci-Annie doll. People could now learn how to do CPR and practice this technique without doing bodily harm as would happen if done on a real person. Resusci-Annie was invented by Asmund S. Laerdal. Laerdal wanted a doll that was life-sized and extremely realistic in appearance so students would be better motivated to learn this lifesaving procedure. Today, the American Red Cross works closely with the American Heart Association to teach people how to save lives using Resusci-Annie dolls.

Then and Now

*First Aid for Injuries    Chapter 15*    **315**

**Ask:**

- What are some possible signs of a heart attack? (difficulty breathing, irregular heartbeat, nausea, pain in the arm or jaw)

- What two actions are used in CPR? (pressure against the chest and rescue breathing)

---

### Chapter 15  Lesson 4

**Overview** In this lesson, students learn first aid techniques for helping victims of heart attack and poisoning.

### Objectives

- To explain the steps of rescue breathing and CPR.

**Student Pages** 315–318
**Audiocassette**
**Teacher's Resource Library**

Activity 58
Workbook Activity 58

## Teaching Suggestions

### ■ Vocabulary

*cardiac arrest, cardiopulmonary resuscitation (CPR), irregular, compression, oral poisoning, contact poisoning, inhalation poisoning*

Have students review the vocabulary words. Challenge each student to make up a short paragraph using all of the words relating to either heart attack or poisoning, leaving a blank for each vocabulary word. Then have pairs of students exchange their paragraphs and fill in the blanks.

### ■ Teaching the Lesson

Tell students that choking is not the only medical emergency that causes someone to stop breathing. Ask if students can name other medical problems that might cause someone to stop breathing. (Students might name problems such as heart attacks.)

Then have students read about first aid for heart attacks on page 315.

### Then and Now

A local fire department, hospital, or Red Cross chapter might have Resusci-Annie dolls that are used to teach CPR and rescue breathing. Your school district might also have some. If so, try to obtain one of the dolls so students can practice rescue breathing.

Have students read about the steps in CPR on pages 316 and 317.

Ask:

• What is the first step in CPR? (Make an open airway. Emphasize that an open airway is needed to get the oxygen the victim needs into the body.)

• After making sure there is an open airway, you need to find out if breathing has stopped. If breathing has stopped, what should you do? (Start rescue breathing. Keep the head tilted back and pinch the nose shut. Take a deep breath, seal your lips around the person's mouth, and give the victim two full breaths. If the person starts to breathe, you can stop the procedure.)

## BACKGROUND INFORMATION

During rescue breathing, the victim receives another person's exhaled air. The air that a person inhales contains 21 percent oxygen. People use only 5 percent of that oxygen and exhale the other 16 percent. So during rescue breathing, the air that the victim is taking in is only 16 percent oxygen. While not a normal percentage, it is still enough to keep the person's vital organs alive and functioning.

## LEARNING STYLES

**Visual** Encourage students to use the Resusci-Annie doll, if possible, to practice the correct positioning of victim and rescuer for the compressions used in CPR. Have them also practice compressions. Do not allow students to practice compressions on one another.

---

It is very important to start CPR as soon as possible. Follow these basic steps.

1. Make an open airway.
   • Tap on the person's shoulder or loudly ask, "Are you all right?" to find out if the person is conscious.
   • Tilt the head back and lift the chin to open the airway.
   • Using the finger sweep method, check for any foreign matter that may be blocking the airway.

2. Find out if breathing has stopped.
   • Look, listen, and feel for breathing for three to five seconds.
   • Keep the head tilted back and pinch the nose shut.
   • Take a deep breath, seal your lips around the person's mouth, and give the victim two full breaths. For babies, seal your lips around the nose and mouth and give a gentle puff once every three seconds.
   • Check for a pulse on the side of the neck for five to ten seconds. If you find a pulse, recheck breathing and only proceed if necessary.

**What would you do if someone stopped breathing?**

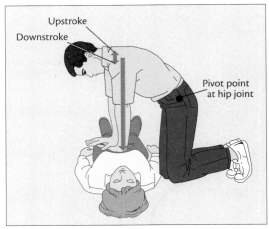

**Figure 15.3.** Cardiopulmonary resuscitation (CPR)

3. Find the proper hand position for **compressions**.
   - Locate the notch at the lower end of the breastbone.
   - Place the heel of your other hand on the breastbone next to your fingers.
   - Remove your hand from the notch and put it on top of your other hand.
   - Use only the heels of your hands, keeping your fingers off the chest.

4. Give fifteen compressions.
   - Position your shoulders over your hands.
   - Compress the breastbone one and one-half to two inches.
   - Do fifteen compressions in about ten seconds.
   - Compress down and up smoothly, keeping hand contact with the chest at all times.
   - After every fifteen compressions, give two full breaths.

### What Is First Aid for Poisoning?

A poison is a substance that causes injury, illness, or even death when it enters the body. A poison might be swallowed, come in contact with the skin, or be inhaled.

### Oral poisoning

**Oral poisoning** occurs when a harmful substance is swallowed. Household cleaners, radiator fluid, and parts of certain plants, such as morning glories, can be poisonous if eaten. Some signs of oral poisoning are sudden, severe abdominal pain, upset stomach, and vomiting. The victim might become sleepy and lose consciousness.

If a person has swallowed a poison, call the local poison control center immediately. Information about the poison and the victim's weight and age is important to give on the phone. The poison control expert will give you instructions on what to do until emergency medical help arrives. Look on the bottle of liquid you think is the poison to see if it says "Do not induce vomiting." This means the chemical will cause more burning in the throat if vomiting occurs.

*First Aid for Injuries    Chapter 15*    **317**

---

Have students read about the steps in CPR and about first aid for poisoning on page 317.

### Ask:

- How do you find the proper hand position for compressions? (Locate the notch at the lower end of the breastbone. Place the heel of your hand on the breastbone next to your fingers. Remove your hand from the notch and put it on top of your other hand. Use only the heels of your hands, keeping your fingers off the chest.)

- How many compressions and breaths should you give while giving CPR? (fifteen compressions and two full breaths)

- What are some signs of oral poisoning? (sudden and severe abdominal pain, upset stomach, vomiting)

- If you think someone has swallowed a poison, what should you do? (Call the local poison control center immediately.)

- What information is important to give to the poison control expert? (Give information about the poison and the victim's weight and age.)

### APPLICATION

**Environment**
Many poisons are household cleaners, paints, and solvents. These substances are also hazardous wastes that can be harmful if they get into the water or soil in the environment. Many communities do not allow such substances to be disposed with regular trash where they could end up in landfills. Some communities have hazardous waste collection days or places where hazardous waste can be dropped off. Encourage students to investigate to find out how these poisons are handled in your community.

Have students read about contact poisoning and inhalation poisoning on page 318.

**Ask:**

- What are some signs of contact poisoning? (severe rash, swelling, blisters, itching, burning)

- What should you do if you suspect someone has contact poisoning? (Remove any clothes that have contacted the poison. Wash the skin with soap and large amounts of water. Apply ice for swelling or calamine lotion to reduce itching.)

- What are some signs of inhalation poisoning? (headache, dizziness, loss of consciousness)

- What should you do for someone who has inhalation poisoning? (Move the person into fresh air at once. If the person is unconscious, check for breathing and pulse. If these are not present, begin CPR immediately.)

## Lesson 4 Review Answers

1) A heart attack occurs when a blood vessel supplying blood to the heart becomes blocked and part of the heart becomes damaged.

2) The fours basic steps of CPR are: (1) Make an open airway. (2) Find out if breathing has stopped. (3) Find the proper hand position for compressions. (4) Give fifteen compressions followed by two full breaths.

3) Oral poisoning occurs when a harmful substance is swallowed. Contact poisoning occurs when a poison comes in contact with the skin. Inhalation poisoning occurs when a person inhales harmful gases.

4) If someone has swallowed a poison, call the poison control center immediately.

5) You should check for breathing and a pulse. If these are not present, begin CPR immediately.

---

**Contact poisoning**
*A poison that comes in contact with the skin*

**Inhalation poisoning**
*A poison that is inhaled*

## Contact poisoning

**Contact poisoning** occurs when a poison comes in contact with the skin. Poisons may be absorbed from plants such as poison ivy, household cleaning products, or lawn and farm chemicals. Signs of this kind of poison are severe rash, swelling, blisters, itching, and burning. Remove any clothes that have contacted the poison. Wash the skin with soap and large amounts of water. You can apply ice for swelling or calamine lotion to reduce itching.

## Inhalation poisoning

**Inhalation poisoning** occurs when someone breathes in, or inhales, harmful gases. Signs of this type of poisoning are headache, dizziness, or loss of consciousness. A person with inhalation poisoning should be moved into fresh air at once. If the victim is unconscious, check for breathing and a pulse. If these are not present, begin CPR immediately.

Remember that this chapter is only your first step toward becoming skilled in giving emergency medical care. Look into taking a first aid class to learn first aid thoroughly.

**LESSON 4 REVIEW** Write the answers to these questions on a separate sheet of paper. Use complete sentences.

1) What is a heart attack?

2) What are four basic steps of CPR?

3) Describe three kinds of poisoning.

4) What is the first thing to do if someone has swallowed a poison?

5) If a victim of inhalation poisoning is unconscious, what is the first thing to do?

---

---

■ Staying calm in an emergency helps you to think clearly and to perform first aid properly.

■ Dialing 911 or 0 for the operator will put you in touch with the local Emergency Medical Service (EMS).

■ Good Samaritan Laws protect emergency caregivers. Universal Precautions protect people from contracting infectious diseases while performing first aid.

■ There are three types of burns. First-degree burns damage only the outer layer of the skin. Second-degree burns affect the outer and underneath layers of the skin. Third-degree burns require immediate professional attention.

■ Overexposure to extreme heat or cold causes trauma to the body. Quick emergency treatment is needed.

■ The signs of shock may include a rapid or slow pulse, fast or slow breathing, pale skin, thirst, or confusion.

■ The Heimlich maneuver is the quick upward thrust under the ribcage that dislodges a foreign object blocking the windpipe.

■ A person is in cardiac arrest if his or her heart has stopped beating and there is no breathing.

■ Cardiopulmonary resuscitation (CPR) combines rescue breathing and pressure against the chest to maintain oxygen flow to vital organs until emergency medical help arrives.

■ Poisoning occurs when a harmful substance is swallowed, comes in contact with the skin, or is inhaled.

*First Aid for Injuries    Chapter 15*    **319**

## ■ Using the Chapter Summary

To further reinforce the facts and concepts presented in the chapter, read and discuss with students the questions that follow.

Ask:

- Why is it important to call 911 or 0 for the operator when there is a medical emergency? (These numbers will put you in touch with the local Emergency Medical Service (EMS).)

- Who do Good Samaritan Laws and Universal Precautions protect? (Good Samaritan Laws protect emergency caregivers. Universal Precautions protect people from contacting infectious diseases while performing first aid.)

- What are signs of shock? (a rapid or slow pulse, fast or slow breathing, pale skin, thirst, confusion)

- What is the Heimlich maneuver? (a quick upward thrust under the ribcage that dislodges a foreign object blocking the windpipe)

- What two processes are involved in CPR? (CPR combines rescue breathing and pressure against the chest to maintain oxygen flow to vital organs until emergency medical help arrives.)

- Name three ways that poisons can enter or contact your body. (Poisoning occurs when a harmful substance is swallowed, comes in contact with the skin, or is inhaled.)

# Chapter 15 Review

The Teacher's Resource Library includes two parallel forms of the Chapter 15 Mastery Test. The difficulty level of the two forms is equivalent. You may wish to use one form as a pretest and the other form as a posttest.

## Review Answers

### Comprehension: Identifying Facts

1) sprain  2) First aid  3) fracture
4) Good Samaritan Laws  5) poison
6) Frostbite  7) cardiac arrest  8) splint
9) hypothermia

---

## Comprehension: Identifying Facts

On a separate sheet of paper, write the correct word or words from the Word Bank to complete each sentence.

| WORD BANK | |
|---|---|
| cardiac arrest | Heimlich maneuver |
| cardiopulmonary resuscitation (CPR) | hypothermia |
| | poison |
| first aid | shock |
| fracture | splint |
| frostbite | sprain |
| Good Samaritan Laws | Universal Precautions |
| heatstroke | |

1) A _____ is the tearing or loosening of ligaments or tendons.

2) _____ is the emergency care given to a sick or an injured person.

3) A bone that is broken is called a _____.

4) The _____ protect an emergency caregiver.

5) A _____ can be swallowed, come in contact with the skin, or be inhaled.

6) _____ is the freezing of tissue due to excessive exposure to cold temperatures.

7) A person whose heart stops beating is in _____.

8) A _____ is used to keep a broken limb in place.

9) Overexposure to severe cold temperatures causes _____.

---

Name _____ Date _____ Period _____

Chapter 15 Mastery Test A

**Directions** Read the words in the Word Bank. Choose the item that *best* completes each sentence. On the blank before each number, write the letter for that item.

| Word Bank | | |
|---|---|---|
| a) calm | f) Good Samaritan Laws | k) cardiac arrest |
| b) shock | g) cardiopulmonary resuscitation | l) heatstroke |
| c) rabies | h) Heimlich maneuver | m) third-degree burn |
| d) cold | i) Universal Precautions | n) hypothermia |
| e) splint | j) poison control center | o) first aid |

_____ 1) The most important thing you can do for a victim in an emergency is to remain _____.

_____ 2) _____ is the immediate emergency care given to a sick or an injured person.

_____ 3) _____ protect rescuers or victims from infectious, or contagious, disease.

_____ 4) If you suspect a sprain or fracture, remember to ICE (immobilize, _____, elevate) it.

_____ 5) _____ protect people who provide first aid in an emergency.

_____ 6) A _____ extends through all layers of skin to the tissues underneath.

_____ 7) The main sign of _____ is a lack of sweating.

_____ 8) _____ is a serious loss of body heat resulting from being exposed to severe cold temperatures.

_____ 9) Animal bites can transmit _____ to humans.

_____ 10) _____ is a physical reaction to severe injury or illness.

Chapter 15 Mastery Test A page 1

Discover Health

---

Name _____ Date _____ Period _____

Chapter 15 Mastery Test A, continued

_____ 11) If a choking victim cannot speak, cough, or breathe, you should do the _____.

_____ 12) If a person's heart stops beating and has no pulse, the person is then in _____.

_____ 13) A _____ is used to keep a broken limb in place.

_____ 14) While waiting for emergency medical help to arrive, perform _____ for anyone whose heart stops beating.

_____ 15) If a person has swallowed a poison, call the local _____ immediately.

Chapter 15 Mastery Test A page 2

Discover Health

## Chapter 15 Mastery Test A

10) Using latex gloves and masks are examples of how
_____ can protect a person from contracting
infectious diseases.

11) The inability to sweat is a main sign of _____.

12) While waiting for emergency medical help to arrive,
perform _____ for anyone whose heart stops
beating.

13) To save a person from choking to death, the
_____ should be performed.

14) Covering a person with blankets will keep a trauma
victim from going into _____.

## Comprehension: Understanding Main Ideas

Write the answers to these questions on a separate sheet
of paper. Use complete sentences.

15) What are three basic guidelines for first aid?

16) Name four types of problems that may require first aid.
Describe the treatment for each type of problem.

17) What is the Heimlich maneuver?

18) How would you start CPR on someone who is having
a heart attack?

## Critical Thinking: Write Your Opinion

19) What would you do if you were baby-sitting and the child
was bitten by a neighbor's dog?

20) What advice would you give someone who is eating large
pieces of meat while talking?

**Test Taking Tip** After you have taken a test, go back and reread the questions
and your answers. Ask yourself, "Do my answers show that
I understood the question?"

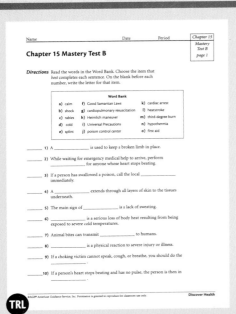

**Chapter 15 Mastery Test B**

---

10) Universal Precautions  11) heatstroke
12) cardiopulminary resuscitation (CPR)
13) Heimlich maneuver  14) shock

## Comprehension: Understanding Main Ideas

15) Three basic guidelines for first aid are
the following: (1) Look around the
area to make sure there is no danger
to yourself or the victim. (2) Find out
if the victim is conscious. If the victim
is not conscious, stay there and ask
someone to call for help. (3) If the
victim is conscious, check for injuries,
cover the victim with a blanket or
coat, and apply pressure to bleeding
areas.

16) Students can name any four of the
problems in lessons 2, 3, and 4,
including the following: Broken bones
or sprains should be immobilized,
iced, and the limb (if it is a limb)
should be elevated. For first- and
second-degree burns, remove the
source of heat, apply cool water, and
cover the area loosely with a bandage.
Call help immediately for third-degree
burns. Treat heat exhaustion by
moving the person out of the heat,
loosening clothing, applying a cool
cloth, and offering sips of water. For
heatstroke, call EMS immediately.
For an unconscious victim, check for
breathing and a pulse. If these are not
present, begin CPR immediately.

17) The Heimlich maneuver is a series of
firm, upward abdominal thrusts that
force out foreign objects blocking an
airway.

18) To start CPR on someone who is
having a heart attack, tilt the head
back and lift the chin to open the
airway. Use the finger sweep method
to check for any foreign matter that
may be blocking the airway.

## Critical Thinking: Write Your Opinion

19) If the child was bitten by a neighbor's
dog, wash the area with soap and
water and apply a dressing. Talk to
the neighbor to find out if the dog
has had rabies shots.

20) Tell the person that he or she should
chew the food well and not talk with
a mouth full of food.

## Chapter 16:
**Preventing Violence**
pages 322–337

**Lessons**

**1) Defining Violence**
pages 323–326

**2) Causes of Violence**
pages 327–330

**3) Preventing Violence**
pages 331–334

**Chapter Summary and Review**
pages 335–337

**Audiocassette** 🎧

**Teacher's Resource Library** **TRL**

Activities 59–61

Workbook Activities 59–61

Student Study Guide 22 pages 1–2

Chapter 16 Mastery Tests A and B

(Answer Keys for the Teacher's
Resource Library begin on page 433
of this Teacher's Edition.)

## Introducing the Chapter

Invite students to tell what they think
about when they hear the word *violence*.
Responses may be as diverse as hitting,
family abuse, weapons, alcohol, drugs,
TV programs, movies, and so on. Then
ask students to give examples of violence
that they have seen or heard about.

Have volunteers read aloud the
introductory material and the Goals
for Learning.

Ask:

• Why do we need to study violence in
health class? (Violence is a growing
threat to the health of young people.)

• How can people avoid violence? (People
can avoid violence by identifying problems
and solving them in peaceful ways.)

**Chapter**
# 16

# Preventing Violence

*I*t is becoming harder to avoid violence. Violence is
shown on TV nearly every day. You can read about it in
newspapers and magazines. The words in some songs
and the images in some pictures are violent. It seems that
violence is being talked about or shown everywhere. So why
do we need to study violence in health class? Violence is a
growing threat to the health of young people. Violence can
affect young people even more strongly than it does adults.
Before we can prevent violence, we need to understand it.

In this chapter, you will learn about different types of violence.
You will look at the causes of violence. You will read about
victims and the high costs of violent acts. You will learn how
people can respect each other and avoid violence. People can
avoid violence by identifying problems and solving them in
peaceful ways.

### Goals for Learning

▶ To define violence and describe its costs
▶ To identify warning signs of conflict
▶ To describe causes of violence
▶ To explain ways to prevent violence and resolve conflicts

---

# Lesson 1

## Defining Violence

**Media**
*Sources of information and entertainment, such as newspapers and TV*

**Violence**
*Actions or words that hurt people or things they care about*

### What Is Violence?

Violence is hard to define. Many people feel they "know it when they see it" but cannot put it into words. Violence can be described as any actions or words that hurt people or things that people care about. Violence makes people feel bad about themselves. They may not even feel safe where they live or work.

### What Is Violent Behavior?

Violent behavior is acting in a way that hurts others. It can include pushing, hitting, or name-calling. Another violent behavior is damaging someone's property or using a weapon. Violence never solves problems. Instead, it creates new problems that are even worse. Suppose you bumped into someone accidentally. What if you said something that hurt someone's feelings, but you didn't mean to? Is this violence?

Usually when we talk about violent behavior, we mean actions that were intended to do harm. However, we might describe an automobile crash as violent, even if it wasn't anyone's fault. When an accident happens, it is a good idea to think about whether it could have been avoided. Could you have been more careful? Could you have chosen your words more thoughtfully before you spoke? One way to avoid violent behavior is to think about what the results of any of your actions might be.

### What Are Some Forms of Violence?

#### Media Violence

One kind of violence is the things we see and hear in the **media**. Newspapers, TV, video games, and movies contain violence. Some of the violence reported is about true things that happen. Some of it is made-up violence that is meant to make a story seem more real. Many people believe that violence on TV or in movies can make children act violently. When children see violence in the media, they may think that it is acceptable. They may then imitate the violent actions they have seen.

*Preventing Violence* *Chapter 16* **323**

## Chapter 16 Lesson 1

**Overview** In this lesson, students learn about several forms of violence, how violence affects people, and the costs of violence.

### Objectives

- To define violence and describe its costs.
- To describe forms of violence.

**Student Pages** 323–326

**Audiocassette**

**Teacher's Resource Library** **TRL**

    Activity 59

    Workbook Activity 59

## Teaching Suggestions

### ■ Vocabulary

*media, violence, conflict, internal conflict, cycle*

Have students review all the vocabulary words. Ask them to pay special attention to the difference between conflict and violence. Ask students to give examples of conflicts that could escalate into violence. Then discuss what could be done in each situation to keep conflict from becoming violence.

### ■ Teaching the Lesson

Ask students what TV shows they watch. Ask them whether these shows contain violence. If they do, have students describe how they think the violence could affect TV viewers.

Have students read about violent behavior and media violence on page 323.

Ask:

- How can you avoid violent behavior? (Think about what the results of any of your actions might be.)

- How might media violence affect the actions of children? (When children see violence in the media, they may think it is acceptable and then imitate the violent actions they have seen.)

Have students read about family violence and random violence on page 324.

Ask:

- How might violent behavior be passed along in families? (If a person was hurt or abused as a child, the violent behavior may be repeated with that person's own children.)

- What is random violence? (Random violence is violence that is not directed at a specific person, such as throwing a rock to damage property.)

- How can people be injured by random violence even though it is not intended to hurt a specific person? (Results are the same whether violence is random or intentional. People can be killed or hurt.)

## APPLICATION

**Environment**
Ask students to consider how violence in the form of vandalism can harm the environment. Students can consider examples such as damaging a tree, dumping toxic material in a river or lake, or setting fire to a building containing toxic substances. Students should write reports in which they explain how this type of violence has harmed people, animals, or land in your community or some other community.

**Family Violence**
Violence in the family is a problem for many people. Parents may become violent toward one another or toward a child. This may be learned from the parents. Suppose a person was hurt or abused as a child. Then the violent behavior may be repeated with that person's own children.

**Random Violence**
Sometimes violence is not directed at a specific person. Someone can damage property by spraying it with paint or throwing a rock at it. The person may not have intended to hurt the property owner, but he or she still acted violently. This is called random violence. People can be injured by random violence. When weapons are used on the street or in other public places, people can be hurt or killed.

There may be times when you can pressure friends not to fight. Let them know you support peaceful solutions to disagreements.

*Health Tip*

**Try to find a compromise to solve conflicts peacefully.**

## How Is Conflict Different From Violence?

Violence is often the result of conflict, but it doesn't have to be. **Conflict** is a disagreement between people. These people may have conflicting ideas about something or want to do something a different way. Conflict is everywhere. Disagreements are normal. Turning to violence is not normal.

Some conflicts are bigger than others. You may disagree with a family member about who should do the chores. Your parents may have different ideas about where to go on vacation. Conflicts can be ongoing or brief. Two schools may have a sports rivalry going for years. Friends may have a different plan about which bus to take to the store. You can even have a conflict within yourself. An **internal conflict** is having two different ideas and not being sure which is best.

Some conflicts have easy solutions. Others take time and care to work out. Government leaders face major conflicts when they decide how to rule a nation. A person is faced with a major conflict if challenged to a fight. The way we respond to conflict determines whether violence will occur.

## Who Does Violence Affect?

Do you think that most violent acts happen among strangers or friends? Unfortunately, violence can happen in many situations. About half of the murders in the United States happen among people who know each other.

Since 1992, an average of 4.3 million Americans have been victims of violent crime. These crimes include robbery, assault, and other attacks. Many of the crime victims were between the ages of 12 and 24. Why do you think so many violent acts happen to young people?

## What Are the Costs of Violence?

When a person is robbed, there is a loss of money or the cost of property. However, the victim may also suffer an emotional loss. He or she may feel unsafe walking down the street. Victims may feel mental or emotional scars. They may have strong feelings of fear, anger, or sadness. Victims may need to see a professional to treat these mental injuries.

*Preventing Violence* Chapter 16 **325**

Have students read about conflict, the people affected by violence, and the costs of violence on page 325.

**Ask:**

- What is the difference between conflict and violence? (Conflict is a disagreement or difference between people. Violence is actions or words that hurt people or things that people care about.)

- Can you think of a nonviolent conflict that has occurred in our community? (Answers will vary. If necessary, suggest any issue that is being debated in your community.)

- What is internal conflict? (Internal conflict is having two different ideas and not being sure which is best.)

- Why do you think about half of the murders in the United States happen between people who know each other? (Many murders occur between people who know each other because conflicts among family, friends, or acquaintances sometimes turn into violence.)

- What kinds of feelings might a victim of violence have? (fear, anger, sadness)

### LEARNING STYLES

**Auditory** Provide several brief newspaper or magazine articles that explain conflicts involving two or more businesses, the government and businesses, individuals and government, or employees and employers. Challenge students to listen carefully as volunteers read the articles to the class. Then ask students questions such as the following: What do you think is the cause of the conflict? What, if anything, are people doing to resolve the conflict? What would you do to resolve the conflict?

Have students read about the costs of violence on page 326.

- **What are the results of physical harm for a victim of violence?** (The victim could have permanent injuries and may need medical care to heal.)

- **What are the costs for a person who commits a violent act?** (A person who commits a violent act might have guilt over what he or she has done, which might lead the person to feel even worse about the situation. If the person does not deal with these feelings, he or she may resort to violence again. The person may serve time in prison and get a criminal record. This could make it hard to make positive changes in life.)

## Lesson 1 Review Answers

1) Violence in the media can make children act violently.
2) Random violence is not directed at a specific person.
3) No, conflicts do not have to lead to violence.
4) Answers will vary. Students may suggest the following costs: loss of money; cost of property; emotional costs, such as mental or emotional scars or feelings of guilt by the person who committed the crime; professional treatment; permanent injuries; and monetary costs for police, courts, and prisons.
5) Violence on TV may lead children to think that violence is acceptable.

## MULTICULTURAL CONNECTION

Inform students that some cultural and religious groups have rules that prohibit alcohol and forbid violence. Amish, Quakers, Mormons, and Muslims are such groups. Have groups of two or three students research such a group to find out more about its attitudes toward alcohol use and violence. Encourage students to give presentations to the class.

---

**Cycle**
*A repetition*

**Why might a victim feel anger? What could that person do to feel better?**

Violence can cause physical harm. Violent acts can cause permanent injuries. Victims may need medical care to heal. Friends and relatives of the victim are affected. They may need to take responsibility for the care of the victim.

The people who commit violent acts may also feel emotional costs for their actions. They may have guilt over what they have done. This might lead them to feel even worse about a situation. If these people do not deal with these feelings, they may resort to violence again.

A person could be arrested for violent behavior. The person may have to go to court and serve time in prison. Once a person has a criminal record, it may be hard to make positive changes in life. A violent past can lead to a **cycle**, or repetition, of violence.

In the end, everyone pays for crime and violence. The costs for police, courts, and prisons add up. When violence occurs, we are all victims.

**LESSON 1 REVIEW** Write the answers to these questions on a separate sheet of paper. Use complete sentences.

1) How might the media contribute to violence?
2) What kind of violence is not directed at a specific person?
3) Do conflicts always lead to violence?
4) What are some of the costs of violence?
5) How might seeing violence on TV affect young people's behavior?

*Chapter 16* *Preventing Violence*

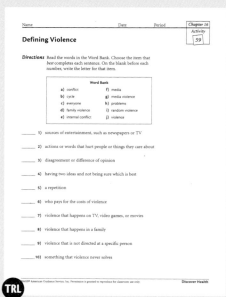

**Activity 59**

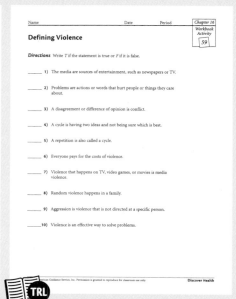

**Workbook Activity 59**

*Chapter 16* *Preventing Violence*

## Causes of Violence

### When Does Conflict Lead to Violence?

You cannot always avoid conflict. We all face difficult situations sometimes. When problems occur, we sometimes do not see how they can be resolved. At times people do not even realize they are in a conflict. A disagreement can quickly turn into an argument with shouting and angry feelings. If people do not stop to think about their actions and words, anger could turn into violence.

Understanding a situation helps you to respond in the right way. Then you can work to find a solution. How do you know when a disagreement is turning into a conflict that needs to be resolved? Below are some warning signs of conflict. If you notice one or more of these signs, work with others to find out what the problem is.

```
WARNING SIGNS OF CONFLICT
• Shouting            • Making fun of others
• Name-calling        • Making threats
• Insults             • Pushing or hitting
• Mean looks
```

### What Causes Violence?

The media often show or describe violent actions or words. This is in part just a reflection of our society. However, when young people see violence, they may think that it is a good way to solve problems.

*Health Tip*

If you are feeling angry, try going for a run or punching a pillow.

Sometimes parents can set a bad example for their children. Parents may feel stress from work and other responsibilities. Increased stress may make parents respond to problems through violent actions or words. The child may take this as an example of how to deal with conflicts. Many criminals come from violent homes. They were not able to break the cycle of violence from their childhood.

*Preventing Violence    Chapter 16*    **327**

---

Ask:

• What are the warning signs of conflict? (shouting, name-calling, insults, mean looks, making fun of others, making threats, pushing or hitting)

• When young people see violence, what might they think? (that violence is a good way to solve problems)

---

## Chapter 16  Lesson 2

**Overview** In this lesson, students learn how conflicts can lead to violence. Students also learn about the causes of violence and the kinds of crimes that are likely to affect young people.

### Objectives

■ To describe causes of violence.

■ To identify warning signs of conflict.

**Student Pages** 327–330

**Audiocassette**

**Teacher's Resource Library**

Activity 60
Workbook Activity 60

## Teaching Suggestions

■ **Vocabulary**
*prejudice*

After reviewing the definition of the vocabulary word, encourage students to give examples of the different types of prejudice mentioned in the definition.

■ **Teaching the Lesson**

Tell students the following story: Two groups of teens were having fun at a park. One group was seated on the grass talking and eating ice cream. A second group was nearby tossing a football. The football accidentally hit one of the people on the grass. The group on the grass immediately got angry. They jumped up and accused the other group of throwing the ball on purpose. They refused to give back the football and began to call the other teens names. The teens who had been throwing the ball got angry and began to shout insulting names back. Soon, everyone was involved in a fight and several teens got hurt. What was the cause of this fight? What could have prevented it?

Have students read about ways conflict can lead to violence on page 327.

Have students read about the causes of violence on page 328.

Ask:

- Why does keeping a gun in the home increase the chances of a violent crime occurring? (A gun in the home increases the chance of accidental death.)

- How do drugs increase the chances of violent crime? (Drugs can prevent a person from using good judgment. People using drugs may do things that they would never do if they did not use drugs.)

- How can gangs encourage violence? (People in gangs sometimes act violently to show their loyalty to a group. Members of a gang often do things that they might not do on their own.)

- What is prejudice? (Prejudice is an opinion based on a a person's religion, gender, culture, or race.)

## GLOBAL CONNECTION

Have students work in small groups to research the gun control laws in another country. Then challenge students to find out about the rate of violent crime in that country. How does it compare to that in the United States? Do the gun control laws seem to have affected the comparative violent crime rates? Encourage each group to make a presentation to the class.

## LEARNING STYLES

**Tactile/Kinesthetic** Encourage groups of students to design a campaign to stop violence for your school. The campaign should educate other students about the causes of violence and give strategies for preventing violence. For example, students might want to design posters, present skits, or plan an assembly with films and speakers.

The examples that parents set influence their children's behavior patterns.

> **Prejudice**
> *An opinion based on a person's religion, race, gender, or culture*

Many people buy guns, which they keep in the home. They may not intend to use the gun. Usually gun owners feel that guns offer protection and peace of mind. Guns, however, are also dangerous to young people. If a child finds a gun, he or she may think that it is a toy. A gun in the home increases the chance of accidental death.

Drugs and alcohol can make people act in dangerous ways. People who use drugs or alcohol commit half of all violent crimes. Drugs can also prevent a person from using good judgment. People using drugs may do things that they would never do if they did not use drugs.

Sometimes people act violently to show their loyalty to a group. Members of a gang often do things that they might not do on their own. This is giving in to peer pressure. They may think they are stronger or more powerful when they are with the gang. However, their actions really make them more likely to get hurt or killed.

**Prejudice** and hatred can lead to violence against a particular group. Prejudice is a person's opinion based on another's race, gender, culture, or religion. A prejudiced person doesn't really know the person in that group. People who commit violence based on prejudice want to prove that they are better. All they really prove is that they are hateful.

## Social Studies    VIOLENCE AND GENOCIDE

During World War II, German Nazis arrested many European Jews and placed them in concentration camps. They were imprisoned for no other reason than their religious background. The Nazis also imprisoned other minority groups. The Nazis felt that their race was superior. Living conditions in these camps were poor. People were killed or tortured. Those who survived would be forever scarred by the memory of the camps. This practice of mass killing or torture based on race, culture, or religion is called genocide. After the war, many Nazi soldiers were tried in court for crimes against humanity. Today, the United Nations and other worldwide organizations guard against genocide. Still, genocide has occurred in areas where people of different backgrounds are competing for power. All people of the world must work to make sure that the horrors of Nazi concentration camps are never repeated because of prejudice and ignorance.

People may turn to violence when they feel they have been insulted or hurt. They are trying to get revenge for the pain or sadness they feel. Figure 16.1 shows how revenge only leads to greater violence. A misunderstanding can lead to violent actions when people take revenge instead of sorting out their problems.

### What Kinds of Crimes Affect Young People?

Young people are just as vulnerable to crime and violence as anyone. In fact, nearly half of all crime victims in the United States are between the ages of 12 and 24. Some crimes affect young children more than others, such as child abuse and kidnapping.

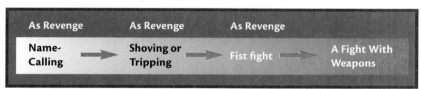

**Figure 16.1.** Pattern of an insult turning into violence

## Healthy Subjects

Ask a volunteer to reread the definition of *genocide*. Challenge students to find out about other instances of genocide in recent history. Have students report on the racial, ethnic, or religious conflicts that have led to violence and mass killing. After students report on the cases that they find and research, discuss the roots of the violence. Why did the violence start? How could it have been stopped before so many people were killed?

Have students read about reasons people might turn to violence and the kinds of crimes that affect young people on page 329.

### Ask:

- How can the attempt to get revenge turn into violence? (The attempt to get revenge can turn into violence when someone feels insulted and hurt and tries to hurt the other person in return. For example, name calling can quickly turn into a fight.)

- In the pattern of insult turning into violence on the bottom of page 329, why is each step more violent than the one before? (The steps become more violent as each party tries to hurt the other more than they were hurt to get revenge.)

### BACKGROUND INFORMATION

Violence is one of the main causes of injury and death in the United States. Since there is no consistent reporting system for nonfatal injuries, complete statistics on injury from violence are hard to obtain. Because of this, public health officials state that the rate of violence and victimization among young people may be even greater than statistics indicate.

Have students read about child abuse and about ways to stay safe from strangers on page 330.

## Ask:

- What are some tips for staying away from dangerous strangers? (Accept any of the following: Walk only in familiar areas; stay with a group whenever possible; never accept offerings from strangers; never go with strangers; avoid dark areas; if you are being followed, walk quickly to a place where there are other people; report suspicious activity to an adult you can trust.)

## Lesson 2 Review Answers

1) No, gun owners are more likely to have violent crimes occur in the home.
2) Name calling might lead to greater violence when people who are being called names become angry and want to get revenge on the name callers. People might take revenge by engaging in violent acts, such as pushing or shoving.
3) Drugs tend to make people more violent because they prevent people from using good judgment. Drug users may do things they would never do if they did not use drugs.
4) Child abuse and kidnapping are violent crimes that are more likely to affect young people.
5) Answers will vary. Students may suggest people might commit violence because of prejudice when they want to prove they are better or when they feel hatred and want to hurt a member of the other group.

---

Often, child abuse comes from within the family. Like other types of violence, child abuse may be part of a cycle of violence. Victims of abuse may be more likely to abuse their own children. Victims of child abuse should get help from an adult, such as a teacher or school nurse. Kidnapping or assault by adult strangers is most likely to happen to children younger than 13 years old. However, it can happen to anyone. Here are some tips for staying away from dangerous strangers:

- Walk only in familiar areas.
- Stay with a group whenever possible.
- Never accept any offerings from strangers. Never go with a stranger anywhere.
- Avoid dark areas such as alleys.
- If you are being followed, walk quickly to a place where there are other people.
- Report any suspicious activity to an adult you can trust, such as a police officer.

**LESSON 2 REVIEW** Write the answers to these questions on a separate sheet of paper. Use complete sentences.

1) Are gun owners safe from violent crimes?
2) How might name-calling lead to greater violence?
3) Do drugs tend to make people more violent or less violent?
4) Name two kinds of violent crimes that are more likely to affect young people.
5) Why would a person commit violence because of prejudice?

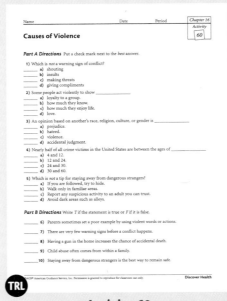

**Activity 60**

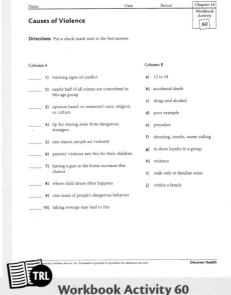

**Workbook Activity 60**

*Preventing Violence*

### How Can Anger Be Managed?

Everybody gets angry sometimes. Someone may say something that hurts your feelings or do something that you think is unfair. When you feel your body tensing up or your heart beating faster, you probably need to be careful not to get too mad. You might blurt something out that you don't really mean. That could make the situation worse.

Try taking a time-out to relax. Take a deep breath and count to ten. Think about what you want to say and come up with some nonviolent solutions to the problem. If the problem doesn't seem so important after you're relaxed, then you probably shouldn't say anything.

### When Should Conflict Be Avoided?

Not all conflicts can be avoided. Some conflicts can be healthy. However, there are some situations where it is best to walk away. It is always a good idea to look at a problem from the other person's perspective. Ask yourself how you would feel if you just forgot about the problem. It may be best to just let it go. You may get along with the other person better the next time.

**STOPPING VIOLENCE IN THE SKY**

Early airports were much simpler than modern airports. There were fewer flights. There were also fewer concerns about violence in the air. In the 1960s and 1970s, however, terrorist activities placed passengers in danger.

In 1973, new security measures were begun. Under these rules, all baggage was X-rayed. Passengers passed through metal detectors. As a result, less terrorism occurred. By the late 1980s, some airports did not enforce these rules. New terrorism occurred in the 1990s. Again, airports became more careful in examining both passengers and luggage. Such checks keep weapons or bombs from being carried onto planes. The government and airlines do their best to provide passenger safety.

*Preventing Violence* Chapter 16 **331**

**Ask:**

- What are some things you can do to manage anger? (try taking a time-out to relax; take a deep breath and count to ten; think about what you want to say and come up with some nonviolent solutions to the problem)

## Chapter 16 Lesson 3

**Overview** In this lesson, students learn methods for avoiding or resolving conflicts before they turn into violence.

### Objectives

■ To explain ways to prevent violence and resolve conflicts.

**Student Pages** 331–334

**Audiocassette**

**Teacher's Resource Library**

Activity 61

Workbook Activity 61

## *Teaching Suggestions*

### ■ Vocabulary

*mediator, neutral*

Review the definitions of the vocabulary words with students. Discuss why a mediator might be needed to resolve a conflict and why it is important for the mediator to be neutral.

### ■ Teaching the Lesson

Ask students to think of well-known situations in your community or in national news in which anger has resulted in family violence. Point out to students that people who need help dealing with family violence can call crisis centers and support groups.

Have students read about ways that anger can be managed and times that conflict should be avoided on page 331.

### Then and Now

Ask students who have flown recently to describe the security measures that were in effect at the airports they used. Did these methods seem as though they would be effective in stopping acts of violence on airplanes?

Have students read about methods for resolving conflicts and about helping others avoid fights on page 332.

Ask:

• What things can you do to resolve a conflict? (listen to what the other person has to say, do not interrupt, keep an open mind, explain your feelings, try to remain calm, keep your emotions under control, focus on your feelings instead of the other person's actions)

• How can a bystander encourage people fighting? (Watching and cheering encourages violence.)

## Action for Health

Have students study the steps for resolving conflict. Challenge them to use the steps the next time they are involved in a conflict that threatens to get out of control. Then have students report to the class on how the process worked.

### APPLICATION

**At Home**
Encourage students to apply conflict resolution skills they learn in this lesson to family disputes at home among siblings or between themselves and their parents. Have students who use these skills report to the class on their effectiveness. If they were not successful, have the class troubleshoot to find out what might have been done to make the process more successful.

### APPLICATION

**In the Community**
Share with students the fact that some communities have volunteer citizen mediators to resolve small conflicts among residents. Encourage students to find out if your community uses citizen mediators. If so, have students report to the class on the program. If possible, have one of the mediators come to class to explain what he or she does and how local conflicts have been resolved without violence.

---

**Mediator**
*A person who helps two sides solve a problem reasonably*

## What Are Some Methods for Resolving Conflict?

When you decide that it is time to resolve a conflict, you can do some things to make it easier. Try to talk to the person alone or with a **mediator**. A mediator helps people work out a problem reasonably. A mediator does not favor one side or the other.

Listen to what the other person has to say. Do not interrupt, act bored, or daydream. Keep an open mind and consider the person's words. When you explain your feelings, try to remain calm. Keep your emotions under control. Focus on your feelings instead of the other person's actions. If you start to feel upset, ask for a time-out to collect yourself.

## How Can You Help Others Avoid Fights?

If you see people fighting, don't encourage it by watching or cheering. That could encourage one of the people to act violently. Let people know that you respect them for being able to walk away from a fight. Give respect to someone who is strong enough to apologize.

**Action for Health**

### STEPS FOR RESOLVING CONFLICT

1. Stay cool. Take a deep breath or go for a walk. Resist acting out in anger.

2. Identify the problem. Take turns listening while the other person talks. Be honest. Avoid insults. Do not interrupt. Ask questions to discover the reasons for the other person's feelings.

3. Use "I" messages to express your feelings. Don't make "you" statements or accusations. That makes the other person defensive.

4. Brainstorm all possible safe solutions. Write down as many solutions as possible. Include even silly solutions. Sometimes they work. For each solution, ask if it is fair, respectful, and true to your sense of right and wrong.

5. Agree on a solution that is fair to everyone. Remember, not every conflict must have a winner and a loser.

6. If you can't resolve the conflict together, perhaps you can seek a mediator.

Peer mediation helps to find solutions to conflicts.

| **Neutral**<br>*Not favoring either side* |
|---|

Sometimes you can take a more active role in preventing violence. You may be able to suggest a peaceful solution to the problem. If people are having trouble working out a solution, offer to be a mediator. Remember, though, that as a mediator you must be **neutral**, not favoring either side. Here are some methods for mediation:

- Let both people know that you are not taking sides.
- Set some rules, such as using calm, reasonable speech.
- Let each person state his or her feelings without interruption.
- Allow each side to ask reasonable questions.
- Encourage them to identify several peaceful solutions.
- Ask them to discuss each solution and agree on one idea.
- Work at a compromise; don't let them give up without really trying.

Have students read about methods for mediation on page 333.

Ask:

- What are some methods people can use for mediation? (Accept any of the following: let both people know that you are not taking sides; set some rules, such as using calm, reasonable speech; let each person state his or her feelings without interruption; allow each side to ask reasonable questions; encourage each side to identify several peaceful solutions; ask each person to discuss each solution and agree on one idea; work at a compromise.)

## LEARNING STYLES

 **Group Learning** Encourage groups of students to role-play a conflict that could turn violent. The role-playing should show the parties in conflict finding a nonviolent solution to the disagreement. After each presentation, have students offer their ideas about how they would have handled the problem.

## APPLICATION

 **Career Connection** Many students think of police officers as people who enforce laws by catching criminals. Inform students that police officers often deal with conflict resolution—trying to calm people down before they get into violent confrontations and commit crimes. Invite a member of your local police department to class to explain the importance of mediation for resolving conflicts. What kinds of conflicts are typical? Encourage the officer to explain the type of training he or she received to do this part of the job.

## Careers

Encourage students to identify other careers for health care workers, including the physician's assistant. These careers can also include physicians, nurses, medical secretaries, receptionists, laboratory technicians, and office managers. Students should report on the training each career requires. If possible, invite a physician's assistant to visit the class to talk about how all of these health care workers function together.

Have students read about ways to deal with serious conflicts on page 334.

Ask:

· Why do you think you should tell a parent, teacher, or other trusted adult if you are faced with a serious conflict? (You should tell a trusted adult if you are faced with a serious conflict because you may not be able to resolve it on your own. By telling someone, you may prevent the conflict from getting worse.)

## Lesson 3 Review Answers

1) Taking a time-out when you feel angry allows you to think calmly about the situation, possibly find a nonviolent solution, or decide that the problem isn't that important after all.

2) It is a good idea to avoid conflict if you can look at the problem and decide that forgetting about it makes more sense than trying to resolve it.

3) "You" statements make the other person defensive.

4) A mediator needs to be neutral so that he or she can see both sides of the conflict.

5) 1. Stay cool. Resist acting out of anger.
   2. Identify the problem.
   3. Use "I" messages to express your feelings.
   4. Brainstorm all possible safe solutions.
   5. Agree on a solution that is fair to everyone.
   6. Seek a mediator if necessary.

### PHYSICIAN'S ASSISTANT

If you are interested in helping people with health care, you might consider becoming a physician's assistant (PA). A physician's assistant works with a doctor to complete some of a doctor's routine work. PAs get medical information from patients, perform physical examinations, and order laboratory tests. In emergencies, PAs treat cuts, scrapes, bruises, and burns. They know how to set broken bones. Sometimes PAs decide what the results of lab tests mean. They may make diagnoses or prescribe treatments. PAs may handle tasks before or after surgery. Physician's assistants need experience in health care. They also must attend college and complete a recognized degree program.

### How Do You Deal With Serious Conflicts?

If you are faced with a serious conflict, don't try to resolve it on your own. Ask a parent, peer mediator, teacher, or counselor for help.

What would you do if you found out that a friend or classmate planned to hurt someone? If you tell someone, it may feel like you are betraying the person. But it is always more important to stop violence than it is to keep a secret. Your friend or classmate will be better off, too, if he or she is prevented from doing something harmful.

**Writing About Health**

Make a list of some of the conflicts you have faced this year. Describe how you dealt with these conflicts. Are the problems solved now or did they become bigger problems?

**LESSON 3 REVIEW** Write the answers to these questions on a separate sheet of paper. Use complete sentences.

1) Why should you take a time-out when you feel angry?

2) When is it a good idea to avoid conflict?

3) Why should you avoid "you" statements?

4) Why does a mediator need to be neutral?

5) What are the steps for resolving conflict?

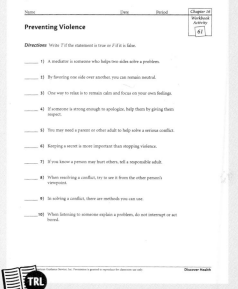

Activity 61

Workbook Activity 61

■ Violence doesn't solve problems. It usually creates even worse problems.

■ Conflicts and disagreements are normal. They may be big, small, or ongoing. It is not normal or healthy for a conflict to turn violent.

■ Some of the costs of violent crimes are permanent injuries, mental scarring, lost peace of mind, and money.

■ It is helpful to identify conflict and potential problems. This is the first step to resolving potential problems and avoiding violence.

■ Some potential causes of violence are the media, family problems, guns, drugs, and gangs. Prejudice and the desire for revenge can also motivate violence.

■ Young children can be affected by crimes such as robbery and assault. They are also vulnerable to child abuse and kidnapping.

■ Everyone feels anger sometimes. People can use a time-out to manage their anger.

■ Sometimes it is best to walk away from conflicts.

■ It is best to talk alone with a person when resolving conflict. Each side should remain calm, avoid insults, and focus on feelings rather than actions.

■ You can prevent others from fighting by not watching or encouraging them. You can also suggest that they work out a peaceful solution.

■ Some problems are too difficult for you to work out on your own. It is okay to ask for help from an adult or peer mediator.

■ It is more important to stop violence than it is to keep a secret. If you know that a friend may hurt someone, tell a trusted adult and try to stop the violence.

■ **Using the Chapter Summary**
To further reinforce the facts and concepts presented in the chapter, read and discuss with students the questions that follow.

Ask:

· What are some of the costs of violent crimes? (permanent injuries, mental scarring, lost peace of mind, money)

· What is the first step to resolving potential problems? (identify the conflict and potential problems)

· What are some potential causes of violence? (media, family problems, guns, drugs, gangs, prejudice, the desire for revenge)

· Why do people use time-outs? (to manage their anger)

· What should each side do when resolving a conflict? (remain calm, avoid insults, focus on feelings rather than actions)

· If you know a friend is about to hurt someone, is it more important to keep the secret or stop the violence? (It is more important to stop the violence by telling a trusted adult.)

# Chapter 16 Review

The Teacher's Resource Library includes two parallel forms of the Chapter 16 Mastery Test. The difficulty level of the two forms is equivalent. You may wish to use one form as a pretest and the other form as a posttest.

## Review Answers

### Comprehension: Identifying Facts

1) intended  2) imitate  3) Conflict
4) ongoing  5) mental  6) Shouting
7) increase  8) loyalty  9) Revenge

---

## Chapter 16 Review

## Comprehension: Identifying Facts

On a separate sheet of paper, write the correct word or words from the Word Bank to complete each sentence.

| WORD BANK | |
|---|---|
| apology | mediator |
| conflict | mental |
| encourage | ongoing |
| imitate | prejudice |
| increase | revenge |
| intended | secret |
| loyalty | shouting |

1) Violence is any actions or words that are _____ to do harm.

2) Children may _____ what they see on TV.

3) _____ is a normal disagreement or difference.

4) Some conflicts are _____, lasting for years.

5) A crime victim may have both physical and _____ injuries.

6) _____ is a warning sign of conflict.

7) Guns _____ the chance of violence in the home.

8) People may act violently to show _____ to a gang.

9) _____ usually leads to increased violence.

---

Name _____ Date _____ Period _____    Chapter 16 Mastery Test A page 1

**Chapter 16 Mastery Test A**

**Directions** Read each sentence. Write *T* if the statement is true or *F* if the statement is false.

_____ 1) Violent behavior is acting in a way that hurts others.

_____ 2) Violence makes people feel safe where they live or work.

_____ 3) Newspapers, TV, and movies contain violence.

_____ 4) Violent behavior in children may be learned from the parents.

_____ 5) Turning to violence is normal.

_____ 6) People are rarely injured by random violence.

_____ 7) An internal conflict is having two different ideas and not being sure which is best.

_____ 8) About half of the murders in the United States happen among people who know each other.

_____ 9) A victim never feels mental or emotional scars.

_____ 10) A violent past can lead to a cycle of violence.

_____ 11) Entering a situation without knowing what is going on is the best way to respond.

_____ 12) People should not stop and think about their actions.

_____ 13) Shouting, insults, and threats are all warning signs of conflict.

_____ 14) When young people see violence, they may think that it is a good way to solve problems.

©AGS® American Guidance Service, Inc. Permission is granted to reproduce for classroom use only.    Discover Health

---

Name _____ Date _____ Period _____    Chapter 16 Mastery Test A page 2

**Chapter 16 Mastery Test A, continued**

_____ 15) Drugs help people use good judgment.

_____ 16) A gun in the home decreases the chance of accidental death.

_____ 17) Members of a gang often do things that they might not do on their own.

_____ 18) Prejudice and hatred can lead to violence against a particular group.

_____ 19) It is okay to accept any offerings from strangers.

_____ 20) Some conflicts can be healthy.

_____ 21) Nearly 75 percent of all crime victims in the United States are between the ages of 12 and 24.

_____ 22) A mediator helps people work out a problem reasonably.

_____ 23) If you see people fighting, encourage it by watching or cheering.

_____ 24) A mediator must remain neutral.

_____ 25) It is always more important to stop violence than it is to keep a secret.

©AGS® American Guidance Service, Inc. Permission is granted to reproduce for classroom use only.    Discover Health

**Chapter 16 Mastery Test A**

**10)** An _____ often helps both sides feel better.

**11)** _____ and hatred can lead to violence against a particular group.

**12)** Don't _____ a fight by watching it.

**13)** A _____ should not choose sides.

**14)** It is more important to prevent violence than it is to keep a _____.

## Comprehension: Understanding Main Ideas

Write the answers to these questions on a separate sheet of paper. Use complete sentences.

**15)** Give some examples of the media.

**16)** What is the cycle of violence?

**17)** What is the term used for violence aimed at a group of people with a particular cultural or religious background?

**18)** What does a mediator need to be?

## Critical Thinking: Write Your Opinion

**19)** Why might using alcohol make a person less likely to compromise and resolve a conflict?

**20)** As a mediator, how might you solve a problem if one person is prejudiced?

**Test Taking Tip** Review your corrected tests. You can learn from previous mistakes.

**10)** apology **11)** Prejudice
**12)** encourage **13)** mediator **14)** secret

## Comprehension: Understanding Main Ideas

**15)** Examples of the media include newspapers, TV, and movies.

**16)** The cycle of violence is repeating violence because of a violent past.

**17)** *Prejudice* is the term used for violence aimed at a group of people with a particular cultural or religious background.

**18)** A mediator needs to be neutral, not favoring either side.

## Critical Thinking: Write Your Opinion

**19)** Accept all reasonable answers. Students may suggest that using alcohol might make a person less likely to compromise and resolve a conflict because alcohol clouds judgment. Students might also suggest that alcohol can make a person feel more powerful and more likely to start fights.

**20)** Accept all reasonable answers. A possible answer might be to find out if the prejudice has something to do with the conflict. If it does, you might try to explain the other person's point of view or suggest compromises to the conflict.

---

**Chapter 16 Mastery Test B**

Name _____ Date _____ Period _____

Chapter 16 Mastery Test B | Chapter 16 Mastery Test B
page 1

**Chapter 16 Mastery Test B**

**Directions** Read each sentence. Write *T* if the statement is true or *F* if the statement is false.

_____ **1)** Members of a gang often do things that they might not do on their own.

_____ **2)** Prejudice and hatred can lead to violence against a particular group.

_____ **3)** It is okay to accept any offerings from strangers.

_____ **4)** Some conflicts can be healthy.

_____ **5)** Nearly 75 percent of all crime victims in the United States are between the ages of 12 and 24.

_____ **6)** A mediator helps people work out a problem reasonably.

_____ **7)** If you see people fighting, encourage it by watching or cheering.

_____ **8)** A mediator must remain neutral.

_____ **9)** It is always more important to stop violence than it is to keep a secret.

_____ **10)** Violent behavior is acting in a way that hurts others.

_____ **11)** Violence makes people feel safe where they live or work.

_____ **12)** Newspapers, TV, and movies contain violence.

_____ **13)** Violent behavior in children may be learned from the parents.

_____ **14)** Turning to violence is normal.

Name _____ Date _____ Period _____

Chapter 16 Mastery Test B, continued | Chapter 16 Mastery Test B page 2

_____ **15)** People are rarely injured by random violence.

_____ **16)** Entering a situation without knowing what is going on is the best way to respond.

_____ **17)** People should not stop and think about their actions.

_____ **18)** Shouting, insults, and threats are all warning signs of conflict.

_____ **19)** When young people see violence, they may think that it is a good way to solve problems.

_____ **20)** Drugs help people use good judgment.

_____ **21)** A gun in the home decreases the chance of accidental death.

_____ **22)** An internal conflict is having two different ideas and not being sure which is best.

_____ **23)** About half of the murders in the United States happen among people who know each other.

_____ **24)** A victim never feels mental or emotional scars.

_____ **25)** A violent past can lead to a cycle of violence.

## Deciding for Yourself

Have students read "Does Gun Control Prevent Violence?" in the Deciding for Yourself lesson on page 338.

### Ask:

- Why might someone who is against gun control not agree with the statement that police departments provide enough protection, so private citizens do not need guns? (Accept all reasonable answers that students can justify. A person who is against gun control might say that police cannot be everywhere, and people should be able to protect themselves when the police cannot do so.)

- Why might someone who is for gun control not agree with the statement that waiting periods and background checks won't stop someone who wants a gun? (Accept all reasonable answers that students can justify. A person who is for gun control might say that these methods might not stop every criminal who wants a gun, but it will stop some of them. The process will also make it more difficult for people to get guns, which could cut down on the number of guns sold.)

### Deciding for Yourself Answers

1) Accept all answers students can justify. They may suggest that arguments supported with statistics are more believable than those based only on opinion.

2) Accept all answers students can justify. They may suggest that arguments with statistics are more believable than those based only on opinion.

3) Answers will vary. If students agree with the question, encourage them to suggest the kinds of laws that might be passed.

### ■ Deciding for Yourself Activity

Have students complete the Unit 6 Deciding for Yourself Activity.

---

### Does Gun Control Prevent Violence?

Many violent crimes involve the use of guns. Sometimes the guns were purchased for legal reasons and were not locked up properly. Some of the guns are stolen or bought illegally.

Some people believe that more gun laws will reduce violence. They work to pass laws such as the Brady Handgun Violence Protection Act. This law requires a five-day waiting period before a person can buy a gun. Other such laws may prohibit people from carrying any concealed weapon. Here are some other arguments in support of gun control.

- Gun laws can help stop convicted criminals and drug abusers from buying guns.
- Without gun control, our schools and neighborhoods will become more violent.
- Americans no longer need guns for self-protection. Today we have police departments to protect us.

Other people believe that gun laws are a bad idea. They think everyone should have the right to buy a gun. Here are some arguments against gun control.

- Waiting periods and background checks won't stop someone who wants a gun.
- Gun laws won't decrease violence and crime.
- Every American has the right to self-protection.
- Americans should have the right to use guns for hunting and other recreational purposes.

### Questions

1) Which statements supporting gun control do you believe? Do you have other reasons to give in support of gun control?

2) Which statements against gun control do you believe? Do you have other reasons to give against gun control?

3) Do you think we need more laws controlling the buying and using of guns? Support your answer with reasons.

---

Name                     Date          Period          Unit 6
Deciding for Yourself Activity 6

**Gun Control**

1) Divide the class into two groups. One group represents the National Rifle Association and is against gun control. The other group represents the Center to Prevent Handgun Violence and is for gun control. The two groups will argue for their position in a debate on gun control.

2) To prepare for the debate, write the arguments for the side you represent here.

3) Listen carefully to each argument. In deciding whether you agree with an argument, ask yourself the following questions:
   - Who is making the statement?
   - What is their position?
   - How accurate or complete is their statement?

4) After listening to the arguments, did you change your opinions on gun control?

5) What is your opinion about the connection between gun control and violence?

Discover Health

**Deciding for Yourself Master 6**

■ To reduce chances of car injuries, don't drive with someone who has been drinking alcohol or using drugs. Serious injuries from a car accident can be reduced by wearing seat belts.

■ Wearing proper safety equipment prevents injuries when doing exercise or sports. Warm up and cool down before and after exercising. Drink plenty of water.

■ Hand guns and rifles should be in locked cabinets. The ammunition should be stored in a separate, and also locked, location.

■ Wiring, appliances, and smoke detectors should be checked twice a year. Checking the house for fire hazards reduces the number of fires. Knowing what to do if a fire breaks out reduces your risk of injury.

■ When baby-sitting, keep your full attention on the children. Know what to do in an emergency.

■ An emergency kit should have flashlights and batteries, candles and matches, a battery-operated radio, and a first aid kit.

■ Plan ahead for what you will do if your area has an earthquake, tornado, hurricane, flood, or severe thunderstorm.

■ To get emergency help, dial 911 or 0. Stay calm and talk slowly. Never hang up until you are told to do so.

■ The Good Samaritan Laws protect people who help victims in an emergency.

■ First-aid providers should use Universal Precautions when possible. These include wearing masks and latex gloves.

■ Heat exhaustion, heatstroke, hypothermia, and frostbite occur in very hot or cold temperatures.

■ Severe bleeding, shock, or a victim not breathing require immediate emergency first aid.

■ The Heimlich maneuver is used for people who are choking.

■ Cardiopulmonary resuscitation (CPR) is emergency first aid for heart attacks.

■ It is more important to stop violence than to keep it a secret. If you know a friend who may hurt someone, tell a trusted adult.

## ■ Using the Unit Summary

To further reinforce the facts and concepts presented in the unit, read and discuss with students the questions that follow.

### Ask:

- Why is it important to avoid getting into a car with someone who has been drinking alcohol or using drugs? (It is important to avoid driving with someone who has been using alcohol or drugs because it is more likely that the driver will have an accident.)

- List three ways that you can prevent sports-related injuries. (wear proper safety equipment, warm up and cool down before and after exercising, drink plenty of water)

- What should be included in an emergency kit? (flashlights and batteries, candles and matches, a battery-operated radio, and a first aid kit)

- What should you do to get emergency help? (Dial 911 or 0.)

- For what kind of emergency is the Heimlich maneuver used? (The Heimlich maneuver is used for people who are choking.)

- What is CPR? (CPR is cardiopulmonary resuscitation, or emergency first aid for heart attacks.)

- If a friend tells you she is going to hurt someone, why is it more important to stop the violence than to keep your friend's secret? (It is more important to stop the violence because you can prevent someone from being hurt.)

## Unit 6 Review

The Teacher's Resource Library includes a two-page Unit Mastery Test pictured on this page. Answers are in the Answer Keys beginning on page 433 of this Teacher's Edition.

### Review Answers

#### Comprehension: Identifying Facts

1) seat belts  2) smoke detector
3) emergency  4) firearms  5) batteries
6) first aid  7) conscious  8) temperature
9) choking

### Comprehension: Identifying Facts

On a separate sheet of paper, write the correct word or words from the Word Bank to complete each sentence.

| WORD BANK | | |
| --- | --- | --- |
| batteries | firearms | shouting |
| choking | first aid | smoke detector |
| conflict | prejudice | temperature |
| conscious | pressure | violence |
| emergency | seat belts | |

1) Wearing _____ can help prevent injuries in car accidents.

2) A _____ can protect you from injury in a household fire.

3) You should dial 911 in an _____.

4) Keep all _____ in locked cabinets.

5) An emergency kit should include a flashlight, _____, a first aid kit, and a radio.

6) Immediate emergency care given to a sick or an injured person is _____.

7) To find out if someone is _____, tap them on the shoulder or ask loudly if the person is OK.

8) For shock, maintain normal body _____ by using a blanket or a coat.

9) The Heimlich maneuver is used when a person is _____.

### Unit 6 Mastery Test, page 1

Name _____ Date _____ Period _____  | Chapters 14–16 / Unit 6 Mastery Test / page 1

**Unit 6 Mastery Test**

**Part A Directions** Read each sentence. Write *T* if the statement is true or *F* if the statement is false.

_____ 1) Call 911 for every minor injury.

_____ 2) An emergency kit should include a radio and a first aid kit.

_____ 3) Drugs rarely change how a person sees a situation.

_____ 4) During a storm, thunder is dangerous.

_____ 5) While baby-sitting, be sure to keep your full attention on the children.

_____ 6) Teens are more at risk of injuring themselves than adults are.

_____ 7) Over 90 percent of house fires are preventable.

_____ 8) People are rarely injured by random violence.

_____ 9) Turning to violence is normal.

_____ 10) A victim never feels mental or emotional scars.

_____ 11) Violent behavior may be learned from the parents.

_____ 12) Members of a gang often do things that they might not do on their own.

_____ 13) People should not stop and think about their actions.

### Unit 6 Mastery Test, page 2

Name _____ Date _____ Period _____  | Chapters 14–16 / Unit 6 Mastery Test / page 2

**Unit 6 Mastery Test, continued**

_____ 14) A gun in the home decreases the chance of accidental death.

_____ 15) A violent past can lead to a cycle of violence.

**Part B Directions** Read the words in the Word Bank. Choose the item that *best* completes each sentence. On the blank before each number, write the letter for that item.

| Word Bank | | |
| --- | --- | --- |
| a) cold | c) hypothermia | e) splint |
| b) heatstroke | d) shock | |

_____ 16) The main sign of _____ is a lack of sweating.

_____ 17) A _____ is used to keep a broken limb in place.

_____ 18) If you suspect a sprain or fracture, remember to ICE (immobilize, _____, elevate) it.

_____ 19) _____ is a physical reaction to severe injury or illness.

_____ 20) _____ is a serious loss of body heat resulting from being exposed to severe cold temperatures.

10) To stop severe bleeding, apply _____ directly to the wound.

11) Hurting people or things people care about is _____.

12) A disagreement between people is a _____.

13) Warning signs of conflict are threatening gestures or _____.

14) Violence aimed at a particular cultural or religious group may result from _____.

## Comprehension: Understanding Main Ideas

Write the answers to these questions on a separate sheet of paper. Use complete sentences.

15) Describe at least two actions that can prevent poisoning.

16) Describe what you should do in a tornado or during an earthquake.

17) What is the most important thing to do in an emergency?

18) What is a poison control center and when should you call it?

## Critical Thinking: Write Your Opinion

19) Describe two ways you could make your own home safer.

20) What are some ways to avoid becoming the victim of a violent crime?

10) pressure  11) violence  12) conflict
13) shouting  14) prejudice

## Comprehension: Understanding Main Ideas

15) Answers will vary. Accept any two of the following: storing medicines and dangerous products safely, following directions for the safe use of all products, using products with dangerous fumes outdoors, removing poisonous plants from outdoor areas.

16) If caught outside in a tornado, move away from it at right angles or lie face down in the lowest spot you can find. If inside during a tornado, go to the basement or lowest floor. If outside during an earthquake, stay in a car or a clear space away from buildings, trees, and power lines. If inside, stay away from windows. Get under a strong table and cover your face and head.

17) The most important thing to do in an emergency is to remain calm.

18) A poison control center provides emergency information on the telephone to victims of poisoning. It is the first number to call if someone has been poisoned.

## Critical Thinking: Write Your Opinion

19) Answers will vary. Students may suggest checking for dangerous products, checking the batteries in smoke detectors, knowing how to use a fire extinguisher, or putting together an emergency kit.

20) Answers will vary. Possible answers: Avoid walking alone at night. Walk only in familiar areas that are well-lighted. If you are being following, walk quickly to a place where there are other people. When home alone, keep the door locked. Do not tell someone over the telephone that you are home alone.

# Planning Guide

## Health and Society

| | Student Pages | Student Lesson | | |
|---|---|---|---|---|
| | | Vocabulary | Lesson Review | Writing About Health |
| **Chapter 17  Consumer Health** | 345–367 | | | |
| Lesson 1  Health Care Information | 346–347 | • | • | |
| Lesson 2  Seeking Health Care | 348–351 | • | • | |
| Lesson 3  Paying for Health Care | 352–353 | • | • | |
| Lesson 4  Being a Wise Consumer | 354–356 | • | • | |
| Lesson 5  Evaluating Advertisements | 357–360 | • | • | |
| Lesson 6  Consumer Protection | 361–364 | • | • | • |
| **Chapter 18  Public Health** | 368–383 | | | |
| Lesson 1  Defining Community | 369–372 | • | • | • |
| Lesson 2  Community Health Resources | 373–376 | • | • | |
| Lesson 3  Community Health Advocacy Skills | 377–380 | • | • | |
| **Chapter 19  Environmental Health** | 384–403 | | | |
| Lesson 1  Health and the Environment | 385–388 | • | • | • |
| Lesson 2  Air Pollution and Health | 389–392 | • | • | |
| Lesson 3  Water and Land Pollution and Health | 393–396 | • | • | |
| Lesson 4  Promoting a Healthy Environment | 397–400 | | • | |

### Unit Activities

**Home Connection**
**What Do You Think?**
**Deciding for Yourself**

### AGS-Related Resources

**Discover Life Skills Handbook**
**Discover Healthy Sexual Development**

### Assessment Options

**Student Text**
  **Lesson Reviews**
  **Chapter Reviews**
  **Unit Review**
**Teacher's Resource Library**
  **Chapter Mastery Tests**
  **Unit Mastery Test**

| Action for Health | Careers | Health, Fitness, and Nutrition Tips | Healthy Subjects | Then and Now | Technology | Background Information | Career Application | Community Application | Environment Application | Global Connection | Home Application | Multicultural Connection | Auditory | Group Learning | LEP/ESL | Tactile/Kinesthetic | Visual | Activities | Mastery Tests | Student Study Guide | Workbook Activities |
|---|---|---|---|---|---|---|---|---|---|---|---|---|---|---|---|---|---|---|---|---|---|
| | | | | | | | | | | | | | | | | | | | • | • | |
| | | 346 | | | | | | | | 347 | | | | | | | | | | | |
| | 349 | | | | | | | 350 | | | 351 | | | | 349 | | | | | | |
| | | 353 | | | | | | 353 | | | | | | | | | | | | | |
| | | | | | | | | | | | | | | 355 | | | | | | | |
| 360 | 359 | | 357 | | 358 | 358 | | | 358 | | | | 359 | | | | | | | | |
| | | | | 364 | | 363 | | | | | 362 | | | | | 363 | 362 | | | | |
| | | | | | | | | | | | | | | | | | | | • | • | |
| | 371 | | | | | | | 372 | | 370 | | 371 | | | 371 | | | | | | |
| | | | | | | 375 | 374 | | 375 | | | | | 374 | | 376 | | | | | |
| 377 | 378 | | 379 | | | | | | | 378 | | | 380 | | | | 379 | | | | |
| | | | | | | | | | | | | | | | | | | | • | • | |
| | | 386 | | | | 386 | 388 | | | | | | | | | | 387 | | | | |
| | | 389 | | | | 391 | | | | 392 | | | | | | 390 | | | | | |
| | | 395 | | | | | | 396 | | | 394 | | | 395 | | | | | | | |
| 400 | 397 | | | 399 | | 398 | | | 398 | | | 399 | | | | | | | | | |

---

## Block Scheduling

Here is a suggested teaching activity if you have extended instructional time, such as a block schedule.

**Health Export** *To increase your understanding of individual and societal issues, problems, consequences, and solutions.*

Create a 1- to 2-minute radio or television public service announcement (PSA) that promotes healthy attitudes and behaviors focused on consumer, public, and/or environmental health. The PSA must contain: (1) a clear and focused message, (2) a mini True-False quiz about the topic, (3) a memorable slogan, and (4) the results of a mini-survey you conducted on a topic that aligns with and supports your message. If time and resources permit, air the PSAs over school or community networks.

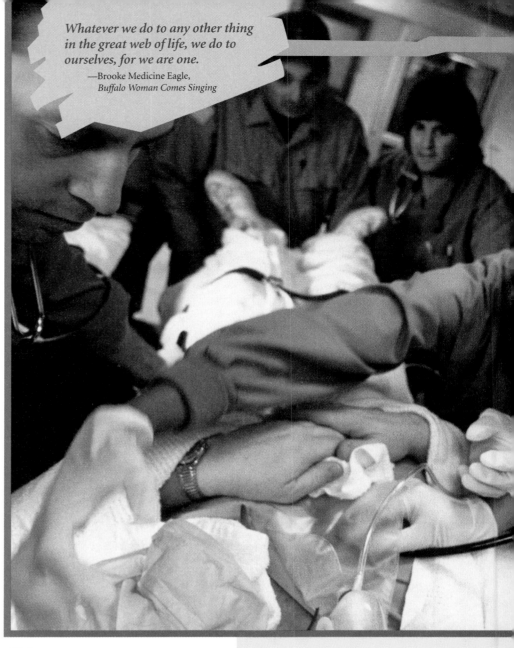

*Whatever we do to any other thing in the great web of life, we do to ourselves, for we are one.*

—Brooke Medicine Eagle,
*Buffalo Woman Comes Singing*

 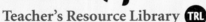
## Other Resources

### Books for Teachers
Guber, Selena S., and Jon Berry. *Marketing to and Through Kids.* New York: McGraw Hill, 1993.

*Understanding Our Environment.* Arlington, VA: National Science Teacher's Association, 1995.

### Books for Students
Engel, Peter. *Scams, Shams, Stings, and Shady Business Practices and How You Can Avoid Them.* New York: St. Martin's Griffin, 1996. (Discusses fraud and deceptive advertising.)

Karni, Karen, Oliver Karni, and Jane Sidney. *Opportunities in Medical Technology Careers.* VGM Career Horizons, 1990. (Shows the challenges and joys of laboratory work in a medical field.)

### Videos
*America's Health Care Dilemma: Who Pays?* (26 minutes). Princeton, NJ: Films for the Humanities & Sciences (1-800-257-5126), 1990. (Examines the rising costs of health care and who should pay for Americans' access to health care services.)

*Quackery Gallery.* (32 minutes). Minneapolis: Great Tapes (1-800-879-8273), 1997. (Provides historical information on quackery and reviews many quack medical devices.)

### Sources of Water Quality Testing Kits
HACH Company, P.O. Box 389, Loveland, CO 80539. (1-800-227-4224).

Science Kit & Boreal Laboratories, 777 East Park Drive, Tonawanda, NY 14150-6784. (1-800-828-7777).

| Name | Date | Period | Unit 7 Home Connection 7 |
|---|---|---|---|

**Discussing Environmental Issues With Your Family**

This activity will give you the opportunity to share what you have learned about environmental health with your family. To do the activity, complete each step below.

*Step 1* **Gathering Information**
Before talking to your family, collect a number of media stories on the environment. Most newspapers feature at least one story a day. Television news programs are another source of information. Clip out written stories or write down summaries of news shows. Set aside a time to meet with family members to discuss your findings.

*Step 2* **Leading a Family Discussion on the Environment**
Tell your family about what you have been learning about the environment and share with them the information you have gathered. Lead a family discussion on this topic. The questions below will help you.

· What environmental issues are discussed in the news stories?
· Are there two sides to the issues?
· What groups of people are involved in environmental issues?
· How does the way we live affect the environment?

When you have finished discussing your news stories, ask your parents if the environment was an important topic when they were teenagers. Discuss whether or not environmental issues have changed over the years.

*Step 3* **Looking Back From the Future**
Now imagine that you are a parent with children. In the space below, write a short paragraph telling your child about the environmental problems that existed when you were a teenager. Share your writing with your parents. You might like to save your paragraph, so that if you do have children, one day they can read it.

(TRL)   **Home Connection Master 7**

# Unit 7

# Health and Society

$A$re the products you buy safe for the environment? Do you help others in your community? Do you take care of yourself to prevent disease? We all have a responsibility to do things that promote public health and safety. We can be wise consumers by buying products that are safe for us and our families. We can promote recycling in our community to protect the environment.

As consumers, we are faced with many decisions that affect our health. We make decisions about choosing health care, doing volunteer work, and preventing air pollution. In this unit, you will learn how to be a wise consumer, promote public health, and protect our global environment.

## Introducing the Unit

Call on a volunteer to read the quote on page 342.

Ask:

- How do you think this quote is connected to community health and safety? (Answers will vary. Prompt students to think about how individuals, communities, and the environment are connected. The health of one affects the health of others. For example, problems in the environment can lead to problems in communities and in individuals.)

- Whose responsibility is it to clean up the environment and keep it clean? (Students should conclude that it is everyone's responsibility to preserve the environment, including business, industry, governments, and individuals.)

- How are you connected to the environment? (Ask students to think about how the environment provides for our needs, such as air, food, and water.)

## What Do You Think?

Have volunteers read the story on page 344.

**Ask:**

- What problems did Nikki notice in her neighborhood? (litter and garbage on the streets, homeless people, lack of health-care facilities and grocery stores nearby, no wheelchair access, no safe places to ride skateboards and bikes in the park)

- Even though all the problems in the neighborhood did not affect Nikki directly, why do you think she was concerned? (Answers will vary. Students might suggest that Nikki is concerned about her community because she realizes that all community problems affect people and the environment.)

- Who might Nikki want to tell about the problems of litter and lack of wheelchair access? (She could raise the issues with neighborhood organizations.)

- What organizations deal with community problems are in your community? (Answers will vary, depending on the resources available in your community.)

- How can you get involved to improve your community? (Answers will vary. Students may suggest they can volunteer or join organizations that serve the community.)

Have students complete the Unit 7 What Do You Think? Activity sheet.

### What Do You Think?

Nikki is concerned about her community. She lives in the city and is pretty happy with life. She loves her family, and she likes to go to school. She tries to do things that protect her health and safety. Lately, though, she has noticed problems in her neighborhood.

On her way to school, Nikki has noticed a lot of litter on the streets. The wind blows the garbage around, and sometimes it blows into her face. Some of the litter smells bad, and Nikki thinks it might be a danger to her health. Besides, it really looks bad.

Sometimes Nikki sees homeless people on the streets. She wonders how they can take care of their health. Where do they go when it is cold? How do they get enough food to eat?

Nikki heard her mother talking about there being no health care facilities near home. It might be difficult to get a doctor when someone gets hurt or sick. There are also no grocery stores within walking distance. People in her neighborhood have to drive to do their shopping. Some people end up buying fast food instead.

Nikki also noticed some other problems in the community. There is no wheelchair access to the park, and there are no safe places to ride bikes or skateboards.

Nikki has heard of some neighborhood organizations. There is a neighborhood action league that deals with problems in the community. There is a food pantry that provides food to people who need it. How can Nikki get involved to improve her community?

---

Name _____ Date _____ Period _____

Unit 7
What Do You Think? Activity
7

**Looking at Your Community**

Read your local newspaper, look at local magazines, or talk with community agencies or your local government to learn more about services available in your community. Then answer these questions.

1) Is litter a problem in your community? What is being done to address the problem of litter? What actions could you take to help clean up your community? Where is your community's landfill?

2) How many homeless people are in your community? What groups provide assistance to homeless people?

3) Are there food shelves in your community to provide food to people who need it? How could you help this effort in your community?

4) Notice buildings in your community that have wheelchair ramps or are accessible to people in wheelchairs. For example, look at public libraries, city government buildings, hospitals, schools, apartment buildings, churches. List those buildings.

5) Are there walking or biking paths in your community? Where are they located?

6) How many health care clinics are in your community? How many hospitals are there? Are they public clinics or private clinics?

AGS® American Guidance Service, Inc. Permission is granted to reproduce for classroom use only.          Discover Health

**TRL**

**What Do You Think? Master 7**

# Consumer Health

H ealth care products and services are available everywhere. Most people buy them every day. You buy health care when you use a product or a service that directly affects your physical and emotional well-being. You buy health care whenever you see a doctor, dentist, or nurse. Becoming a wise health buyer takes effort. It means learning how to judge the products and services you use. It means knowing when and where to seek health care and ways to pay for it.

In this chapter, you will learn what wise health consumers know and what a consumer's rights are. You will learn what influences people's health choices, how to judge products and services, and how to clear up consumer problems. You will learn when to use self-care and when and where to seek professional health care. You will learn how health care expenses are paid.

## Goals for Learning

▶ To identify sources for health care

▶ To learn when self-care or professional treatment is best

▶ To explain ways to pay for health care

▶ To explain the advantages of being a wise health consumer

▶ To describe ways to judge products and services

▶ To describe how advertising influences health care consumers

## Introducing the Chapter

Bring to class magazine or newspaper advertisements that deal with the subject of health products or services. Discuss the purpose of each ad—to sell a product or service—and ask students to decide whether the ad seems sensible and accurate.

Have students read the chapter opener and Goals for Learning on page 345.

### Ask:

• What are some examples of health care products and services? (Answers will vary and may include medicine; hygiene products; doctor, dentist, and nurse care; and hospitals. Accept all reasonable answers.)

---

Student Study Guide 23, page 1

Student Study Guide 23, page 2

## Lesson at a Glance

### Chapter 17 Lesson 1

**Overview** This lesson describes health care services and products.

### Objectives

- To describe health care.
- To identify the products and services that make up health care.
- To identify places where medical care is given.

**Student Pages** 346–347

**Audiocassette**

**Teacher's Resource Library** (TRL)

Activity 62

Workbook Activity 62

## Teaching Suggestions

### ■ Vocabulary

*over-the-counter medicine, specialist*

Have students read the paragraph in which the word *specialist* and *over-the-counter medicine* appear. Ask if students have any questions about the meaning of the words and discuss them. Ask for examples of the use of the word.

### ■ Teaching the Lesson

Have students generate a list of words that they associate with health care. Encourage them to think of products or services they use themselves, such as soap, medicine, and visits to a doctor. Keep and add to this list as you proceed through this chapter. At the end of each lesson, the class can add and delete words as students refine their definition of what health care is.

Have students read about health care and who provides it on page 346.

---

## Lesson 1 — Health Care Information

**Specialist**
*A doctor who works only on certain types of medical problems*

As a person who buys health care, you need to be aware of what is available to you. You also need to know how you can get the health care you need.

### What Is Health Care?

Health care includes many different activities, including preventive medicine and regular doctor checkups. Sometimes special measures need to be taken to preserve your body's health. You may need a medical procedure, an operation, or emergency medical care to treat an illness or a disease.

However, health care is also something that you can do every day. When you eat a balanced diet and exercise regularly, you are practicing preventive medicine. Using grooming products to keep your body clean and healthy is another form of health care. If your doctor has prescribed medication or recommended vitamin supplements, then taking these is also a part of your health care.

### Who Can Help You With Health Care?

You probably know about medical professionals such as doctors or nurses. You may have been to a medical **specialist**, such as an orthopedic surgeon or a pediatrician. However, there are many other people in the health care industry. Pharmacists at the drugstore can help you pick out over-the-counter medicine, or things you can buy at the store. They will also help you understand how to take any medication your doctor has prescribed. Employees at an insurance company can help their customers understand what health care is available to them and how they can pay for it. There are also many workers at companies that make health care products. All these people are a part of our health care system.

**Health Tip**

Make regular appointments with a doctor and dentist twice a year, and an eye doctor once a year.

---

Ask:

- What are some ways that you can practice preventive medicine? (eat a balanced diet, exercise regularly)

- Who are some people that help provide health care? (Answers will vary. Accept all reasonable answers, such as doctors, dentists, nurses, pharmacists, workers who make health care products, and so on.)

Make regular appointments with your doctor.

## What Health Care Products Are Available?

Grooming products, over-the-counter medicine, and prescription medication are some health care products that you may already be familiar with. Health care centers may have more specialized types of products. Most hospitals and clinics carry equipment, machines, and computers that are not available elsewhere. From medical syringes to heart monitors, many products can help diagnose and treat illness or disease.

## How Is Medical Care Given?

Medical care can be given from a doctor's office, clinic, or hospital. For routine procedures, you probably would want to go to an office that is near your home. If your medical care is managed through an insurance company, you may need to see a doctor who is in the company's plan.

**LESSON 1 REVIEW** Write the answers to these questions on a separate sheet of paper. Use complete sentences.

1) How is eating a balanced diet a part of health care?

2) Name three types of health care professionals besides doctors and nurses.

3) What are some health care products you can buy?

4) Where would you go for a routine medical checkup?

5) How does a pharmacist assist a doctor in administering health care?

Have students read page 347 to get an overview about health care products and where medical care is provided.

Ask:

- Can people buy all their health care products over the counter? (No. Some products are available only with a prescription. Other products may be available only at a hospital or clinic.)

- Why might it be important for your doctor's office to be near your home? (A doctor's office near your home is more convenient for making regular appointments. It is also makes it easier to visit the doctor when you are sick.)

## Lesson 1 Review Answers

1) Eating a balanced diet helps prevent health problems.

2) Medical specialists, pharmacists, and health insurance employees are health care professionals.

3) You can buy over-the-counter medicine, prescription medicine, and grooming products.

4) You would go to your doctor or a clinic for a routine medical checkup.

5) A pharmacist assists a doctor by helping the patient to understand the medication.

### GLOBAL CONNECTION

Different countries organize and regulate their health care systems differently. This affects who provides health care, how medical care is given, and what health care products are available. Challenge students to find out more about the national health care systems of countries such as Canada, England, or Sweden. Students can focus on different topics, such as how much people spend on medical care, whether they can choose their own doctors, and how easy it is to obtain routine, preventive care.

---

Name _____ Date _____ Period _____  | Chapter 17 / Activity / 62

**Health Care Information**

*Directions* Write *T* if the statement is true or *F* if it is false.

_____ 1) Health care includes regular checkups with a doctor.

_____ 2) Health care includes medical procedures and emergency treatments.

_____ 3) Health care includes eating too many sweets.

_____ 4) Health care includes preventive medicine.

_____ 5) You need a prescription to buy over-the-counter medicine.

_____ 6) On orthopedic surgeon is an example of a specialist.

_____ 7) If you are part of managed health care, you may need to see a doctor in the company's plan.

_____ 8) Many health care products can help diagnose and treat illnesses.

_____ 9) Employees at a health care insurance company are part of the health care industry.

_____ 10) Workers at companies that make health care products are part of the health care industry.

**Activity 62**

---

Name _____ Date _____ Period _____  | Chapter 17 / Workbook Activity / 62

**Health Care Information**

*Directions* Write *T* if the statement is true or *F* if it is false.

_____ 1) Health care includes medical procedures and emergency treatments.

_____ 2) You need a doctor's written order to buy prescription medicine.

_____ 3) A general practitioner is an example of a specialist.

_____ 4) Health care includes having a healthy diet.

_____ 5) Managed health care may require you to see a doctor in the company's plan.

_____ 6) Only a few health care products can help diagnose and treat illnesses.

_____ 7) Health care includes preventive medicine.

_____ 8) Employees at a health care insurance company are part of the health care industry.

_____ 9) Workers at companies that make health care products are part of the health care industry.

_____ 10) Health care includes oversleeping twice a week.

**Workbook Activity 62**

## Lesson at a Glance

### Chapter 17 Lesson 2

**Overview** This lesson explains the people who can provide health care services and where they are available.

### Objectives

- To explain how to practice self-care.
- To determine when professional help is needed.
- To name the professionals who provide health care services.
- To describe types of health care facilities.

**Student Pages** 348–351

**Audiocassette**

**Teacher's Resource Library** **TRL**

Activity 63

Workbook Activity 63

## Teaching Suggestions

### ■ Vocabulary

*prevention, nurse practitioner, primary care physician, health care facility, inpatient, outpatient, pediatrics, rehabilitation, hospice, terminally ill*

Read the vocabulary words and discuss their meanings with the class. Ask students to name the words that are neither a person nor a place. *(prevention, pediatrics, rehabilitation, terminally ill)* Then have students classify each of the remaining words as either a person or a place.

### ■ Teaching the Lesson

Ask students to think of some things that they do to keep themselves healthy. As students share ideas, encourage responses that characterize prevention, good hygiene, and self-care.

Have students read about self-care and questions to ask yourself about a doctor on page 348.

---

## Lesson 2

### Seeking Health Care

**Prevention**
*Appropriate, ongoing self-care*

W̱ise health consumers know how to take care of themselves. They also know when it is best to see a doctor.

#### When Is Self-Care Appropriate?

One way to take care of yourself is to use **prevention**, or appropriate, ongoing self-care. Good nutrition, regular exercise, and safety practices help to prevent illness or injuries. Not smoking and not being around smokers are also preventive measures. Prevention also means not using tobacco, alcohol, or any other drugs unless they have been prescribed by a health professional. Keeping a healthy body weight that's right for your height and age can help to prevent heart and other problems.

It is a good idea to use self-care for colds and other minor illnesses. For example, sound self-care for a cold is to drink plenty of liquids and get extra rest. If a minor illness or injury does not get better within a few days, you should consult a doctor.

#### When Should People Seek Professional Help?

Sometimes it is best not to treat your own health problem. As a rule, consult a health professional whenever you notice something unusual about your body, behavior, or thoughts. Here are some examples of situations for which you should seek professional help:

- An injury that is more than a minor cut or bruise or any blow to the head
- Any unusual bleeding, such as blood in the urine or feces
- Any sharp pain, such as in the stomach
- A patch of skin or a mole that has changed shape or color
- A minor problem—such as a cold, flu, cough, or sore throat—that lasts more than a week
- Feelings of sadness that last more than a few days

**QUESTIONS TO ASK YOURSELF ABOUT A DOCTOR**

- Does the doctor ask about your health problem and history?
- Does the doctor listen carefully and answer all your questions?
- Do you feel comfortable with the doctor?
- Does the doctor give you enough time and attention?
- Does the doctor clearly explain the purpose of tests and procedures?
- Does the doctor clearly explain the tests or diagnosis?
- Does the doctor encourage you to take preventive action?
- Is the doctor willing to refer you elsewhere when necessary?

**348** *Chapter 17 Consumer Health*

---

**Ask:**

- What should you do for a cold that lasts three days? What if the cold lasts eight days? (You can treat a cold with self-care, such as drinking plenty of fluids and getting extra rest, for the first few days. After that, you should seek professional help.)

- Why should you seek professional care for a blow to the head? (A blow to the head could cause a major injury that cannot be treated with self-care. A health professional should help you decide how to treat such an injury.)

**Nurse practitioner**
*A registered nurse with special training for providing health care*

**Primary care physician**
*A doctor who treats people for routine problems*

## Who Are Some Health Care Professionals?

There are many choices for professional health care. Most often people see a doctor for health care. A **primary care physician** treats people for routine or usual problems. For example, a primary care physician may do preventive checkups and handle illness or injury such as the flu or a muscle sprain. A primary care physician usually has a focus in family or general practice. If a problem is too difficult for a primary care physician to handle, he or she may refer you to a specialist.

People often see a **nurse practitioner** for minor problems. A nurse practitioner is a registered nurse with special training for providing primary health care. The nurse practitioner can do many of the things that a doctor does.

Sometimes doctors refer people to other kinds of health care providers. For example, a doctor might refer someone to a physical therapist or a registered dietitian. A physical therapist helps people to regain their muscle functions. A registered dietitian provides nutritional counseling for people who have special dietary needs. A dietitian might help someone with diabetes.

### MEDICAL SPECIALISTS

Medical specialists need special training so that they understand and can treat all the conditions and problems related to their field. Here are the names of some medical specialists and descriptions of what they do.

Allergists diagnose and treat allergies such as hay fever and hives. Dermatologists diagnose and treat skin disease. Obstetricians deal with pregnancy and childbirth. Oncologists treat cancer and its symptoms. Ophthalmologists diagnose and treat eye problems. Orthopedic surgeons diagnose and treat bone and joint problems. Pediatricians provide primary care for babies, children, and adolescents.

Have you been to any medical specialists? Did they use special equipment or a procedure that was new to you?

---

Have students read about health care professionals on page 349.

Ask:

- To which health care professional do most people go for routine problems? (a primary care physician or a nurse practitioner)

- How might a doctor treat a person with diabetes? (A doctor might refer a person with diabetes to a dietitian for nutritional counseling.)

## Healthy Subjects

Ask students to name some medical specialists. Have them describe what the specialist does. Ask students why they think medical specialists are needed. Encourage volunteers to read a paragraph in the feature. Allow students to share their answers to the questions in the feature.

### LEARNING STYLES

**LEP/ESL** The names of the specialists in the Careers feature can be difficult for students to pronounce. Help students make sense of the terms by breaking the words down into their roots. You can also point out the similarity between some of the names and the conditions they treat. For example, allergists treat allergies.

Have students read about choosing health care professionals and facilities on page 350.

Ask:

- Why should you ask for recommendations and examine qualities before choosing your health care provider? (It is important to have a doctor that you are comfortable with and who you feel is responsive to your needs.)

- What are some reasons that an inpatient may need to stay overnight at a health care facility? (to recover from surgery or an illness or to receive rehabilitation for an injury)

**Health care facility**
*A place where people go for medical, dental, and other care*

**Inpatient**
*Someone receiving health care who stays in a facility overnight or longer*

**Outpatient**
*Someone receiving health care without staying overnight*

**Pediatrics**
*Child health care*

**Rehabilitation**
*Help to recover from surgery, illness, or injury*

## How Can You Find a Health Care Professional?

One way to find a health care professional for your needs is to ask a trusted person for a recommendation. Family members or friends may know someone who they feel is qualified. Another doctor or nurse could also give you a recommendation. Directories in the public library list physicians, their specialty, and where and when they received their training.

Once you have a list of names, you can decide what kind of qualities are important to you. Do you prefer a male or female health care provider? Do you want to see a young health professional or one with more years of experience? If you feel uncomfortable with a health care provider, you may want to choose a different provider.

## What Are Some Health Care Facilities?

A **health care facility** is a place where people go for medical, dental, or other types of care. A dental or medical office is one kind of health care facility. You may go to a medical office for routine checkups and to test and diagnose injuries, diseases, or other problems.

A clinic may provide **outpatient** care for people who do not need to stay overnight. Outpatient clinics offer primary care and same-day surgery. The patient can go home the same day. Most clinics treat all kinds of medical problems. Others have a specific focus, such as **pediatrics**, or child health care.

When receiving **inpatient** care, a person must stay overnight or longer. Sometimes patients need to recover from surgery, an illness, or an injury. They can receive nursing care and possibly **rehabilitation**, or help to get better, while in inpatient care.

A hospital is equipped to provide complete health care services. People can receive both outpatient and inpatient care at a hospital. Hospital emergency rooms offer care twenty-four hours a day. These centers treat people who cannot wait for an appointment at a doctor's office.

## Sources for Health Care

| Health Care Professionals | Health Care Facilities | Insurance |
|---|---|---|
| **Dentist**<br>Treats routine or usual teeth problems<br>**Dermatologist**<br>Diagnoses and treats skin problems<br>**Doctor**<br>Diagnoses and treats routine or usual problems<br>**Nurse Practitioner**<br>Provides primary health care<br>**Physical Therapist**<br>Helps people regain their muscle functions<br>**Psychiatrist**<br>Diagnoses and treats mental and emotional problems<br>**Registered Dietitian**<br>Provides nutritional counseling | **Dental or Medical Offices**<br>Provide routine examinations and tests to diagnose and treat injuries, diseases, and problems<br>**Hospital**<br>Provides complete health care services<br>**Long-Term Care Facility**<br>Provides health care for people who require extended recovery and rehabilitation after surgery<br>**Outpatient Clinic**<br>Provides primary health care for people who do not need to stay overnight | **Health Maintenance Organization (HMO)**<br>Provides care within certain limits to enrolled members and their families<br>**Preferred Provider Organization (PPO)**<br>Provides their members more coverage if they choose health care providers in the plan<br>**Medicare**<br>Provides insurance for people age 65 or older<br>**Medicaid**<br>Provides medical aid for people whose incomes are below an established level |

**Hospice**
*A long-term care facility for people who are dying*

**Terminally ill**
*Dying from a disease, an injury, or an illness, sometimes over a long period*

Nursing homes and other long-term care facilities offer everyday care for people who cannot care for themselves. They help older adults or people living with a disability. Long-term care facilities can also help people who require extended recovery and rehabilitation after surgery. A **hospice** is a kind of long-term care facility for people who are **terminally ill**, or certain to die from a disease.

**LESSON 2 REVIEW** Write the answers to these questions on a separate sheet of paper. Use complete sentences.

1) What kind of health care is prevention?

2) When is it wise to seek professional medical help?

3) What does a primary care physician do?

4) What are the two kinds of health care facilities?

5) Why would a primary care physician need to refer you to a medical specialist?

*Consumer Health* Chapter 17 **351**

Have students read about sources for health care and long-term health care facilities on page 351.

**Ask:**

- Do nursing homes provide inpatient or outpatient care? (inpatient, or long-term care)

- Why would a person need hospice care? (A person who is terminally ill, or certain to die from a disease, would need hospice care.)

### Lesson 2 Review Answers

1) Prevention is self-care.

2) You should seek professional medical help if a minor problem lasts for more than a few days or if you notice a change in your body, behavior, or thoughts.

3) A primary care physician administers regular checkups and tests and diagnoses illness, injury, or disease.

4) Nursing home, hospices, hospitals, and clinics are all health care facilities.

5) A primary care physician would refer you to a medical specialist if the medical problem was too difficult for the primary care physician to handle.

### MULTICULTURAL CONNECTION

Challenge students to research practices and customs dealing with the elderly in various cultures. In the United States, many of the elderly move to nursing homes when they cannot take care of themselves. In some cultures, it is more common for older people to live with their children or grandchildren in an extended family. Students can research this topic by looking for books about other countries and cultures or by talking with people from other cultures.

## Chapter 17 Lesson 3

**Overview** This lesson discusses methods and options for paying health care expenses.

### Objectives

■ To explain how health insurance works.

■ To compare private health insurance, managed care, and government programs such as Medicare and Medicaid.

■ To explain how individuals can lower health care costs.

**Student Pages** 352–353

**Audiocassette**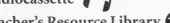

**Teacher's Resource Library** TRL

    Activity 64

    Workbook Activity 64

## Teaching Suggestions

### ■ Vocabulary

*deductible, health insurance, out-of-pocket, premium, Medicaid, Medicare*

Write the vocabulary words on the chalkboard. Ask students which of the words they have heard and where they have heard them. Have students write what they think each word means on a sheet of paper. Tell them to keep the paper and compare their definitions to the definitions and descriptions in the textbook as they read the lesson.

### ■ Teaching the Lesson

Tell students to think about something that they wanted to buy but for which did not have enough money. Ask how they solved their problem. Did they save the money, do extra chores to earn it, or borrow it from their parents? Have students discuss different ways to pay for large expenses.

Have students read about health insurance on pages 352.

---

### Paying for Health Care

**Deductible**
*The initial amount a patient must pay before insurance covers health care costs*

**Health insurance**
*A plan that pays all or part of medical costs*

**Out-of-pocket**
*Straight from a person's income or savings*

**Premium**
*An amount of money paid to an insurance company at regular intervals*

*I*t can be very expensive to pay for health care. When someone suffers from an injury or illness, the care and equipment needed to make him or her well can be very costly. Some people can pay for their medical expenses **out-of-pocket** from their income or savings. Most people, however, have **health insurance** to cover their medical expenses.

#### How Does Health Insurance Work?

Health insurance is a system where you pay a **premium**, or a set amount of money to a company at regular intervals. The company then pays for all or part of your medical costs. This may include medicines, surgery, tests, hospital stays, and regular doctors' visits. Health insurance covers large medical expenses that people might otherwise not be able to afford. Three major kinds of health insurance are private, managed care, and government supported.

#### Private Health Insurance

In private insurance, people pay for a policy themselves or through their employer. An individual may also need to pay a **deductible**, or an initial amount before the insurance pays the costs. For example, if a deductible is $100, you must pay the first $100 of your medical expenses each year.

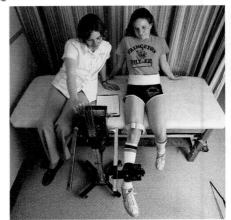

Health insurance covers larger medical expenses that people might otherwise not be able to afford.

---

**Ask:**

• How does health insurance benefit people? (Health insurance can pay for large health care expenses that a person might otherwise not be able to afford.)

**Medicaid**
*Health insurance for people with low incomes*

**Medicare**
*Health insurance for people age 65 or older or who receive Social Security disability*

## Managed Care

People in a managed care plan usually pay a premium, just as in private insurance. However, they may not have to pay a deductible as long as they see medical professionals who are part of the managed care plan. Plans usually have a number of qualified professionals to choose from.

## Government-Supported Health Insurance

The U.S. government provides aid to people who otherwise may not be able to afford health care. **Medicare** provides insurance for people age 65 or older and people on Social Security disability. It pays for hospital and nursing home care. Individuals must pay for some uncovered expenses, such as physician care. **Medicaid** provides similar aid for people with incomes below a certain level.

## How Can Individuals Lower Health Costs?

There are many ways to keep medical expenses down. The cheapest form of health care is preventive medicine. Regular doctor visits and maintaining a healthy lifestyle are two ways of avoiding costly medical treatments.

*Health Tip*

If your health insurance has a preventive care policy, take advantage by going for regular checkups.

Outpatient care is almost always less expensive than inpatient care, which requires overnight stays. When possible, you can choose procedures that allow you to leave the hospital the same day.

You can also receive health care from low-cost facilities. Neighborhood health clinics, alternative birthing centers, and hospices are some places that provide various health care services at a lower cost than most hospitals.

**LESSON 3 REVIEW** Write the answers to these questions on a separate sheet of paper. Use complete sentences.

1) What is a deductible?

2) What are three kinds of health insurance?

3) Who qualifies for Medicare?

4) Which is cheaper, inpatient care or outpatient care? Why?

5) How does health insurance help people receive health care?

---

Have students read about managed care, government-supported insurance, and lowering health costs on page 353.

**Ask:**

- What are the three major kinds of health insurance? (private, managed care, government supported)

- Who benefits from Medicare? (people age 65 or older and people on Social Security disability)

- Who benefits from Medicaid? (people with incomes below a certain level)

- What are some ways of lowering your health costs? (practicing preventive medicine, choosing outpatient care when possible, going to low-cost clinics or other health care facilities)

## Lesson 3 Review Answers

1) A deductible is the amount you must pay before insurance covers health care costs.

2) Three kinds of health insurance are individual, managed care, and government-supported.

3) People who are age 65 or over or who are on Social Security disability qualify for Medicare.

4) Outpatient care is cheaper because you do not have to pay the costs of an overnight hospital stay.

5) Health insurance helps people receive care that they otherwise could not afford.

## APPLICATION

 **In the Community**
Challenge students to research and compare the prices for similar care in different health care facilities. For example, they might call a hospital, health clinic, and other community resources to compare prices for a flu shot. Encourage students to include research and government-sponsored clinics or programs, as well as any resources for senior citizens. Students can create a bar graph or similar chart to present their information.

---

**Activity 64**

Name _____ Date _____ Period _____   Chapter 17 / Activity 64

**Paying for Health Care**

**Part A Directions** Put a check mark next to the *best* answer.

1) Health insurance is a system where you pay _____
  a) a premium.
  b) one large amount of money.
  c) less money the longer you stay in the hospital.
  d) for a policy through government money.

2) The initial amount you pay before your health insurance covers health care costs is a _____
  a) conductant.
  b) premium.
  c) reduction.
  d) deductible.

3) Outpatient care is almost always _____ inpatient care.
  a) less expensive than
  b) more expensive than
  c) the same cost as
  d) better than

4) A government health care plan is called _____
  a) Medicare.
  b) Blue Cross.
  c) managed care.
  d) well-patient care.

5) Medicare is for people _____
  a) who have a yearly income above $100,000.
  b) age 65 and older who receive Social Security.
  c) who have yearly medical expenses of more than $25,000.
  d) who work in the U.S. government.

**Part B Directions** Write *T* if the statement is true or *F* if it is false.

____ 6) Medicaid provides health care for people with incomes below a certain amount.

____ 7) You pay a premium to receive health care.

____ 8) Health insurance is meant to cause out-of-pocket expenses to rise.

____ 9) Preventive medicine is the most expensive form of health care.

____ 10) Outpatient care requires a patient to stay overnight at a hospital.

---

**Workbook Activity 64**

Name _____ Date _____ Period _____   Chapter 17 / Workbook Activity 64

**Paying for Health Care**

**Directions** Write *T* if the statement is true or *F* if it is false.

____ 1) The initial amount you pay before your health insurance covers health care costs is a conductant.

____ 2) Outpatient care is almost always better than inpatient care.

____ 3) A government health care plan is called Medicare.

____ 4) Medicare is for people age 65 and older who receive Social Security.

____ 5) Medicaid provides health care for people with incomes below a certain amount.

____ 6) You pay a premium to receive health care.

____ 7) Health insurance is meant to cause out-of-pocket expenses to rise.

____ 8) Preventive medicine is the most expensive form of health care.

____ 9) Outpatient care requires a patient to stay overnight at a hospital.

____ 10) Health insurance is a system where you pay less money the longer you stay in a hospital.

## Lesson at a Glance

### Chapter 17 Lesson 4

**Overview** This lesson discusses how to make wise health care decisions.

### Objectives

- To explain why it is important to be a wise consumer.

- To identify things that can influence consumer choices, such as recommendations and quackery.

- To describe some ways to judge products and services.

**Student Pages** 354–356

**Audiocassette**

**Teacher's Resource Library**

Activity 65

Workbook Activity 65

## Teaching Suggestions

### ■ Vocabulary

*consumer, defective, count, quackery, word of mouth, bogus, generic*

Write the vocabulary words and their definitions on the chalkboard. Ask students to write sentences, leaving blanks for the missing vocabulary words. Then have students exchange papers and write in the missing words.

### ■ Teaching the Lesson

Have students brainstorm a list of products and services that they use. Ask if they are satisfied with these products and services. Discuss how they or their parents decided that these products or services were the best for them.

Have students read about the advantages of being a wise consumer on page 354.

### Ask:

• What can you do if a product you buy is defective? (Bring your complaint to the proper source. You may get your money back or a replacement product.)

---

## Being a Wise Consumer

| Consumer |
| --- |
| *A person who buys goods and services* |
| Defective |
| *Not working properly* |

*T*o stay healthy, you need to be a wise **consumer**. A consumer is someone who buys goods or services. For example, you buy goods such as soap or aspirin. You buy services such as dental or medical care.

### What Advantages Does a Wise Consumer Have?

As a wise consumer, you can make good choices that protect and improve your health. This means you avoid buying products that are useless or harmful. You recognize signals that you need health care, and you get help quickly.

Wise consumers can also save money by getting the best product or service for the least money. It will take some time to find the best value, but it pays off in the long run. For example, you can check publications with information about consumer products. They will help you compare features, benefits, and prices of different products.

A wise consumer has increased self-confidence. Speaking up for your rights means taking care of yourself. For example, if a product is **defective**, or doesn't work properly, you can make a complaint to the proper source. Usually you can get your money back or have the product replaced. The satisfaction of researching and finding the right product or service also can boost your self-confidence. Knowing and exercising your rights is part of being a wise consumer.

### What Influences Consumers' Choices?

Many things influence consumers' choices. Advertisers use techniques that influence people without their realizing it. For example, you may keep singing a catchy tune that you heard advertise a product. Without thinking about the reason, you may buy that product. It takes careful thought to consider how accurate advertising claims are.

**Count**
*The number of items in a package*

**Quackery**
*A medical product or service that is unproved or worthless*

**Word of mouth**
*Information about a product that you hear from a friend or family member*

Another influence on consumers is the advice or opinions of family and friends. For example, if your friend tells you that he likes a certain brand of deodorant, you may decide to try it. You may also buy a product because your family has always used it. **Word of mouth** can be helpful when you consider a purchase. Keep in mind, however, that what is right for another person may not be right for you.

The price of a product can influence your decision to buy it or not. Well-advertised brand-name products are familiar but usually cost more than less-known brands. However, the advertised brand might appeal to a consumer because it has a recognizable name. If consumers are concerned about the safety and quality of a product, they may feel influenced to buy a brand they are familiar with.

The size of a product can affect its price and its overall value. It is important to compare the price with its weight, volume, or **count**—the number of items in a package—to determine the best value.

Where a product is sold can affect its price. For example, the cost of a product in a convenience store may be higher than in a drugstore or discount store. The wise consumer will shop around for the best price.

Ask your pharmacist to advise about the medication you are taking.

### How Does Quackery Influence Consumers?

**Quackery** is the promotion of medical products or services that are unproved or worthless. Each year Americans spend billions of dollars on products that make false claims of curing diseases and reversing conditions.

Anyone can be fooled by quackery. People who are terminally ill, overweight, or unhappy with aging are targets of quackery. Quackery can fool even cautious people.

Have students read about consumer choices on pages 354 and 355.

Ask:

- When might you follow a recommendation by word of mouth? (when you trust the person who is giving the recommendation)

- Is it always best to buy the cheapest product? (No. You should look at other qualities, such as weight, volume, or count, to determine the best value.)

### LEARNING STYLES

**Group Learning** Have students work in small groups to do a comparison-shopping activity for health care products. Assign a product such as soap, toothpaste, or shampoo to each group. Group members can gather information on different brands, such as price, weight, volume, count, and ingredients. Have the groups compare the different brands and decide which is the best value. Have students present their findings so that everyone can benefit.

Have students read about quackery and about judging products and services on pages 355 and 356.

**Ask:**

- What is wrong with quackery? (These products or services are fake treatments or worthless medications and may be harmful to your health because you are not getting proper treatment.)

- Could quackery cause people to mistrust other health professionals? (Yes, if people do not realize the difference between quackery and sound medical advice.)

- Where can you find information about the ingredients of a product (on the product label)

## Lesson 4 Review Answers

1) You can make a complaint to the proper source about a defective product. You may get your money back or the product replaced.

2) We might buy the product we saw advertised if the advertising convinced us that the product is better than other brands.

3) Quackery promotes unproven or worthless products that may prevent people with illness from getting proper treatment.

4) The best source of information about health care products is your doctor, pharmacist, or a respected health care agency.

5) Answers may vary. Possible answer: It is good that producers advertise their products because the companies make improvements and more information is available about the products.

**Bogus**
*Nongenuine*

**Generic**
*Nonbrand-name*

People would like to believe that every disease and condition has a cure and that pain and suffering always can be eased. This is not always the case. Sometimes there is no real cure for a medical condition. Other times, these nongenuine, or **bogus**, products prevent people from seeking proper treatment. At best, people waste their money on these products and services. At worst, people who buy fake treatments or worthless medications delay getting appropriate treatment until the problem is severe. People who do not get proper treatment may become sicker. They could even die.

### How Can Products and Services Be Judged?

The best way to decide if a product is worth the cost and is right for you is to study its ingredients. This involves making a habit of reading labels. Federal law requires that manufacturers list ingredients on the label of every food, drug, and cosmetic or grooming product. For example, if you were buying a pain reliever, you might look both at brand-name and **generic**, or nonbrand-name, products. Both have labels listing their ingredients. Food labels usually are easy to read. Labels for cosmetic and grooming products and drugs can be more difficult to read. Reading the label provides important information.

The best source of information about a health care product or treatment is your doctor, pharmacist, or a respected agency. A wise consumer should keep in mind that if something sounds too good to be true, it probably is.

**LESSON 4 REVIEW** Write the answers to these questions on a separate sheet of paper. Use complete sentences.

1) What can you do if a product is defective?

2) How might advertising influence our consumer decisions?

3) How does quackery hurt consumers?

4) What is the best source of information about health care products?

5) What is the best way to decide if a product is right for you?

356    *Chapter 17    Consumer Health*

**Activity 65**

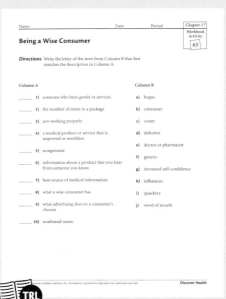

**Workbook Activity 65**

## Evaluating Advertisements

M̲ost products are advertised on TV and radio or in newspapers and magazines. Companies spend large amounts of money to encourage people to buy their products. Why do they do it? Sometimes people choose products that they have seen advertised. But is this the best way to decide if a product is good or not? What if it affects your health? A wise consumer should look critically at claims made in advertisements before deciding whether to buy a product.

### What Are Some Methods of Advertising a Product?

Advertisers use a number of methods and catchphrases to convince you to buy their products.

### New Product

Words like *new* and *improved* appeal to the buyer's desire to be different. Sometimes the product is the same; only the packaging is new.

### Old-Fashioned

Advertisers appeal to the ideals of tradition and happy memories. Consumers may buy the product because it reminds them of a relative or something from their past.

**Healthy Subjects**

**Consumer Science**

**CONSUMER REPORTS**

The magazine *Consumer Reports* tests and evaluates thousands of products every year. It tests all kinds of household items and other consumer products, from radios and phones to cars and washing machines. It rates different brands by performance, reliability, and specific features. It also provides a chart that shows the rate of repairs for each brand.

*Consumer Reports* is a useful resource for rating various products and testing the claims they make in advertising. The magazine does not have any product advertising. This is so that it can stay impartial, or fair. The magazine judges the products only on their quality.

---

## Chapter 17  Lesson 5

**Overview**  This lesson explains the effects of advertising on consumer choices.

### Objectives

- To identify methods of advertising.
- To discuss the reasons for advertising health care products or services.
- To describe ways advertisements of harmful drugs are being regulated.

**Student Pages** 357–360

**Audiocassette**

**Teacher's Resource Library**  **TRL**

   Activity 66

   Workbook Activity 66

## Teaching Suggestions

### ■ Vocabulary

*competition, minor*

Have students write clues for the vocabulary words. For example: He is under age 21. He is a _____. Allow students to show their clues to classmates who name the word for each clue.

### ■ Teaching the Lesson

Discuss with students what they think makes a good advertisement. Do they prefer pictures, humor, factual information, or a friendly face in an ad? Ask if they think a bad product could be sold because of a good ad.

Have students read about advertising methods and the Healthy Subjects feature on page 357.

Ask:

- What catch phrases might advertisers use to sell a product? (new, improved)

### Healthy Subjects

Bring several issues of *Consumer Reports* to class. Ask students what they think this magazine is about. Have volunteers each read a paragraph from the feature. Choose an article from the health section of the magazine and discuss it with the class.

Have students read about other advertising methods on page 358.

Have students read about other advertising methods on page 358.

Ask:
_____

- Why would an advertiser say that its product is expensive? (The advertiser wants people to believe that its product is the best.)

## Technology

If you have Internet access in your school, lead your class in an exploration of some sites with advertisements. Look for sites that would appeal to teenagers or that have health-related information. Be careful to screen these sites beforehand to make sure that the content is appropriate. Have volunteers each read a paragraph from the feature. Discuss whether students like the idea of advertisers keeping track of their interests. Discuss how information about the likes and dislikes of people of a particular age is obtained by companies. (surveys, focus groups, customer numbers)

---

### APPLICATION

**Environment**
Some products make advertising references or claims to preserving the environment. Ask students why a product might make such a claim. (This is a twist on the healthy product advertising method. People may feel that a product that preserves the environment is also healthy for their bodies.) Discuss with students whether this makes a product good. (As with any advertising claim, a consumer should examine and verify the facts before making a decision. Some advertising claims are misleading or completely false.)

---

**What group of people would a cartoon animal character appeal to?**

**Expensive and Superior**
These products are more expensive. This appeals to people who want the best.

**Inexpensive and a Bargain**
Advertisers try to convince people they are getting the best bargain.

**Recommended by Someone Famous**
Advertisements use an athlete or a TV or movie star to encourage people to buy a product. Advertisers hope this gives their product instant name recognition.

**Healthy Product**
Some products claim "no cholesterol" or "no fat" or make other references to health, such as "all natural."

All of these advertising claims should be examined before a consumer makes a decision about a product. Consumers need to be careful, especially when the product affects their health.

### technology

#### ADVERTISING ON THE INTERNET

The Internet has become very popular. Millions of people log on and browse every day. Because of this, many companies want to get advertisements of their products on Web sites. Some of these advertisements are just words and pictures, like in a magazine. Some have graphic animation that is fun to watch. If you click on some of these advertisements, you will be taken to a new Web page with more information about the product.

Some advertisers are now using information from your computer to figure out what you like. They can put advertisements on the Web browser that are tailored to your interests. Some people think this is an invasion of privacy. Others think it would be useful and convenient to have advertisements for things they like. What do you think?

---

**358**    *Chapter 17   Consumer Health*

---

### BACKGROUND INFORMATION

The Federal Trade Commission (FTC) sets the rules for truth in advertising. Advertising must be truthful and nondeceptive. If an ad makes specific scientific claims, it must have conducted a study or survey, or it should have other factual information to back up the claim. A company that runs a false or deceptive ad can be penalized. The FTC may order the company to stop running the ad, issue a retraction of its claims, or pay a monetary fine or other penalty.

### Careers

## MEDICAL RECORDS TECHNICIAN

Can you keep track of lots of details? If so, you might want to think about a career as a medical records technician. Medical records technicians gather and report patient information. This may include symptoms, medical history, examination results, lab test results, and treatments. All records must be properly arranged. Technicians translate disease names and treatments into coding systems. It is important to be organized and keep detailed records. Most medical records technicians work on computers and need excellent typing skills. Technicians may work in hospitals, clinics, health agencies, insurance companies, nursing homes, or other health care facilities. A high school diploma with on-the-job training is required. Sometimes a medical records course at a community college may be required. The job outlook for medical records technicians is excellent.

---

**Competition**
*Many companies trying to sell similar products*

## Why Advertise a Health Care Product?

Many over-the-counter products advertise because there is so much **competition**. Competition is many companies trying to sell similar products. Advertisements for pain reliever medications use many numbers and figures to try to convince consumers that their product is the best. They may also claim that their product is "recommended by most doctors."

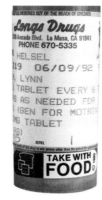

Sometimes hospitals, drug manufacturers, or insurance companies advertise. They may be trying to increase their business, or they may be trying to raise awareness of a new product.

---

*Consumer Health    Chapter 17*    **359**

---

## Careers

Ask students if they have ever seen their own medical record. Explain that a medical record keeps track of any conditions that a person might have. It also describes any procedures or operations a person has had. Discuss with students the importance of keeping an accurate medical record for an individual. Then read the feature with students. Ask what might happen if a medical record was misplaced or had incorrect information. (A patient could be treated improperly because of incomplete or incorrect information on the record. This might result in serious injury or illness.)

Have students read page 359 for information about advertising health care products.

### Ask:

- What method could be used to convince people that a health care product is good? (Advertisers may promote that their product is "recommended by doctors," or use numbers or figures to convince consumers that their product is the best.)

### LEARNING STYLES

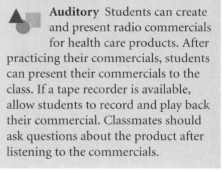

**Auditory** Students can create and present radio commercials for health care products. After practicing their commercials, students can present their commercials to the class. If a tape recorder is available, allow students to record and play back their commercial. Classmates should ask questions about the product after listening to the commercials.

---

## Action for Health

Give students a few days to gather ads from magazines and newspapers or to write down messages from TV and radio advertisements. As a class, discuss the questions in the feature. Allow time for students to make the advertisements and share their ideas in class.

Have students read about advertising harmful drugs on page 360.

### Ask:

- How can advertising for products like alcohol and tobacco be harmful? (These products can be harmful to your health. The ads may also appeal to children and encourage them to smoke or drink.)

- How does the government regulate advertising of harmful products? (The government puts limits on where cigarette advertising can be placed and what it can show.)

## Lesson 5 Review Answers

1) It wants the product to appeal to people who value tradition.
2) The person may bring instant name recognition to the product.
3) They might advertise to sell their product or to let the public know about a new product or service.
4) Answers may vary. Possible answer: The company might be trying to appeal to young children.
5) Answers may vary. Possible answer: Advertising does not always give accurate information, and it drives up the price of products.

## Action for Health

### ANALYZING ADVERTISEMENTS

Cut several advertisements from magazines and newspapers, or record or write down the message from a TV or radio show.

What was being sold? What kind of claims does the advertisement make about its product? Is it convincing? Were any health risks portrayed in the advertisements? Was there any depiction of violence or use of drugs, such as alcohol or tobacco? Make your own advertisement for the product. Then think about how you would advertise preventive health care.

---

**Minor**
*A person under age 18 or 21*

### What Are the Effects of Advertising Harmful Drugs?

There are many advertisements for harmful drugs such as tobacco and alcohol. Although these products cannot be sold to **minors**, people under age 18 or 21, the advertisements can be seen by anyone. Sometimes these advertisements use cartoon or animal characters to sell their products. Many people have felt that these companies were trying to make their product appealing to children. Recent government regulations put new limits on cigarette advertising, including where the ads can be placed and what they can show.

**LESSON 5 REVIEW** Write the answers to these questions on a separate sheet of paper. Use complete sentences.

1) Why would a company claim that its product was old-fashioned?
2) How might a famous person help sell a product?
3) Why might a hospital or drug company advertise?
4) Why would a company use a cartoon character to sell its product?
5) What are some problems with advertising?

---

## Consumer Protection

**Consumer advocate**
*A person or group that helps consumers correct problems*

Quackery or other poor medical products or services are a problem for consumers. Quackery may be misleading or confusing. Quackery makes it hard for the consumer to decide what is right and make wise choices. Fortunately, government agencies and **consumer advocates** work to enforce laws and rules that protect consumers.

Consumer advocate groups help consumers find the best way to receive satisfactory answers for their complaints. Consumers can consult these agencies and decide on the best course of action to protect their rights.

### What Are a Consumer's Rights?

Consumers have some basic rights that protect them from quackery and other misleading or confusing practices. The U.S. government has established the Consumer Bill of Rights, which gives every consumer these rights:

- *The right to safety*—Consumers have the right to be protected from unhealthy products.
- *The right to be informed*—People can ask for the facts they need to protect them from misleading advertising and to make wise choices.
- *The right to choose*—People have the right to make their own choices.
- *The right to be heard*—When consumers aren't satisfied, they have the right to speak out. This often helps to make laws that protect consumers.
- *The right to redress*—Consumers have the right to get a wrong corrected.
- *The right to consumer education*—People have the right to be educated about the products and services they buy.

- What document established consumer rights? (the Consumer Bill of Rights)

- What are the rights of every consumer? (the rights to safety, to be informed, to choose, to be heard, to redress, to consumer education)

Have students read page 362 for an overview of the Patient's Bill of Rights.

**Ask:**

- Do patients have a right to an explanation of their medical bills? (Yes, this is a part of the Patient's Bill of Rights.) Why is this important? (Answers will vary. Students may suggest it is important so that patients can see the cost for their care.)

- Who should you contact with a complaint about a product? (the manufacturer)

## LEARNING STYLES

**Visual** Students who would benefit from a visual aid can create posters illustrating the Consumer Bill of Rights and the Patient's Bill of Rights. Students can use pictures from magazines to create scenes that illustrate each right. Provide markers and other art supplies for students to draw additional scenes. Posters can be displayed in class and used as a study tool for students.

## APPLICATION

**At Home** Ask students to bring in warranties from appliances from home. Discuss the terms of the warranties, what is covered, and the length of coverage. Encourage students to look in their warranties for an address or phone number to contact in case the product breaks. Let students share their findings with the class.

---

Hospital patients are protected by a similar set of rights—the Patient's Bill of Rights. These rights were established by the American Hospital Association. They are shown below. Many individual hospitals, medical centers, and dental and medical offices have established similar lists of rights. You may have been given a copy of such a list or seen one posted.

### Patient's Bill of Rights

1. The right to considerate and respectful care
2. The right to complete, current information about your condition in terms you can understand
3. The right to receive all information necessary to give informed consent before any treatment
4. The right to refuse treatment to the extent permitted by law and to be informed of the consequences
5. The right to privacy during examinations and confidentiality concerning your care and records
6. The right to expect a reasonable response when you ask for help
7. The right to be told if your treatment will be part of a research project and to refuse to take part in the project
8. The right to expect good follow-up care
9. The right to an explanation of your bill
10. The right to know hospital rules that apply to your conduct as a patient

### How Can a Consumer's Problem Be Corrected?

Sometimes people buy a defective product or have a bad experience with a health care provider. When consumers' rights are violated or broken, they can respond to correct the problem.

The first step is to deal directly with the manufacturer of the product or with the health care provider. Many manufacturers have toll-free numbers. Call and explain your complaint.

## Writing About Health

Think of a time you had a complaint about a product or service. Write what you did about it. Which items in the Consumer Bill of Rights justified your complaint?

Ask for your money back or for a fair exchange. Record the names of people you talked with, the dates, and what they said they would do.

If you aren't satisfied, the second step is to contact one of the agencies listed below. It is best to submit the complaint in writing. Give the details of your problem, including any lack of cooperation from the manufacturer or caregiver. Send the original letter to the appropriate agency.

---

**Sources of Help for the Consumer**
For complaints about a product or service, false advertising, or irresponsible behavior:

**Better Business Bureau**
Check the phone book for
the local bureau.                    Web site: www.bbb.org

Also for complaints about false advertising:
**Federal Trade Commission Office of Public Affairs**
600 Pennsylvania Ave., NW      Web site: www.ttc.gov
Washington, DC 20580            E-mail: webmaster@ftc.gov

For complaints about foods, drugs, or cosmetics:
**Food and Drug Administration**
5600 Fishers Ln.                Web site: www.fda.gov
Rockville, MD 20857            E-mail: webmail@oc.fda.gov

Also for complaints about food:
**Food Safety and Inspection Service**
U.S. Department of Agriculture   Web site: www.fsis.usda.gov
1400 Independence Ave., SW     E-mail: fsis.webmaster@usda.gov
Washington, DC 20250

For complaints about dangerous products:
**U.S. Consumer Product Safety Commission**
Check the phone book           Web site: www.cpsc.gov
for the field office near you.  E-mail: info@cpsc.gov

*Consumer Health    Chapter 17*    **363**

---

Have students read pages 362 and 363 for information about correcting consumer problems.

### Ask:

- What agency would you contact with a complaint about unsafe food? (the Food and Drug Administration)

- What agency would you contact about dangerous products? (the U.S. Consumer Product Safety Commission)

### LEARNING STYLES

**Tactile/Kinesthetic** Create a blank "complaint form" for students to fill in. Leave blanks for the name of the product, the manufacturer, the complaint, and the name of the government agency students will write to if they do not get a reply. Encourage students to fill in the information, using a product for which they have a warranty or have them make up a product and company name.

### BACKGROUND INFORMATION

The Consumer Product Safety Commission was established in 1973. Since that time, thousands of products have been taken off the market or recalled. When a product is recalled, consumers either receive a refund or a replacement for the product. The company that manufactured the defective product is responsible for disposing of the defective merchandise or correcting the problem.

## Then and Now

Ask students if they have ever tried a product for which they heard or read false claims. Ask how they felt when they found out the product did not do what was advertised. How would they have felt if that product had affected their health? Have volunteers read the feature.

Have students read about other actions consumers can take on page 364.

**Ask:**

- When should a consumer take legal action against a manufacturer or health care provider? (When all other methods of correcting the problem do not work, then consumers can take legal action against the manufacturer or health care provider.)

## Lesson 6 Review Answers

1) Consumers are protected against quackery by government agencies and consumer advocates who enforce laws and rules to protect consumers.

2) The American Hospital Association established the Patient's Bill of Rights.

3) The first step is to contact the manufacturer of the product or the health care provider directly.

4) Consumers can go to the Federal Trade Commission Office of Public Affairs.

5) A consumer group might help a person reclaim losses by taking legal action.

**Then and Now**

### ELECTRICITY AND HEALING

In 1910, a new product called the White Cross Electric Vibrator Chair promised to help with many problems. These included rheumatism, backaches, and stomach, kidney, hearing, and vision problems. This was quackery, or false medical help, because its claims were not true.

The government began regulating medical devices in 1938. Since then, electricity has been used to treat many illnesses. Small battery-operated devices are placed in the body to help control the heart or other organs. Larger electrical devices produce healing magnetic or radio waves. Treatments with these devices have helped many people with arthritis and Lyme disease.

You should also send a copy to the company or person the complaint is against. Keep a copy for your records. If you don't get a response within six weeks, send a follow-up letter with a copy of the first letter.

### What Other Actions Can a Consumer Take?

If other methods of correcting the problem do not work, consumers may consider taking legal action against the manufacturer or health care provider. The government may be able to help make a case against the offender. If the offenses are severe enough, it may even be able to bring criminal charges against the offender.

**LESSON 6 REVIEW** Write the answers to these questions on a separate sheet of paper. Use complete sentences.

1) What protection do consumers have against quackery?

2) What organization established the Patient's Bill of Rights?

3) What is the first step to correcting a consumer problem?

4) Where can consumers go with a false advertising complaint?

5) How might a consumer group help a person who had been severely injured by an unsafe medical practice?

---

Name _____ Date _____ Period _____ | Chapter 17 Activity 67

**Consumer Protection**

*Directions* Write *T* if the statement is true or *F* if it is false.

_____ 1) The U.S. government established the Patient's Bill of Rights.

_____ 2) The U.S. government established the Consumer Bill of Rights.

_____ 3) Consumer advocates represent companies that advertise their products.

_____ 4) The first step to correcting a consumer problem is to contact the Better Business Bureau.

_____ 5) As a patient, you have the right to considerate and respectful care.

_____ 6) As a consumer, you have the right to be informed.

_____ 7) If contacting a manufacturer or caregiver doesn't solve your problem, then you can contact a government agency like the Food and Drug Administration.

_____ 8) The government can help you take legal action against a manufacturer.

_____ 9) The American Hospital Association established the Patient's Bill of Rights.

_____ 10) If a manufacturer doesn't respond to your request or problem in two days, send a follow-up letter.

Discover Health

**Activity 67**

---

Name _____ Date _____ Period _____ | Chapter 17 Workbook Activity 67

**Consumer Protection**

*Directions* Write *T* if the statement is true or *F* if it is false.

_____ 1) The U.S. government established the Patient's Bill of Rights.

_____ 2) The U.S. government established the Consumer Bill of Rights.

_____ 3) Consumer advocates represent companies that advertise their products.

_____ 4) The first step to correcting a consumer problem is to contact the Better Business Bureau.

_____ 5) As a patient, you have the right to considerate and respectful care.

_____ 6) As a consumer, you have the right to be informed.

_____ 7) If contacting a manufacturer or caregiver doesn't solve your problem, then you can contact a government agency like the Food and Drug Administration.

_____ 8) The government can help you take legal action against a manufacturer.

_____ 9) The American Hospital Association established the Patient's Bill of Rights.

_____ 10) If a manufacturer doesn't respond to your request or problem in two days, send a follow-up letter.

Discover Health

**Workbook Activity 67**

■ Health care includes many things, from major surgery to hygiene and healthy living every day.

■ The health care industry includes many people in different jobs and many products and services.

■ Prevention and taking care of colds and minor illnesses are wise forms of self-care.

■ You should consult a health care professional for anything out of the ordinary about your body or behavior.

■ Health care professionals include primary care physicians, specialists, nurse practitioners, and providers such as physical therapists.

■ You may choose a health care professional based on recommendations from others, medical directories, and your personal preferences.

■ Individuals can pay for health care costs out-of-pocket or through private insurance or managed care.

■ Government-supported health insurance includes Medicare for people over 65 and Medicaid for people with low incomes.

■ Individuals can help lower health care costs by practicing prevention, taking part in their own health care, and choosing low-cost alternatives when possible.

■ A wise consumer saves money, protects and improves his or her health, and increases self-confidence.

■ Advertisers use a number of methods and catchphrases to convince consumers to buy their product.

■ Consumers need to be critical of advertisements and evaluate which claims may be exaggerations and which may be useful information.

■ The U.S. government protects consumers with some basic rights. Many health care organizations also set forth rights for patients.

■ Wise consumers should read product labels and consult a doctor or other qualified medical professional to determine whether a product is appropriate.

■ Consumers who buy a defective product or have a bad experience with a health care provider can follow some steps to correct the problem.

*Consumer Health    Chapter 17*    **365**

## ■ Using the Chapter Summary

To further reinforce the facts and concepts presented in the chapter, read and discuss with students the questions that follow.

### Ask:

- What kind of health care can you take part in every day? (You can practice preventive medicine every day by eating a balanced diet and exercising regularly.)

- Which health care products would you get from a pharmacist? (prescription medication)

- What should you do if you have feelings of sadness that last more than a few days? (consult a health care professional)

- What health care professional provides assistance to a primary care physician and treats minor problems? (a nurse practitioner)

- What kind of health care can a hospital provide? (Most hospitals are equipped to provide complete health care services, including both inpatient and outpatient care.)

- What should a wise consumer look at before buying a product? (the ingredient list; label information; and overall value, price, and quantity)

- How do advertisers convince consumers to buy their products? (Advertisers use a number of methods to convince consumers to buy their products.)

- What steps can you take to remedy a problem with a product or service? (Call or write the manufacturer or service provider. Explain your complaint and ask for your money back or a fair exchange. If you do not get a response, contact a government agency or consumer advocate group for assistance.)

## Chapter 17 Review

The Teacher's Resource Library includes two parallel forms of the Chapter 17 Mastery Test. The difficulty level of the two forms is equivalent. You may wish to use one form as a pretest and the other form as a posttest.

### Review Answers
#### Comprehension: Identifying Facts
1) pharmacist  2) Prevention
3) health professional  4) checkups
5) muscle  6) regular  7) managed care
8) value  9) specialist  10) expensive

---

## Comprehension: Identifying Facts

On a separate sheet of paper, write the correct word or words from the Word Bank to complete each sentence.

| WORD BANK | |
| --- | --- |
| Better Business Bureau | muscle |
| checkups | pharmacist |
| competition | prevention |
| expensive | regular |
| health professional | rights |
| hospice | specialist |
| managed care | value |

1) A _____ can help you pick out over-the-counter medicine and understand your prescription.

2) _____ includes keeping a healthy body weight and not using tobacco or alcohol.

3) A person should seek a _____ if the flu or a fever lasts more than a week.

4) You go to a primary care physician for preventive _____.

5) A physical therapist helps people regain their _____ functions.

6) A premium is money paid at _____ intervals.

7) In _____, you may have a limited choice of doctors.

8) Wise consumers find the best _____.

9) Your primary care physician may refer you to a _____ to address a certain illness.

10) An advertiser may say a product is _____ because it is the best.

---

### Chapter 17 Mastery Test A

Name _____ Date _____ Period _____    Chapter 17 Mastery Test A page 1

**Directions** Read the words in the Word Bank. Choose the item that *best* completes each sentence. On the blank before each number, write the letter for that item.

| Word Bank | | |
| --- | --- | --- |
| a) Better Business Bureau | f) long-term | k) pharmacist |
| b) deductible | g) managed care | l) physical therapists |
| c) health care professional | h) Medicare | m) prevention |
| d) health insurance | i) nurse practitioner | n) product labels |
| e) improved | j) outpatient | o) rights |

_____ 1) _____ includes good nutrition, not smoking, and regular exercise.

_____ 2) You should consult a _____ for anything out of the ordinary about your body or behavior.

_____ 3) Health care professionals include primary care physicians, specialists, nurse practitioners, and providers such as _____.

_____ 4) Government-supported health insurance includes _____ for people over 65.

_____ 5) A _____ can help you pick out over-the-counter medicine and understand your prescription.

_____ 6) In _____, you may have a limited choice of doctors.

_____ 7) A _____ is a registered nurse with special training for providing primary care.

_____ 8) Nursing homes and other _____ care facilities offer care for people who cannot care for themselves.

_____ 9) If a manufacturer or provider does not respond to a consumer complaint, you could contact the _____.

Name _____ Date _____ Period _____    Chapter 17 Mastery Test A page 2

### Chapter 17 Mastery Test A, continued

_____ 10) An advertiser may use the words new and _____ to appeal to the buyer.

_____ 11) The American Hospital Association established a list of _____ for patients.

_____ 12) A _____ is the initial amount a patient must pay before insurance covers health care costs.

_____ 13) A clinic may provide _____ care for people who do not need to stay overnight.

_____ 14) A wise consumer should read _____.

_____ 15) _____ covers large medical expenses that people may otherwise not be able to afford.

TRL    TRL

### Chapter 17 Mastery Test A

11) Companies advertise and make claims about their products so that they sell better than the _____.

12) You might go to live in a _____ if you were terminally ill.

13) The American Hospital Association established a list of _____ for patients.

14) If a manufacturer or provider does not respond to a consumer complaint, you could contact the _____.

## Comprehension: Understanding Main Ideas

Write the answers to these questions on a separate sheet of paper. Use complete sentences.

15) If you have a low income, how could you pay for health care?

16) If you need to have a medical procedure, what are two ways you could lower costs?

17) Why would a generic brand be cheaper than a name brand?

18) What kind of people might be fooled by quackery?

## Critical Thinking: Write Your Opinion

19) Why might a recommendation by word of mouth for a pain reliever be more reliable than an advertisement claim?

20) Why do we need a Consumer Bill of Rights?

**Test Taking Tip**  When taking a matching test, match all the items that you are sure go together. Cross those items out. Then try to match the items that are left.

11) competition  12) hospice  13) rights
14) Better Business Bureau

## Comprehension: Understanding Main Ideas

15) You could get government support through Medicaid.

16) First, you could have an outpatient procedure instead of an inpatient one if possible. Second, you could go to a clinic or other less costly health care facility.

17) Generic brands are cheaper because they do not spend money on advertising.

18) Anybody can be fooled by quackery. However, people who are terminally ill, overweight, or unhappy about aging are especially vulnerable.

## Critical Thinking: Write Your Opinion

19) A recommendation by word of mouth might be more reliable if you trusted the opinion of the person who gave you the recommendation.

20) The Consumer Bill of Rights protects consumers from quackery and other misleading or confusing practices.

---

**Chapter 17 Mastery Test B**

Name _____ Date _____ Period _____

Chapter 17 Mastery Test B

*Chapter 17 Mastery Test B page 1*

**Directions** Read the words in the Word Bank. Choose the item that *best* completes each sentence. On the blank before each number, write the letter for that item.

**Word Bank**

| | | |
|---|---|---|
| a) Better Business Bureau | f) long-term | k) pharmacist |
| b) deductible | g) managed care | l) physical therapists |
| c) health care professional | h) Medicare | m) prevention |
| d) health insurance | i) nurse practitioner | n) product labels |
| e) improved | j) outpatient | o) rights |

_____ 1) A wise consumer should read _____ .

_____ 2) _____ covers large medical expenses that people may otherwise not be able to afford.

_____ 3) If a manufacturer or provider does not respond to a consumer complaint, you could contact the _____ .

_____ 4) An advertiser may use the words new and _____ to appeal to the buyer.

_____ 5) _____ includes good nutrition, not smoking, and regular exercise.

_____ 6) You should consult a _____ for anything out of the ordinary about your body or behavior.

_____ 7) Health care professionals include primary care physicians, specialists, nurse practitioners, and providers such as _____ .

_____ 8) The American Hospital Association established a list of _____ for patients.

_____ 9) A _____ is the initial amount a patient must pay before insurance covers health care costs.

Name _____ Date _____ Period _____

Chapter 17 Mastery Test B, continued

*Chapter 17 Mastery Test B page 2*

_____ 10) Government-supported health insurance includes _____ for people over 65.

_____ 11) A _____ can help you pick out over-the-counter medicine and understand your prescription.

_____ 12) In _____ , you may have a limited choice of doctors.

_____ 13) A clinic may provide _____ care for people who do not need to stay overnight.

_____ 14) A _____ is a registered nurse with special training for providing primary care.

_____ 15) Nursing homes and other _____ care facilities offer care for people who cannot care for themselves.

TRL  TRL

### Chapter 18:
**Public Health**
pages 368–383

### Lessons

**1) Defining Community**
pages 369–372

**2) Community Health Resources**
pages 373–376

**3) Community Health Advocacy Skills** pages 377–380

**Chapter Summary and Review**
pages 381–383

**Audiocassette**

**Teacher's Resource Library**

    **Activities** 68–70

    **Workbook Activities** 68–70

    **Student Study Guide 24** pages 1–2

    **Chapter 17 Mastery Tests A and B**

    (Answer Keys for the Teacher's Resource Library begin on page 433 of this Teacher's Edition.)

## Introducing the Chapter

Discuss what the word *public* means. Have students name some communities that they belong to or are familiar with. Challenge them to think of situations, events, or other things that affect the health of these communities. Keep a list of responses and allow students to make additions or changes to it throughout the chapter.

Have a volunteer read the introductory information, as well as the Goals for Learning.

### Ask:

• What are the public health resources in your community? (Answers will vary, depending on the resources available in your community.)

• What are some characteristics of a healthy community? (Answers will vary. Responses may include people taking care of themselves and one another and helping those who are sick or in need.)

# Chapter 18

# Public Health

*P*ublic health, or the health of the community, depends on a balance of community resources and personal responsibility. The health of your community is important because it affects the health of every community member.

In this chapter, you will learn what makes a community and how health is a community concern. You will learn about resources that are available and how community members support these resources. You will learn how to help promote public health.

### Goals for Learning

▶ To identify what makes up a community

▶ To analyze the importance of health for community members

▶ To identify the health resources available in a community

▶ To explain how resources are funded

▶ To describe ways that community members can make wise decisions to strengthen their community

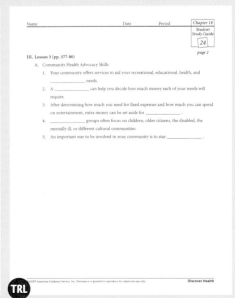

**Student Study Guide 24, page 1**     **Student Study Guide 24, page 2**

# Defining Community

**Common association**
*Similar cultural, racial, or religious ties*

**Common identity**
*Similar interests or goals*

**Community**
*A group of people who live in the same place or have common interests*

**A** **community** is a group of people who live in the same place or share common interests. Strong communities have members who work together for the good of everyone. When problems affect a community, they affect all community members.

## How Do You Identify a Community?

Communities come in different sizes. Some small towns may be considered a single community. In larger cities, there may be many communities. Community boundaries may be created by natural formations, such as lakes, rivers, or hills. Other communities may be created by artificial boundaries, such as highways or buildings. Usually, communities exist because a group of people share certain qualities that make them unique. These qualities may be economic or social concerns.

In most strong communities, members also share similar interests and goals, or a **common identity**. Some communities may want to preserve the history of their neighborhoods and the appearance of their houses. Others may want to improve their neighborhoods with new housing or business developments. Many communities hold festivals or other celebrations to promote community pride.

Besides a common identity, some community members may share common cultural, racial, or religious ties. This is called a **common association**. Sometimes the people in a community such as this do not live in the same area. People with similar political or economic needs can be called a community. For example, senior citizens may identify themselves as a part of the senior community. As a community, groups of senior citizens can ask for greater

### Writing About Health

Make a list of the different communities you belong to. Explain how your membership in each community affects you and your health. Then name some contributions you make to each community.

---

## Chapter 18  Lesson 1

**Overview** This lesson explains what a community is and what affects the health of the community.

### Objectives

- To explain what makes up a community.

- To describe the importance of community health.

- To identify factors that affect community health.

**Student Pages** 369–372

**Audiocassette**

**Teacher's Resource Library**

    Activity 68
    Workbook Activity 68

## Teaching Suggestions

### ■ Vocabulary

*common association, common identity, community, communicable, epidemic, resource, economics*

Read and discuss the definitions of the vocabulary words. Have students write descriptive sentences that contain one or more of the words. For example: People in a *community* usually have a *common identity*. A *communicable* disease could turn into an *epidemic* if it is not controlled. Encourage volunteers to read their sentences to the class.

### ■ Teaching the Lesson

Ask students for examples of some tasks that can be better accomplished by a group. Discuss the idea that communities make it easier for individuals to get the resources they need. Give an example, such as fire protection or education. Invite students to list other resources that a community provides.

Have students read about the characteristics of a community on pages 369 and 370.

---

Ask:

- How might a community show its common identity? (Some communities preserve the history of the neighborhood, others improve their neighborhoods with new housing or business developments. Many communities hold festivals or celebrations to promote community pride.)

Have students read about community health concerns on pages 370 and 371.

Ask:

- What can communities do if an epidemic occurs? (If an epidemic occurs, communities may need to set up special clinics to care for the sick. Doctors and scientists can work on a vaccine, or a cure, for the disease. Sometimes, communities can only treat the disease and try to prevent it from spreading.)

- How does health care availability affect a community? (If there is not enough health care available, people cannot get the services they need.)

## GLOBAL CONNECTION

Homelessness is a community health problem. Ask students to research statistics on homelessness in other countries and the associated health problems that affect the rest of the population. Students can contact the World Health Organization (WHO) for information on this subject.

**Epidemic**
*A disease that spreads quickly*

**Resource**
*A source of supply and support*

**resources**, sources of supply and support, to meet their unique health and social needs. Other groups of people can organize themselves into communities to make sure their needs are met.

### How Is Health a Community Concern?

The health of every community member is a community concern. People with communicable diseases, such as influenza, can infect others. Communicable diseases can be passed along to others. If a disease becomes uncontrollable, it is called an epidemic. An epidemic spreads quickly and affects many people at the same time. If an epidemic occurs, communities may need to set up special clinics to care for the sick. Doctors and scientists can also start working on a vaccine, or a cure, for the disease. Sometimes, however, communities can only treat the disease and try to prevent it from spreading to others.

People with similar economic needs can be called a community.

The number of health resources available in a community affect the people who live there. When people become ill or injured, what kind of health care will they receive? Are there enough health care workers so that all patients receive the treatment they need? Sometimes a certain group of people does not get the health care they need. For example, in some areas, pregnant women may have to wait weeks to see a doctor. If the woman does not get proper care during her pregnancy, the baby may be affected. This would end up hurting the community into which the baby is born.

Economics
*The way in which money and other resources are divided among community members*

People dependent on drugs can have a harmful effect on the community. They may be less productive at work and more likely to become ill. They may become violent. A good community resource is a clinic that can treat drug addiction. Clinics can also treat people with mental disabilities.

## How Is Economics a Community Concern?

**Economics** is the way in which money and other **resources** are divided among community members. All health care has a cost. Doctors and other caregivers need to be paid for their work. Supplies and equipment need to be paid for. What happens when individuals do not have enough money to pay for the care they need?

The number of people unable to afford health care is increasing. Many do not have enough health insurance. The company they work for may not offer insurance. They may be unemployed and cannot afford to buy insurance. This means they may not be able to afford needed health care for themselves or their family. By not getting proper treatment, their health problems could get worse.

Poverty is a major health concern. It puts people at risk for many serious health problems. When people cannot afford a nutritionally balanced diet, malnutrition and other health problems can result. Poverty is the main reason that some children do not get proper vaccinations and other necessary care.

## What Are Some National Health Goals?

Most communities do not exist independently from the rest of the world. Federal and state governments can affect and influence many aspects of a community. They may provide communities with assistance to address problems. They may also set rules or goals that a community must meet.

*Health Tip*

If you need vaccinations, find out if they will be offered in a neighborhood health center or a school in your community.

Have students read about how economics affects health care on page 371.

Ask:

- Why do people have to pay for health care? (The people that provide the care need to be paid for what they do, and the supplies and equipment need to be paid for.)

- What are some health problems that can result from poverty? (malnutrition, children not getting proper vaccinations, lack of other necessary health care)

## LEARNING STYLES

**ESL/LEP** Preview the lesson with LEP students by reading the question heads and discussing the pictures. Point out the picture on page 370 and explain how this is a community. Review other vocabulary words and key concepts in the chapter.

## MULTICULTURAL CONNECTION

Discuss some problems that immigrants might face in getting health care services. Immigrants may not be able to afford proper health care in this country, they may have language difficulties, and they may be fearful or suspicious of health clinics. Ask students to propose some solutions to this problem. For example, health agencies could have translators that help immigrants understand what is being done. Spokespeople might also find out about cultural traditions and try to respect these traditions or even integrate them into the health-care process.

Have students read about national health goals and how changes affect community health on pages 371 and 372.

## Ask:

· Which of the U.S. government's public health goals would benefit people who cannot afford to pay for health care? (all of them)

· Are changes good or bad for the health of a community? (Changes can be both good and bad. People are living longer and that is a good change because it shows that people are healthier. However, since people are getting older, it also poses special challenges. Older people have special health needs that should be considered.)

## Lesson 1 Review Answers

**1)** No, a community may have a common association other than area.

**2)** People addicted to drugs are less productive and are more likely to become ill. They may also become violent.

**3)** Poverty puts people at risk for many serious health problems such as malnutrition.

**4)** the goal to increase health and quality of life for older Americans

**5)** The number of people 65 years and older will increase because people are living longer than they used to.

Every ten years, the U.S. government sets public health goals on which to work. These public health goals include the following.

· To provide equal health care for all Americans, including children, adolescents, older people, and people with disabilities

· To increase health and quality of life for older people

· To increase the ability of all Americans to obtain the use of preventive health services

## How Do Changes Affect Community Health?

All communities go through changes. Community members grow older and die, and new ones are born. Some people move in, and others move away. It is expected that the population of the United States will increase over the coming years. Most likely, the population of your community will increase, too. Communities need to change as their members change.

The number of people 65 years old or older will increase. This is because more people are living longer than they used to. This is positive for communities because it shows that people are healthier. However, it also poses special challenges. Older people have special health needs that should be considered. They can also contribute to society in different ways.

**LESSON 1 REVIEW** Write the answers to these questions on a separate sheet of paper. Use complete sentences.

**1)** Do all members of a community have to live in the same area?

**2)** What effect can drugs have on a community?

**3)** How can poverty cause health problems?

**4)** Which public health goal might be a concern for your parents or grandparents?

**5)** Why will the number of people over age 65 increase in the United States?

**Activity 68**

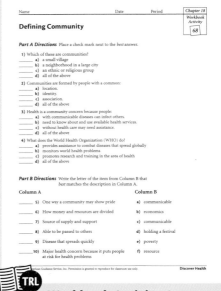

**Workbook Activity 68**

## Community Health Resources

**Private resource**
*A group of people not associated with the government*

**Public resource**
*A health service that is run by a local, state, or national government*

**Volunteer resource**
*A group of people who donate their time to provide services*

Many factors contribute to community health. Many programs and services—from local to national—can keep community members healthy.

### What Are Some Local Health Resources?

Public, private, and volunteer services are available in most communities. **Public resources** are health services that are run by a local, state, or national government. Emergency Medical Service (EMS) is a public resource that provides emergency care for people with injury or illness. An ambulance with paramedics transports patients to an appropriate care facility, such as a hospital.

Other public resources include a poison control hotline, clinics, and agencies that focus on special care. Most public resources offer free or low-cost care. In addition, public programs can help pay for other types of health care.

**Private resources** are groups not associated with the government. Private hospitals, insurance companies, and privately run clinics are some examples of private resources. Generally, individuals pay for services received from private resources.

**Volunteer resources** are made up of people who donate their time to provide health information or services. There may be volunteer programs at a hospital or clinic. There are also special volunteer groups, such as the Red Cross and the American Cancer Society.

People with similar health problems or concerns may also form support groups. This may include emotional support for alcoholics and their families, single parents, and people with disabilities. For example, the Center for Independent Living (CIL) began as a local self-help group. CIL helps people who are blind or who have physical disabilities. Now the CIL is a national organization. Volunteer resources can provide health care services that might not otherwise be available.

*Public Health* Chapter 18 **373**

### Ask:

- What roles do volunteers play in providing health services? (Volunteers provide services that might otherwise not be available or affordable.)

- What type of resource is EMS and what does it provide? (EMS is a public resource that provides emergency care for people with injury or illness.)

## Lesson at a Glance

### Chapter 18 Lesson 2

**Overview** This lesson describes some community resources and how they can improve the health of a community.

### Objectives

- To identify local, state, national, and international health resources.

- To describe how these resources can affect the health of a community.

- To identify how these resources are funded.

**Student Pages** 373–376

**Audiocassette**

**Teacher's Resource Library**

Activity 69
Workbook Activity 69

## Teaching Suggestions

### ■ Vocabulary

*private resource, public resource, volunteer resource, screening service, statistics, grant, recall, charitable organization*

Read the vocabulary words and discuss their meanings with the class. Ask a volunteer to describe the difference between private, public, and volunteer resources. Ask students to write sentences, leaving blanks for the missing vocabulary words. Then have students exchange papers and write in the missing words.

### ■ Teaching the Lesson

Ask students to think about where they go when they feel sick. Discuss the importance of a community being able to provide health care resources to its members.

Have students read about local health resources on page 373 and 374.

Have students read about state and national health resources on page 374.

Ask:

- How might statistics be used by a state health department? (Statistics might keep track of the type of diseases that have been treated in the community.)

- How do vaccination and education programs help improve the health of a community? (These programs are free services that support community clinics and substance abuse programs. These programs may also link people to other programs that will help pay for medical expenses.)

- Which agency requires that food labels contain a list of ingredients? (the FDA)

## APPLICATION

**Career Connection**
Challenge students to research a state health department to learn about the types of programs that are run by the department, how they are funded, and what training is needed to become a public health official. Encourage volunteers to present their findings to the class.

## LEARNING STYLES

**Group Learning** Encourage students to role-play the members of a community organization. Their organization might provide food for the needy, transportation to health facilities, or health care information. In groups, have students divide up the tasks that need to be done in their organization. Students should list specific duties that they would perform each day, week, or month.

Screening service
*An exam that provides prevention, such as eye and ear exams*

Statistics
*Important information*

Schools are another local health resource. Schools provide health education. They also provide prevention or **screening services**, such as eye and ear exams. Schools may form a partnership with a community agency to provide additional preventive services. This helps young people stay healthy and find out about problems before they occur.

### What Are Some State Health Resources?

States, and sometimes cities and counties, have public health departments. These departments enforce health laws. They also provide information to help caregivers understand and treat public health problems. Health departments keep **statistics**, or important information, about public health. They might keep track of the types of diseases that have been treated in the community.

Health departments also provide free services such as vaccination and education programs. They support community clinics and substance abuse programs. They may also link people to programs that will help pay for medical expenses.

### What Are Some National Health Resources?

The United States has many agencies that deal with and affect people's health. The Department of Health and Human Services (DHHS) is concerned with the health and well-being of the entire country. Many agencies operate under this department. The agencies under the Public Health Service focus on health needs and problems.

### Food and Drug Administration (FDA)

The FDA tests the foods, drugs, and cosmetics we use. It requires that all food manufacturers label the ingredients on their food containers. This helps people with allergies or special diets to make smart choices about the food they eat.

### Centers for Disease Control (CDC)

The CDC works to prevent the spread of disease in the United States. It keeps track of illnesses and tries to prevent an epidemic from occurring. The CDC also helps scientists develop vaccines and treatments for disease.

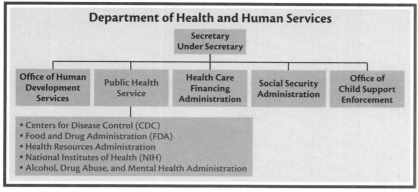

**Department of Health and Human Services**

A branch of the Department of Health and Human Services, the Public Health Service is involved with health care concerns

**Grant**
*An amount of money given*

**Recall**
*An order to return unsafe items*

### National Institutes of Health (NIH)

The NIH conducts research into health problems. It provides **grants**, or money, to colleges and research centers. The NIH makes sure that the information from this research is available to everyone. This research can help in the treatment of injury or illness. The research also provides information to help prevent similar problems from occurring.

A separate agency, called the Consumer Product Safety Commission (CPSC), deals with the safety of products. The CPSC can determine if a product is unsafe or damaged. It may require a **recall**, or a return of all items, to take an unsafe product off the market. The CPSC can also help people make claims against a company if they have been hurt by its product.

### What Are Some International Health Resources?

Many people study how disease moves over the world. The World Health Organization (WHO) is an international organization that fights diseases that spread globally. It monitors conditions that could become world health problems. The WHO shares its information and makes decisions about distributing health resources. It can help to avoid an epidemic and save lives. The WHO promotes training and helps countries to set up effective health programs.

Have students read about the NIH and WHO on page 375.

Ask:

- Which agency conducts research into health problems? (the NIH)

- Why would a product be recalled? (A product would be recalled if it is unsafe.)

- Which organization fights diseases that spread globally? (WHO)

**BACKGROUND INFORMATION**

The United Nations founded the World Health Organization (WHO) in 1948. Besides working to provide worldwide health services, it also collects and shares medical and scientific information and promotes international standards for drugs and vaccines. WHO has made major contributions to the prevention of diseases such as malaria, polio, leprosy, and tuberculosis, and to the eradication of smallpox. Its main headquarters are in Geneva, Switzerland.

**APPLICATION**

**Environment**
Ask students to think of some environmental problems that might cause a public health problem. Students may describe oil spills or toxic fumes and smoke in the air. Make a list of students' responses. Discuss how each problem would affect the environment. What are some steps that could be taken to prevent these problems?

Have students read about how health care programs are funded on page 376.

## Ask:

- What are some ways a volunteer organization might raise money? (holding a special fund drive, asking for donations on the street or door-to-door, asking businesses for contributions)

## Lesson 2 Review Answers

1) Three kinds of local health resources are public, private, and volunteer.
2) Volunteer groups can help serve needs that public and private resources do not serve or that might be unavailable or unaffordable.
3) Public health departments keep track of the types of diseases that have been treated in the community.
4) Charities raise money through donations.
5) The CDC might provide information about a disease and how to treat or prevent it.

Most food shelf programs function through the help of volunteers of all ages.

**Charitable organization**
*A group of people who give funds to health care programs*

## How Are Health Care Programs Funded?

Community health care programs get money from several sources. Federal and state governments can provide funds for prevention and special treatment programs. Other support comes from local taxes and private charities. **Charitable organizations**, such as the United Way, give funds to many different programs. These groups sometimes raise money through special fund drives. Volunteers may ask for donations from people on the street or door-to-door. They may also ask businesses to contribute. Many programs are kept running by the caring and generosity of fellow community members. These people know that the programs keep the whole community strong and healthy.

**LESSON 2 REVIEW** Write the answers to these questions on a separate sheet of paper. Use complete sentences.

1) What are three kinds of local health resources?
2) How do volunteer groups help communities?
3) What do public health departments keep track of?
4) How do charities help fund health care programs?
5) What does the CDC do?

---

**Activity 69**

**Workbook Activity 69**

## Community Health Advocacy Skills

Community members need to develop skills to find and manage resources. They also need to contribute to the community and be ready to change to meet new community needs.

### How Do You Find Community Services?

Every community offers a range of services and programs. To participate in your community, you need to find the services that are right for you. You may have a wide range of needs, including recreational, educational, health, and housing. You will also want to know what to do in an emergency. By contacting a community service or local government, you can find out which agencies can help you.

Everyone in your community pays for the services that are offered. People pay taxes on things they buy, property they own, income they make, and business they conduct. This is how the community gets the funds that keep services going.

**Action for Health**

### FINDING HEALTH RESOURCES IN YOUR COMMUNITY

Make a list of local health agencies and organizations in your community. Check with parents, librarians, teachers, and the phone book for ideas. Think about issues such as disease prevention, health promotion, and treatment programs.

Divide into pairs or teams to gather information about the agencies. Phone each agency and ask about the items below. Prepare for the interview in advance. Record the answers.

- Name, address, and phone number of the agency
- Days and hours of operation
- Types of services and health professionals on staff
- Who qualifies for services
- Fees, if any
- Whether the services are confidential
- Languages other than English spoken

*Public Health    Chapter 18*    **377**

---

## Lesson at a Glance

### Chapter 18  Lesson 3

**Overview** This lesson discusses how people can manage their resources to maintain a healthy community.

### Objectives

- To explain how to find community services.

- To identify ways people can manage their resources.

- To describe how communities can manage their resources and how people can improve their community.

**Student Pages** 377–380

**Audiocassette**

**Teacher's Resource Library**

    **Activity** 70
    **Workbook Activity** 70

## Teaching Suggestions

### ■ Vocabulary

*budget, expense, income, advocacy group*

Write the vocabulary words on the chalkboard. Have students write what each word means on a sheet of paper. Tell them to keep the paper and compare their meanings to the definitions in the textbook as they go through the lesson.

### ■ Teaching the Lesson

Tell students that in this lesson they will learn about services in the community and some ways that they can help improve these resources. Have students read about finding community services on page 377.

### Action for Health

Provide a phone book and other references for students. Have them research community health resources. Review some interviewing guidelines with students and help them write questions for gathering information about an agency. Students should take notes during the phone interview and keep a list of questions handy. Invite students to share the information they received from the interviews.

---

**Ask:**

- What are some needs that the community might help people with? (recreational, educational, health, housing)

Have students read about the ways people manage their resources on page 378.

Ask:

- How can a budget help a person know how much he or she can spend for entertainment? (It can show how much money the person will have left after paying for food, clothing, and shelter.)

## Careers

Have students read the feature on home health aides. Discuss who might need a home health aide. Ask students why CPR is an important skill for a home health aide. (CPR is important because a home health aide may need to administer emergency care before an ambulance is able to assist a person in need.)

---

### APPLICATION

 **At Home**
Encourage students to work with their parents to make up their own budget. Expenses can include games, snacks, bus fare, and so on. Income would be any allowance and extra money earned. Students should create a monthly budget and indicate how much, if any, of their money goes into a savings account.

---

Individuals play a significant role in helping to address public health problems.

| **Budget** |
| *A written plan for spending money* |

### How Can People Manage Their Resources?

Sometimes it is difficult to know where to spend money first. You need food, clothing, and shelter. You need proper health care to stay healthy. You also want to do things that are fun and help you be happy. It helps to have a **budget**, or written plan for spending money. This will help you decide how much money you will need for each of your needs.

**Careers**

### HOME HEALTH AIDE

Living at home is important for most people, especially when they are ill. Home health aides help sick people to stay at home by performing routine tasks for them. They change bed linens, prepare meals, clean, do laundry, and run errands. Aides help bathe and clean people. They may read aloud or play games with them. Under a doctor's or nurse's direction, aides give medication. Usually, health care agencies employ home health aides. Some hospitals run home care programs that employ home health aides. Home health aides should know CPR. Many states don't require training for home health aides. However, some states are developing training standards.

Your **income** is the amount of money that you receive or earn from a job. Your **expenses** are the things that you need to spend money on. If your expenses are greater than your income, you will go into debt. Some expenses are fixed and more important than others are. You should pay for things like food, clothing, rent or mortgage, and utility bills first. Then you can allow for some other expenses, like going to the movies or taking a vacation. It is a good idea to set aside some extra money for emergencies.

By saving money, families can have additional money available if needed for medical emergencies. They also can relax knowing that all their expenses are paid and they have money left over. They may want to use some of that money for preventive care to ensure that they stay healthy.

## Then and Now

### POPULATION CHANGES

In 1900, there were many young children 5 to 13 years old. They made up over 20 percent of the total population. At the same time, the number of people over 65 was very small. Since then, there have been many changes in the population of people 65 years and older. This is because many more people are living longer than they did years ago. Examine the graph below. How do you think this will affect communities? What health resources might people age 65 or older need?

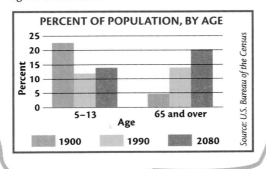

**PERCENT OF POPULATION, BY AGE**

*Source: U.S. Bureau of the Census*

Percent — Age — 5–13, 65 and over

■ 1900  ■ 1990  ■ 2080

*Public Health  Chapter 18*  **379**

---

Have students read about income and expenses on page 379.

## Ask:

- Which expenses are fixed expenses, or things that you must pay? (food, clothing, rent or mortgage, utility bills)

- Where would be a good place to put extra money left over from the budget? (Extra money can be put away in savings so that it is available for emergencies.)

## Then and Now

After reading the selection, ask students what kinds of changes they think might take place by 2080. Encourage them to think about housing for the elderly, health care, and the costs involved. Ask them how they would like to live when they are 65 years old. Would they prefer to live with other people the same age, at home with family, or by themselves?

### LEARNING STYLES

**Visual** Students can create graphs to illustrate their own budgets. A bar graph could show income versus expenses. A circle graph could show how much each expense (food, school supplies, transportation, and so on) is in relation to the whole. Encourage students to display their graphs on poster board.

Have students read about the ways a community manages resources and how students can contribute to the community on page 380.

**Ask:**

- How can information about diseases, violence, or substance abuse help a community stay healthy? (Providing information about health problems can decrease the risk of these problems occurring.)

- How does it benefit your community for you to be healthy? (When you are healthy, you are able to contribute to the community.)

## Lesson 3 Review Answers

1) The community pays for its services through taxes.
2) A person would use a budget to help decide how much money is needed for his or her needs.
3) Preventive care costs less than treatment of illness. It reduces the demands on the health care system. Preventive care allows the community to provide more care for less money.
4) An advocacy group provides health services or helps people find affordable health services. The group may work with government to try to change laws or policies.
5) By saving money, families can have additional money available if they have a medical emergency.

---

## LEARNING STYLES

**Auditory** Have pairs of students take turns role-playing a conversation between someone answering a phone at an advocacy group and someone seeking affordable health services. Encourage auditory learners to listen carefully and to take notes about the conversation. Students should try to answer each question that the caller asks. Encourage each pair to evaluate each other's responses.

---

**Advocacy group**
*An organization that works to benefit a specific group*

## How Can a Community Manage Resources?

A community can benefit from local, national, and international health promotion. Preventive care costs less than treatment of illness. It reduces the demands on the health care system. This allows the community to provide more care for less money.

Health promotion and disease prevention should be goals for every community. Health education is another wise use of resources. Providing information about health problems can decrease the risk of these problems occurring. Communities can make information available about diseases, violence, physical fitness, nutrition, and substance abuse.

Prevention organizations that work with specific groups are called **advocacy groups**. Advocacy groups may provide health services or help people find affordable health services. They may work with government to try to change laws or policies. Advocacy groups often focus on children, senior citizens, people with disabilities, or different ethnic communities.

## How Can You Contribute to the Community?

You can do many things to get involved in and improve your community. Staying healthy is an important way to be involved in your community. When you are healthy, you are able to contribute to the community. You might choose to volunteer with a group in your community. You could also be an advocate by writing letters to lawmakers asking for change.

**LESSON 3 REVIEW** Write the answers to these questions on a separate sheet of paper. Use complete sentences.

1) How does the community pay for its services?
2) Why would a person use a budget?
3) How does preventive care save money for a community?
4) What does an advocacy group do?
5) How can people prepare for medical emergencies?

*Health Tip*

**Check into volunteer opportunities that interest you and that benefit public health.**

---

---

**Activity 70**

Name ___ Date ___ Period ___  Chapter 18 Activity 70

**Community Health Advocacy Skills**

**Directions** Write *T* if the statement is true or *F* if it is false.

____ 1) Community services can tell you about agencies that can help in emergencies.
____ 2) A budget is a written plan for managing money.
____ 3) A budget will not help you plan how to spend money.
____ 4) Always try not to spend more than your income.
____ 5) Taxes pay for community services.
____ 6) Renting a video game is an example of a fixed expense.
____ 7) It is better to treat an illness than prevent it.
____ 8) There are many ways to contribute to your community.
____ 9) An advocacy group tries to help anyone in need.
____ 10) Fixed expenses are usually more important than others are.

**Workbook Activity 70**

Name ___ Date ___ Period ___  Chapter 18 Workbook Activity 70

**Community Health Advocacy Skills**

**Directions** Write *T* if the statement is true or *F* if it is false.

____ 1) Taxes pay for community services.
____ 2) Community services can tell you about agencies that can help in emergencies.
____ 3) A budget is a written plan for managing money.
____ 4) A budget will not help you plan how to spend money.
____ 5) Always try not to spend more than your income.
____ 6) Fixed expenses are more important than others are.
____ 7) Renting a video game is an example of a fixed expense.
____ 8) It is better to treat an illness than prevent it.
____ 9) There are many ways to contribute to your community.
____ 10) An advocacy group tries to help anyone in need.

---

■ Physical boundaries, common identity, common interests, and other ties are factors in forming a community.

■ A community's health depends on the health of all its members.

■ A strong community has health care programs.

■ Poverty contributes to disease and other public health problems.

■ Public, private, and volunteer resources provide care to members of a community.

■ School health programs enhance community resources.

■ State health departments help with disease control and help provide care for people who cannot afford it.

■ National health resources are concerned with the health and safety of the entire country.

■ Federal agencies regulate food and drugs and prevent spread of disease. Some agencies conduct medical research and determine product safety.

■ Funding for community health programs comes from many sources, including national, state, and local governments.

■ Charities raise and contribute money to many community causes.

■ Health services are available through community programs to those who otherwise could not afford them.

■ Community members help finance services by paying taxes.

■ A budget can help you manage money and plan for health emergencies.

■ Communities can manage resources through prevention, education, and planning.

■ You can fulfill your responsibility to your community by protecting your own health and volunteering to help others.

## ■ Using the Chapter Summary

To further reinforce the facts and concepts presented in the chapter, read and discuss with students the questions that follow.

Ask:

- On what does a community's health depend? (the health of all its members)

- How can poverty affect the health of a community? (Poverty contributes to disease and other public health problems.)

- What do state health departments do? (State health departments help with disease control and help provide care for people who cannot afford it.)

- What are some concerns of national health resources? (the health and safety of the entire country)

- What kind of group usually raises and contributes money to many community causes? (charities)

- Who pays for community services? (Community members help finance services by paying taxes.)

- How can a budget help you? (A budget can help you manage money and plan for health emergencies.)

- How can you fulfill your responsibility to your community? (by protecting your own health and volunteering to help others)

# Chapter 18 Review

The Teacher's Resource Library includes two parallel forms of the Chapter 18 Mastery Test. The difficulty level of the two forms is equivalent. You may wish to use one form as a pretest and the other form as a posttest.

## Review Answers

### Comprehension: Identifying Facts

**1)** identity  **2)** epidemic  **3)** area
**4)** health resources  **5)** Poverty
**6)** goals  **7)** increase  **8)** Emergency Medical Service (EMS)  **9)** donate

## Comprehension: Identifying Facts

On a separate sheet of paper, write the correct word or words from the Word Bank to complete each sentence.

| WORD BANK | |
|---|---|
| advocacy group | health resources |
| area | identity |
| budget | increase |
| donate | poverty |
| Emergency Medical Service (EMS) | screening services |
| | taxes |
| epidemic | World Health Organization (WHO) |
| goals | |

**1)** In a strong community, members share a common _____.

**2)** If a disease becomes uncontrollable, it is called an _____.

**3)** A community with a common association may not live in the same _____.

**4)** The _____ available in a community affect the people who live there.

**5)** _____ is the main reason that some children do not get proper vaccinations.

**6)** The United States has set several public health _____.

**7)** The U.S. population will likely _____ in the coming years.

**8)** _____ provides emergency care for people with injury or illness.

**9)** Volunteers _____ their time.

---

**Chapter 18 Mastery Test A**

**10)** Schools provide _____, such as eye exams.

**11)** The _____ fights diseases that spread globally.

**12)** Community services are partly funded by _____.

**13)** It helps to have a _____, or written plan for spending money.

**14)** An _____ might try to change a law.

## Comprehension: Understanding Main Ideas

Write the answers to these questions on a separate sheet of paper. Use complete sentences.

**15)** What is an epidemic?

**16)** What kind of information do state health departments provide?

**17)** Which Public Health Service agency would be concerned about reports of a new disease?

**18)** What happens if your expenses are greater than your income?

## Critical Thinking: Write Your Opinion

**19)** Why are health promotion and prevention programs important?

**20)** What might a charitable organization do to fight an epidemic?

**Test Taking Tip**  When you read true-false questions, the statement must be absolutely correct. Words like *always* and *never* tell you the question is probably false.

**10)** screening services  **11)** World Health Organization (WHO)  **12)** taxes  **13)** budget  **14)** advocacy group

## Comprehension: Understanding Main Ideas

**15)** An epidemic is a disease that spreads quickly.

**16)** State health departments provide statistics about public health. They also provide free services such as vaccination and education programs.

**17)** The CDC would be concerned about reports of a new disease.

**18)** You cannot pay some of your expenses, and you go into debt.

## Critical Thinking: Write Your Opinion

**19)** Health promotion and prevention programs are important because by providing information about health problems, these programs can decrease the risk of these problems occurring. Because preventive care costs less than treating diseases, the community can save money.

**20)** Answers will vary. Students may suggest that charitable organizations might start a new fundraising campaign to support research for a cure.

---

**Chapter 18 Mastery Test B**

Name _____ Date _____ Period _____   | Chapter 18 Mastery Test B page 1

**Chapter 18 Mastery Test B**

**Directions** Read the words in the Word Bank. Choose the item that best completes each sentence. On the blank before each number, write the letter for that item.

**Word Bank**

| | | |
|---|---|---|
| a) taxes | f) epidemic | k) common identity |
| b) budget | g) federal agencies | l) public resource |
| c) charities | h) health resources | m) common association |
| d) poverty | i) advocacy group | n) volunteer resources |
| e) healthy | j) increase | o) World Health Organization (WHO) |

_____ 1) A _____ can help you manage money and plan for health emergencies.

_____ 2) An _____ might try to change a law.

_____ 3) When you are _____, you are able to contribute to the community.

_____ 4) _____ regulate food and drugs and prevent the spread of disease.

_____ 5) The _____ is an international organization that fights diseases that spread globally.

_____ 6) In most strong communities, members also share similar interest and goals, or a _____.

_____ 7) A _____ is when some community members share similar cultural, racial, or religious ties.

_____ 8) If a disease becomes uncontrollable, it is called an _____.

_____ 9) Emergency Medical Service (EMS) is a _____ that provides emergency care.

©AGS® American Guidance Service, Inc. Permission is granted to reproduce for classroom use only.    Discover Health

Name _____ Date _____ Period _____   | Chapter 18 Mastery Test B page 2

**Chapter 18 Mastery Test B, continued**

_____ 10) _____ are made up of people who donate their time to provide health information or services.

_____ 11) The number of _____ available in the community affect the people who live there.

_____ 12) _____ contributes to disease and other public health problems.

_____ 13) In the United States, the number of people 65 years old or older will _____.

_____ 14) _____ raise and contribute money to many community causes.

_____ 15) Community members help finance services by paying _____.

©AGS® American Guidance Service, Inc. Permission is granted to reproduce for classroom use only.    Discover Health

# Environmental Health

Humans are not alone on this planet. We share the earth with many living things. In recent years, there have been reports and studies on how our environment is changing. People now understand that the land, air, water, and living things are all valuable resources. These resources must be protected so that they can be available for future generations.

In this chapter, you will learn about the environment and how it affects your health. You will learn about environmental problems and what can be done to solve these problems. You will also learn how you can help to protect and preserve the environment.

### Goals for Learning

▶ To explain how the environment affects health

▶ To identify causes and effects of air pollution

▶ To identify causes and effects of water and land pollution

▶ To identify actions that protect and promote a healthy environment

## Introducing the Chapter

Show students side-by-side pictures of a clean body of water such as a lake or river and a body of water with obvious pollution and debris. Have students discuss the difference between the two pictures and the effect those differences could have on nearby living things.

Have a volunteer read the introduction and the Goals for Learning.

Ask:

• What is the difference between these two bodies of water? (Students should notice differences such as the water looks clear in one and dirty in another; one has no floating debris, while the other has floating garbage or scum; the shores of one are clean, while the shores of the other have waste or sewage flowing from factories or pipes.)

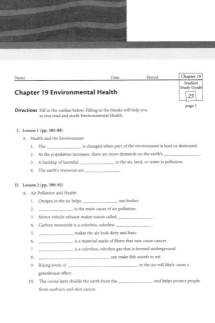

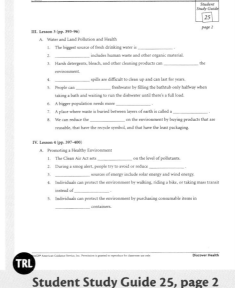

**Student Study Guide 25, page 1**

**Student Study Guide 25, page 2**

# Lesson 1

## Health and the Environment

**Environment**
*The system that connects air, land, water, plants, and animals*

$A$ll living things depend on air, water, and land for survival. The system that connects air, land, water, plants, and animals is called the **environment**. Changes in the environment affect the health of all living things.

### How Does the Environment Achieve Balance?

Everything on the earth contributes to the environment. Water and minerals in the land help plants to grow. Plants give off oxygen, which animals need to breathe. Animals turn the oxygen into carbon dioxide, which plants need to survive. All parts of the environment contribute to one another. This creates a healthy balance in nature. When a part of the environment is hurt or destroyed, the balance is changed.

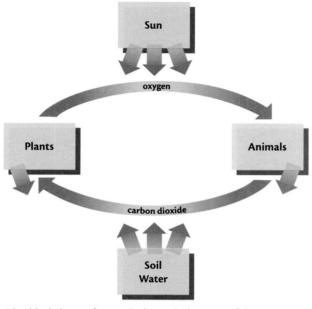

A healthy balance of nature is changed when part of the environment is hurt or destroyed.

*Environmental Health   Chapter 19*   **385**

## Lesson at a Glance

### Chapter 19 Lesson 1

**Overview** In this lesson, students learn what the environment is, how their lives depend on a healthy environment, and what can destroy a healthy environment.

### Objectives

■ To explain how the environment affects health.

**Student Pages** 385–388

**Audiocassette**

**Teacher's Resource Library**

   Activity 71
   Workbook Activity 71

## Teaching Suggestions

### ■ Vocabulary

*environment, pollution, ecology*

Write the vocabulary words on the chalkboard. Tell students to write definitions of the words. Then read the definitions from the textbook. Have students compare their previous ideas with the actual definitions.

### ■ Teaching the Lesson

Ask students to brainstorm about things that all people need to live. Remind them to include things in nature that make life possible. (Students might mention air, food, water, sunlight, and soil.)

Then have students read about the environment on page 385.

Ask:

· Why do changes in the environment affect all living things? (Changes in the environment affect all living things because the environment is the system that connects land, air, water, plants, and animals.)

· How does the environment achieve balance? (Plants give off oxygen waste, which animals need to breathe. Animals turn the oxygen into carbon dioxide, which plants need to survive.)

## Healthy Subjects

Disasters such as Hurricane Mitch can devastate the natural environment as well as the lives of people. Forests can be destroyed, bodies of water can be churned up and filled with debris, pollutants from destroyed structures can be accidentally released. Encourage students to look at newspaper articles about Hurricane Mitch to find out how the natural environment was affected by the hurricane. Have students report their findings to the class.

Have students read about events that can disturb the environment's balance on pages 386 and 387.

Ask:

• How does the increasing population affect the environment? (As more people inhabit the earth, there are more demands on the earth's resources. There is less land for plants and animals to live.)

• Name two resources that people take from the environment that cannot be replaced. (Accept any two of the following: metals, minerals, coal, oil.)

## RESULTS OF A NATURAL DISASTER

In 1998, a storm named Hurricane Mitch swept through Central America. Winds reached 180 miles per hour, and four feet of rain fell in a few days. This caused severe floods and mudslides. At least 11,000 people were killed by the storm. Millions of people were left homeless. It was the worst storm to hit the region in over one hundred years.

Many countries around the world provided aid to the people of Central America. They needed help to rebuild their homes. Also, food and drinking water were in short supply after the storm. How have people responded to natural disasters in your community?

### What Disturbs the Environment's Balance?

Since many things contribute to the environment, any event can affect its balance. Natural events, such as earthquakes, volcanoes, and floods, can cause damage. But nature usually recovers from these kinds of disasters. For example, new plants grow over land damaged by a fire. In fact, the changes that natural events produce can have positive effects by renewing the environment.

### Writing About Health

If a tree is cut down, what do you think will happen to the living things that used the tree as a source of food? Write your thoughts.

Human activity can also disturb the environment. Humans are the only animals who have the ability to change their environment. They do this by building houses, farming, and using the earth's resources. As more people inhabit the earth, there are more demands on the earth's resources. There is less land for plants and animals to live. This puts a strain on the environment.

Some of the resources that people use from the environment cannot be replaced. Metals and minerals are taken from the ground to make things that people use. Coal and oil are mined to heat homes or fuel vehicles, such as cars. Trees are cut down to make wood for houses and paper for writing.

**386**   *Chapter 19   Environmental Health*

As with natural disasters, the environment will change in response to these events. Nature will try to re-create a balance. However, human activity could permanently upset the balance of nature. Land that has been mined or stripped of trees may be so damaged that it can no longer grow trees or crops. It may even be unsafe for humans to live on. People must be careful that they do not damage the environment so much that it cannot recover.

### How Does the Environment Affect Our Health?

Problems in the environment cause problems for humans, too. Some effects can be noticed right away, such as a flood in an area where there are homes. Other effects may not be noticed until many years have passed. The result is **pollution**, the buildup of harmful wastes in the air, land, or water.

Over time, nature breaks down most normal wastes. However, some pollution consists of dangerous chemicals or other harmful wastes that nature cannot clean. These wastes come from human activity such as manufacturing. The products from these factories make our lives easier. However, chemicals needed to make the products can make factory workers sick. Wastes from factories and vehicles harm the air and water that humans need to live.

Pollution is a buildup of harmful wastes in the air, land, or water.

Have students read about how the environment affects our health on page 387.

Ask:

- What is pollution? (Pollution is the buildup of harmful wastes in the air, land, or water.)

- Nature breaks down most normal wastes. Why doesn't nature clean up pollution by breaking it down? (Some pollution consists of dangerous or other harmful wastes that nature cannot clean.)

- What are some sources of pollution? (Accept all reasonable answers. Sources of pollution include factories, power plants, vehicles, sewage from households, and pesticides and herbicides from farms.)

- Some factories contribute to polluting the environment. How do individual people contribute to creating pollution? (Accept all reasonable answers. Students might say that people contribute to pollution by using the products that factories produce.)

### LEARNING STYLES

**Visual** Challenge students to take a walk through some part of the community to look for a source of air, water, or land pollution. Encourage students to take a picture of the source or draw a sketch of it. Invite each student to make a presentation to the class showing the source of pollution, identifying what facility is releasing or creating it, and explaining how the pollutant is affecting the environment around it (for example, polluting a pond, or fouling the air). If the class has an interest, have students choose one source of pollution to investigate as a group. Have them find out what the pollution is and what the polluter is doing to stop it. Students might want to bring their findings to the attention of community officials or to find out what community regulations cover this type of pollution.

Have students read about keeping the environment healthy on page 388.

Ask:

· How can ecology be helpful in preserving a healthy environment? (By studying ecology, people can find ways to repair the harm they have caused the environment.)

## Lesson 1 Review Answers

1) Plants give off oxygen, which animals need to breathe. Animals turn the oxygen into carbon dioxide, which plants need to survive.
2) Land that has been mined may be so damaged that it can no longer grow trees or crops. It may be unsafe for humans to live on.
3) Nature can break down normal wastes. Pollution consists of dangerous chemicals that nature cannot clean.
4) Ecology is the study of how living things are connected.
5) Nature can usually recover from the results of natural disasters over time. But human activity can disturb the environment in ways from which nature cannot recover.

## APPLICATION

**Career Connection**

Career Connection

If students have ever visited a national or state park, they have probably encountered park rangers and naturalists. Rangers and naturalists take care of the natural environment of parks, forests, and wilderness areas. They also conduct educational programs and tours for the public, allowing people to enjoy and understand the ecology of these natural places. Encourage students to find out about jobs as a park ranger or naturalist for the National Park Service or your state park system. If possible, invite a ranger or naturalist to visit the class with a slide presentation on the ecology of a nearby protected area. Encourage students to ask questions about a career as a ranger or naturalist in a park, as well as about the park's ecology.

---

**Ecology**
*The study of how living things are connected*

## How Can We Keep a Healthy Environment?

It is important to understand the problems in the environment. Then we can take steps to fix them. People now know that the earth's resources are limited. The environment is delicate and all of its parts are connected. It is important for us to preserve the environment for ourselves and future generations.

By studying the environment, you can find ways to make changes to improve it. **Ecology** is the study of how living things are connected in the environment. By careful study, humans can find ways to repair the harm they have caused to the environment.

**LESSON 1 REVIEW** Write the answers to these questions on a separate sheet of paper. Use complete sentences.

It is important to preserve a healthy environment for future generations.

1) How do plants and animals contribute to one another through the environment?
2) How can mining hurt the environment?
3) How is some pollution different from normal wastes?
4) What is the study of how living things are connected?
5) What is the difference between a natural disaster and a damage to the environment by human causes?

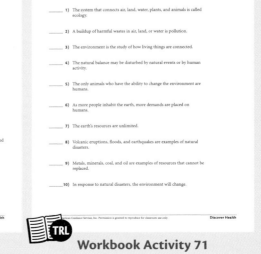

**Activity 71**　　　　　**Workbook Activity 71**

By-product
*An unwanted result*

Hydrocarbon
*A toxin caused by motor vehicle exhaust*

Toxin
*A dangerous chemical*

$L$iving things depend on clean air to breathe and live. Indoor and outdoor air pollution can affect your health. Problems in the air can also affect other living things in the environment.

### Why Do We Need Clean Air?
We breathe in and out about 3,000 gallons of air every day. We use the oxygen in the air to help fuel our bodies. If the air is polluted, then **toxins**, or dangerous chemicals, will enter our bodies. Over time, these toxins can affect our lungs or other parts of our bodies. It may take years for the damage to be noticeable. If the level of toxins is high enough, there can be damaging effects in weeks or months.

### What Causes Air Pollution?
The main cause of air pollution is burning. Whenever a substance is burned, harmful gases and particles are produced. The burning of fuels, such as oil, coal, or gasoline, creates smoke and exhaust. This is a **by-product**, or unwanted result, of the burning. Some other sources of air pollution are tobacco smoke, furnaces that burn waste material, and leaf burning.

Pollution can also be caused when chemicals or gases are released into the air. Usually these chemicals do not occur naturally. For example, pesticides and asbestos are made by humans.

### How Does Outdoor Pollution Affect Health?
Sometimes you can see air pollution, such as smoke. Other times you cannot see pollution because the particles are so small. However, the pollutants can still harm us.

The toxins caused by the burning of motor vehicle exhaust are called **hydrocarbons**. Hydrocarbons can also enter the air when natural gas escapes into the air or when liquid fuel evaporates. Hydrocarbons can irritate your nose and throat and make your eyes water. They can also cause cancer.

*Health Tip*

To reduce pollution, limit how often you drive a car.

*Environmental Health   Chapter 19*   **389**

---

**Ask:**

- How does breathing in polluted air affect the body? (Breathing in polluted air brings toxins into the body. These toxins affect the lungs and other parts of the body.)

- What is the main cause of air pollution? (burning of fuels, such as oil, coal, or gasoline)

- What are by-products of the burning of fuels? (smoke and exhaust)

- What are hydrocarbons? (Hydrocarbons are toxins caused by motor vehicle exhaust.)

---

## Lesson at a Glance

### Chapter 19 Lesson 2
**Overview** In this lesson, students learn about the different types of air pollution and how they can affect health.

### Objectives
- To identify causes and effects of air pollution.

**Student Pages** 389–392
**Audiocassette**
**Teacher's Resource Library**  **TRL**

   Activity 72
   Workbook Activity 72

## Teaching Suggestions

### ■ Vocabulary
*by-product, hydrocarbon, toxin, carbon monoxide, fossil fuel, smog, acid rain, asbestos, particulate, radon, greenhouse effect, ozone layer*

Have students take turns reading the vocabulary words and definitions aloud. Discuss each word and have students use each word correctly in a sentence. Invite students to share their sentences with the class.

### ■ Teaching the Lesson
Ask students to recall the last time they encountered a smell outside that was unpleasant. (Students might mention exhaust from a truck or bus, odor from a sewer, skunk scent, or odor from a factory.) Have students discuss how the smell made them feel. (Students might mention that the smell made them sick or forced them to hold their nose.) Ask students if substances in the air can affect health. (Students should answer that they can.)

Then have students read about the importance of clean air, what causes air pollution, and how outdoor pollution affects health on page 389.

Have students read about carbon monoxide, fossil fuels, and smog on page 390.

Ask:

- What is carbon monoxide? (Carbon monoxide is a pollutant caused by car exhaust.)

- Why is it difficult to know if you are being exposed to carbon monoxide? (Carbon monoxide is difficult to detect because it is a colorless, odorless gas.)

- Name two fossil fuels. (coal and oil)

- What substance does the burning of fossil fuels often produce? (sulfur dioxide)

- If you are experiencing irritation in your eyes and throat, is the gas you are breathing carbon monoxide or sulfur dioxide? (sulfur dioxide)

- What is smog? (Smog is air pollution formed by car exhaust and other pollutants.)

- How does ozone affect the body? (Ozone interferes with our ability to absorb oxygen from the air. Some people may have trouble breathing. Ozone can cause asthma, bronchitis, and emphysema.)

## LEARNING STYLES

**Tactile/Kinesthetic** Have groups of students place white coffee filters inside large glass jars. Direct them to place the jars outdoors in various places around the school or in different parts of the community. The jars must be open and should be left in places where they will not be disturbed. After a certain amount of time, have students collect the jars and examine the residue left on the filters with a magnifying glass. Encourage students to report their findings to the class.

Car exhaust is one of the causes of smog.

**Carbon monoxide**
*A pollutant caused by car exhaust*

**Fossil fuel**
*A burnable substance formed in the earth from plant or animal material*

**Smog**
*Air pollution formed by car exhaust and other pollutants*

**Carbon monoxide** is a pollutant that car exhaust and tobacco smoke cause. It is a colorless, odorless gas that is poisonous at high levels. If you are in an area with high carbon monoxide levels, your health may be affected. You may experience headaches, dizziness, blurred vision, and fatigue. High carbon monoxide levels in areas can cause death. Over many years, carbon monoxide contributes to heart and lung disease.

When factories and power plants burn **fossil fuels**, such as coal or oil, they produce sulfur dioxide. Fossil fuels are burnable substances that are formed in the earth from plant or animal material. Sulfur dioxide irritates the eyes, throat, and lungs and makes breathing difficult.

Many big cities have a problem with **smog**. Smog is caused when there is a great deal of exhaust and other pollutants in an area. Smog makes the air look dirty and hazy. It also creates ozone, which interferes with our ability to absorb oxygen from the air. Some people may have trouble breathing in an area with a lot of smog. Ozone can cause conditions such as asthma, bronchitis, and emphysema.

**390** *Chapter 19 Environmental Health*

**Acid rain**
*Rain, snow, sleet, or hail with large amounts of sulfuric acid or nitric acid*

**Asbestos**
*A material made of fibers that is used as an insulator; it can cause lung cancer*

**Particulate**
*A small pollutant, such as dust, ash, or dirt*

**Radon**
*A colorless, odorless, poisonous gas that is formed underground*

**Particulates** are small pollutants, such as dust, ash, or dirt, that hang in the air. Particulates, such as pesticides, can harm the body when they are inhaled. They can irritate the eyes, nose, throat, and lungs. Lead is a particulate that can be absorbed through the lungs or the skin. Lead enters the bloodstream and can cause lead poisoning. Symptoms include high blood pressure, loss of appetite, and brain damage.

### How Does Indoor Pollution Affect Health?

If a building is insulated, or sealed up tightly, the indoor air may not circulate enough. This will cause a buildup of any toxins that may be present in the building. Glue, paint, pesticides, and household cleaners can release harmful gases into the air. Tobacco smoke can cause breathing problems for both smokers and nonsmokers.

Indoor air pollution can cause shortness of breath, coughing, and nose and throat irritation. Other symptoms are eye irritation, upset stomach, headaches, dizziness, and fatigue. Some indoor air pollutants can cause lung disease or cancer.

Houses that contain **asbestos** can be dangerous for people living in them. Asbestos is a material made of fibers. It was used as an insulator in older buildings. Asbestos fibers in the air can affect the lungs and cause cancer. Asbestos has now been banned. It is being removed from homes and other buildings.

**Radon** is a colorless, odorless gas that is formed underground. It can seep into houses through walls or floors. Radon is a serious indoor pollutant. It may cause lung cancer. There are methods for detecting and removing radon gas. The Environmental Protection Agency (EPA) can help if you have radon in your home.

### How Can Air Pollution Hurt the Environment?

High levels of pollution can affect the entire planet. Chemicals in the air can cause **acid rain**. Rain, snow, sleet, or hail with large amounts of sulfuric acid or nitric acid is called acid rain. It damages rivers, lakes, and plant and animal life. It can destroy forests and make fish unsafe to eat.

*Environmental Health  Chapter 19*  **391**

Have students read about particulates, indoor air pollution, and acid rain on page 391.

Ask:

- **What are particulates?** (Particulates are small pollutants, such as dust, ash, or dirt, that hang in the air.)

- **How can the air in tightly sealed buildings be harmful to health?** (The indoor air may not circulate enough. This could cause a buildup of any toxins that may be present in the building.)

- **Name two materials that cause indoor air pollution.** (asbestos fibers and radon)

- **What is radon?** (Radon is a colorless, odorless gas that is formed underground.)

- **Why is acid rain harmful to the environment?** (Acid rain damages rivers, lakes, and plant and animal life. It can destroy forests and make fish unsafe to eat.)

 **BACKGROUND INFORMATION**

Acid rain forms when precipitation falls through air containing pollutants such as sulfur dioxide and nitrogen oxide. The pollutants form weak acids when they mix with the precipitation, falling as acidic rain, snow, sleet, or hail. Most acid rain is formed by pollutants that come from power plants that burn fossil fuels (especially coal).

Have students read about the greenhouse effect and the ozone layer on page 392.

Ask:

- What is the greenhouse effect? (The greenhouse effect is the gradual warming of the earth's atmosphere.)

- Why would the loss of the ozone layer be harmful to the earth? (The ozone layer shields the earth from the sun's harmful rays. The ozone layer helps protect us from sunburn and skin cancer.)

- How would using fewer CFCs help preserve the ozone layer? (Using fewer CFCs would help preserve the ozone layer because CFCs may be responsible for the decrease in the ozone layer.)

## Lesson 2 Review Answers

1) The main cause of air pollution is the burning of fuels.
2) Smog makes the air look dirty and hazy. It creates ozone. Some people may have trouble breathing.
3) Radon gas is one natural cause of indoor air pollution.
4) The ozone layer shields the earth from the sun's harmful rays.
5) Air pollution causes acid rain, a greenhouse effect, and a reduction of the ozone layer.

### GLOBAL CONNECTION

Warnings about the depletion of the ozone layer date back to the 1970s. The nations of the world have tried to act together to ban the production and use of chemicals such as CFCs that destroy ozone. One such attempt is a 1987 treaty called the Montreal Protocol. Encourage students to research the efforts being taken to protect the ozone and deal with other global air pollution problems, such as global warming. Lead a class discussion centering on what students find.

---

**Greenhouse effect**
*A gradual warming of the earth's atmosphere*

**Ozone layer**
*A region in the atmosphere that protects the earth from the sun's harmful rays*

Many scientists think that the rising levels of carbon dioxide in the air will cause a **greenhouse effect**. The glass ceiling of a greenhouse traps the sun's heat inside. The pollution in the air that surrounds the earth might have the same effect. If air pollution makes the earth's temperature rise, there will be other changes in the environment. Rainfall and weather patterns could change. This could lead to food shortages and more deserts. Melting of the polar ice caps could cause the sea level to rise. Coastal areas would be flooded.

Another problem that air pollution may have caused is the reduction of the **ozone layer**. Although ozone is harmful for people to breathe, it is helpful in the atmosphere. High above the earth's surface, the ozone layer shields the earth from the sun's harmful rays. The ozone layer helps protect us from sunburn and skin cancer. In 1985, scientists discovered a hole in the ozone layer over Antarctica. The size of the hole was as big as the United States. In addition, the whole ozone layer appears to be thinning.

Scientists think that chlorofluorocarbons (CFCs) in the air may be responsible for the decrease in the ozone layer. CFCs are chemicals that were used as cooling agents in refrigerators and air conditioners. These chemicals may have risen up to the ozone layer. They react with the ozone and turn it into oxygen molecules, which cannot protect us from the sun's harmful rays.

**LESSON 2 REVIEW** Write the answers to these questions on a separate sheet of paper. Use complete sentences.

1) What is the main cause of air pollution?
2) What are some of the effects of smog?
3) What is one natural cause of indoor air pollution?
4) How does the ozone layer help us?
5) Name three ways air pollution harms the environment.

**Activity 72**

**Workbook Activity 72**

## Lesson 3

# Water and Land Pollution and Health

| Groundwater<br>*Water beneath the earth's surface* |
|---|

Water and land are important resources. If we use them up or pollute them, they will not be easy to replace. We have to use sparingly, or conserve, and protect our water and land to keep our environment healthy.

## Why Is Water Important to Health?

People need freshwater to live. Three-quarters of the earth's surface is covered with water. However, most of that is saltwater, which cannot be used for drinking or watering crops. Freshwater is as important as air in sustaining life.

Water beneath the earth's surface is called **groundwater**. Groundwater is our biggest source of drinking water. Any toxins in the groundwater will be transferred to us when we drink it. As the world becomes more populated, freshwater is harder to find. If groundwater is not kept clean and free of pollution, we could run out of freshwater sources.

## What Causes Water Pollution?

For many years, humans have dumped wastes into oceans, lakes, and rivers. Many of these wastes cannot be broken down. They remain for a long time and cause damage.

### Industrial Wastes

Factories and other operations dump industrial wastes and by-products into the water. These may include substances like mercury, lead, acids, and other chemicals that cannot be broken down. These toxic substances pollute the water supply and hurt marine life.

### Sewage

The wastewater from drains and toilets is usually carried off as a part of a sewage disposal system. Sewage includes human waste and other organic material. It contains bacteria and can cause disease. If raw sewage gets into groundwater, it can kill wildlife and plants. If it enters the water supply, it can harm humans. Most cities have a sewage treatment plan. Sewage is treated before it is released back into the environment.

*Environmental Health    Chapter 19    **393***

### Ask:

- How can pollution get into groundwater? (Factories and other operations dump industry wastes and by-products into the water.)

- Why do cities need sewage treatment plants? (Sewage treatment plants clean up sewage before it is released back into the environment.)

### Chapter 19  Lesson 3

**Overview** In this lesson, students find out about the causes of water and land pollution.

### Objectives

- To identify causes and effects of water and land pollution.

**Student Pages** 393–396

**Audiocassette**

**Teacher's Resource Library**

Activity 73
Workbook Activity 73

## Teaching Suggestions

### ■ Vocabulary

*groundwater, famine, landfill*

Have students review the definitions of the vocabulary words. Then have each student write a short sentence in which two of the words are used. Invite students to read their sentences aloud in class. Encourage classmates to evaluate whether the words were used correctly.

### ■ Teaching the Lesson

Point to the oceans on a world globe or map. Tell students that oceans contain saltwater—water that we cannot use for drinking, bathing, or cooking. Tell students that the water we use is freshwater. Have students guess what percentage of the water on Earth is fresh. Write their guesses on the board. Then tell students that less than one percent of the water on Earth is freshwater. Ask students to think about why freshwater is a precious resource.

Have students read about why water is important to health and the causes of water pollution on page 393.

Have students read about the health dangers of household chemicals, agricultural runoff, and oil leaks and spills on page 394.

## Ask:

- How can the fertilizer a farmer puts on a field of corn have an effect on the fish you eat? (The chemicals from the fertilizer sink into the groundwater or streams. As the level of chemicals builds up, they can be harmful to the fish we eat.)

- Why are oil spills bad for the environment? (The spilled oil does not mix with the water. Instead, it sits on top of the water like a thick skin. The oil can kill wildlife and leave behind dangerous toxins. The effects of oil spills can last for years.)

## APPLICATION

**At Home**
Have students do a home inventory of household products that could be considered hazardous substances. Students can look at the labels to make this determination. Substances such as cleaning products for drains, ovens, tile, and toilets often contain harmful substances that can pollute the environment. Encourage students to talk with their families about how they dispose of these products and their containers. Tell them to contact the department of sanitation or public works to get suggestions about how these substances should be thrown away.

### Household Chemicals
Some products that people use every day can have harmful effects if they get into the water supply. Harsh detergents, bleach, and other cleaning products can pollute the environment. You can read the ingredient list on products to see if they contain anything harmful. The labels should also tell you how to dispose of the product safely.

### Agricultural Runoff
Farmers use fertilizers and other chemicals to help grow crops. When these chemicals sink into the groundwater or streams, they can have harmful effects. As the level of chemicals builds up, they can be harmful to fish, animals, and people.

### Oil Leaks and Spills
All over the world, people use oil and the products that come from it, such as gasoline. Oil is often shipped across the oceans. Sometimes the oil leaks or spills. The spilled oil does not mix with the water. Instead, it sits on top of the water like a thick skin. The oil can kill wildlife and leave behind dangerous toxins. Oil spills are difficult to clean up. The effects of an oil spill can last for years.

Oil spills kill wildlife and leave behind toxins that can affect humans.

## How Can Freshwater Be Conserved?

Reducing the amount of pollutants in our water is important. By protecting the water we have, we can avoid a shortage later. We can look for cleaner ways to dispose of waste, chemicals, and other products. Another way to protect freshwater is to conserve it. Here are some ways you can conserve water:

- Turn off the water in the shower while you lather and clean. Limit your time in the shower to five minutes.
- Fill the tub only halfway when you take a bath.
- Turn off the water when you are not using it. Don't let it run while you brush your teeth.
- Wait to run the clothes washer or dishwasher until there is a full load.

## How Can Land Pollution Affect Your Health?

The number of people on the earth keeps growing, and the amount of open space keeps shrinking. We need to manage carefully the land we have so that we can meet our needs. We also must find solutions to problems like overpopulation and ways to manage solid waste.

**Health Tip**

Reduce your waste by not buying things that you don't need.

### Population Growth

There are nearly six billion people on the earth. That number may grow to nine billion over the next fifty years. A larger population needs more food. There is, however, only a limited amount of land. How can we grow more crops on less land? Many countries already have problems with **famine**, or a shortage of food. This can happen when there is not enough rain to grow crops.

A larger population would also need more cars and other products. This can cause problems because the cars and factories that make products also cause pollution. Increased pollution can cause more problems for the environment.

Have students read about the conservation of freshwater and how land pollution can affect health on page 395.

Ask:

- List four ways you can conserve freshwater. (Turn off the water in the shower while you lather and clean. Limit your time in the shower to five minutes. Fill the tub only halfway when you take a bath. Turn off the water when you are not using it. Don't let it run while you brush your teeth. Wait to run the clothes washer or dishwasher until there is a full load.)

- How can a population that is too large lead to famine? (If a population becomes too large, land that could be used to grow food would be needed for more houses, roads, and factories. There would not be enough land to grow more crops.)

- How can a larger population create more pollution? (A larger population would need more cars and other products. Because the cars and factories make products that cause pollution, increased pollution can cause more problems for the environment.)

### LEARNING STYLES

**Group Learning** What is the population trend in your community and your state? Encourage groups of students to research in the library or on the Internet to find census figures that show the population of your community today and how it has changed over the last twenty years. Is the trend up or down? What might be accounting for the population change? If the trend is up, what stresses are being placed on the environment? Have each group make a presentation to the class.

Have students read about solid waste and how to reduce stress on the environment on page 396.

Ask:

• Name three things each of us can do to preserve the environment and conserve our resources. (Buy products that can be used again and again, look for products with the recycle symbol, and buy products that have the least packaging.)

## Lesson 3 Review Answers

1) Groundwater is the source for most of our drinking water.

2) The effects of an oil spill last for years because the oil spills are difficult to clean up since the spilled oil sits on top of the water.

3) You can conserve water in the shower by turning off the shower while you lather and clean and limit your time in the shower to five minutes.

4) If a landfill gets too full, some of the trash may be burned. This pollutes the air.

5) A larger population requires more food, which strains land resources and our ability to feed everyone. A larger population will also need more cars and other products. This can cause the use of more resources and create more pollution.

---

## APPLICATION

### In the Community

Recycling can save resources and decrease pollution. Have students find out what type of recycling program your community has. Does your school participate in this program? What is recycled? When and where are recyclables collected? Where do the recyclables go? Encourage students to report on what they find. If possible, make arrangements for the class to visit a local recycling center, landfill, or incineration facility to find out where the garbage goes after it leaves the school or their homes.

---

**Landfill**
*A place where waste is buried between layers of earth*

## Solid Waste

Getting rid of the waste we create is a big job. Solid waste is usually dumped in a **landfill**. A landfill is a place where waste is buried between layers of earth. When landfills get too full, some of the trash may be burned. However, this pollutes the air. Sometimes toxic waste is dumped in a landfill. If it is not disposed of properly, the toxic waste can seep into the ground and poison the water.

Recycling paper and aluminum cans reduces the stress on the environment.

## How Can We Reduce the Stress on the Environment?

Every person must work at preserving the environment and conserving our resources. Here are some actions you can take to keep the earth a healthy place to live:

• Buy products that can be used again and again.

• Look for products with the recycle symbol.

• Buy products that have the least packaging.

**LESSON 3 REVIEW** Write the answers to these questions on a separate sheet of paper. Use complete sentences.

1) What is the source for most of our drinking water?

2) Why would the effects of an oil spill last for years?

3) How can you conserve water in the shower?

4) What might happen when a landfill gets too full?

5) How does a larger population strain the earth's resources?

---

### Activity 73

**Name** _____ **Date** _____ **Period** _____ | Chapter 19 Activity 73

**Water and Land Pollution and Health**

*Directions* Put a check mark next to the best answer.

1) People need freshwater so that they _____
   a) have bath water.
   b) can go deep-sea fishing.
   c) can go boating.
   d) can live.

2) If groundwater is contaminated, then _____
   a) toxins may be transferred to people.
   b) cleanup becomes easier.
   c) our trees may be shorter.
   d) winter ice may dilute the water.

3) Toxic by-products _____
   a) include substances like hydrogen and oxygen.
   b) are also called contaminated groundwater.
   c) can be cleaned up with industrial chemicals.
   d) pollute the water supply and hurt marine life.

4) To treat raw sewage, most cities _____
   a) ship it to Europe.
   b) bury it in landfills.
   c) ignore the problem.
   d) have a sewage treatment plant.

5) Some _____ that are used every day can harm the water supply.
   a) household chemicals
   b) cars
   c) buses
   d) automobile exhausts

6) Two threats to groundwater are _____
   a) agricultural runoff and oil spills.
   b) chemicals and the ozone layer.
   c) lawn sprinklers and raw sewage.
   d) water towers and dams.

7) One way to conserve our groundwater is _____
   a) turn off the water in the shower while you lather and clean.
   b) let the water run when you brush your teeth.
   c) wash as much laundry as you can.
   d) fill up the tub when taking a bath.

8) Famine is _____
   a) a shortage of food.
   b) pollution of groundwater.
   c) a place where waste is buried.
   d) an illness in a family.

9) A place where waste is buried between layers of earth is called _____
   a) a landfill.
   b) a famine.
   c) a chemical hazard.
   d) industrial waste.

10) To keep the earth healthy, you should buy products _____
    a) from South America.
    b) that can be used over and over.
    c) that are packaged in plastic.
    d) all of the above.

*American Guidance Service, Inc. Permission is granted to reproduce for classroom use only.* Discover Health

---

### Workbook Activity 73

**Name** _____ **Date** _____ **Period** _____ | Chapter 19 Workbook Activity 73

**Water and Land Pollution and Health**

*Directions* Write T if the statement is true or F if it is false.

_____ 1) People need freshwater so that they can go boating.

_____ 2) If groundwater is contaminated, then toxins may be transferred to people.

_____ 3) Toxic by-products pollute the water supply and hurt marine life.

_____ 4) To treat raw sewage, most cities ship it to Europe.

_____ 5) Some household chemicals that are used every day can harm the water supply.

_____ 6) Two threats to groundwater are overuse of water towers and rundown reservoirs.

_____ 7) One way to conserve our groundwater is to let the water run while you brush your teeth.

_____ 8) Famine is an illness in a family.

_____ 9) A place where waste is buried between layers of earth is called a landfill.

_____ 10) To keep the earth healthy, you should buy products from South America.

*American Guidance Service, Inc. Permission is granted to reproduce for classroom use only.* Discover Health

---

## Promoting a Healthy Environment

Protecting the environment is everyone's job. Governments, industries, and individuals can work together to make the earth a healthy place to live.

### How Can Governments Protect the Environment?

The U.S. government has passed laws to protect the environment and people's health. The Clean Air Act was passed in 1970, and changes have been made to improve it since then. It sets limits on the level of pollutants. There are also laws about water safety and the disposal of solid and toxic wastes.

The government uses these laws as guidelines for keeping the environment clean. For example, it might fine a factory for polluting the air or water.

Local governments and communities can also work on protecting the environment. They can set up programs and educate people on how they can contribute. Sometimes cities will issue a smog alert. Everyone should try to avoid or reduce driving on those days. People who have health problems should stay indoors because the air may be unhealthy.

**Careers**

### ENVIRONMENTAL PROTECTION WORKER

If you are concerned about the environment, you could become an environmental protection worker. Environmental protection workers support good health and environmental practices. Using computers and other equipment, they check for poisons in samples of air, water, and soil. They also make sure laws about health standards are followed. They may check sewage treatment plants to make sure the water is cleaned properly. Environmental protection workers also check the air for dangerous gases. Training and certification vary by state. Specialties such as those working with asbestos require training and certification from the Occupational Safety and Health Administration (OSHA).

*Environmental Health*   *Chapter 19*   **397**

## Lesson at a Glance

### Chapter 19 Lesson 4

**Overview** In this lesson, students learn how the government protects the environment. They also learn what industries and individuals can do to protect the environment.

### Objectives

■ To identify actions that protect and promote a healthy environment.

**Student Pages** 397–400

**Audiocassette**

**Teacher's Resource Library** **TRL**

  Activity 74

  Workbook Activity 74

## Teaching Suggestions

### ■ Teaching the Lesson

Draw a three-column chart on the chalkboard with these heads: Government, Industry, Individuals. Ask students to brainstorm ways that government, industries, and individuals can protect and improve the environment. Leave the chart on the board as students read the lesson. After the lesson, have students revise their list.

Have students read about how governments protect the environment on page 397.

### Careers

Ask students if they think it is important for a group of professionals to monitor the safety of the environment. Ask what they think an environmental protection worker might do. After reading the feature, ask students if the number and types of duties of environmental protection workers is surprising to them.

**Ask:**

- Name some ways that the federal government works to protect the environment. (The federal government passes laws that set limits on the level of pollutants. There are also laws about water safety and the disposal of solid and toxic wastes.)

- What should people do during a smog alert? (Everyone should try to avoid or reduce driving on those days. People who have health problems should stay indoors because the air may be unhealthy.)

Have students read about future environmental solutions on page 398.

Ask:

- How would alternative sources of energy, such as wind energy and solar energy, help the environment? (Wind energy and solar energy do not pollute the environment and would keep the air and water clean.)

- How might electric cars preserve a healthy environment? (Electric cars put out little or no pollution.)

## BACKGROUND INFORMATION

Inform students that the federal Environmental Protection Agency (EPA) and state environmental agencies maintain sets of air quality monitors to track the level of some pollutants in the air. Some of the major pollutants monitored are carbon monoxide, lead, sulfur dioxide, nitrogen oxides, ozone, and particulates. Monitors must show the air to be within acceptable levels established to maintain health. If the pollutants in the air exceed those levels, states must begin to implement plans to bring the pollution levels down or face penalties.

## APPLICATION

### Environment

Encourage students to work in groups to research the air quality monitoring network in your area. Find out from state or federal authorities (or the local health department) where the air quality monitors in your community or a nearby community are located. Have students ask which pollutants they monitor. Then find out whether your area is in compliance with federal air quality guidelines. If not, what is being done to bring the area into compliance? Invite each group to report their findings to the class.

Hoover Dam supplies water and electric power for a large area of the Pacific Southwest.

### What Are Some Future Environmental Solutions?

Scientists and other researchers are trying to find new ways of protecting the environment. An alternative source of energy that does not pollute the environment would keep the air and the water clean. Solar energy and wind energy are some examples.

The government and the automobile industry are also working on more efficient cars that put out less pollution. For example, California is working to increase the number of electric cars on its roads. Electric cars put out little or no pollution. They may be more energy efficient than gasoline-powered cars. Alternative fuels are another possibility for automobile improvements. Natural gas and hydrogen are some possibilities for the future.

Engineers are also working on ways to grow more crops in a smaller area. Perhaps some of the farmland that is saved can be changed back to wetland or forest.

### DISAPPEARING WETLANDS

Wetlands create a rich home for plants and wildlife in our environment. They prevent floods because they can hold a great deal of water. Wetlands also absorb pollutants and help keep the water clean. One hundred years ago, wetlands covered much of the United States, especially in the Midwest. Today, about half of all U.S. wetlands have been lost. Farms, houses, or other buildings have replaced them. Wetlands are also sensitive to changes in the environment. Some groups of people are trying to raise awareness of the importance of wetlands. Some wetland areas are now protected. Researchers are also trying to find ways to create new wetlands to replace the ones that were lost.

## How Can Individuals Protect the Environment?

Individuals can make a difference. Everyone can take actions that will improve the environment. Here are some things you can do:

- Walk, ride a bike, or take mass transit instead of driving.
- Turn off the lights when you leave a room.
- Set air conditioners no lower than 75 degrees in summer.
- Keep the furnace set no higher than 68 degrees in winter.
- Recycle newspapers, cans, bottles, plastic, and paper. Reuse items like paper clips.
- Select products that contain the least amount of packaging. Larger containers usually hold more product with less packaging.
- Purchase consumable items, such as detergent, in refillable containers.
- Find alternatives to toxic products around your home. For example, use baking soda and water instead of oven cleaners and harsh cleansers. Wash windows with vinegar and water.

## Then and Now

Are there any wetlands in your community? Have students create a natural history of the area, reporting on plants and animals of the wetland and its importance to the local environment. Encourage students to be creative by taking pictures, making videotapes, and interviewing ecologists and others about the area. If the area is being considered for development, have students report on the controversy, laying out both sides of the issue. Allow time for students to make presentations to the class.

Have students read about how individuals can protect the environment on page 399.

### Ask:

- How can walking, taking mass transit, and riding bicycles help protect the environment? (Walking, taking mass transmit, and riding bicycles means that there will be fewer cars on the roads to release pollution into the air.)

- How would purchasing and using nontoxic alternatives to household products help protect the environment? (If you use nontoxic alternatives to household products, you will not be adding toxins to the environment.)

### MULTICULTURAL CONNECTION

Inform students that Native Americans have attitudes toward the environment, influenced by their culture, that govern the way they treat it. Native Americans have traditionally had great respect for the environment and have treated it as something they are a part of, not something to be conquered. Encourage students to look into the environmental beliefs and practices of Native Americans.

Have students read the Action for Health on page 400.

## Action for Health

Encourage interested students to begin a recycling program for the classroom or for your floor of the school. Have students coordinate their efforts with the custodial staff and the school administration. Students should make a plan that includes the items that will be recycled, the placement of containers for dropping off recyclables, a pick-up schedule, and a list of jobs to be handled by student volunteers. Have students submit their plan to you and other school staff for approval.

## Lesson 4 Review Answers

1) During a smog alert, you should try to avoid or reduce driving. People who have health problems should stay indoors.
2) Solar energy and wind energy are alternative energy sources.
3) Electric cars put out little or no pollution.
4) The government helps protect the environment by passing laws that limit the level of pollutants and the disposal of solid and toxic wastes.
5) Accept any five of the following: Walk, ride a bike, or take mass transit instead of driving. Turn off the lights when you leave a room. Set air conditioners no lower than 75 degrees in summer. Keep the furnace set no higher than 68 degrees in winter. Recycle newspapers, cans, bottles, plastic, and paper and reuse items like paper clips. Select products that contain the least amount of packaging. Purchase consumable items, such as detergent, in refillable containers. Find alternatives to toxic products around your home.

### Action for Health

### RECYCLING

Recycling means reusing materials instead of buying new ones. You can make a difference in your community's environment by recycling. It saves natural resources and also reduces solid waste. Newspapers, cardboard, aluminum cans, glass, and some paper and plastics can be recycled. Find out if your community has a recycling program, what materials it takes, and how it works. Organize a drive to collect materials and take them to a recycling center.

**LESSON 4 REVIEW** Write the answers to these questions on a separate sheet of paper. Use complete sentences.

1) What would you try to avoid during a smog alert?
2) Name some alternative energy sources.
3) Why might an electric car be better for the environment?
4) How does the government help protect the environment?
5) Name five ways individuals can help protect the environment.

---

Name _____ Date _____ Period _____ | Chapter 19 Activity 74

**Promoting a Healthy Environment**

*Directions* Write *T* if the statement is true or *F* if it is false.

____ 1) The U.S. government has passed laws that protect the environment.

____ 2) The Clean Air Act sets limits on the levels of pollutants.

____ 3) When the air is clean, cities sometimes issue smog alerts.

____ 4) Scientists are looking for alternative sources of energy that pollute the earth.

____ 5) Electric cars pollute more than regular cars.

____ 6) By growing more food in smaller areas, farmland may be changed back to wetlands.

____ 7) Individuals can have little effect on improving the environment.

____ 8) Solar energy is an example of an alternative energy source.

____ 9) Recycling is a good way to help keep the environment clean.

____ 10) A mixture of vinegar and water can be used to clean your windows.

AGS® American Guidance Service, Inc. Permission is granted to reproduce for classroom use only.   Discover Health

**Activity 74**

---

Name _____ Date _____ Period _____ | Chapter 19 Workbook Activity 74

**Promoting a Healthy Environment**

*Directions* Place a check mark beside the *best* answer.

1) The _____ has passed laws that protect the environment.
____ a) U.S. government       ____ b) president of the United States
____ c) PTA                   ____ d) National Pollution Center

2) The Clean Air Act sets limits on the levels of _____.
____ a) pollutants.           ____ b) automobiles.
____ c) noise pollution.      ____ d) leaf burning.

3) When the air is _____, cities sometimes issue smog alerts.
____ a) clean                 ____ b) dark
____ c) dirty                 ____ d) breathable

4) Scientists are looking for alternative sources of energy that _____ the earth.
____ a) pollute               ____ b) use resources of
____ c) do not pollute        ____ d) exhaust

5) Electric cars pollute _____ regular cars.
____ a) more than             ____ b) as much as
____ c) less than             ____ d) just like

6) By growing more food in smaller areas, _____ may be changed back to wetlands.
____ a) downtown areas        ____ b) landfills
____ c) farmland              ____ d) deserts

7) Individuals can have a great effect on improving _____.
____ a) environment.          ____ b) average score.
____ c) stock market index.   ____ d) work efficiency.

8) Solar energy is an example of an _____.
____ a) way of life.          ____ b) energy source.
____ c) landfill.             ____ d) transportation method.

9) Recycling is a good way to help keep the _____ clean.
____ a) environment           ____ b) bathroom
____ c) bathtub               ____ d) park

10) A mixture of _____ can be used to clean your windows.
____ a) oil and water         ____ b) vinegar and oil
____ c) vinegar and water     ____ d) soap and oil

AGS® American Guidance Service, Inc. Permission is granted to reproduce for classroom use only.   Discover Health

**Workbook Activity 74**

■ All parts of the environment contribute to one another.

■ Humans are the only animals capable of changing their environment.

■ The environment recovers from natural events and disasters. These events sometimes renew the environment.

■ Human activity could damage the environment and upset its balance.

■ Pollution can endanger human health and life as well as other forms of life.

■ Understanding environmental problems is the first step in finding solutions.

■ Burning is the main cause of outdoor air pollution.

■ Pollutants, such as hydrocarbons, smog, ozone, and carbon monoxide, can cause harm to humans.

■ Indoor air pollutants can be a problem in a building without good circulation.

■ Indoor air pollutants include gases and fumes from household items, tobacco smoke, radon, and asbestos.

■ The greenhouse effect, thinning of the ozone layer, and acid rain are some global air pollution problems.

■ Freshwater is an important and limited resource that is necessary for human life. Most freshwater comes from groundwater.

■ Industrial wastes, sewage, oil leaks, agricultural runoff, and toxic chemicals can cause water pollution.

■ The growing world population may cause many environmental problems, including increased land pollution.

■ The U.S. government has passed laws that help maintain a healthy environment.

■ Alternative energy and fuel sources will help to protect our environment.

■ Individuals can take actions to protect the environment.

## ■ Using the Chapter Summary

To further reinforce the facts and concepts presented in the chapter, read and discuss with students the questions that follow.

### Ask:

- What animals are capable of changing the environment? (humans)

- What is the main cause of outdoor air pollution? (burning of fuels)

- Name four pollutants that can cause harm to humans. (hydrocarbons, smog, ozone, carbon monoxide)

- Name four examples of indoor air pollutants. (gases and fumes from household items, tobacco smoke, radon, asbestos)

- What are two global air pollution problems? (greenhouse effect, acid rain)

- What five things can cause water pollution? (industrial wastes, sewage, oil leaks and spills, agricultural runoff, toxic chemicals)

- What can a growing world population cause? (It may cause many environmental problems, including increased land pollution.)

- What will help protect our environment? (alternative energy and fuel sources)

# Chapter 19 Review

The Teacher's Resource Library includes two parallel forms of the Chapter 19 Mastery Test. The difficulty level of the two forms is equivalent. You may wish to use one form as a pretest and the other form as a posttest.

## Review Answers

### Comprehension: Identifying Facts

**1)** carbon dioxide  **2)** balance
**3)** pollution  **4)** Ecology  **5)** toxin
**6)** Ozone  **7)** pollutant  **8)** skin cancer
**9)** groundwater

## Comprehension: Identifying Facts

On a separate sheet of paper, write the correct word or words from the Word Bank to complete each sentence.

| WORD BANK | |
| --- | --- |
| bacteria | landfill |
| balance | ozone |
| carbon dioxide | pollutant |
| Clean Air Act | pollution |
| ecology | skin cancer |
| famine | solar energy |
| groundwater | toxin |

**1)** Plants give off oxygen, which animals turn back into _____.

**2)** Natural events and human activity can upset the _____ of nature.

**3)** Harmful wastes that cannot be broken down by nature create _____.

**4)** _____ is the study of how living things are connected.

**5)** A _____ is a dangerous chemical.

**6)** _____ is created by smog.

**7)** Radon gas is an indoor _____.

**8)** The ozone layer helps protect us against sunburn and _____.

**9)** Most of our drinking water comes from _____.

---

**Chapter 19 Mastery Test A**

**10)** Sewage treatment kills _____ that can cause disease.

**11)** A country may experience a _____ if it does not have enough crops to feed all the people.

**12)** The _____ sets limits on the level of pollutants allowed in the United States.

**13)** _____ is an alternative energy source that does not pollute the environment.

**14)** A _____ is a place where waste is buried between layers of earth.

## Comprehension: Understanding Main Ideas

Write the answers to these questions on a separate sheet of paper. Use complete sentences.

**15)** What is a by-product of burning fossil fuels?

**16)** Which pollutant has been used as insulation?

**17)** What air pollution problem could cause global temperatures to rise?

**18)** Where are most solid wastes stored?

## Critical Thinking: Write Your Opinion

**19)** If acid rain killed all the fish in a lake, how might other animals in the area be affected?

**20)** What would you do if you wanted to get rid of some old cleaning supplies that you found in the basement?

---

**Test Taking Tip**   When taking a short-answer test, first answer the questions you know for sure. Then go back to spend time on the questions about which you are less sure.

---

**10)** bacteria  **11)** famine
**12)** Clean Air Act  **13)** Solar energy
**14)** landfill

## Comprehension: Understanding Main Ideas

**15)** By-products of burning fossil fuels include smoke and exhaust.

**16)** Asbestos is a pollutant that has been used for insulation.

**17)** The greenhouse effect could cause global temperatures to rise.

**18)** Most solid wastes are stored in landfills.

## Critical Thinking: Write Your Opinion

**19)** Accept all reasonable answers. Students might suggest that if all the fish in a lake died, the populations of animals that depend on those fish for food would decrease or disappear.

**20)** Accept all reasonable answers. Students might suggest that you read the labels to find out if the supplies are toxic substances. If they are, you should check with your local department of sanitation or public works to find out how to properly dispose of them. You should not just throw them in the household trash or pour them in the sink or toilet.

**Chapter 19 Mastery Test B**

## Deciding for Yourself

Have students read "The Clean Water Supply" in the Deciding for Yourself lesson on page 404.

### Ask:

- Why do we need clean water? (We need clean water for cooking, washing, and drinking.)

- Why do some communities need to pipe in clean water from long distances? (They do not have enough clean water to support the population.)

- What can people do to avoid a water shortage? (Use less water and decide how to conserve water.)

### Deciding for Yourself Answers

1) Answers will vary. Students may say that they would think about whether there might be a water shortage in the future.

2) Answers will vary. Students might suggest that letting water run while brushing teeth, taking long showers, or sprinkling lawns in the middle of the day are poor uses of water.

3) We can keep our water clean by reducing waste and pollution that could get into the water supply.

4) The following are some ways to conserve water: Turn off the water in the shower while you lather and clean. Limit your time in the shower to five minutes. Fill the tub only halfway when you take a bath. Turn off the water tap when you are not using it. Don't let water run while you brush your teeth. Wait to run the washing machine or dishwasher until there is a full load.

### ■ Deciding for Yourself Activity

Have students complete the Unit 7 Deciding for Yourself Activity.

---

### Deciding for Yourself

### The Clean Water Supply

Clean water is important for our health. We need clean water for cooking, washing, and drinking. Getting a clean water supply is important for all communities. Some communities have difficulty providing enough water for everyone. For example, in Los Angeles, water is piped in from hundreds of miles away. Other communities might have to dig very deep wells to find groundwater.

As the population grows, the demand for clean water is becoming greater. Communities that ship out water to other places may find that they need it for themselves. Pollution can also make it harder to find clean water.

There has been a population boom in Arizona. Many people want to move there because the weather is usually warm and dry. People who are elderly or sick may move there to improve their health. But much of Arizona is dry and desert-like. The population needs water to live. New lawns and golf courses that have been built need to be watered to be maintained. This creates a water shortage problem. People in Arizona and in other places where there is a water shortage need to decide how to conserve water. What is the best use of water? What uses are wasteful? This is a problem that will continue to grow as the population grows and pollution problems get worse.

### Questions

1) Before moving into a community, would you consider where it gets its water?

2) What would you describe as a poor use of water?

3) How can we keep our water clean?

4) What are some ways to conserve water?

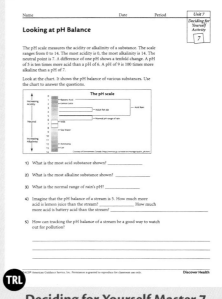

**Deciding for Yourself Master 7**

■ The health care industry includes many people in different jobs and many products and services.

■ Prevention and taking care of colds and minor illnesses are wise forms of self-care.

■ Individuals can pay for health care costs out-of-pocket or through private insurance or managed care.

■ The U.S. government protects consumers with some basic rights. Many health care organizations also set forth rights for patients.

■ Consumers should read product labels and consult a medical professional to decide whether to buy a product.

■ Public, private, and volunteer resources provide care to members of a community.

■ National health resources are concerned with the health and safety of the entire country.

■ Some funding for community health programs comes from national, state, and local governments. Community members help finance services by paying taxes.

■ You can fulfill your responsibility to your community by protecting your own health and volunteering to help others.

■ Understanding environmental problems is the first step in finding solutions.

■ Pollutants, such as hydrocarbons, smog, ozone, and carbon monoxide, can cause harm to humans.

■ The greenhouse effect, thinning of the ozone layer, and acid rain are some global air pollution problems.

■ The growing world population may cause many environmental problems, including increased land pollution.

■ Individuals can take actions to protect the environment.

## ■ Using the Unit Summary

To further reinforce the facts and concepts presented in the unit, read and discuss with students the questions that follow.

### Ask:

- How can individuals pay for health care costs? (out-of-pocket or through private insurance or managed care)

- What should consumers do to decide whether to buy a product? (read the label and consult a medical professional)

- Who provides care to members of a community? (public, private, and volunteer resources)

- Who funds community health programs? (When services are funded by the government, everyone pays for them through taxes.)

- Name four pollutants that can cause harm to humans. (hydrocarbons, smog, ozone, carbon monoxide)

- What are three global air pollution problems? (the greenhouse effect, a thinning of the ozone layer, acid rain)

## Unit 7 Review

The Teacher's Resource Library includes a two-page Unit Mastery Test. Answers are in the Answer Key beginning on page 433 of this Teacher's Edition.

### Review Answers

**Comprehension: Identifying Facts**

1) Prevention  2) health professional
3) managed care  4) specialist  5) rights
6) Better Business Bureau  7) Poverty
8) donate

### Comprehension: Identifying Facts

On a separate sheet of paper, write the correct word or words from the Word Bank to complete each sentence.

| WORD BANK | |
| --- | --- |
| Better Business Bureau | poverty |
| carbon dioxide | prevention |
| Clean Air Act | rights |
| donate | skin cancer |
| health professional | solar energy |
| managed care | specialist |
| pollution | taxes |

1) _____ includes keeping a healthy body weight and not using tobacco or alcohol.

2) A person should seek a _____ if the flu or a fever lasts more than a week.

3) In _____, you may have a limited choice of doctors.

4) Your primary care physician may refer you to a _____ for a certain illness.

5) The American Hospital Association established a list of _____ for patients.

6) If a manufacturer or provider does not respond to a consumer complaint, you could contact the _____.

7) _____ is the main reason that some children do not get proper vaccinations.

8) Volunteers _____ their time.

Unit 7 Mastery Test, page 1

Unit 7 Mastery Test, page 2

9) Community services are partly funded by
_____.

10) Plants give off oxygen, which animals turn back into
_____.

11) Harmful wastes that cannot be broken down by nature
create _____.

12) The ozone layer helps protect us against sunburn and
_____.

13) The _____ sets limits on the level of
pollutants allowed in the United States.

14) _____ is an alternate energy source that does
not pollute the environment.

## Comprehension: Understanding Main Ideas

Write the answers to these questions on a separate sheet of
paper. Use complete sentences.

15) If you have a low income, how could you pay for
health care?

16) What is an epidemic?

17) What is a by-product of burning fossil fuels?

18) What air pollution problem could cause global
temperatures to rise?

## Critical Thinking: Write Your Opinion

19) Why do we need a Consumer Bill of Rights?

20) Why are health promotion and prevention programs
important?

9) taxes  10) carbon dioxide
11) pollution  12) skin cancer
13) Clean Air Act  14) Solar energy

## Comprehension:
### Understanding Main Ideas

15) If you have a low income, you can
get government support through
Medicaid.

16) An epidemic is a disease that is out of
control, spreading to many people at
the same time.

17) Sulfur dioxide is a by-product of
burning fossil fuels.

18) The greenhouse effect could cause
global temperatures to rise.

## Critical Thinking:
### Write Your Opinion

19) We need a Consumer Bill of Rights
to protect consumers from being
cheated or lied to by manufacturers.

20) Health promotion and prevention
programs are important because
they prevent people from needing
health resources and they save the
community money.

# Appendix A: Nutrition Tables

**Table A.1.** The Six Essential Nutrient Classes

| NUTRIENT | BEST FOOD SOURCES | WHY THEY ARE NEEDED |
|---|---|---|
| Protein | Cheese, eggs, fish, meat, milk, poultry, soybeans, nuts, dry beans, and lentils | To promote body growth; to repair and maintain tissue |
| Carbohydrate | Bread, cereal, flour, potatoes, rice, sugar, dry beans, fruit | To supply energy; to furnish heat; to save proteins to build and regulate cells |
| Fat | Butter, margarine, cream, oils, meat, whole milk, nuts, avocado | To supply energy; to furnish heat; to save proteins to build and regulate cells; to supply necessary fat-soluble vitamins and other nutrients |
| **MINERALS** | | |
| Calcium | Milk, cheese, leafy green vegetables, oysters, almonds | To give rigidity and hardness to bones and teeth; for clotting of blood, osmosis, action of heart and other muscles, and nerve response |
| Iron | Meats (especially liver), oysters, leafy green vegetables, legumes, dried apricots or peaches, prunes, raisins | To carry oxygen in the blood |
| Iodine | Seafood, iodized salt | To help the thyroid gland regulate cell activities for physical and mental health |
| **VITAMINS** | | |
| Vitamin A | Whole milk, cream, butter, liver, egg yolk, leafy green vegetables, dark yellow fruits and vegetables | To promote health of epithelial tissues; for health of eyes and development of teeth |
| Thiamin | Present in many foods, abundant in few; pork, some animal organs, some nuts, whole grains, yeast, dry beans, and peas | To promote healthy nerves, appetite, digestion, and growth; for metabolism of carbohydrates |
| Riboflavin | Milk, glandular organs, lean meats, cheese, eggs, leafy green vegetables, whole grains | To make for better development, greater vitality, freedom from disease, metabolism of carbohydrates, fats, and proteins |
| Niacin | Lean meats, liver, poultry, peanuts, legumes, yeasts | To promote good digestion, healthy skin, and a well-functioning nervous system |
| Vitamin C | Citrus fruits, strawberries, tomatoes, broccoli, cabbage, green peppers | To enhance iron absorption; for deposit of intercellular cement in tissues and bone |
| Vitamin D | Milk, salmon, tuna, action of sun | To help absorb and use calcium and phosphorus |
| **WATER** | | |
| | Drinking water, foods | To supply body fluids, regulate body temperature |

**Table A.2.** Fiber Content of Selected Foods

|  | Serving size | Dietary Fiber (g) |
|---|---|---|
| **GRAINS** | | |
| Bread, white | 1 slice | 0.6 |
| Bread, whole wheat | 1 slice | 1.5 |
| Oat bran, dry | 1/3 cup | 4.0 |
| Oatmeal, dry | 1/3 cup | 2.7 |
| Rice, brown, cooked | 1/2 cup | 2.4 |
| Rice, white, cooked | 1/2 cup | 0.8 |
| **FRUITS** | | |
| Apple, with skin | 1 small | 2.8 |
| Apricots, with skin | 4 fruit | 3.5 |
| Banana | 1 small | 2.2 |
| Blueberries | 3/4 cup | 1.4 |
| Figs, dried | 3 fruit | 4.6 |
| Grapefruit | 1/2 fruit | 1.6 |
| Pear, with skin | 1 large | 5.8 |
| Prunes, dried | 3 medium | 1.7 |
| **VEGETABLES** | | |
| Asparagus, cooked | 1/2 cup | 1.8 |
| Broccoli, cooked | 1/2 cup | 2.4 |
| Carrots, cooked, sliced | 1/2 cup | 2.0 |
| Peas, green, frozen, cooked | 1/2 cup | 4.3 |
| Potato, with skin, raw | 1/2 cup | 1.5 |
| Tomato, raw | 1 medium | 1.0 |
| **LEGUMES** | | |
| Kidney beans, cooked | 1/2 cup | 6.9 |
| Lima beans, canned | 1/2 cup | 4.3 |
| Pinto beans, cooked | 1/2 cup | 5.9 |
| Beans, white, cooked | 1/2 cup | 5.0 |
| Lentils, cooked | 1/2 cup | 4.7 |
| Peas, blackeye, canned | 1/2 cup | 4.7 |

**Table A.3.** Calcium and Fat Content of Dairy Products*

| PRODUCT | CALORIES | FAT (grams) | CALCIUM (milligrams) |
|---|---|---|---|
| Skim milk (also called nonfat or fat free) | | | |
| Plain | 86 | 0 | 301 |
| Chocolate | 144 | 1 | 292 |
| 1% milk (also called lowfat or light) | | | |
| Plain | 102 | 2$\frac{1}{2}$ | 300 |
| Chocolate | 158 | 2$\frac{1}{2}$ | 288 |
| 2% milk (now called reduced fat, not lowfat) | | | |
| Plain | 121 | 5 | 298 |
| Chocolate | 179 | 5 | 285 |
| Whole milk | | | |
| Plain | 150 | 8 | 290 |
| Chocolate | 209 | 8 | 280 |
| Buttermilk (lowfat) | 100 | 2 | 300 |
| Buttermilk (whole) | 150 | 8 | 300 |
| Sweetened condensed milk | 246 | 7 | 217 |

*All nutrition information is based on a one-cup serving except sweetened condensed milk, based on a quarter-cup serving

### FRAME SIZE

To determine your frame size:

1. Extend your arm in front of your body bending your elbow at a ninety-degree angle to your body (your arm is parallel to your body).

2. Keep your fingers straight and turn the inside of your wrist to your body.

3. Place your thumb and index finger on the two prominent bones on either side of your elbow, measure the distance between the bones with a tape measure or calipers.

4. Compare to the medium frame chart below. Select your height based on how tall you are barefoot. If you are below the listed inches, your frame is small. If you are above, your frame is large.

### ELBOW MEASUREMENTS FOR MEDIUM FRAME

| Height in 1" Heels | Elbow Breadth |
|---|---|
| **Men** | |
| 5'2"–5'3" | $2\frac{1}{2}$"–$2\frac{5}{8}$" |
| 5'4"–5'7" | $2\frac{5}{8}$"–$2\frac{7}{8}$" |
| 5'8"–5'11" | $2\frac{3}{4}$"–3" |
| 6'0"–6'3" | $2\frac{3}{4}$"–$3\frac{1}{8}$" |
| 6'4" | $2\frac{7}{8}$"–$3\frac{1}{4}$" |
| **Women** | |
| 4'10"–4'11" | $2\frac{1}{4}$"–$2\frac{1}{2}$" |
| 5'0"–5'3" | $2\frac{1}{4}$"–$2\frac{1}{2}$" |
| 5'4"–5'7" | $2\frac{3}{8}$"–$2\frac{5}{8}$" |
| 5'8"–5'11" | $2\frac{3}{8}$"–$2\frac{5}{8}$" |
| 6'0" | $2\frac{1}{2}$"–$2\frac{3}{4}$" |

**Table B.1.** Top 10 Fat-Blasting Exercises

| ACTIVITY | CALORIES BURNED (per 30 minutes) | ACTIVITY | CALORIES BURNED (per 30 minutes) |
|---|---|---|---|
| Bicycling, vigorous (15 MPH) | 340 | Spinning class (indoor cycling) | 312 |
| Jogging (10- to 12-minute miles) | 340 to 272 | Jumping rope, slowly | 272 |
| Swimming, vigorous | 340 | Tennis, singles | 272 |
| Cross-country ski machine | 323 | Hiking, uphill | 238 |
| | | Inline skating | 238 |
| | | Walking, uphill (3.5 MPH) | 204 |

**Table B.2.** Recommended Height and Weight for Women

| Height Feet Inches | Small Frame | Medium Frame | Large Frame |
|---|---|---|---|
| 4'10" | 102–111 | 109–121 | 118–131 |
| 4'11" | 103–113 | 111–123 | 120–134 |
| 5'0" | 104–115 | 113–126 | 122–137 |
| 5'1" | 106–118 | 115–129 | 125–140 |
| 5'2" | 108–121 | 118–132 | 128–143 |
| 5'3" | 111–124 | 121–135 | 131–147 |
| 5'4" | 114–127 | 124–138 | 134–151 |
| 5'5" | 117–130 | 127–141 | 137–155 |
| 5'6" | 120–133 | 130–144 | 140–159 |
| 5'7" | 123–136 | 133–147 | 143–163 |
| 5'8" | 126–139 | 136–150 | 146–167 |
| 5'9" | 129–142 | 139–153 | 149–170 |
| 5'10" | 132–145 | 142–156 | 152–173 |
| 5'11" | 135–148 | 145–159 | 155–176 |
| 6'0" | 138–151 | 148–162 | 158–179 |

Weights at ages 25–59 based on lowest mortality.

Weight in pounds according to frame (in indoor clothing weighing 3 lb.; shoes with 1" heels).

**Table C.3.** Recommended Height and Weight for Men

| Height Feet Inches | Small Frame | Medium Frame | Large Frame |
|---|---|---|---|
| 5'2" | 128–134 | 131–141 | 138–150 |
| 5'3" | 130–136 | 133–143 | 140–153 |
| 5'4" | 132–138 | 135–145 | 142–156 |
| 5'5" | 134–140 | 137–148 | 144–160 |
| 5'6" | 136–142 | 139–151 | 146–164 |
| 5'7" | 138–145 | 142–154 | 149–168 |
| 5'8" | 140–148 | 145–157 | 152–172 |
| 5'9" | 142–151 | 148–160 | 155–176 |
| 5'10" | 144–154 | 151–163 | 158–180 |
| 5'11" | 146–157 | 154–166 | 161–184 |
| 6'0" | 149–160 | 157–170 | 164–188 |
| 6'1" | 152–164 | 160–174 | 168–192 |
| 6'2" | 155–168 | 162–178 | 172–197 |
| 6'3" | 158–172 | 167–182 | 176–202 |
| 6'4" | 162–176 | 171–187 | 181–207 |

Weights at ages 25–59 based on lowest mortality.

Weight in pounds according to frame (in indoor clothing weighing 5 lb.; shoes with 1" heels).

## Leading Causes of Death

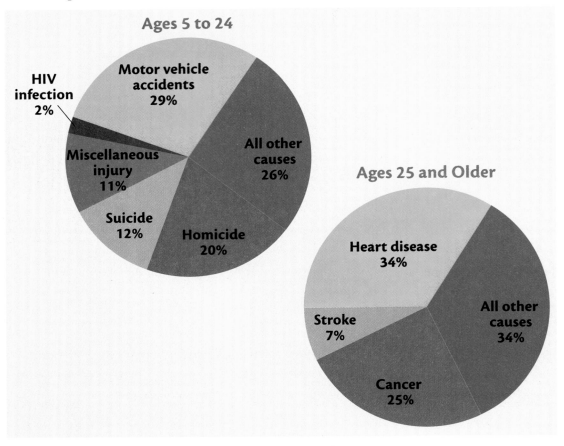

### Ages 5 to 24

- Motor vehicle accidents 29%
- All other causes 26%
- Homicide 20%
- Suicide 12%
- Miscellaneous injury 11%
- HIV infection 2%

### Ages 25 and Older

- Heart disease 34%
- All other causes 34%
- Cancer 25%
- Stroke 7%

**Table B.4.** The Most Common Places for Cancer in Men and Women

| Men | Women |
| --- | --- |
| Prostate Gland 184,500 | Breast 178,700 |
| Lung 91,400 | Lung 80,100 |
| Colon & Rectum 64,600 | Colon & Rectum 67,000 |
| Urinary Bladder 39,500 | Uterus 36,100 |
| Non-Hodgkin's Lymphoma 31,100 | Ovary 25,400 |
| Skin—Melanoma 24,300 | Non-Hodgkin's Lymphoma 24,300 |
| Mouth 20,600 | Skin—Melanoma 17,300 |
| Kidney 17,600 | Urinary Bladder 14,900 |
| Blood 16,100 | Pancreas 14,900 |
| Stomach 14,300 | Cervix 13,700 |
| All Sites 627,900 | All Sites 600,700 |

*Source: American Cancer Society, Inc., 1998.*

## The ABCDs of Melanoma

Melanoma is usually curable if you find it early. Follow this A-B-C-D self-examination guide adapted from the American Academy of Dermatology:

■ *A is for asymmetry*—Symmetrical round or oval growths are usually benign. Look for irregular shapes where one half is a different shape than the other half.

■ *B is for border*—Irregular, notched, scalloped, or vaguely defined borders need to be checked out.

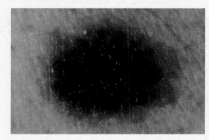

■ *C is for color*—Look for growths that have many colors or an uneven distribution of color. Generally, growths that are the same color all over are benign.

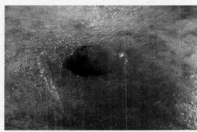

■ *D is for diameter*—Have your doctor check out any growths that are larger than 6 millimeters, about the diameter of a pencil eraser.

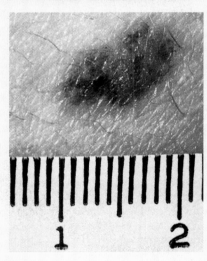

# Glossary

**Absorption**—The moving of nutrients from the digestive system to the circulatory system (p. 140)

**Acid rain**—Rain, snow, sleet, or hail with large amounts of sulfuric acid or nitric acid (p. 391)

**Acne**—Clogged skin pores that causes pimples or blackheads (p. 55)

**Acquired disease**—A disease caused by infection or human behavior (p. 232)

**Adapt**—Change (p. 89)

**Additive**—A chemical added to food to make it better in some way (p. 171)

**Adolescent**—A child between the ages of 13 and 17 (p. 69)

**Adrenal gland**—The endocrine gland that releases several hormones (p. 46)

**Adrenaline**—The hormone that increases certain body functions (p. 46)

**Advocacy group**—An organization that works to benefit a specific group (p. 380)

**Aerobic exercise**—An exercise that raises the heart rate (p. 59)

**Aggression**—Any act that is meant to harm someone (p. 101)

**AIDS**—Acquired immunodeficiency syndrome, a disorder of the immune system (p. 243)

**Alateen**—A support group for teens (p. 218)

**Alcohol**—A chemical that depresses the central nervous system (p. 198)

**Alcohol abuse**—Drinking too much alcohol or drinking too frequently (p. 199)

**Alcoholic beverage**—A drink that contains alcohol (p. 198)

**Alcoholics Anonymous (AA)**—An organization that helps people live alcohol-free lives (p. 201)

**Alcoholism**—A disease in which a person is dependent on the use of alcohol (p. 200)

**Amino acid**—The smaller units of protein (p. 144)

**Amphetamine**—A synthetic stimulant (p. 204)

**Anabolic steroid**—A synthetic drug that resembles the hormone testosterone (p. 207)

**Anorexia**—An eating disorder in which a person chooses not to eat (p. 112)

**Antibiotic**—A drug used to fight bacterial infections (p. 187)

**Antibody**—A protein that is stimulated by the immune system to fight disease (p. 188)

**Antihistamine**—A medicine used for treating allergy symptoms (p. 187)

**Anus**—The opening through which solid wastes leave the body (p. 33)

**Anxiety**—An unpleasant feeling like fear but without reasons that are clear (p. 106)

**Aorta**—The largest artery in the body (p. 38)

**Arteriosclerosis**—A chronic disease in which the walls of the arteries thicken (p. 256)

**Artery**—A blood vessel that carries blood away from the heart (p. 38)

**Arthritis**—A group of diseases marked by swollen and painful joints (p. 268)

**Asbestos**—A material made of fibers that is used as an insulator; it can cause lung cancer (p. 391)

**Asthma**—A disease that affects the lungs, making it difficult to breathe (p. 263)

**Atherosclerosis**—A narrowing of the arteries due to a buildup of fat (p. 256)

### B

**Benign tumor**—A mass of cells that are not harmful (p. 259)

**Bloated**—swollen (p. 162)

**Blood pressure**—The force of the blood against the walls of the arteries when the heart beats (p. 59)

**Body image**—The way each person sees himself or herself (p. 112)

**Body system**—A group of organs that work together to carry out a certain job (p. 25)

**Bogus**—Nongenuine (p. 356)

**Bond**—An emotional feeling of closeness (p. 119)

**Budget**—A written plan for spending money (p. 378)

**Bulimia**—An eating disorder in which a person eats large amounts of food and then vomits (p. 113)

**By-product**—An unwanted result (p. 389)

### C

**Caffeine**—A stimulant found in coffee, tea, chocolate, and some soft drinks (p. 204)

**Calorie**—The unit used to measure the amount of energy in foods (p. 141)

**Cancer**—A group of diseases marked by the abnormal and harmful growth of cells (p. 259)

**Capillary**—A tiny blood vessel (p. 36)

**Carbohydrate**—A nutrient needed mostly for energy (p. 142)

**Carbon monoxide**—A pollutant caused by car exhaust (p. 390)

**Cardiac arrest**—A condition in which the heart has stopped beating and there is no pulse (p. 315)

**Cardiopulmonary resuscitation (CPR)**—An emergency procedure for cardiac arrest (p. 315)

**Cardiovascular**—Relating to the heart and blood vessels (p. 188)

**Cardiovascular disease**—A disease of the heart and blood vessels (p. 255)

**Cardiovascular fitness**—The condition of the heart, lungs, and blood vessels (p. 59)

**Cardiovascular medicine**—A drug used for the heart and blood vessels (p. 188)

**Caries**—Cavities in the teeth (p. 56)

**Cataract**—A clouding of the lens of the eye (p. 267)

**Cell**—The basic unit that makes up your body (p. 24)

**Cell membrane**—The outer wall of a cell (p. 24)

**Central nervous system**—The brain and the spinal cord (p. 42)

**Cerebellum**—The lower part of the brain, which controls balance and coordination (p. 40)

**Cerebrum**—The top part of the brain, which controls thinking (p. 40)

**Charitable organization**—A group of people who give funds to health care programs (p. 376)

**Chemotherapy**—A cancer treatment that uses drugs to kill cancer cells (p. 261)

**Child abuse**—An action that harms a child (p. 73)

**Chlamydia**—A sexually transmitted disease that often has no symptoms (p. 249)

**Cholesterol**—A waxy, fatlike substance found in animal products (p. 145)

**Chronic**—Lasting (p. 247)

**Chronic disease**—A disease that lasts a long time (p. 268)

**Circulatory system**—The body system that pumps blood through the body (p. 36)

**Cocaine**—A dangerous and illegal stimulant drug made from the coca plant (p. 204)

**Codeine**—A prescription medicine that relieves severe pain (p. 191)

**Commitment**—Love, dedication; a pledge of trust (p. 67)

**Common association**—Similar cultural, racial, or religious ties (p. 369)

**Common identity**—Similar interests or goals (p. 369)

**Communicable**—Able to be passed from one person to another (p. 245)

**Community**—A group of people who live in the same place or have common interests (p. 369)

**Competition**—Many companies trying to sell similar products (p. 359)

**Complete protein**—A protein that has all nine essential amino acids (p. 144)

**Compression**—The act of pressing down (p. 317)

**Compromise**—An agreement in which both sides give in a little (p. 95)

**Conflict**—A disagreement or difference of opinion (p. 325)

**Consumer**—A person who buys goods and services (p. 354)

**Consumer advocate**—A person or group that helps consumers correct problems (p. 361)

**Contact poisoning**—A poison that comes in contact with the skin (p. 318)

**Contaminate**—Infect by contact with germs or toxins (p. 172)

**Contract**—Shorten (p. 28)

**Convulsion**—A drawing tightly together and relaxing of a muscle (p. 203)

**Cope**—Deal with a problem (p. 102)

**Count**—The number of items in a package (p. 355)

**Crack cocaine**—A form of cocaine that is smoked (p. 204)

**Cycle**—A repetition (p. 326)

**Cytoplasm**—The jelly-like material inside the cell membrane (p. 24)

**Daily Values**—The part of the food label that tells about the percent of nutrients in the food, based on 2,000 calories per day (p. 169)

**Decibel**—A unit that measures sound (p. 57)

**Decongestant**—A medicine that opens lung and nasal passages (p. 187)

**Deductible**—The initial amount a patient must pay before insurance covers health care costs (p. 352)

**Defective**—Not working properly (p. 354)

**Depressant**—A drug that slows down the central nervous system (p. 198)

**Depressed**—Extremely sad (p. 71)

**Depression**—Extreme sadness (p. 92)

**Dermatologist**—A doctor who takes care of skin (p. 56)

**Dermis**—The middle layer of the skin (p. 26)

**Designated driver**—The person in a group who will not drink alcohol and will drive the group home (p. 200)

**Designer drug**—An illegal manufactured drug that is almost the same as a legal drug (p. 208)

**Detoxification**—The removal of a drug from the body (p. 217)

**Diabetes**—A disease in which the body does not make enough insulin (p. 188)

**Digestion**—The breaking down of food into nutrients (p. 140)

**Digestive system**—The body system that breaks food down (p. 32)

**Discipline**—Correct behavior (p. 68)

**Disease**—A disorder of normal body function (p. 232)

**Disinfectant**—A chemical used to prevent the spread of disease (p. 198)

**Divorce**—The end of a marriage (p. 71)

**Drug**—A substance that changes the way the mind or body works (p. 186)

**Drug abuse**—The improper use of legal or illegal drugs (p. 213)

**Drug dependence**—The need for a drug that results from the frequent use of that drug (p. 213)

**Earthquake**—A shaking of the rocks that make up the earth's crust (p. 297)

**Eating disorder**—A health problem in which a person loses control over eating patterns (p. 112)

**Ecology**—The study of how living things are connected (p. 388)

**Economics**—The way in which money and other resources are divided among community members (p. 371)

**Elevate**—Raise (p. 307)

**E-mail**—Messages sent and received over the Internet (p. 294)

**Emergency kit**—A collection of items that are useful in almost any kind of emergency (p. 295)

**Emergency Medical Service (EMS)**—An intercommunity emergency system that sends out fire, police, and ambulances by dialing 911 or 0 for operator (p. 305)

**Emotional abuse**—A mistreatment through words, gestures, or lack of affection (p. 73)

**Emotions**—Feelings (p. 86)

**Emphysema**—A serious disease of the lungs that causes difficulty in breathing (p. 195)

**Endocrine system**—The body system that uses chemicals to send and receive messages (p. 44)

**Enrichment**—Adding extra nutrients to a food (p. 171)

**Environment**—The system that connects air, land, water, plants, and animals (p. 385)

**Epidemic**—A disease that spreads quickly (p. 370)

**Epidermis**—The outer layer of skin that you can see (p. 26)

**Epilepsy**—A chronic disease that is caused by disordered brain activity (p. 270)

**Esophagus**—The tube that connects the throat and the stomach (p. 32)

**Ethyl alcohol**—A kind of alcohol found in beer, wine, and hard liquors (p. 200)

**Excretory system**—The body system that rids the body of waste and extra water (p. 32)

**Expense**—Something you need to spend money on (p. 379)

**Extended family**—A family who includes many people from different generations (p. 67)

**Family life cycle**—The changes in a family over time (p. 67)

**Famine**—A shortage of food (p. 395)

**Febrile seizure**—A seizure that is common in young children (p. 272)

**Fiber**—The parts of food that the body cannot digest (p. 143)

**Firearm**—A handgun or rifle (p. 287)

**First aid**—The immediate care given to a sick or an injured person before professional help arrives (p. 305)

**Flood**—A condition in which a body of water overflows and covers land that is not usually under water (p. 300)

**Flood warning**—A situation in which flooding has occurred (p. 300)

**Flood watch**—A situation in which flooding is possible (p. 300)

**Food and Drug Administration (FDA)**— A government agency that oversees the testing and sale of medicines (p. 189)

**Food Guide Pyramid**—A chart that can be used to choose a healthy diet (p. 151)

**Fortification**—Adding a nutrient that a food lacks (p. 171)

**Fossil fuel**—A burnable substance formed in the earth from plant or animal material (p. 390)

**Fracture**—A cracked or broken bone (p. 307)

**Frostbite**—A tissue injury causing the tissue to freeze due to overexposure to cold temperatures (p. 310)

**Frustration**—An unpleasant feeling that happens when goals are blocked (p. 101)

**Gene**—Parts of a cell that are passed from parent to child (p. 232)

**Generic**—Nonbrand-name (p. 356)

**Genital herpes**—A sexually transmitted chronic infection (p. 247)

**Gestational diabetes**—Diabetes that develops during pregnancy (p. 266)

**Gland**—A group of cells that produces a special substance to help the body work (p. 26)

**Glaucoma**—An eye disease in which pressure damages the main nerve of the eye (p. 267)

**Gonorrhea**—A sexually transmitted disease that often has no symptoms (p. 248)

**Good Samaritan Laws**—The laws that protect people who assist victims in an emergency (p. 306)

**Gossip**—The spreading of rumors, usually untrue, about people (p. 128)

**Grand mal seizure**—A seizure that affects a person's motor skills (p. 270)

**Grant**—An amount of money given (p. 375)

**Greenhouse effect**—A gradual warning of the earth's atmosphere (p. 392)

**Grief**—A mixture of painful emotions that result from loss (p. 91)

**Groundwater**—Water beneath the earth's surface (p. 393)

**Guilt**—An emotion felt when a person does something wrong (p. 90)

**Hallucination**— A distortion of the senses caused by mental disease or drugs (p. 205)

**Hallucinogen**—A drug that confuses the way the brain processes information (p. 202)

**Hassle**—A small, annoying event or problem (p. 104)

**Hazard**—A danger (p. 288)

**Health care facility**—A place where people go for medical, dental, and other care (p. 350)

**Health insurance**—A plan that pays all or part of medical costs (p. 352)

**Heart attack**—A condition in which the blood supply to the heart is greatly reduced or stopped (p. 257)

**Heart rate**—The number of times the heart pumps blood each minute (p. 59)

**Heat exhaustion**—A condition resulting from physical exertion in very hot temperatures (p. 309)

**Heatstroke**—A condition resulting from being in high heat too long (p. 309)

**Heimlich maneuver**—Firm, upward abdominal thrusts that force out foreign objects blocking an airway (p. 312)

**Heroin**— A dangerous and illegal narcotic drug (p. 202)

**HIV**—Human immunodeficiency virus, the virus that causes AIDS (p. 243)

**HIV negative**—Not having HIV in the blood (p. 244)

**HIV positive**—Having HIV in the blood (p. 244)

**Hormone**—A chemical messenger produced by a gland (p. 45)

**Hospice**—A long-term care facility for people who are dying (p. 351)

**Hurricane**—A tropical storm that forms over the ocean (p. 299)

**Hurricane warning**—A situation in which a hurricane has reached land (p. 299)

**Hurricane watch**—A warning to prepare for a hurricane (p. 299)

**Hydrocarbon**—A toxin caused by motor vehicle exhaust (p. 389)

**Hypertension**—High blood pressure (p. 255)

**Hypothermia**—A serious loss of body heat resulting from being exposed to severe cold temperatures (p. 309)

**Ice**—A form of an amphetamine that is smoked (p. 204)

**Immune**—Resistant to infection (p. 236)

**Immune system**—A system of organs, tissues, and cells that fight infection (p. 235)

**Immunization**—Means of making a body immune from a disease (p. 236)

**Income**—The amount of money received or earned from a job (p. 379)

**Infection**—A sickness caused by a pathogen in the body (p. 233)

**Infectious**—Contagious (p. 306)

**Infectious disease**—A disease caused by a pathogen (p. 233)

**Inflammatory response**—The body's first response to a pathogen (p. 235)

**Inhalant**—A substance that is breathed (p. 206)

**Inhalation poisoning**—A poison that is inhaled (p. 318)

**Inherited disease**—A disease passed through genes (p. 232)

**Inject**—Use a needle to take medicine into the body (p. 190)

**Inpatient**—Someone receiving health care who stays in a facility overnight or longer (p. 350)

**Internal conflict**—A situation in which a person doesn't know what to do (p. 325)

**Internet**—The worldwide computer network that provides information to users (p. 291)

**Intoxicated**—Excited or stimulated by a drug (p. 199)

**Involuntary muscle**—A muscle that moves whether you think about it or not (p. 31)

**Irregular**—Not normal (p. 315)

**Joint**—A place where two bones come together (p. 28)

**Kaposi's sarcoma**—A rare type of cancer affecting the skin or internal organs (p. 244)

**Keratin**—A protein that makes nails hard (p. 26)

**Landfill**—A place where waste is buried between layers of earth (p. 396)

**Large intestine**—The tube that connects the small intestine and the rectum (p. 33)

**Life-threatening emergency**—Any situation in which a person might die if medical treatment isn't provided immediately (p. 292)

**Look-alike drug**—An illegal manufactured drug that imitates the effect of other drugs (p. 208)

**Lot number**—A number that identifies a group of packages (p. 167)

**Lung cancer**—A disease of the lungs caused primarily by smoking tobacco (p. 195)

**Malignant tumor**—A mass of cells that are harmful (p. 259)

**Malnutrition**—A condition in which the body does not get enough to eat (p. 162)

**Marijuana**—An illegal drug from the hemp plant that produces intoxication (p. 207)

**Media**—Sources of information and entertainment, such as newspapers and TV (p. 323)

**Mediator**—A person who helps two sides solve a problem reasonably (p. 332)

**Medicaid**—Health insurance for people with low incomes (p. 353)

**Medicare**—Health insurance for people age 65 or older or who receive Social Security disability (p. 353)

**Medicine**—A drug used to treat or prevent a disease or health problem (p. 186)

**Medulla**—The part of the brain that connects to the spinal cord (p. 40)

**Melanin**—A chemical that gives skin and hair its color (p. 26)

**Menstruation**—The monthly flow of an egg and extra tissue from the uterus (p. 48)

**Metabolism**—The process of cells using nutrients for energy and other needs (p. 140)

**Metastasize**—Spread cancer to distant tissues (p. 259)

**Microscope**—A tool used to see cells (p. 24)

**Mineral**—A nutrient from the earth that is needed to help the body use energy from other nutrients (p. 147)

**Minor**—A person under age 18 or 21 (p. 360)

**Mitosis**—The dividing process that makes new cells (p. 25)

**Mucous membrane**—The thin, moist tissue that lines body openings (p. 233)

**Mucus**—The sticky fluid produced by mucous membranes (p. 233)

**Multiply**—Increase in number (p. 233)

**Muscular dystrophy**—An inherited disease in which the muscles do not develop normally (p. 232)

**Muscular system**—The body system made up of your muscles (p. 28)

**Narcotic**—A drug that dulls the senses or relieves pain (p. 202)

**Natural disaster**—A destructive event that happens because of natural causes (p. 297)

**Need**—Something important or necessary to have (p. 93)

**Nervous system**—The body system that sends and receives messages throughout the body (p. 40)

**Neutral**—Not favoring either side (p. 333)

**Nicotine**—A chemical in tobacco to which people become addicted (p. 194)

**Nucleus**—The control center of the cell (p. 24)

**Nurse practitioner**—A registered nurse with special training for providing health care (p. 349)

**Nutrient**—The basic unit of food that the body can use (p. 140)

**Nutrition Facts**—The part of a food label that tells about the calories and nutrients in the food (p. 168)

**Obesity**—A condition in which one is more than 20 percent overweight (p. 162)

**Ointment**—A medicine for minor skin infections (p. 187)

**Ophthalmologist**—A doctor who specializes in diseases of the eye (p. 58)

**Opiate**—A drug made from opium poppy plants; another name for narcotic (p. 202)

**Optometrist**—A specialist in eye examinations and corrective lenses (p. 57)

**Oral poisoning**—A poison that is eaten or swallowed (p. 317)

**Organ**—A group of tissues that work together (p. 25)

**Orthodontist**—A dentist who treats crooked or crowded teeth (p. 57)

**Osteoarthritis**—A type of arthritis that causes a person's joints to get worse with age (p. 269)

**Out-of-pocket**—Straight from a person's income or savings (p. 352)

**Outpatient**—Someone receiving health care without staying overnight (p. 350)

**Ovary**—The female organ that stores eggs (p. 47)

**Over-the-counter medicine**—A medicine that can be bought without a doctor's written order (p. 186)

**Ovulation**—The monthly process of releasing an egg (p. 47)

**Ozone layer**—A region in the atmosphere that protects the earth from the sun's harmful rays (p. 392)

**Particulate**—A small pollutant, such as dust, ash, or dirt (p. 391)

**Pathogen**—A disease-causing germ (p. 232)

**Pediatrics**—Child health care (p. 350)

**Peer**—A person in the same age group (p. 108)

**Peer pressure**—The influence people of the same age have on one another (p. 108)

**Penicillin**—An antibiotic used to treat diseases such as gonorrhea (p. 248)

**Penis**—The male organ used to deliver sperm and to urinate (p. 49)

**Peripheral nervous system**—All the nerves in the body outside the brain and the spinal cord (p. 42)

**Perspiration**—Sweat (p. 26)

**Petit mal seizure**—A seizure that affects a person's mental functions (p. 271)

**Pharmacist**—A person trained and licensed to prepare and sell prescription drugs (p. 186)

**Physical fitness**—The body's ability to work, exercise, and play without tiring (p. 59)

**Pituitary gland**—The endocrine gland attached to the base of the brain (p. 46)

**Plaque**—A layer of bacteria on teeth (p. 56)

**Plasma**—The liquid part of blood (p. 38)

**Pollution**—The buildup of harmful wastes in the air, land, or water (p. 387)

**Polyunsaturated fat**—A fat that is found mostly in plant foods (p. 145)

**Prejudice**—An opinion based on a person's religion, race, gender, or culture (p. 328)

**Premium**—An amount of money paid to an insurance company at regular intervals (p. 352)

**Prescription**—A written order from a doctor for a medicine (p. 186)

**Preservative**—A chemical added to food to prevent spoiling (p. 171)

**Prevention**—Appropriate ongoing self-care (p. 348)

**Primary care physician**—A doctor who treats people for routine problems (p. 349)

**Private resource**—A group of people not associated with the government (p. 373)

**Protein**—A nutrient needed for growth and repair of body tissues (p. 142)

**Psychedelic drug**—Another term for hallucinogen (p. 205)

**Psychoactive medicine**—A medicine that changes the function of the brain (p. 188)

**Puberty**—The period when children develop into adults and reach sexual maturity (p. 47)

**Public resource**—A health service that is run by a local, state, or national government (p. 373)

**Quackery**—A medical product or service that is unproved or worthless (p. 355)

**Rabies**—A disease transmitted to humans through animal bites (p. 310)

**Radiation**—A type of treatment that uses energy waves to destroy cancer cells (p. 261)

*Discover Health    Glossary*   **419**

**Radon**—A colorless, odorless, poisonous gas that is formed underground (p. 391)

**Recall**—An order to return unsafe items (p. 375)

**Rectum**—The organ that stores solid waste before it leaves the body (p. 33)

**Rehabilitation**—Help to recover from surgery, illness, or injury (p. 350)

**Relationship**—A connection between people (p. 125)

**Reproductive system**—The body system responsible for making a baby (p. 47)

**Resist**—Act against (p. 109)

**Resource**—A source of supply and support (p. 370)

**Respiratory system**—The body system responsible for breathing (p. 36)

**Rheumatoid arthritis**—A type of arthritis caused by a defect in the immune system (p. 268)

**Rheumatoid factor**—The antibody associated with rheumatoid arthritis (p. 268)

**Risk factor**—A trait or habit that increases a person's chances of having or getting a disease (p. 258)

**Saliva**—The liquid in the mouth that begins digestion (p. 32)

**Saturated fat**—A fat that is found mostly in animal products (p. 145)

**Screening service**—An exam that provides prevention, such as eye and ear exams (p. 374)

**Secondhand smoke**—Tobacco smoke breathed by nonsmokers (p. 195)

**Secrete**—Form and give off (p. 45)

**Seizure**—A physical or mental reaction to disordered brain activity (p. 270)

**Self-esteem**—The way a person feels about himself or herself (p. 104)

**Separation**—A period when a married couple stops living together (p. 71)

**Septic arthritis**—A swelling of the joints caused by an infection (p. 269)

**Serving size**—A way to measure the amount of different foods that should be eaten each day (p. 152)

**Sexual abuse**—Any sexual contact that is forced on a person (p. 73)

**Sexual intercourse**—Inserting the penis into the vagina (p. 49)

**Sexually transmitted disease**—A disease spread by sexual contact (p. 216)

**Shame**—An emotion that results from disapproval or rejection (p. 91)

**Shock**—The physical reaction to injury in which the circulatory system fails to provide enough blood to the body (p. 311)

**Shyness**—Feelings of discomfort around others (p. 127)

**Side effect**—An unexpected and often harmful result of taking medicine (p. 191)

**Skeletal system**—The body system made up of your bones and joints (p. 28)

**Small intestine**—Where most of digestion takes place (p. 32)

**Small talk**—Talk about things that are interesting but not important (p. 123)

**Smog**—Air pollution formed by car exhaust and other pollutants (p. 390)

**Smokeless tobacco**—Tobacco that is chewed (p. 195)

**Social emotions**—Emotions that have to do with relationships with others (p. 90)

**Specialist**—A doctor who works only on certain types of medical problems (p. 346)

**Sperm**—The male sex cell (p. 48)

**Spinal cord**—The cable of nerve cells within the bones of the spine (p. 40)

**Splint**—A rigid object that keeps a broken limb in place (p. 307)

**Sponsor**—A recovering alcoholic who helps a new AA member (p. 218)

**Sprain**—The sudden tearing or stretching of tendons or ligaments (p. 307)

**Statistics**—Important information (p. 374)

**Sterile**—Unable to have children (p. 207)

**Steroid**—A chemical that occurs naturally in the body or is made in a laboratory (p. 207)

**Stimulant**—A drug that speeds up the central nervous system (p. 194)

**Stress**—The way the body reacts to a change or to something that can hurt you (p. 87)

**Stress response**—The body's reaction to stress (p. 105)

**Stroke**—A condition in which the blood supply to a person's brain is suddenly blocked (p. 257)

**Subcutaneous layer**—The deepest layer of the skin (p. 27)

**Support group**—A group of people with similar problems who help one another (p. 218)

**Suppository**—A cylinder containing medicine to be inserted into the rectum (p. 190)

**Synthetic**—A narcotic drug that is manufactured in laboratories (p. 202)

**Syphilis**—A sexually transmitted disease that has three stages (p. 249)

**Tar**—A substance in tobacco that can form a thick, brown, sticky substance in the lungs (p. 195)

**Terminally ill**—Dying from a disease, an injury, or an illness, sometimes over a long period (p. 351)

**Testis**—The male organ that makes sperm (p. 48)

**Testosterone**—The male hormone that produces male characteristics, such as facial hair and a deep voice (p. 207)

**Therapeutic effect**—A helpful result of taking medicine (p. 191)

**Threat**—A situation that puts a person's well-being in danger (p. 104)

**Thunderstorm**—A severe weather condition that produces thunder, lightning, and rain (p. 299)

**Thyroid gland**—The endocrine gland that affects a person's energy (p. 46)

**Tissue**—A group of cells that do the same job (p. 25)

**Tolerance**—A condition in which a person must take more and more of a drug to get the same effect (p. 202)

**Tornado**—A whirling, funnel-shaped storm that forms over land (p. 300)

**Tornado warning**—An alert issued when a tornado has been spotted in an area (p. 300)

**Tornado watch**—A situation in which a tornado may develop (p. 300)

**Toxin**—A dangerous chemical (p. 389)

**Trachea**—The tube that connects the throat to the lungs (p. 36)

**Transfusion**—The transfer of blood from one person to another (p. 245)

**Transmit**—Spread (p. 310)

**Tremor**—Severe shaking (p. 203)

**Type I diabetes**—Insulin-dependent diabetes (p. 265)

**Type II diabetes**—Non-insulin-dependent diabetes (p. 266)

**Universal Precautions**—The methods of self-protection that prevent contact with blood or other body fluids (p. 306)

**Ureter**—The tube that carries urine from the kidney to the bladder (p. 34)

**Urethra**—The tube through which urine passes out of the body (p. 34)

**Urine**—The liquid waste formed in the kidneys (p. 34)

**Uterus**—The female organ that holds a growing baby (p. 48)

**Vaccination**—An injection of dead or weakened viruses to make the body immune to the virus (p. 236)

**Vaccine**—A medicine that stimulates the immune system to fight off a disease (p. 188)

**Vagina**—The birth canal through which a baby is born (p. 48)

**Vein**—A blood vessel that carries blood back to the heart (p. 38)

**Violence**—Actions or words that hurt people or things they care about (p. 323)

**Violent**—Doing actions or words that hurt people (p. 72)

**Vitamin**—A nutrient needed to help the body use energy from other nutrients (p. 147)

**Voluntary muscle**—A muscle that moves when you think about it (p. 31)

**Volunteer resource**—A group of people who donate their time to provide services (p. 373)

**Withdraw**—Pull away (p. 102)

**Withdrawal**—A physical reaction to the absence of a drug (p. 196)

**Withdrawal symptoms**—The body's physical reaction to the absence of a drug (p. 214)

**Word of mouth**—Information about a product that you hear from a friend or family member (p. 355)

# Index

## B

Baby, effect of medicines on unborn, 192
Baby-sitters, safety for, 291
Banting, Frederick, 45
Barbiturates, 202–203
Barton, Clara, 308
Behavior
    changing, 89
    and emotions, 93–96
    violent, 323
Benign tumors, 259
Better Business Bureau, 363
Biofeedback, 107
Birth defects, preventing, 192
Black Death, 235
Blackheads, 55
Bladder, 34, 35
Bleeding, first aid for severe, 311
Blindness, 267
Bloating, 162
Blood, functions of, 37–38
Blood clots, 256
Blood pressure, 59, 61
    high, 255, 267
Blood tests
    in detecting AIDS, 244
    in detecting syphilis, 249
*The Bluest Eye* (Morrison), 94
Body chemistry and drug reactions, 191
Body image, 112
Body systems, 23. *See also* specific body systems
    definition of, 25
Bogus, 356
Bond, 119
Brady Handgun Violence Protection Act, 338
Brain
    functions of, 40–41
    parts of, 40
Breast cancer, 50, 261
Breasts, self-exam of, 50
Breath analyzers, 200
Bronchitis, 390
Bubonic plague, 235
Budget, 378
Bulimia, 113, 161, 162
Burns
    degree of, 308
    first aid for, 308
By-product, 389

## C

Caffeine, 204, 284
Calcium, 149
Calories, 61, 141, 167
Cannabis sativa, 207

Cancer, 259
    breast, 50, 261
    lung, 195, 261
    prostate, 261
    self-exam for early signs of, 50
    skin, 261
    survival rates from, 260
    symptoms and warning signs of, 259
    testes, 50
    treatment for, 262
    types of, 260–261
Capillaries, 36, 38
Carbohydrates, 142–143
    complex, 143
    simple, 142
Carbon dioxide, 36, 38, 385
Carbon monoxide, 391
Cardiac arrest, 315
Cardiopulmonary resuscitation (CPR), 315–317, 318
Cardiovascular diseases, 188
    arteriosclerosis, 256
    atherosclerosis, 256
    definition of, 255
    heart attacks, 257
    and high blood pressure, 255
    risk factors for, 258
    strokes, 257
Cardiovascular fitness, 59
Cardiovascular medicines, 188
Careers
    dietary aide, 163
    drug abuse counselor, 220
    environmental protection worker, 397
    fitness instructor, 61
    food technologist, 141
    health service coordinator, 234
    home health aide, 378
    industrial safety specialist, 287
    laboratory assistant, 250
    medical records technician, 359
    medical specialists, 349
    mental health assistant, 95
    occupational therapy assistant, 257
    pharmacy clerk, 190
    physician's assistant, 334
    registered nurse, 314
    resident assistant, 114
    residential counselor, 124
Caries, 56
Cataracts, 267
Cell membrane, 24
Cells, 24
    metabolism in, 141
    parts of, 24–25
Center for Independent Living (CIL), 373
Centers for Disease Control (CDC), 374
Central nervous system, 42

*Discover Health    Index*    **431**

Tars, 195
TDD (telecommunications device for the deaf), 306
Teens, safety for, 291–293
Teeth, taking care of, 56–57
Terminal care, 351
Testes, 48
 cancer of, 50
 self-exam of, 50
Testosterone, 207
Threats, 104
Thunderstorm, 299
Thyroid gland, 46
Tissue, 25
Tobacco, 194
 effects of, 194, 195, 219
 and lung cancer, 261
 reasons for using, 194
 and rights of nonsmokers, 196–197
 and secondhand smoke, 195, 196–198
 stopping use of, 196
Tolerance, 202, 213
Tonsillitis, 236
Tonsils, 236
Tornado, 300
Tornado warning, 300
Tornado watch, 300
Toxins, 389
Trachea, 36
Tranquilizers, 202–203
Transfusions and spread of AIDS, 245
Transmission, 310
Tremors, 203
Tumors
 benign, 259
 malignant, 259
Type I diabetes, 265
Type II diabetes, 266

United Way, 376
Universal Precautions, 306
Ureters, 34, 35
Urethra, 34, 35, 49
Urine, 34, 35
Uterus, 48

Vaccinations, 236–237
 tracking, 238
Vaccines, 188
Vagina, 48, 49
Valium, 224

Values
 importance of, 122
 in relationships, 126
Veins, 38, 59
Violence
 causes of, 327–329
 versus conflict, 324
 conflict as cause of, 327
 costs of, 326
 and crime, 329–330
 cycle of, 326, 327, 330
 definition of, 323
 and drug dependence, 215
 effects of, 325
 in families, 72–73, 324
 family, 324
 and genocide, 329
 gun control in preventing, 338
 media, 323
 preventing, 331–334
 random, 324
Violent behavior, 323
Vitamins, 147–48
Voluntary muscles, 31, 41
Volunteer resources, 373

Warm-up, 60
Wastes
 removal of liquid, from body, 34–35
 removal of solid, from body, 33
Water, 147, 150
 importance of, to health, 393
 importance of clean, 404
Water pollution, causes of, 393–394
Weight
 calculating ideal, 154
 maintaining healthy, 160
Westermarck, Alexander, 127
Wetlands, disappearing, 399
Wheezing, 263
White blood cells, 24, 38
White Cross Electric Vibrator Chair, 364
Withdrawal from drugs, 196, 214
Withdrawing, frustration and, 102
Women in sports 62
Word of mouth, 355
World Health Organization (WHO), 375

Young people, impact of crime on, 329–330

# Teacher's Resource Library Answer Key

## Activities

**Activity 1—Cells, Tissues, and Organs**
1) e  2) c  3) j  4) d  5) g  6) f  7) i  8) h  9) a  10) b

**Activity 2—The Body's Protective Covering**
1) d  2) e  3) a  4) i  5) b  6) f  7) j  8) c  9) h  10) g

**Activity 3—Skeletal and Muscular Systems**
1) h  2) e  3) j  4) b  5) o  6) f  7) o  8) j  9) f  10) a  11) b  12) e
13) i  14) j  15) b

**Activity 4—Digestive and Excretory Terms**
1) e  2) o  3) h  4) k  5) i  6) a  7) m  8) f  9) c  10) a  11) b
12) g  13) d  14) i  15) l

**Activity 5—Circulatory and Respiratory Terms**
1) k  2) a  3) d  4) l  5) a  6) f  7) j  8) c  9) b  10) n  11) i  12) i
13) g  14) b  15) k

**Activity 6—The Nervous System**
1) f  2) c  3) a  4) h  5) i  6) b  7) d  8) e  9) g  10) j

**Activity 7—The Endocrine System**
1) d  2) i  3) e  4) h  5) j  6) a  7) b  8) g  9) f  i c

**Activity 8—The Reproductive System**
1) L  2) F  3) E  4) C  5) M  6) I  7) E  8) K  9) J  10) O  11) I
12) B  13) G  14) H  15) N

**Activity 9—Hygiene**
1) a  2) b  3) c  4) h  5) g  6) e  7) f  8) j  9) d  10) i

**Activity 10—Fitness**
1) h  2) d  3) g  4) c  5) a  6) i  7) e  8) j  9) f  10) e

**Activity 11—The Family Life Cycle**
1) g  2) e  3) b  4) d  5) a  6) f  7) j  8) i  9) c  10) h

**Activity 12—Family Problems**
1) i  2) b  3) a  4) b  5) f  6) l  7) j  8) k  9) k  10) o  11) n  12) e
13) f  14) m  15) d

**Activity 13—Emotions and Their Causes**
1) d  2) i  3) j  4) e  5) b  6) a  7) c  8) f  9) h  10) g

**Activity 14—Social Emotions**
1) j  2) d  3) i  4) c  5) b  6) f  7) h  8) g  9) a  10) e

**Activity 15—Emotions and Behavior**
1) g  2) f  3) b  4) c  5) d  6) h  7) i  8) e  9) j  10) a

**Activity 16—Managing Frustration**
1) a  2) f  3) e  4) i  5) c  6) b  7) j  8) g  9) h  10) d

**Activity 17—Managing Stress and Anxiety**
1) T  2) F  3) T  4) F  5) F  6) F  7) T  8) F  9) T  10) F  11) T
12) F  13) T  14) F  15) T

**Activity 18—Responding to Peer Pressure**
1) c  2) d  3) a  4) c  5) a  6) d  7) a  8) e  9) c  10) b

**Activity 19—Eating Disorders**
1) T  2) T  3) T  4) T  5) T  6) b  7) c  8) d  9) e  10) a

**Activity 20—Being a Friend to Yourself**
1) T  2) F  3) T  4) T  5) F  6) F  7) T  8) T  9) F  10) T

**Activity 21—Making Friends**
1) F  2) F  3) F  4) F  5) T  6) b  7) c  8) a  9) d  10) a

**Activity 22—Healthy Relationships**
1) T  2) F  3) T  4) F  5) T  6) F  7) T  8) F  9) F  10) T

**Activity 23—Food for Energy**
1) b  2) a  3) c  4) b  5) a  6) d  7) d  8) d  9) a  10) c

**Activity 24—Carbohydrates and Protein**
1) T  2) T  3) T  4) T  5) F  6) F  7) F  8) T  9) T  10) T

**Activity 25—Fats and Cholesterol**
1) T  2) T  3) T  4) T  5) F  6) F  7) F  8) T  9) T  10) F

**Activity 26—Vitamins, Minerals, and Water**
1) b  2) c  3) c  4) a  5) a  6) d  7) b  8) c  9) a  10) d

**Activity 27—Dietary Guidelines**
1) b  2) b  3) d  4) d  5) a  6) T  7) F  8) T  9) F  10) T

**Activity 28—Food Choices and Health**
1) j  2) h  3) a  4) e  5) d  6) b  7) c  8) g  9) i  10) f

**Activity 29—Influences on Food Choices**
1) T  2) F  3) T  4) T  5) T  6) c  7) d  8) a  9) c  10) c

**Activity 30—Reading Food Labels**
1) d  2) b  3) e  4) a  5) c  6) c  7) a  8) b  9) d  10) a

**Activity 31—Making Foods Safe**
1) j  2) a  3) h  4) c  5) b  6) i  7) f  8) e  9) g  10) d

**Activity 32—Prescriptions and Over-the-Counter Medicines**
1) c  2) b  3) e  4) a  5) d  6) h  7) j  8) f  9) g  10) i

**Activity 33—The Effect of Medicines and Drugs on the Body**
1) e  2) d  3) c  4) a  5) b  6) h  7) f  8) i  9) j  10) g

**Activity 34—Tobacco**
1) T  2) T  3) T  4) F  5) F  6) T  7) F  8) F  9) F  10) T  11) F
12) T  13) F  14) T  15) T

**Activity 35—Alcohol**
1) g  2) e  3) a  4) i  5) d  6) h  7) f  8) c  9) j  10) b

**Activity 36—Narcotics, Depressants, Stimulants, and Hallucinogens**
1) a  2) h  3) b  4) j  5) c  6) k  7) e  8) m  9) i  10) n  11) f
12) d  13) l  14) o  15) g

**Activity 37—Other Dangerous Drugs**
1) d  2) a  3) b  4) d  5) a  6) d  7) c  8) b  9) d  10) d

**Activity 38—The Problem of Drug Dependence**
1) j  2) g  3) i  4) f  5) b  6) a  7) d  8) e  9) c  10) h

**Activity 39—Solutions to Drug Dependence**
1) g  2) i  3) j  4) m  5) b  6) e  7) a  8) h  9) d  10) n  11) c
12) k  13) o  14) f  15) l

**Activity 40—Causes of Disease**
1) j  2) o  3) m  4) i  5) h  6) a  7) b  8) g  9) k  10) c  11) e  12) l
13) n  14) d  15) f

**Activity 41—The Body's Protection From Disease**
1) h  2) f  3) b  4) i  5) e  6) c  7) a  8) j  9) d  10) g

**Activity 42—AIDS**
1) g  2) f  3) d  4) c  5) i  6) j  7) n  8) c  9) a  10) c  11) m  12) o
13) k  14) h  15) k

### Activity 43—Sexually Transmitted Diseases
1) e  2) g  3) f  4) j  5) m  6) m,c  7) j  8) b  9) e  10) c  11) l  12) h  13) j  14) l  15) j

### Activity 44—Cardiovascular Diseases and Disorders
1) d  2) e  3) b  4) c  5) f  6) h  7) g  8) i  9) d  10) a

### Activity 45—Cancer
1) e  2) j  3) h  4) b  5) f  6) i  7) d  8) a  9) c  10) g

### Activity 46—Asthma
1) F  2) T  3) F  4) F  5) F  6) T  7) F  8) T  9) F  10) T

### Activity 47—Diabetes
1) b  2) f  3) e  4) a  5) c  6) h  7) i  8) j  9) g  10) d

### Activity 48—Arthritis
1) T  2) T  3) T  4) T  5) T  6) d  7) a  8) b  9) d  10) c

### Activity 49—Epilepsy
1) F  2) T  3) T  4) T  5) F  6) T  7) T  8) F  9) T  10) F  11) d  12) e  13) a  14) b  15) c

### Activity 50—Promoting Safety
1) T  2) T  3) F  4) F  5) T  6) T  7) T  8) F  9) T  10) F

### Activity 51—Reducing Risks of Fire
1) T  2) F  3) F  4) F  5) T  6) T  7) F  8) T  9) T  10) T

### Activity 52—Safety for Teens
1) j  2) g  3) a  4) i  5) d  6) b  7) c  8) h  9) e  10) f

### Activity 53—Emergency Equipment
1) g  2) h  3) j  4) b  5) f  6) a  7) e  8) i  9) c  10) d

### Activity 54—Safety During Natural Disasters
1) F  2) F  3) F  4) T  5) F  6) T  7) F  8) F  9) T  10) F  11) T  12) F  13) T  14) F  15) T

### Activity 55—What to Do First
1) F  2) T  3) F  4) T  5) T  6) F  7) T  8) T  9) T  10) T

### Activity 56—Caring for Common Injuries
1) d  2) m  3) o  4) n  5) j  6) g  7) h  8) k  9) e  10) l  11) b  12) i  13) c  14) a  15) f

### Activity 57—First Aid for Bleeding, Shock, and Choking
1) a  2) i  3) d  4) e  5) c  6) h  7) f  8) j  9) g  10) b

### Activity 58—First Aid for Heart Attacks and Poisoning
1) T  2) F  3) F  4) T  5) F  6) T  7) T  8) T  9) T  10) F

### Activity 59—Defining Violence
1) f  2) j  3) a  4) e  5) b  6) c  7) g  8) d  9) i  10) h

### Activity 60—Causes of Violence
1) d  2) a  3) a  4) b  5) a  6) T  7) F  8) T  9) T  10) T

### Activity 61—Preventing Violence
1) i  2) d  3) c  4) f  5) g  6) h  7) j  8) a  9) b  10) e

### Activity 62—Health Care Information
1) T  2) T  3) F  4) T  5) F  6) T  7) T  8) T  9) T  10) T

### Activity 63—Seeking Health Care
1) g  2) d  3) h  4) i  5) f  6) e  7) c  8) a  9) b  10) j

### Activity 64—Paying for Health Care
1) a  2) d  3) a  4) a  5) b  6) T  7) T  8) F  9) F  10) F

### Activity 65—Being a Wise Consumer
1) d  2) b  3) c  4) j  5) i  6) a  7) f  8) e  9) g  10) h

### Activity 66—Evaluating Advertisements
1) F  2) T  3) T  4) F  5) F  6) T  7) F  8) F  9) T  10) F

### Activity 67—Consumer Protection
1) F  2) T  3) F  4) F  5) T  6) T  7) T  8) T  9) T  10) F

### Activity 68—Defining Community
1) d  2) b  3) f  4) a  5) c  6) e  7) d  8) d  9) d  10) d

### Activity 69—Community Health Resources
1) b  2) h  3) d  4) f  5) e  6) a  7) c  8) g  9) i  10) j

### Activity 70—Community Health Advocacy Skills
1) T  2) T  3) F  4) T  5) T  6) F  7) F  8) T  9) F  10) T

### Activity 71—Health and the Environment
1) c  2) i  3) b  4) f  5) d  6) h  7) e  8) g  9) j  10) a

### Activity 72—Air Pollution and Health
1) e  2) a  3) l  4) i  5) b  6) c  7) o  8) j  9) h  10) n  11) m  12) k  13) f  14) d  15) g

### Activity 73—Water and Land Pollution and Health
1) d  2) a  3) d  4) d  5) a  6) a  7) a  8) a  9) a  10) b

### Activity 74—Promoting a Healthy Environment
1) T  2) T  3) F  4) F  5) F  6) T  7) F  8) T  9) T  10) T

## Workbook Activities

### Workbook Activity 1—Cells, Tissues, and Organs
1) b  2) h  3) f  4) j  5) c  6) d  7) a  8) i  9) e  10) g

### Workbook Activity 2—The Body's Protective Covering
1) F  2) T  3) F  4) T  5) F  6) T  7) F  8) F  9) F  10) T

### Workbook Activity 3—The Skeletal and Muscular Systems
1) h  2) f  3) j  4) a  5) d  6) i  7) b  8) c  9) e  10) g

### Workbook Activity 4—The Digestive and Excretory Systems
1) g  2) b  3) h  4) e  5) f  6) a  7) j  8) d  9) i  10) c

### Workbook Activity 5—The Respiratory and Circulatory Systems
1) d  2) c  3) a  4) i  5) f  6) b  7) j  8) e  9) h  10) g

### Workbook Activity 6—The Nervous System
1) i  2) j  3) c  4) d  5) f  6) b  7) a  8) e  9) h  10) g

### Workbook Activity 7—The Endocrine System
1) F  2) T  3) F  4) F  5) T  6) T  7) T  8) F  9) T  10) T

### Workbook Activity 8—The Reproductive System
1) T  2) F  3) T  4) T  5) F  6) T  7) T  8) F  9) F  10) T

### Workbook Activity 9—Hygiene
Part A: 1) F  2) T  3) F  4) F  5) F  6) F
Part B: 7) b  8) c  9) d  10) c

### Workbook Activity 10—Fitness
1) F  2) F  3) F  4) T  5) F  6) T  7) F  8) T  9) F  10) T

### Workbook Activity 11—The Family Life Cycle
1) e  2) b  3) g  4) c  5) j  6) f  7) i  8) h  9) a  10) d

### Workbook Activity 12—Dealing With Family Problems
Part A: 1) b  2) c  3) c  4) c  5) d
Part B: 6) a  7) d  8) c  9) e  10) b

### Workbook Activity 13—Emotions and Their Causes
1) c  2) i  3) e  4) j  5) h  6) f  7) b  8) a  9) d  10) g

### Workbook Activity 14—Social Emotions
1) j  2) d  3) i  4) e  5) c  6) b  7) h  8) a  9) f  10) g

### Workbook Activity 15—Emotions and Behavior
1) g  2) j  3) i  4) b  5) d  6) e  7) h  8) f  9) a  10) c

**Workbook Activity 16—Managing Frustration**
Part A: 1) b  2) a  3) d  4) e  5) c
Part B: 6) F  7) F  8) T  9) T  10) T

**Workbook Activity 17—Managing Stress and Anxiety**
Part A: 1) e  2) c  3) a  4) b  5) d
Part B: 6) T  7) F  8) T  9) F  10) F  11) F  12) T  13) F  14) T
15) F

**Workbook Activity 18—Responding to Peer Pressure**
Part A: 1) b  2) d  3) a  4) e  5) c
Part B: 6) a  7) c  8) d  9) a  10) c

**Workbook Activity 19—Eating Disorders**
Part A: 1) a  2) a  3) c  4) d  5) e
Part B: 6) T  7) T  8) T  9) T  10) T

**Workbook Activity 20—Being a Friend to Yourself**
1) T  2) F  3) T  4) T  5) F  6) T  7) T  8) F  9) T  10) F

**Workbook Activity 21—Making Friends**
Part A: 1) b  2) c  3) a  4) d  5) a
Part B: 1) F  2) F  3) T  4) F  5) F

**Workbook Activity 22—Healthy Relationships**
1) T  2) T  3) F  4) T  5) F  6) T  7) F  8) T  9) F  10) F

**Workbook Activity 23—Food for Energy**
1) b  2) a  3) c  4) b  5) a  6) d  7) d  8) d  9) a  10) c

**Workbook Activity 24—Carbohydrates and Protein**
1) T  2) T  3) T  4) F  5) T  6) F  7) F  8) F  9) T  10) T

**Workbook Activity 25—Fats and Cholesterol**
1) T  2) T  3) T  4) T  5) F  6) F  7) F  8) F  9) T  10) T

**Workbook Activity 26—Vitamins, Minerals, and Water**
1) d  2) b  3) c  4) c  5) a  6) a  7) d  8) b  9) c  10) a

**Workbook Activity 27—Dietary Guidelines**
Part A: 1) T  2) T  3) F  4) T  5) F
Part B: 6) a  7) b  7) b  8) d  10) d

**Workbook Activity 28—Food Choices and Health**
1) d  2) j  3) h  4) a  5) e  6) f  7) b  8) c  9) g  10) i

**Workbook Activity 29—Influences on Food Choices**
Part A: 1) c  2) b  3) d  4) a  5) c
Part B: 6) T  7) T  8) F  9) T  10) T

**Workbook Activity 30—Reading Food Labels**
Part A: 1) a  2) c  3) a  4) b  5) d
Part B: 6) c  7) d  8) b  9) e  10) a

**Workbook Activity 31—Making Foods Safe**
1) b  2) j  3) a  4) h  5) c  6) d  7) i  8) f  9) e  10) g

**Workbook Activity 32—Prescription and Over-the-Counter Medicines**
Part A: 1) c  2) e  3) a  4) b  5) d
Part B: 1) c  2) b  3) e  4) a  5) d

**Workbook Activity 33—The Effect of Medicines and Drugs on the Body**
Part A: 1) b  2) c  3) a  4) d  5) e
Part B: 6) e  7) d  8) c  9) a  10) b

**Workbook Activity 34—Tobacco**
1) T  2) T  3) T  4) T  5) F  6) F  7) T  8) F  9) F  10) F  11) T
12) F  13) T  14) F  15) T

**Workbook Activity 35—Alcohol**
1) b  2) g  3) e  4) a  5) i  6) d  7) h  8) f  9) c  10) j

**Workbook Activity 36—Narcotics, Depressants, Stimulants, and Hallucinogens**
1) g  2) a  3 h  4) b  5) j  6) c  7) k  8) e  9) m  10) i  11) n  12) f
13) d  14) l  15) o

**Workbook Activity 37—Other Dangerous Drugs**
1) d  2) d  3) a  4) b d  6) a  7) d  8) c  9) b  10) d

**Workbook Activity 38—The Problems of Drug Dependence**
Part A: 1) c  2) a  3) e  4) d  5) b
Part B: 6) F  7) T  8) T  9) T  10) T

**Workbook Activity 39—Solutions to Drug Dependence**
1) d  2) c  3) h  4) i  5) f  6) e  7) g  8) b  9) a  10) j

**Workbook Activity 40—Causes of Disease**
1) a  2) b  3) h  4) e  5) d  6) c  7) f  8) g  9) j  10) i

**Workbook Activity 41—The Body's Protection From Disease**
1) j  2) f  3) c  4) d  5) h  6) a  7) b  8) e  9) i  10) g

**Workbook Activity 42—AIDS**
1) g  2) h  3) f  4) d  5) e  6) j  7) c  8) a  9) i  10) b

**Workbook Activity 43—Sexually Transmitted Diseases**
Part A: 1) a  2) a, c  3) b, c  4) b
Part B: 5) T  6) T  7) F  8) T  9) T  10) T  11) T  12) F  13) T
14) T  15) T

**Workbook Activity 44—Cardiovascular Diseases and Disorders**
Part A: 1) c  2) d  3) a  4) b  5) e  6) g  7) f  8) h
Part B: 9) T  10) F

**Workbook Activity 45—Cancer**
1) b  2) e  3) j  4) h  5) g  6) f  7) i  8) d  9) a  10) b

**Workbook Activity 46—Asthma**
1) F  2) F  3) T  4) T  5) F  6) T  7) T  8) T  9) T  10) F

**Workbook Activity 47—Diabetes**
1) c  2) b  3) f  4) e  5) a  6) d  7) h  8) i  9) j  10) g

**Workbook Activity 48—Arthritis**
Part A: 1) d  2) a  3) b  4) d  5) c
Part B: 1) T  2) T  3) T  4) T  5) T

**Workbook Activity 49—Epilepsy**
Part A: 1) d  2) e  3) a  4) b  5) c
Part B: 6) F  7) T  8) T  9) T  10) F  11) T  12) T  13) F  14) T
15) F

**Workbook Activity 50—Promoting Safety**
1) F  2) T  3) T  4) F  5) F  6) T  7) T  8) T  9) F  10) T

**Workbook Activity 51—Reducing Risks of Fire**
1) T  2) T  3) F  4) F  5) F  6) T  7) T  8) F  9) T  10) T

**Workbook Activity 52—Safety for Teens**
1) f  2) j  3) g  4) a  5) i  6) d  7) b  8) c  9) h  10) e

**Workbook Activity 53—Emergency Equipment**
1) d  2 i  3) h  4) k  5) b  6) f  7) a  8) e  9) j  10) c

**Workbook Activity 54—Safety During Natural Disasters**
1) T  2) F  3) F  4) F  5) T  6) F  7) T  8) F  9) F  10) T  11) F
12) T  13) F  14) T  15) F

**Workbook Activity 55—What to Do First**
1) T  2) T  3) T  4) F  5) T  6) T  7) F  8) T  9) T  10) T

**Workbook Activity 56—Caring for Common Injuries**
1) h  2) d  3) m  4) o  5) n  6) j  7) g  8) f  9) k  10) e  11) l  12) b
13) i  14) c  15) a

**Workbook Activity 57—First Aid for Bleeding, Shock, and Choking**
1) b  2) a  3) i  4) d  5) e  6) c  7) h  8) f  9) j  10) g

**Workbook Activity 58—First Aid for Heart Attacks and Poisoning**
1) F  2) T  3) F  4) F  5) T  6) F  7) T  8) T  9) T  10) T

**Workbook Activity 59—Defining Violence**
1) T  2) F  3) T  4) F  5) T  6) T  7) T  8) F  9) F  10) F

**Workbook Activity 60—Causes of Violence**
1) f  2) a  3) e  4) i  5) g  6) d  7) a  8) j  9) c  10) h

**Workbook Activity 61—Preventing Violence**
1) T  2) F  3) T  4) T  5) T  6) F  7) T  8) T  9) T  10) T

**Workbook Activity 62—Health Care Information**
1) T  2) T  3) F  4) T  5) T  6) F  7) T  8) T  9) T  10) T

**Workbook Activity 63—Seeking Health Care**
1) T  2) T  3) F  4) T  5) T  6) T  7) T  8) T  9) F  10) T

**Workbook Activity 64—Paying for Health Care**
1) F  2) F  3) T  4) T  5) T  6) T  7) F  8) F  9) F  10) F

**Workbook Activity 65—Being a Wise Consumer**
1) b  2) c  3) d  4) i  5) a  6) j  7) e  8) g  9) h  10) f

**Workbook Activity 66—Evaluating Advertisements**
1) F  2) T  3) T  4) F  5) F  6) T  7) F  8) F  9) T  10) F

**Workbook Activity 67—Consumer Protection**
1) F  2) T  3) F  4) F  5) T  6) T  7) T  8) T  9) T  10) F

**Workbook Activity 68—Defining Community**
Part A: 1) d  2) d  3) d  5) d
Part B: 5) d  6) b  7) f  8) a  9) c  10) e

**Workbook Activity 69—Community Health Resources**
Part A: 1) b  2) h  3) d  4) f  5) e  6) a  7) c  8) g
Part B: 9) b  10) d

**Workbook Activity 70—Community Health Advocacy Skills**
1) T  2) T  3) T  4) F  5) T  6) T  7) F  8) F  9) T  10) F

**Workbook Activity 71—Health and the Environment**
1) F  2) T  3) F  4) T  5) T  6) F  7) F  8) T  9) T  10) T

**Workbook Activity 72—Air Pollution and Health**
1) a  2) l  3) b  4) e  5) g  6) c  7) j  8) i  9) h  10) m  11) o  12) k  13) f  14) n  15) d

**Workbook Activity 73—Water and Land Pollution and Health**
1) F  2) T  3) T  4) F  5) T  6) F  7) F  8) F  9) F  10) F

**Workbook Activity 74—Promoting a Healthy Environment**
1) a  2) a  3) c  4) c  5) c  6) c  7) a  8) b  9) a  10) c

## Chapter Mastery Tests

**Chapter 1 Mastery Test A**
1) b  2) c  3) a  4) b  5) d  6) c  7) a  8) b  9) c  10) a  11) d  12) b  13) a  14) d  15) b

**Chapter 1 Mastery Test B**
1) b  2) d  3) c  4) d  5) a  6) b  7) d  8) c  9) a  10) a  11) b  12) a  13) c  14) b  15) b

**Chapter 2 Mastery Test A**
1) F  2) T  3) F  4) F  5) T  6) F  7) T  8) T  9) F  10) T  11) F  12) T  13) F  14) T  15) T

**Chapter 2 Mastery Test B**
1) F  2) F  3) T  4) T  5) F  6) T  7) T  8) F  9) F  10) T  11) F  12) T  13) F  14) T  15) F

**Chapter 3 Mastery Test A**
1) c  2) h  3) i  4) l  5) j  6) a  7) n  8) k  9) d  10) b  11) f  12) o  13) e  14) m  15) g

**Chapter 3 Mastery Test B**
1) l  2) j  3) m  4) g  5) k  6) d  7) c  8) h  9) a  10) n  11) i  12) b  13) f  14) o  15) e

**Chapter 4 Mastery Test A**
1) T  2) T  3) F  4) T  5) F  6) T  7) F  8) T  9) T  10) F  11) F  12) T  13) T  14) F  15) F  16) T  17) F  18) T  19) T  20) F  21) T  22) F  23) T  24) T  25) F

**Chapter 4 Mastery Test B**
1) T  2) F  3) T  4) F  5) T  6) F  7) T  8) T  9) F  10) F  11) T  12) F  13) F  14) T  15) F  16) T  17) T  18) F  19) T  20) T  21) T  22) F  23) T  24) T  25) F

**Chapter 5 Mastery Test A**
1) b  2) d  3) a  4) c  5) b  6) a  7) d  8) c  9) a  10) b  11) d  12) b  13) a  14) c  15) b

**Chapter 5 Mastery Test B**
1) c  2) b  3) a  4) b  5) b  6) d  7) d  8) b  9) b  10) a  11) a  12) c  13) d  14) c  15) a

**Chapter 6 Mastery Test A**
1) c  2) a  3) b  4) d  5) a  6) a  7) d  8) c  9) a  10) b  11) c  12) a  13) c  14) d  15) a

**Chapter 6 Mastery Test B**
1) d  2) a  3) a  4) b  5) c  6) a  7) b  8) c  9) a  10) d  11) a  12) a  13) c  14) d  15) c

**Chapter 7 Mastery Test A**
1) f  2) g  3) k  4) h  5) m  6) d  7) e  8) b  9) o  10) i  11) a  12) c  13) j  14) l  15) n

**Chapter 7 Mastery Test B**
1) h  2) m  3) d  4) e  5) a  6) c  7) j  8) l  9) n  10) f  11) g  12) k  13) b  14) o  15) i

**Chapter 8 Mastery Test A**
1) c  2) a  3) b  4) b  5) a  6) c  7) d  8) c  9) d  10) b  11) c  12) a  13) d  14) b  15) c

**Chapter 8 Mastery Test B**
1) b  2) c  3) d  4) b  5) c  6) a  7) c  8) a  9) a  10) c  11) b  12) b  13) d  14) c  15) d

**Chapter 9 Mastery Test A**
1) i  2) a  3) n  4) j  5) h  6) m  7) k  8) o  9) c  10) g  11) b  12) e  13) f  14) l  15) d

**Chapter 9 Mastery Test B**
1) l  2) d  3) c  4) g  5) i  6) a  7) n  8) b  9) e  10) f  11) k  12) o  13) j  14) h  15) m

**Chapter 10 Mastery Test A**
1) m  2) e  3) c  4) f  5) g  6) l  7) i  8) d  9) b  10) a  11) j  12) h  13) n  14) o  15) k

**Chapter 10 Mastery Test B**
1) g  2) l  3) i  4) n  5) o  6) k  7) m  8) e  9) c  10) d  11) b  12) f  13) a  14) j  15) h

**Chapter 11 Mastery Test A**
1) b  2) d  3) a  4) c  5) d  6) a  7) b  8) a  9) b  10) c  11) d  12) b  13) a  14) c  15) d

**Chapter 11 Mastery Test B**
1) b  2) a  3) a  4) b  5) a  6) c  7) d  8) c  9) d  10) b  11) c  12) d  13) d  14) a  15) b

**Chapter 12 Mastery Test A**
1) b  2) a  3) d  4) c  5) a  6) d  7) b  8) c  9) a  10) c  11) b  12) d  13) c  14) a  15) d

**Chapter 12 Mastery Test B**
1) a  2) d  3) a  4) c  5) b  6) a  7) d  8) b  9) d  10) c  11) b  12) c  13) c  14) a  15) d

**Chapter 13 Mastery Test A**
1) c  2) a  3) d  4) b  5) d  6) a  7) c  8) b  9) c  10) d  11) b  12) a  13) d  14) c  15) a

**Chapter 13 Mastery Test B**
1) d  2) c  3) a  4) d  5) b  6) a  7) c  8) a  9) d  10) b  11) d  12) a  13) c  14) b  15) c

**Chapter 14 Mastery Test A**
1) T  2) F  3) T  4) F  5) F  6) T  7) T  8) T  9) F  10) T  11) F  12) F  13) T  14) T  15) F  16) T  17) F  18) T  19) T  20) F

**Chapter 14 Mastery Test B**
1) T  2) F  3) F  4) F  5) T  6) F  7) T  8) T  9) F  10) T  11) F  12) F  13) F  14) T  15) T  16) T  17) T  18) F  19) F  20) T

**Chapter 15 Mastery Test A**
1) a  2) o  3) i  4) d  5) f  6) m  7) l  8) n  9) c  10) b  11) h  12) k  13) e  14) g  15) j

**Chapter 15 Mastery Test B**
1) e  2) g  3) j  4) m  5) l  6) n  7) c  8) b  9) h  10) k  11) a  12) o  13) i  14) d  15) f

**Chapter 16 Mastery Test A**
1) T  2) F  3) T  4) T  5) F  6) F  7) T  8) T  9) F  10) T  11) F  12) F  13) T  14) T  15) F  16) F  17) T  18) T  19) F  20) T  21) F  22) T  23) F  24) T  25) T

**Chapter 16 Mastery Test B**
1) T  2) T  3) F  4) T  5) F  6) T  7) F  8) T  9) T  10) T  11) F  12) T  13) T  14) F  15) F  16) F  17) F  18) T  19) T  20) F  21) F  22) T  23) T  24) F  25) T

**Chapter 17 Mastery Test A**
1) m  2) c  3) l  4) h  5) k  6) g  7) i  8) f  9) a  10) e  11) o  12) b  13) j  14) n  15) d

**Chapter 17 Mastery Test B**
1) n  2) d  3) a  4) e  5) m  6) c  7) l  8) o  9) b  10) h  11) k  12) g  13) j  14) i  15) f

**Chapter 18 Mastery Test A**
1) m  2) k  3) f  4) h  5) d  6) j  7) l  8) n  9) g  10) o  11) c  12) a  13) b  14) i  15) e

**Chapter 18 Mastery Test B**
1) b  2) i  3) e  4) g  5) o  6) m  7) k  8) f  9) l  10) n  11) h  12) d  13) j  14) c  15) a

**Chapter 19 Mastery Test A**
1) d  2) b  3) a  4) b  5) c  6) a  7) d  8) c  9) a  10) d  11) b  12) c  13) b  14) c  15) a

**Chapter 19 Mastery Test B**
1) b  2) c  3) a  4) d  5) b  6) a  7) b  8) d  9) b  10) c  11) d  12) c  13) a  14) c  15) a

## Unit Mastery Tests

**Unit 1 Mastery Test**
Part A: 1) b  2) a  3) d  4) c  5) a  6) b  7) c  8) a  9) a  10) d
Part B: 1) T  2) F  3) F  4) T  5) T
Part C: 1) c  2) d  3) b  4) a  5) e

**Unit 2 Mastery Test**
Part A: 1) T  2) F  3) F  4) T  5) F  6) T  7) F  8) T  9) T  10) F
Part B: 1) d  2) c  3) a  4) d  5) a  6) c  70) d  8) a  9) c  10) c

**Unit 3 Mastery Test**
Part A: 1) d  2) e  3) f  4) c  5) a  6) j  7) g  8) b  9) h  10) i
Part B: 1) c  2) b  3) a  4) d  5) c  6) d  7) c  8) a  9) b  10) c

**Unit 4 Mastery Test**
Part A: 1) g  2) h  3) f  4) i  5) b  6) e  7) c  8) d  9) a  10) j
Part B: 1) i  2) b  3) c  4) h  5) e  6) a  7) f  8) d  9) j  10) g

**Unit 5 Mastery Test**
1) b  2) d  3) d  4) b  5) b  6) d  7) a  8) b  9) c  10) d  11) c  12) c  13) b  14) c  15) d  16) d  17) c  18) c  19) b  20) a

**Unit 6 Mastery Test**
Part A: 1) F  2) T  3) F  4) F  5) T  6) T  7) T  8) F  9) F  10) F  11) T  12) T  13) F  14) F  15) T
Part B: 1) b  2) e  3) a  4) d  5) c

**Unit 7 Mastery Test**
Part A: 1) d  2) b  3) j  4) e  5) m  6) k  7) a  8) f  9) l  10) h  11) i  12) n  13) g  14) c  15) o
Part B: 1) a  2) b  3) c  4) a  5) d

## Midterm Mastery Test

Part A: 1) e  2) h  3) b  4) g  5) d  6) i  7) j  8) f  9) a  10) c
Part B: 1) F  2) F  3) T  4) T  5) T  6) T  7) T  8) F  9) F  10) T
Part C: 1) b  2) e  3) h  4) f  5) j  6) d  7) g  8) a  9) c  10) i
Part D: 1) c  2) b  3) a  4) a  5) c  6) b  7) b  8) c  9) d  10) b  11) b  12) a  13) a  14) b  15) c  16) b  17) a  18) c  19) a  20) a

## Final Mastery Test

Part A: 1) m  2) f  3) e  4) d  5) i  6) g  7) a  8) b  9) k  10) j  11) o  12) h  13) n  14) c  15) l
Part B: 1) F  2) T  3) F  4) T  5) T  6) T  7) F  8) T  9) T  10) F  11) T  12) F  13) T  14) F  15) T
Part C: 1) i  2) n  3) g  4) j  5) m  6) l  7) k  8) e  9) f  10) d  11) o  12) c  13) a  14) h  15) b
Part D: 1) a  2) a  3) c  4) b  5) d  6) b  7) a  8) b  9) c  10) d  11) a  12) a  13) b  14) d  15) a  16) d  17) a  18) d  19) c  20) c  21) b  22) c  23) c  24) d  25) a  26) a  27) d  28) d  29) d  30) a

# Student Study Guides

## Student Study Guide Chapter 1

**I.**
- **A.** Cells
- **B.** cytoplasm; nucleus
- **C.** tissues

**II.**
- **A.** body
- **B.** Dermis

**III.**
- **A.** frame
- **B.** bones
- **C.** voluntary

**IV.**
- **A.** food
- **B.** rectum
- **C.** Urine

**V.**
- **A.** oxygen
- **B.** blood
- **C.** heart

**VI.**
- **A.** spinal cord
- **B.** cerebellum

**VII.**
- **A.** glands
- **B.** Hormones

**VIII.**
- **A.** ovaries
- **B.** sperm
- **C.** egg

## Student Study Guide Chapter 2

**I.**
- **A.**
  - **1.** soap; water
  - **2.** pores
- **B.**
  - **1.** brushing
  - **2.** germs
- **C.**
  - **1.** Plaque
  - **2.** orthodontist
- **D.**
  - **1.** helmet
  - **2.** optometrist
- **E.**
  - **1.** hearing loss
  - **2.** ears
  - **3.** earplugs

**II.**
- **A.**
  - **1.** heart
  - **2.** blood pressure
  - **3.** heart rate
  - **4.** blood; body
  - **5.** five
  - **6.** exercise
- **B.**
  - **1.** energy
- **C.**
  - **1.** friends
- **D.**
  - **1.** stress

**E.**
- **1.** tired
- **2.** eight; nine

## Student Study Guide Chapter 3

**I.**
- **A.**
  - **1.** marry
  - **2.** child
- **B.**
  - **1.** interests; tasks
- **C.**
  - **1.** rules
  - **2.** communication
- **D.**
  - **1.** home
  - **2.** hobbies
  - **3.** limitations
  - **4.** wisdom

**II.**
- **A.**
  - **1.** Unexpected
  - **2.** emotional
- **B.**
  - **1.** worried
- **C.**
  - **1.** denial
  - **2.** acceptance
- **D.**
  - **1.** Child
  - **2.** Emotional
  - **3.** responsible
- **E.**
  - **1.** strengthens
  - **2.** attitude

## Student Study Guide Chapter 4

**I.**
- **A.**
  - **1.** mental
  - **2.** act
  - **3.** thoughts
  - **4.** stress
  - **5.** nervous
  - **6.** think
  - **7.** adapting
  - **8.** ups; downs

**II.**
- **A.**
  - **1.** relationships
  - **2.** guilty
  - **3.** shame
  - **4.** grief
  - **5.** sadness
  - **6.** Positive

**III.**
- **A.**
  - **1.** automatic
  - **2.** need; solve
  - **3.** expect
  - **4.** reasonable; compromise
  - **5.** normal
  - **6.** Physical

## Student Study Guide Chapter 5

I.
    A.
1. goals
2. aggression
3. pull away; problems
4. cope
5. harder

II.
    A.
1. helps
2. threatened; needs
3. reaction
4. three; flight
5. Preparing
6. Anxiety
7. reason

III.
    A.
1. influence; pressure
2. safe
3. resist
4. respect
5. someone else
6. leave

IV.
    A.
1. body
2. unhealthy; unhappy
3. anorexia
4. bulimia
5. overweight

## Student Study Guide Chapter 6

I.
    A.
1. nicely; kindly
2. Self-talk
3. never; always
4. compliment
5. alone

II.
    A.
1. respect
2. common
3. values
4. small
5. listener
6. spend time
7. pressure

III.
    A.
1. alone
2. think
3. equally
4. values
5. shy
6. them
7. gossip
8. friend

## Student Study Guide Chapter 7

I.
    A.
1. Nutrients
2. bloodstream
3. energy
4. fat

II.
    A.
1. fuel
2. complex
3. digestive
4. proteins
5. amino

III.
    A.
1. polyunsaturated
2. animals
3. blood

IV.
    A.
1. stored
2. variety
3. earth
4. Calcium
5. high
6. eight

V.
    A.
1. Pyramid
2. size
3. dietary
4. menstruating

## Student Study Guide Chapter 8

I.
    A.
1. activity level
2. vegetables
3. nutrients
4. change
5. fat
6. Malnutrition

II.
    A.
1. anger
2. feelings
3. available
4. culture
5. fun

III.
    A.
1. ingredients
2. calories
3. sodium
4. weight
5. priced

IV.
  A.
    1. chemicals
    2. additive
    3. spoiling
    4. grades
    5. poisoning
    6. minerals
    7. spoil
    8. utensils

## Student Study Guide Chapter 9
I.
  A.
    1. prescription
    2. germs
    3. cure
    4. Cardiovascular
    5. Psychoactive
II.
  A.
    1. Medicines
    2. therapeutic
    3. Body
    4. alcohol
III.
  A.
    1. blood pressure
    2. throat
    3. gum
IV.
  A.
    1. think
    2. drink alcohol
    3. control
    4. cure
V.
  A.
    1. Narcotics
    2. central
    3. stop
    4. brain
    5. hallucinogen
VI.
  A.
    1. inhalants
    2. testosterone
    3. Marijuana
    4. Designer
    5. look-alike

## Student Study Guide Chapter 10
I.
  A.
    1. disease
    2. brain
    3. memory; performance
    4. withdrawal
  B.
    1. death
    2. drug
    3. school; judgment

II.
  A.
    1. admit
    2. detoxification
    3. drugs
  B.
    1. treatment
  C.
    1. Alcoholics Anonymous
    2. Alateen
  D.
    1. Peer pressure
    2. away; honest
    3. physically; interests

## Student Study Guide Chapter 11
I.
  A.
    1. inherited
    2. acquired
    3. pathogens
  B.
    1. mucus
    2. Hairs
    3. cut
    4. multiply
    5. infectious
  C.
    1. Wash
    2. eggs
II.
  A.
    1. inflammatory
  B.
    1. antibodies
    2. immune
  C.
    1. viruses
    2. antibodies

## Student Study Guide Chapter 12
I.
  A.
    1. immune system
    2. HIV
    3. bloodstream
    4. six; ten
    5. AIDS
  B.
    1. communicable
    2. shares
    3. birth
    4. hugging
II.
  A.
    1. blisters
    2. cure
    3. sterility
    4. antibiotics
    5. eye infections
    6. identity

**Student Study Chapter Guide 13**

I.
  A.
    1. artery
    2. fat
    3. fats
    4. heart attack
    5. stroke
    6. inherited

II.
  A.
    1. tissue
    2. benign
    3. sore
    4. breast
    5. prostate
    6. Lung
    7. radiation
    8. chemotherapy

III.
  A.
    1. wheezing
    2. animal
    3. prevent

IV.
  A.
    1. insulin
    2. Type II
    3. Gestational
    4. blurred

V.
  A.
    1. rheumatoid
    2. joints
    3. cartilage

VI.
  A.
    1. malfunctions
    2. thought
    3. cause
    4. medicines

**Student Study Guide Chapter 14**

I.
  A.
    1. chances
    2. traffic
    3. water
    4. locked

II.
  A.
    1. carelessness
    2. month
    3. small
    4. escape routes

III.
  A.
    1. drowning
    2. one
    3. shock
    4. talk
    5. strangers
    6. chat

IV.
  A.
    1. flashlights
    2. first aid

V.
  A.
    1. earthquake
    2. wall
    3. table
    4. Thunder
    5. hurricane
    6. tornado
    7. flood

**Student Study Chapter Guide 15**

I.
  A.
    1. calm
    2. breathing
    3. sued
    4. latex

II.
  A.
    1. splint
    2. cold
    3. blister
    4. Third-degree
    5. forward
    6. sweating
    7. Hypothermia
    8. rub
    9. animal

III.
  A.
    1. heart
    2. shock
    3. index
    4. speak
    5. thrusts

IV.
  A.
    1. blood vessel
    2. cardiopulmonary resuscitation (CPR)
    3. poison control
    4. water
    5. inhalation

**Student Study Chapter Guide 16**

I.
  A.
    1. problems
    2. results
    3. newspapers
    4. specific
    5. Conflict
    6. murders
    7. emotional

II.
  A.
    1. understand
    2. violent
    3. gun
    4. prejudice
    5. strangers

III.
- A.
  1. angry
  2. perspective
  3. emotions
  4. apologize
  5. mediator
  6. secret

**Student Study Guide Chapter 17**
I.
- A.
  1. Preventive
  2. professionals
  3. specialized

II.
- A.
  1. doctor
  2. primary
  3. library
  4. Outpatient
  5. older

III.
- A.
  1. private
  2. managed care
  3. cheapest

IV.
- A.
  1. rights
  2. price
  3. quackery
  4. labels

V.
- A.
  1. superior
  2. competition
  3. children

VI.
- A.
  1. Bill; Rights
  2. money
  3. legal

**Student Study Guide Chapter 18**
I.
- A.
  1. common
  2. epidemic
  3. negative
  4. increasing
  5. poverty
  6. equal; older
  7. community

II.
- A.
  1. public
  2. Private
  3. volunteer
  4. health
  5. Disease
  6. research
  7. WHO
  8. donations

III.
- A.
  1. housing
  2. budget
  3. emergencies
  4. Advocacy
  5. healthy

**Student Study Chapter Guide 19**
I.
- A.
  1. balance
  2. resources
  3. wastes
  4. limited

II.
- A.
  1. fuel
  2. Burning
  3. hydrocarbons
  4. gas
  5. Smog
  6. Asbestos
  7. Radon
  8. Acid rain
  9. carbon dioxide
  10. sun

III.
- A.
  1. groundwater
  2. Sewage
  3. pollute
  4. Oil
  5. conserve
  6. food
  7. landfill
  8. stress

IV.
- A.
  1. limits
  2. driving
  3. Alternative
  4. driving
  5. refillable

## Home Connections

**Home Connection 1—Dealing With Stress in the Family**
Answers will vary.

**Home Connection 2—Family Practice in Assertiveness**
Answers will vary.

**Home Connection 3—Family Health Profile and Action Plan**
Answers will vary.

**Home Connection 4—Family Quiz on Substances**
**1-8)** True

**Home Connection 5—Family AIDS Awareness Assessment**
**1)** F  **2)** T  **3)** F  **4)** F
Ways AIDS is acquired include through exchange of body fluids, sexual activity with an infected partner, sharing needles among drug users, and passage from mother to child.
Ways AIDS is not acquired are casual social contact such as shaking hands, hugging, kissing, crying, coughing, sneezing, sharing eating utensils, bathing in the same water, and bites from sucking insects.
Sexually transmitted diseases are prevented by avoiding contact with the pathogens that cause them or avoiding sexual activity.

**Home Connection 6—Family Quiz on Accidents and Injuries**
**1-4)** T  **5)** F  **6-7)** T  **8-9)** F

**Home Connection 7—Discussing Environmental Issues With Your Family**
Answers will vary.

## What Do You Think? Activities

**Unit 1 What Do You Think? Activity—Choosing an Activity**
**1)** Practiced many hours, eaten well, gotten plenty of rest, and kept a good attitude.  **2)** Believe that you will do the best you can and try your best no matter what happens  **3)** Answers will vary.
**4a)** Answers will vary.  **4b)** Answers will vary.  **4c)** Answers will vary.  **4d)** Answers will vary.

**Unit 2 What Do You Think? Activity—Getting Started**
Answers will vary.

**Unit 3 What Do You Think? Activity—Nutrition**
Answers will vary.

**Unit 4 What Do You Think? Activity—Test Your Knowledge**
**1)** d  **2)** c  **3)** a  **4)** a

**Unit 5 What Do You Think? Activity—Test Your Knowledge About Diseases**
**1)** c  **2)** b  **3)** c  **4)** c  **5)** a  **6)** a  **7)** b  **8)** b  **9)** b  **10)** a

**Unit 6 What Do You Think? Activity—Home Safety Checklist**
**1)** Smoke detectors outside bedroom doors will alert you if a fire is just outside your room.  **2)** Answers will vary.  **3)** Answers will vary.  **4)** Answers will vary.
Answers will vary about how to make the home safer.

**Unit 7 What Do You Think? Activity—Looking at Your Community**
**1-6)** Answers will vary.

## Deciding for Yourself Activities

**Unit 1 Deciding for Yourself Activity—Making a Fitness Plan**
**1-4)** Answers will vary.

**Unit 2 Deciding for Yourself Activity—Using Body Language**
Answers to question 5 will vary.

**Unit 3 Deciding for Yourself Activity—Food Advertising Words and Questions**
**1)** Answers will vary. Some examples might be low-fat, wholesome, goodness, light, no-fat, low-sodium, low-cholesterol, healthy  **2)** Answers will vary. Students' answers should reflect critical thinking about advertising techniques.  **3)** Answers will vary.

**Unit 4 Deciding for Yourself Activity—Skills for Handling Stress**
**1-3)** Answers will vary.

**Unit 5 Deciding for Yourself Activity—Staying Healthy**
Answers to questionnaire and to questions will vary.

**Unit 6 Deciding for Yourself Activity—Gun Control**
Answers will vary.

**Unit 7 Deciding for Yourself Activity—Looking at pH Balance**
**1)** The most acid substance on the chart is battery acid.  **2)** Lye is the most alkaline substance shown on the chart.  **3)** A stream's normal pH range is 5 to 6.  **4)** Lemon juice is $10 \times 10 \times 10 = 1,000$ times more acid than the stream; battery acid is $10 \times 10 \times 10 \times 10 = 10,000$ times more acid than the stream.  **5)** Answers will vary. A changing pH could show something is polluting the stream. It could show the environment is changing in some other way.